VIBRATION PROBLEMS IN ENGINEERING

By

S. TIMOSHENKO

Professor Emeritus of Engineering Mechanics
Stanford University

THIRD EDITION

In collaboration with

D. H. YOUNG

Professor of Engineering Mechanics
Stanford University

D. VAN NOSTRAND COMPANY, Inc.

PRINCETON, NEW JERSEY

TORONTO
LONDON

NEW YORK

D. VAN NOSTRAND COMPANY, INC.
120 Alexander St., Princeton, New Jersey (*Principal office*)
24 West 40 Street, New York 18, New York

D. VAN NOSTRAND COMPANY, LTD.
358, Kensington High Street, London, W.14, England

D. VAN NOSTRAND COMPANY (Canada), LTD.
25 Hollinger Road, Toronto 16, Canada

First Edition, October 1928

Two Reprintings

Second Edition, July 1937

Eight Reprintings

Third Edition, January 1955

*Reprinted, August 1956, February 1959,
September 1961, May 1964,
January 1966*

PRINTED IN THE UNITED STATES OF AMERICA

PREFACE TO THE THIRD EDITION

Since the appearance of the first edition of Vibration Problems in 1928, the subject has become a standard part of almost every Mechanical Engineering curriculum; it is becoming of more and more interest to Structural Engineers; and many new developments, particularly in the field of non-linear vibrations, have taken place. To make the book more suitable for teaching purposes and to incorporate some of the more important new developments have been the chief aim in this revision.

The first chapter, dealing with systems having one degree of freedom, has been very thoroughly revised to cover a wide range of applications, and a considerable number of problems have been added. Chapter II, dealing with non-linear vibrations, has been greatly expanded and many new methods of treating such problems are presented. To simplify the book for students having only the usual elementary course in dynamics, the use of Lagrangian equations in Chapters III and IV has been dropped and all derivations are based on the more familiar d'Alembert's principle. Aside from this, these chapters dealing with systems having several degrees of freedom are not greatly different from previous editions. Chapter V on vibrations of elastic bodies again has been very completely revised and several new topics, such as combined bending and torsional vibrations of beams, are discussed. Finally, the Appendix, dealing with vibration measuring instruments, has been omitted. So many new developments in vibration measuring techniques have taken place in recent years that they far outrun the confines of a volume of this size. Readers interested in such material are referred to the *Handbook of Experimental Stress Analysis*, edited by M. Hetényi.

S. TIMOSHENKO
D. H. YOUNG

PALO ALTO, CALIFORNIA
November, 1954

iii

PREFACE TO THE FIRST EDITION

With the increase of size and velocity in modern machines, the analysis of vibration problems becomes more and more important in mechanical engineering design. It is well known that problems of great practical significance, such as the balancing of machines, the torsional vibration of shafts and of geared systems, the vibrations of turbine blades and turbine discs, the whirling of rotating shafts, the vibrations of railway track and bridges under the action of rolling loads, the vibration of foundations, can be thoroughly understood only on the basis of the theory of vibration. Only by using this theory can the most favorable design proportions be found which will remove the working conditions of the machine as far as possible from the critical conditions at which heavy vibrations may occur.

In the present book, the fundamentals of the theory of vibration are developed, and their application to the solution of technical problems is illustrated by various examples, taken, in many cases, from actual experience with vibration of machines and structures in service. In developing this book, the author has followed the lectures on vibration given by him to the mechanical engineers of the Westinghouse Electric and Manufacturing Company during the year 1925, and also certain chapters of his previously published book on the theory of elasticity.*

The contents of the book in general are as follows:

The first chapter is devoted to the discussion of harmonic vibrations of systems with one degree of freedom. The general theory of free and forced vibration is discussed, and the application of this theory to balancing machines and vibration-recording instruments is shown. The Rayleigh approximate method of investigating vibrations of more complicated systems is also discussed, and is applied to the calculation of the whirling speeds of rotating shafts of variable cross-section.

Chapter two contains the theory of the non-harmonic vibration of systems with one degree of freedom. The approximate methods for investigating the free and forced vibrations of such systems are discussed. A particular case in which the flexibility of the system varies with time is considered in detail, and the results of this theory are applied to the investigation of vibrations in electric locomotives with side-rod drive.

* *Theory of Elasticity*, Vol. II (1916)—St. Petersburg, Russia.

In chapter three, systems with several degrees of freedom are considered. The general theory of vibration of such systems is developed, and also its application in the solution of such engineering problems as: the vibration of vehicles, the torsional vibration of shafts, whirling speeds of shafts on several supports, and vibration absorbers.

Chapter four contains the theory of vibration of elastic bodies. The problems considered are: the longitudinal, torsional, and lateral vibrations of prismatical bars; the vibration of bars of variable cross-section; the vibrations of bridges, turbine blades, and ship hulls; the theory of vibration of circular rings, membranes, plates, and turbine discs.

Brief descriptions of the most important vibration-recording instruments which are of use in the experimental investigation of vibration are given in the appendix.

The author owes a very large debt of gratitude to the management of the Westinghouse Electric and Manufacturing Company, which company made it possible for him to spend a considerable amount of time in the preparation of the manuscript and to use as examples various actual cases of vibration in machines which were investigated by the company's engineers. He takes this opportunity to thank, also, the numerous friends who have assisted him in various ways in the preparation of the manuscript, particularly Messr. J. M. Lessells, J. Ormondroyd, and J. P. Den Hartog, who have read over the complete manuscript and have made many valuable suggestions.

He is indebted, also, to Mr. F. C. Wilharm for the preparation of drawings, and to the Van Nostrand Company for their care in the publication of the book.

S. TIMOSHENKO

ANN ARBOR, MICHIGAN,
May 22, 1928.

CONTENTS

CHAPTER I

PAGE

CHAPTER II

CHAPTER III

CONTENTS

CHAPTER IV

SYSTEMS WITH SEVERAL DEGREES OF FREEDOM

CHAPTER V

VIBRATIONS OF ELASTIC BODIES

CONTENTS

CHAPTER I

SYSTEMS WITH ONE DEGREE OF FREEDOM

1. Free Harmonic Vibrations.—If an elastic system, such as a loaded beam, a twisted shaft or a deformed spring, be disturbed from its position of equilibrium by an impact or by the sudden application and removal of an additional force, the elastic forces of the member in the disturbed position will no longer be in equilibrium with the loading, and vibrations will ensue. Generally an elastic system can perform vibrations of different modes. For instance, a string or a beam while vibrating may assume different shapes depending on the number of nodes subdividing the length of the member. In the simplest cases the configuration of the vibrating system can be determined by one coordinate only. Such systems are called *systems with one degree of freedom.*

Let us consider the case shown in Fig. 1. If the arrangement be such that only vertical displacements of the weight W are possible and the mass of the spring is small in comparison with that of the weight W, the system can be considered as having *one degree of freedom.* The configuration will be determined completely by the vertical displacement of the weight.

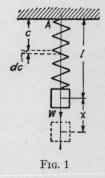

By an impulse or a sudden application and removal of an external force, vibrations of the system can be produced. Such vibrations which are maintained by the elastic force in the spring alone are called *free* or *natural* vibrations. An analytical expression for these vibrations can be found from the differential equation

Fig. 1

of motion, which always can be written down if the forces acting on the moving body are known.

Let k denote the load necessary to produce a unit extension of the spring. This quantity is called the *spring constant.* If the load is measured in pounds and extension in inches the spring constant will be obtained in *lb per in.* The static deflection of the spring under the action of the weight W will be

$$\delta_{st} = \frac{W}{k}.$$

1

Denoting a vertical displacement of the vibrating weight from its position of equilibrium by x and considering this displacement as positive if it is in a downward direction, the expression for the tensile force in the spring corresponding to any position of the weight becomes

$$F = W + kx. \tag{a}$$

In deriving the differential equation of motion we will use Newton's principle stating that the product of the mass of a particle and its acceleration is equal to the force acting in the direction of acceleration. In our case the mass of the vibrating body is W/g, where g is the acceleration due to gravity; the acceleration of the body is given by the second derivative of the displacement x with respect to time and will be denoted by $\ddot{x}$; the forces acting on the vibrating body are the gravity force W, acting downwards, and the force F of the spring (eq. a) which, for the position of the weight indicated in Fig. 1, acts upwards. Thus the differential equation of motion in the case under consideration is

$$\frac{W}{g}\ddot{x} = W - (W + kx). \tag{b}$$

This equation holds for any position of the body. If, for instance, the body in its vibrating motion takes a position above the position of equilibrium and such that a compressive force in the spring is produced, expression (a) becomes negative, and both terms on the right side of eq. (b) have the same sign. Thus in this case the force in the spring is added to the gravity force as it should be.

Introducing the notation

$$p^2 = \frac{kg}{W} = \frac{g}{\delta_{st}}, \tag{c}$$

eq. (b) can be represented in the following form

$$\ddot{x} + p^2 x = 0. \tag{1}$$

This equation will be satisfied if we put $x = C_1 \cos pt$ or $x = C_2 \sin pt$, where C_1 and C_2 are arbitrary constants. By adding these solutions, the general solution of eq. (1) will be obtained:

$$x = C_1 \cos pt + C_2 \sin pt. \tag{2}$$

It is seen that the vertical motion of the weight W has a vibratory character, since $\cos pt$ and $\sin pt$ are periodic functions which repeat themselves after an interval of time τ such that

$$p(\tau + t) - pt = 2\pi. \tag{d}$$

This interval of time is called the *period* of vibration. Its magnitude, from eq. (d), is

$$\tau = \frac{2\pi}{p}$$

or, by using notation (c),

$$\tau = 2\pi \sqrt{\frac{W}{kg}} = 2\pi \sqrt{\frac{\delta_{st}}{g}}. \tag{3}$$

It is seen that the period of vibration depends only on the magnitude of the weight W and of the spring constant k and is independent of the magnitude of oscillations. We can say also that the period of oscillation of the suspended weight W is the same as that of a mathematical pendulum, the length of which is equal to the statical deflection δ_{st}. If the statical deflection δ_{st} is determined theoretically or experimentally the period τ can be calculated from eq. (3).

The number of cycles per unit time, say per second, is called the *frequency* of vibration. Denoting frequency by f we obtain

$$f = \frac{1}{\tau} = \frac{1}{2\pi} \sqrt{\frac{g}{\delta_{st}}}. \tag{4}$$

A vibratory motion represented by eq. (2) is called a *harmonic motion*. In order to determine the constants of integration C_1 and C_2, the initial conditions must be considered. Assume, for instance, that at the initial moment ($t = 0$) the weight W has a displacement x_0 from its position of equilibrium and that its initial velocity is $\dot{x}_0$. Substituting $t = 0$ in eq. (2) we obtain

$$x_0 = C_1. \tag{e}$$

Taking now the derivative of eq. (2) with respect to time and substituting in this derivative $t = 0$, we have

$$\frac{\dot{x}_0}{p} = C_2. \tag{f}$$

Substituting in eq. (2) the values of the constants (e) and (f), the following expression for the vibratory motion of the weight W will be obtained:

$$x = x_0 \cos pt + \frac{\dot{x}_0}{p} \sin pt. \tag{5}$$

It is seen that in this case the vibration consists of two parts: a vibration which is proportional to $\cos pt$ and depends on the initial displacement of the weight and another which is proportional to $\sin pt$ and depends on the initial velocity $\dot{x}_0$. Each of these parts can be represented graphically, as shown in Figs. 2a and 2b, by plotting displacements against time. The total displacement x of the oscillating weight W at any instant t is obtained by adding together the ordinates of the two curves for that instant to obtain the curve shown in Fig. 2c.

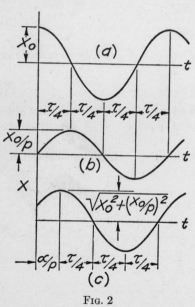

Fig. 2

Another method of representing vibrations is by means of rotating vectors. Imagine a vector $\overline{OA}$ (Fig. 3) of magnitude x_0 rotating with constant angular velocity p around a fixed point, O. This velocity is called the *angular frequency* of vibration. If at the initial moment ($t = 0$) the vector $\overline{OA}$ coincides with the x-axis, the angle which it makes with the same axis at any instant t is equal to pt. The projection OA_1 of this vector on the x-axis is equal to $x_0 \cos pt$ and represents the first term of expression (5). Taking now another vector $\overline{OB}$ equal to $\dot{x}_0/p$ and perpendicular to the vector $\overline{OA}$, its projection on the x-axis gives the second term of expression (5). The total displacement x of the oscillating weight is obtained now by adding the projections on the x-axis of the two perpendicular vectors $\overline{OA}$ and $\overline{OB}$, rotating with the angular velocity p.

The same result will be obtained if, instead of vectors $\overline{OA}$ and $\overline{OB}$, we consider the vector $\overline{OC}$, equal to the geometrical sum of the previous two vectors, and take the projection of this vector on the x-axis. The magnitude of this vector, from Fig. 3, is

$$\overline{OC} = \sqrt{x_0{}^2 + \left(\frac{\dot{x}_0}{p}\right)^2}, \qquad (g)$$

and the angle which it makes with the x-axis is

$$pt - \alpha,$$

where

$$\alpha = \arctan \frac{\dot{x}_0}{px_0}, \qquad (h)$$

From the above discussion, it is evident that eq. (5) can be expressed in the equivalent form

$$x = \overline{OC} \cos{(pt - \alpha)}. \qquad (6)$$

where $\overline{OC}$ and α, as represented by expressions (g) and (h), are new constants depending on the initial conditions of motion. It is seen that the addition of two simple harmonic motions, one proportional to $\cos pt$ and the other to $\sin pt$, is again a simple harmonic motion proportional to $\cos{(pt - \alpha)}$ as represented graphically in Fig. 2c. The maximum ordinate of this curve, equal to the vector $\overline{OC}$ in Fig. 3, represents the maximum displacement of the vibrating body from its position of equilibrium; it is called the *amplitude of vibration*.

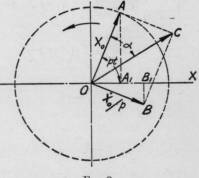

Fig. 3

Due to the angle α between the two rotating vectors $\overline{OA}$ and $\overline{OC}$ the maximum ordinate of the curve (Fig. 2c) is displaced with respect to the maximum ordinate of the curve (Fig. 2a) by the amount α/p. In such a case it may be said that the vibration, represented by the curve (Fig. 2c) is behind the vibration represented by the curve (Fig. 2a) and the angle α is called the *phase difference* of these two vibrations.

EXAMPLES

1. A weight $W = 30$ lb is vertically suspended on a steel wire of length $l = 50$ in. and of cross-sectional area $A = 0.001$ in.^{2}. Determine the frequency of free vibrations

of the weight if the modulus for steel is $E = 30 \cdot 10^6$ lb per sq in. Determine the amplitude of this vibration if the initial displacement $x_0 = 0.01$ in. and initial velocity $\dot{x}_0 = 1$ in. per sec.

Solution. Static elongation of the wire is $\delta_{st} = 30 \cdot 50/(30 \cdot 10^6 \cdot 0.001) = 0.05$ in. Then, from eq. (4), $f = 3.13\sqrt{20} = 14.0$ sec^{-1}. The amplitude of vibration, from eq. (*g*), is $\sqrt{x_0{}^2 + (\dot{x}_0/p)^2} = \sqrt{(0.01)^2 + [1/(2\pi \cdot 14)]^2} = 0.01513$ in.

2. A load W is supported by a beam of length l, Fig. 4. Determine the spring constant and the frequency of free vibration of the load in the vertical direction, neglecting the mass of the beam.

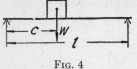

FIG. 4

Solution. The static deflection of the beam under the load is

$$\delta_{st} = \frac{Wc^2(l - c)^2}{3lEI}.$$

Here c is the distance of the load from the left end of the beam and EI, the flexural rigidity of the beam in the vertical plane. It is assumed that this plane contains one of the two principal axes of the cross section of the beam, so that vertical loads produce only vertical deflections. By definition the spring constant in this case is

$$k = \frac{3lEI}{c^2(l - c)^2}.$$

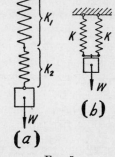

FIG. 5

Substituting δ_{st} in eq. (4), the required frequency can be calculated. The effect of the mass of the beam on the frequency of vibration will be discussed later.

3. A load W is vertically suspended on two springs as shown in Fig. 5*a*. Determine the resultant spring constant and the frequency of vertical vibration of the load if the spring constants of the two springs are k_1 and k_2. Determine the frequency of vibration of the load W if it is suspended on two equal springs as shown in Fig. 5*b*.

Solution. In the case shown in Fig. 5*a* the statical deflection of the load W is

$$\delta_{st} = \frac{W}{k_1} + \frac{W}{k_2} = \frac{W(k_1 + k_2)}{k_1 k_2}.$$

The resultant spring constant is $k_1 k_2/(k_1 + k_2)$. Substituting δ_{st} in eq. (4), the frequency of vibration becomes

$$f = \frac{1}{2\pi} \sqrt{\frac{g k_1 k_2}{W(k_1 + k_2)}}.$$

In the case shown in Fig. 5*b*,

$$\delta_{st} = \frac{W}{2k} \quad \text{and} \quad f = \frac{1}{2\pi} \sqrt{\frac{2gk}{W}}.$$

4. Determine the period of horizontal vibrations of the frame, shown in Fig. 6, supporting a load W applied at the center. The mass of the frame should be neglected in this calculation.

Solution. We begin with a statical problem and determine the horizontal deflection δ of the frame which a horizontal force H acting at the point of application of the load W will produce. Neglecting deformations due to tension and compression in the members and considering only bending, the horizontal bar AB is bent by two equal couples of magnitude $Hh/2$. Then the angle α of rotation of the joints A and B is

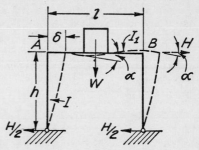

$$\alpha = \frac{Hhl}{12EI_1}.$$

Considering now the vertical members of the frame as cantilevers bent by the horizontal forces $H/2$, the horizontal deflection δ will

Fig. 6

consist of two parts, one due to bending of the cantilevers and the second due to the rotation α of the joints A and B calculated above. Hence

$$\delta = \frac{Hh^3}{6EI} + \frac{Hh^2l}{12EI_1} = \frac{Hh^3}{6EI}\left(1 + \frac{1}{2}\frac{l}{h}\frac{I}{I_1}\right).$$

The spring constant in such case is

$$k = \frac{H}{\delta} = \frac{6EI}{h^3\left(1 + \dfrac{1}{2}\dfrac{l}{h}\dfrac{I}{I_1}\right)}.$$

Substituting in eq. (3), we obtain

$$\tau = 2\pi\sqrt{\frac{Wh^3\left(1 + \dfrac{1}{2}\dfrac{l}{h}\dfrac{I}{I_1}\right)}{6gEI}}.$$

If the rigidity of the horizontal member is large in comparison with the rigidity of the verticals, the term containing the ratio I/I_1 is small and can be neglected. Then

$$\tau = 2\pi\sqrt{\frac{Wh^3}{6gEI}}$$

and the frequency is

$$f = \frac{1}{2\pi}\sqrt{\frac{6gEI}{Wh^3}}.$$

5. Assuming that the load W in Fig. 7 represents the cage of an elevator moving down with constant velocity v_0 and the spring consists of a steel cable, determine the maximum stress in the cable if during motion the upper end A of the cable is suddenly stopped. Assume that the weight $W = 10,000$ lb, $l = 60$ ft, the cross-sectional area of the cable $A = 2.5$ sq in., modulus of elasticity of the cable $E = 15 \cdot 10^6$ lb per sq in., $v_0 = 3$ ft per sec. The weight of the cable is to be neglected.

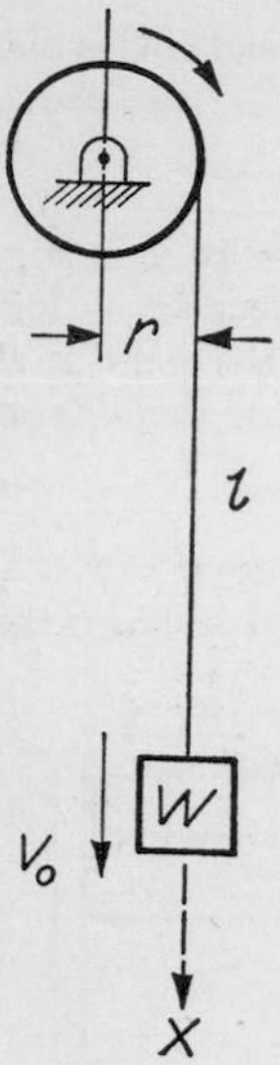

Solution. During the uniform motion of the cage the tensile force in the cable is equal to $W = 10,000$ lb and the elongation of the cable at the instant of the accident is $\delta_{st} = Wl/AE = 0.192$ in. Due to the velocity v_0 the cage will not stop suddenly and will vibrate on the cable. Counting time from the instant of the accident, the displacement of the cage from the position of equilibrium at that instant is zero and its velocity is v_0. From eq. (5) we conclude that the amplitude of vibration will be equal to v_0/p, where $p = \sqrt{g/\delta_{st}} = 44.8$ sec^{-1} and $v_0 = 36$ in. per sec. Hence the maximum elongation of the cable is $\delta_d = \delta_{st} + v_0/p = 0.192 + 36/44.8 = 0.192 + 0.803 = 0.995$ in. and the maximum stress is $(10,000/2.5)(0.995/0.192) = 20,750$ lb per sq in. It is seen that due to the sudden stoppage of the upper end of the cable the stress in the cable increased in this case about five times.

Fig. 7

PROBLEMS

1. The helical spring in Fig. 1 has a mean coil diameter $D = 1$ in., a wire diameter $d = 0.1$ in., and contains $n = 20$ coils. The modulus of elasticity of the wire in shear is $G = 12(10)^6$ lb per sq in. and the suspended weight $W = 30$ lb. Calculate the period of free vibration.

Answer. $\tau = 0.64$ sec.

2. The beam shown in Fig. 4 has a span $l = 12$ ft and a T cross section as shown in Fig. 8. The material is aluminum for which the modulus of elasticity $E = 10(10)^6$ lb per sq in. The weight $W = 500$ lb. Calculate the frequency of free vertical vibrations

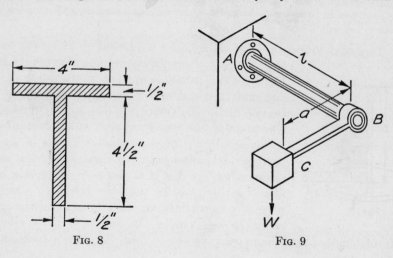

Fig. 8   Fig. 9

when the load W has the position for which $c = 4$ ft. Neglect the effect of the mass of the beam itself.

Answer. $f = 6.47$ osc. per sec.

3. What maximum dynamical deflection δ_{max} will be produced if the weight W of the preceding problem is dropped onto the beam at mid-span from a height $h = 1$ in. above the level of the supports?

Answer. $\delta_{max} = 1.125$ in.

4. Calculate the frequency of free vertical vibration of the weight $W = 10$ lb in Fig. 9. The solid circular shaft AB is firmly fixed to the wall at A and has length $l = 3$ ft and diameter $d = 1$ in. The cantilever strip BC is rigidly attached to the shaft at B and has length $a = 1$ ft, width $b = 1$ in. and thickness $t = \frac{1}{4}$ in. All material is of steel for which $E = 30(10)^6$ lb per sq in. and $G = 12(10)^6$ lb per sq in.

Answer. $f = 5.74$ osc. per sec.

5. To reduce the maximum dynamical stress occurring under the conditions of Ex. 5, a short spring having the spring constant $k = 2000$ lb per in. is inserted between the lower end of the cable and the elevator cage. Calculate the maximum dynamical stress that will result in this case when the upper end of the cable is suddenly stopped. Take the same numerical data as given in Ex. 5.

Answer. $\sigma_{max} = 7200$ lb per sq in.

6. A portal frame consists of a heavy 24 in. I-beam 20 ft long supported by two relatively flexible columns each 14 ft long as shown in Fig. 10. Each column is a channel section having cross-sectional area $A = 4.02$ sq in. and least radius of gyration $r = 0.62$ in. $E = 30(10)^6$ lb per sq in. Calculate the

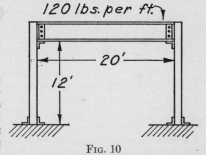

Fig. 10

natural period of lateral vibration in the plane of the frame: a) assuming complete fixity at A and B; b) assuming hinges at A and B. Neglect bending of the I-beam.

Answer. $\tau_1 = 0.813$ sec, $\tau_2 = 1.62$ sec.

2. Torsional Vibration.—Let us consider a vertical shaft to the lower end of which a circular horizontal disc is attached, Fig. 11. If a torque is applied in the plane of the disc and then suddenly removed, free torsional vibration of the shaft with the disc will be produced. The angular position of the disc at any instant can be defined by the angle φ which a radius of the vibrating disc makes with the direction of the same radius when the disc is at rest. As the spring constant in this case we take the torque k which is necessary to produce an angle of twist of the shaft equal to one radian. In the case of a circular shaft of length l and diameter d we obtain from the known formula for

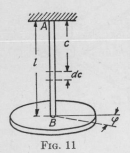

Fig. 11

the angle of twist

$$k = \frac{\pi d^4 G}{32l}.$$ (a)

For any angle of twist φ during vibration the torque in the shaft is $k\varphi$. The equation of motion in the case of a body rotating with respect to an immovable axis states that the moment of inertia of the body with respect to this axis multiplied by the angular acceleration is equal to the moment of the external forces acting on the body with respect to the axis of rotation. In our case this moment is equal and opposite to the torque $k\varphi$ acting on the shaft and the equation of motion becomes

$$I\ddot{\varphi} = -k\varphi$$ (b)

where I denotes the moment of inertia of the disc with respect to the axis of rotation, which in this case coincides with the axis of the shaft, and $\ddot{\varphi}$ is the angular acceleration of the disc. Introducing the notation

$$p^2 = \frac{k}{I},$$ (c)

the equation of motion (b) becomes

$$\ddot{\varphi} + p^2\varphi = 0.$$ (7)

This equation has the same form as eq. (1) of the previous article, hence its solution has the same form as solution (5) and we obtain

$$\varphi = \varphi_0 \cos pt + \frac{\dot{\varphi}_0}{p} \sin pt,$$ (8)

where φ_0 and $\dot{\varphi}_0$ are the angular displacement and angular velocity, respectively, of the disc at the initial instant $t = 0$. Proceeding as in the previous article, we conclude from eq. (8) that the period of torsional vibration is

$$\tau = \frac{2\pi}{p} = 2\pi \sqrt{\frac{I}{k}}$$ (9)

and its frequency is

$$f = \frac{1}{\tau} = \frac{1}{2\pi} \sqrt{\frac{k}{I}}.$$ (10)

In the case of a circular disc of uniform thickness and of diameter D,

$$I = \frac{WD^2}{8g},$$

where W is the weight of the disc. Substituting this in eqs. (9) and (10), and using expression (a), we obtain

$$\tau = 2\pi \sqrt{\frac{4WD^2l}{\pi g d^4 G}}, \quad f = \frac{1}{2\pi} \sqrt{\frac{\pi g d^4 G}{4WD^2l}}. \tag{d}$$

It was assumed in our discussion that the shaft has a constant diameter d. When the shaft consists of parts of different diameters it can be readily reduced to an *equivalent shaft* having a constant diameter. Assume, for instance, that a shaft consists of two parts of lengths l_1 and l_2 and of diameters d_1 and d_2, respectively. If a torque M_t is applied to this shaft the angle of twist produced is

$$\varphi = \frac{32M_t l_1}{\pi d_1^4 G} + \frac{32M_t l_2}{\pi d_2^4 G} = \frac{32M_t}{\pi d_1^4 G} \left(l_1 + l_2 \frac{d_1^4}{d_2^4} \right).$$

It is seen that the angle of twist of a shaft with two diameters d_1 and d_2 is the same as that of a shaft of constant diameter d_1 and of a reduced length L given by the equation

$$L = l_1 + l_2 \frac{d_1^4}{d_2^4}.$$

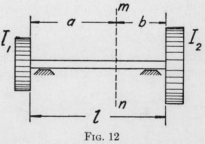

Fig. 12

The shaft of length L and diameter d_1 has the same spring constant as the given shaft of two different diameters and is an *equivalent* shaft in this case.

In general if we have a shaft consisting of portions with different diameters we can, without changing the spring constant of the shaft, replace any portion of the shaft of length l_n and of diameter d_n by a portion of a shaft of diameter d and of length l determined from the equation

$$l = l_n \frac{d^4}{d_n^4}. \tag{11}$$

The results obtained for the case shown in Fig. 11 can be used also in the case of a shaft with two rotating masses at the ends as shown in Fig. 12.

Such a case is of practical importance since an arrangement of this kind may be encountered very often in machine design. A propeller shaft with the propeller on one end and the engine on the other is an example of this kind.* If two equal and opposite twisting couples are applied at the ends of the shaft in Fig. 12 and then suddenly removed, torsional vibrations will be produced during which the masses at the ends are always rotating in opposite directions.† From this fact it can be concluded at once that there is a certain intermediate cross section mn of the shaft which remains immovable during vibrations. This cross section is called the *nodal cross section*, and its position will be found from the condition that both portions of the shaft, to the right and to the left of the nodal cross section, must have the same period of vibration, since otherwise the condition that the masses at the ends always are rotating in opposite directions will not be fulfilled.

Applying eq. (9) to each of the two portions of the shaft, we obtain

$$\sqrt{\frac{I_1}{k_1}} = \sqrt{\frac{I_2}{k_2}}, \quad \text{or} \quad \frac{k_1}{k_2} = \frac{I_1}{I_2}, \tag{e}$$

where k_1 and k_2 are the spring constants for the left and for the right portions of the shaft respectively. These quantities, as seen from eq. (a), are inversely proportional to the lengths of the corresponding portions of the shaft and from eq. (e) follows

$$\frac{a}{b} = \frac{I_2}{I_1}$$

and, since $a + b = l$, we obtain

$$a = \frac{lI_2}{I_1 + I_2}, \quad b = \frac{lI_1}{I_1 + I_2}. \tag{f}$$

Applying now to the left portion of the shaft eqs. (9) and (10) we obtain

---

* This is the case in which engineers for the first time found it of practical importance to go into investigation of vibrations, see H. Frahm, *Z. Ver. deut. Ing.*, p. 797, 1902.

† This follows from the principle of moment of momentum. At the initial instant the moment of momentum of the two discs with respect to the axis of the shaft is zero and must remain zero since the moment of external forces with respect to the same axis is zero (friction forces are neglected). The equality to zero of moment of momentum requires that both masses rotate in opposite directions.

$$\tau = 2\pi \sqrt{\frac{I_1}{k_1}} = 2\pi \sqrt{\frac{32lI_1I_2}{\pi d^4 G(I_1 + I_2)}}, \tag{12}$$

$$f = \frac{1}{2\pi} \sqrt{\frac{\pi d^4 G(I_1 + I_2)}{32lI_1I_2}}. \tag{13}$$

From these formulas the period and the frequency of torsional vibration can be calculated, provided the dimensions of the shaft, the modulus G and the moments of inertia of the masses at the ends are known. The mass of the shaft is neglected in our present discussion and its effect on the period of vibration will be considered later.

It can be seen from eq. (f) that if one of the rotating masses has a very large moment of inertia in comparison with the other, the nodal cross section can be taken at the larger mass and the system with two masses (Fig. 12) reduces to that with one mass (Fig. 11).

EXAMPLES

1. Determine the frequency of torsional vibration of a shaft with two circular discs of uniform thickness at the ends, Fig. 12, if the weights of the discs are $W_1 = 1000$ lb and $W_2 = 2000$ lb and their outer diameters are $D_1 = 50$ in. and $D_2 = 75$ in. respectively. The length of the shaft is $l = 120$ in. and its diameter $d = 4$ in. Modulus in shear $G = 12 \cdot 10^6$ lb per sq in.

Solution. From eqs. (f) the distance of the nodal cross section from the larger disc is

$$a = \frac{120 \cdot 1000 \cdot 50^2}{1000 \cdot 50^2 + 2000 \cdot 75^2} = \frac{120}{1 + 4.5} = 21.8 \text{ in.}$$

Substituting in the second of eqs. (d) we obtain

$$f = \frac{1}{2\pi} \sqrt{\frac{\pi \cdot 386 \cdot 4^4 \cdot 12 \cdot 10^6}{4 \cdot 2000 \cdot 75^2 \cdot 21.8}} = 9.80 \text{ osc. per sec.}$$

2. In what proportion will the frequency of vibration of the shaft considered in the previous example increase if along a length of 64 in. the diameter of the shaft will be increased from 4 in. to 8 in.?

Solution. The length of 64 in. of 8 in. diameter shaft can be replaced by a 4 in. length of 4 in. diameter shaft. Thus the length of the equivalent shaft is $4 + 56 = 60$ in., which is only one-half of the length of the shaft considered in the previous problem. Since the frequency of vibration is inversely proportional to the square root of the length of the shaft (see eq. 13), we conclude that as the result of the reinforcement of the shaft its frequency increases in the ratio $\sqrt{2}:1$.

3. Determine the frequency of vibration of the ring, Fig. 13, about the axis O, assuming that the center of the ring remains fixed and that rotation of the rim is accompanied by some bending of the spokes indicated in the figure by dotted lines. Assume that the total mass of the ring is distributed along the center line of the rim and take the length of the spokes equal to the radius r of this center line. Assume also that the bending

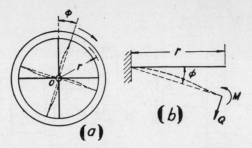

Fig. 13

of the rim can be neglected so that the tangents to the deflection curves of the spokes have radial directions at the rim. The total weight of the ring W and the flexural rigidity B of spokes are given.

Solution. Considering each spoke as a cantilever of length r, Fig. 13b, at the end of which a shearing force Q and a bending moment M are acting and using the known formulas for bending of a cantilever, the following expressions for the slope φ and the deflection $r\varphi$ at the end are obtained

$$\varphi = \frac{Qr^2}{2B} - \frac{Mr}{B}, \quad r\phi = \frac{Qr^3}{3B} - \frac{Mr^2}{2B},$$

from which

$$M = \frac{Qr}{3} = \frac{2B\phi}{r}.$$

If M_t denotes the torque applied to the rim we have

$$M_t = 4Qr - 4M = \frac{16B\phi}{r}.$$

The torque required to produce an angle of rotation of the rim equal to one radian is the spring constant and is equal to $k = 16B/r$. Substituting in eq. (10), we obtain the required frequency

$$f = \frac{1}{2\pi}\sqrt{\frac{16B}{rI}} = \frac{1}{2\pi}\sqrt{\frac{16gB}{Wr^3}}.$$

PROBLEMS

1. Determine the frequency of torsional vibration of the disc shown in Fig. 14 if the ends of the shaft are built in at A and B. The two portions of the shaft have the same diameter d but different lengths l_1 and l_2. The disc has moment of inertia I.

Answer. $\quad f = \dfrac{1}{2\pi} \sqrt{\dfrac{\pi d^4 G(l_1 + l_2)}{32 I l_1 l_2}}.$

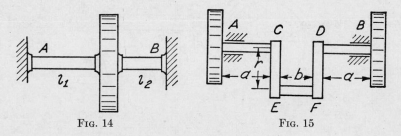

FIG. 14   FIG. 15

2. Determine the equivalent length l of a straight shaft having the same torsional rigidity C_1 as the journals of the crankshaft shown in Fig. 15. The crank webs CE and DF have flexural rigidity B. Assume that the bearings at A and B have sufficient clearance to allow free lateral deflection of C and D during twist of the crankshaft. The crankpin EF has torsional rigidity C_2 and throw-radius r.

Answer. $\quad l = 2a + \dfrac{C_1}{C_2} b + 2 \dfrac{C_1}{B} r.$

3. Two parallel shafts AB and CD are supported in bearings and geared together as shown in Fig. 16. Each shaft carries a heavy disc at its outer end and the system per-

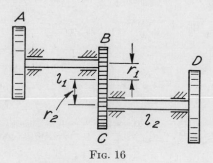

FIG. 16

forms torsional vibrations. Calculate the period of vibration for the following numerical data: $I_a = I_b = 1000$ lb-sec^2-in.; $l_1 = l_2 = 60$ in.; $d_1 = d_2 = 3$ in.; $r_1/r_2 = \tfrac{1}{2}$. Neglect the inertia of the two gears and shafts. Shear modulus $G = 12(10)^6$ lb per sq in.

Answer. $\quad \tau = 0.249$ sec.

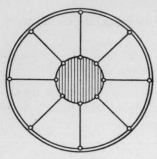

FIG. 17

4. Referring again to the system in Fig. 16, find the general expression for the equivalent length l of a single shaft of diameter d_1 connecting the two discs A and D.

Answer. $l = l_1 + \left(\dfrac{d_1}{d_2}\right)^4 \left(\dfrac{r_2}{r_1}\right)^2 l_2.$

5. A circular steel rim of weight W and mean radius r is attached to a fixed hub of radius r_0 by n radial spokes, each of which carries a high initial tension S_0, Fig. 17. Determine the period of torsional oscillation of the rim, assuming that the tension in each spoke remains constant for small amplitudes of oscillation. The spokes are pinned at the ends and cannot suffer bending.

Answer. $\tau = 2\pi \sqrt{\dfrac{Wr(r - r_0)}{ngS_0r_0}}.$

3. Application of Equation of Energy in Vibration Problems.—Natural frequencies of vibrating systems can sometimes be advantageously calculated by using the law of conservation of energy, providing that damping is negligible. Consider, for example, the system shown in Fig. 1. Neglecting the mass of the spring and considering only the mass of the suspended body, the kinetic energy of the system during vibration is

$$\frac{W}{2g} \dot{x}^2. \qquad (a)$$

The potential energy of the system in this case consists of two parts: (1) the potential energy of deformation of the spring and (2) the potential energy of the weight W by virtue of its position. Considering the energy of deformation, the tension in the spring corresponding to any displacement x from the equilibrium position, is $k(\delta_{st} + x)$ and the corresponding strain energy is $k(\delta_{st} + x)^2/2$. At the position of equilibrium ($x = 0$) this energy is $k\delta^2{}_{st}/2$. Hence the energy stored in the spring during the displacement x is

$$\frac{k(\delta_{st} + x)^2}{2} - \frac{k\delta^2{}_{st}}{2} = Wx + \frac{kx^2}{2}. \qquad (b)$$

The energy due to position of the load diminishes during the displacement x by the amount Wx. Hence the total change of the potential energy of the system is, simply,

$$\frac{kx^2}{2}. \qquad (c)$$

Having expressions (*a*) and (*c*) and neglecting damping, the equation of energy becomes

$$\frac{W}{2g}\dot{x}^2 + \frac{kx^2}{2} = \text{const.} \tag{d}$$

The magnitude of the constant on the right side of this equation is determined by the initial conditions. Assuming that at the initial instant, $t = 0$, the displacement of the body is x_0 and the initial velocity is zero, the initial total energy of the system is $kx_0^2/2$ and eq. (*d*) becomes

$$\frac{W}{2g}\dot{x}^2 + \frac{kx^2}{2} = \frac{kx_0^2}{2}. \tag{e}$$

It is seen that during vibration the sum of the kinetic and potential energy remains always equal to the initial strain energy. When in the oscillatory motion x becomes equal to x_0 the velocity $\dot{x}$ becomes equal to zero and the energy of the system consists of the potential energy only. When x becomes equal to zero, i.e., the vibrating load is passing through its middle position, the velocity has its maximum value and we obtain, from eq. (*e*),

$$\frac{W}{2g}\dot{x}^2{}_{\max} = \frac{kx_0^2}{2}. \tag{14}$$

Thus the maximum kinetic energy is equal to the strain energy stored in the system during its displacement to the extreme position, $x = x_0$.

In all cases in which it can be assumed that the motion of a vibrating body is a simple harmonic motion, which is usually correct for small vibrations,* we can use eq. (14) for the calculation of the frequency of vibration. We assume that the motion is given by the equation $x = x_0 \sin pt$. Then $(\dot{x})_{\max} = x_0 p$. Substituting in eq. (14) we obtain

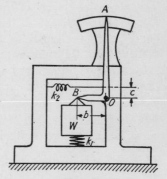

$$p^2 = \frac{kg}{W}. \tag{f}$$

Fig. 18

This coincides with the result, previously obtained, p. 2.

The use of eq. (14) in calculating frequencies is especially advantageous if instead of a simple problem, as in Fig. 1, we have a more complicated

* Some exceptional cases are discussed in Chapter II.

system. As an example let us consider the frequency of free vibrations of the weight W of an *amplitude meter* shown in Fig. 18.

In order to obtain the frequency of the free vibrations of the instrument with greater accuracy, not only the weight W and the spring k_1, but also the arm AOB and the spring k_2 must be taken into consideration. Let x denote a small vertical displacement of the weight W from the position of equilibrium. Then the potential energy of the two springs with the spring constants k_1 and k_2 will be

$$\frac{k_1 x^2}{2} + \frac{k_2}{2}\left(\frac{c}{b}\right)^2 x^2. \tag{g}$$

The kinetic energy of the weight W will be, as before,

$$\frac{W}{2g}\dot{x}^2. \tag{h}$$

The angular velocity of the arm AOB rotating about the point O is

$$\frac{\dot{x}}{b}$$

and the kinetic energy of the same arm is

$$\frac{I}{2}\frac{\dot{x}^2}{b^2}, \tag{i}$$

where I is the moment of inertia of the arm with respect to point O.

Now the equation of motion, corresponding to eq. (d) above, will be from (g), (h) and (i),

$$\left(\frac{W}{2g} + \frac{I}{2b^2}\right)\dot{x}^2 + \left(\frac{k_1}{2} + \frac{k_2}{2}\frac{c^2}{b^2}\right)x^2 = \text{const.} \tag{j}$$

We see that this equation has the same form as eq. (d); only instead of the mass W/g we have now the *modified* mass

$$\frac{W}{g} + \frac{I}{b^2}$$

and instead of the spring constant k we have the *modified spring constant* $k_1 + k_2(c^2/b^2)$.

As another example let us consider torsional vibrations of a shaft one end of which is fixed and to the other end is attached a disc connected with a piston as shown in Fig. 19. We consider only small rotatory oscillations about its middle position given by the angle α. If φ is the angle of twist of the shaft at any instant, the potential energy of the system, which in this case is the strain energy of torsion of the shaft, is equal to $k\varphi^2/2$, where k is the spring constant of the shaft. In calculating the kinetic energy of the system we have to consider the kinetic energy of the rotating parts, equal to $I\dot\varphi^2/2$ and also the kinetic energy of the reciprocating masses.* In calculating the kinetic energy of the reciprocating masses, the total weight of which we denote by W, it is necessary to have the ex-

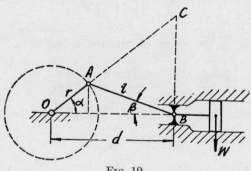

Fig. 19

pression for the velocity of these masses during torsional vibration. The angular velocity $\dot\theta$ of the connecting rod AB with respect to the instantaneous center C, Fig. 19, can be obtained from the consideration of the velocity of the point A. Considering this point as belonging to the disc its velocity during vibration is $r\dot\varphi$. The velocity of the same point, as belonging to the connecting rod, is $\overline{AC}\theta$ and we obtain

$$r\dot\varphi = \overline{AC}\theta = \frac{l\cos\beta}{\cos\alpha}\theta \qquad (k)$$

where l is the length of the connecting rod and β its angle of inclination to the horizontal. From this equation

$$\dot\theta = \frac{r\dot\varphi\cos\alpha}{l\cos\beta} \qquad (l)$$

* The mass of the connecting rod can be replaced by two masses, $m_1 = I_1/l^2$ at the crankpin and $m_2 = m - m_1$ at the crosshead, where m is the total mass of the connecting rod and I_1 its moment of inertia about the center of the crosshead. This is the usual way of replacing the connecting rod, see Max Tolle, *Regelung der Kraftmaschinen*, 3d Ed., p. 116, 1921.

and the velocity of the reciprocating masses is

$$\dot{x} = \dot{\theta}\overline{BC} = \dot{\theta}(l \cos \beta + r \cos \alpha) \tan \alpha = r\dot{\varphi} \sin \alpha \left(1 + \frac{r \cos \alpha}{l \cos \beta}\right). \quad (m)$$

We obtain also from the figure

$$r \sin \alpha = l \sin \beta.$$

Hence

$$\sin \beta = \frac{r}{l} \sin \alpha; \quad \cos \beta = \sqrt{1 - \frac{r^2}{l^2} \sin^2 \alpha} \approx 1 - \frac{1}{2}\frac{r^2}{l^2} \sin^2 \alpha. \quad (n)$$

If the ratio r/l is small we can assume with sufficient accuracy that $\cos \beta \approx 1$. Then the velocity of the reciprocating masses is

$$\dot{x} \approx r\dot{\varphi} \sin \alpha \left(1 + \frac{r}{l} \cos \alpha\right) \quad (o)$$

and the total kinetic energy of the system is

$$\frac{I\dot{\varphi}^2}{2} + \frac{W}{2g} r^2\dot{\varphi}^2 \sin^2 \alpha \left(1 + \frac{r}{l} \cos \alpha\right)^2.$$

The energy equation in this case becomes

$$\frac{I\dot{\varphi}^2}{2} + \frac{W}{2g} r^2\dot{\varphi}^2 \sin^2 \alpha \left(1 + \frac{r}{l} \cos \alpha\right)^2 = \frac{k\varphi_0^2}{2}. \quad (p)$$

The effect of the reciprocating masses on the frequency of torsional vibrations is the same as an increase in the moment of inertia of the disc obtained by adding to the circumference of the disc of a modified mass equal to

$$\frac{W}{g} \sin^2 \alpha \left(1 + \frac{r}{l} \cos \alpha\right)^2. \quad (q)$$

It is seen that the frequency depends on the magnitude of the angle α. When α is zero or π, the reciprocating masses do not affect the frequency and the effect becomes a maximum when α is approximately equal to $\pi/2$.

EXAMPLES

1. Calculate the frequencies of small vibrations of the pendulums shown in Figs. 20a, b, c, by using the equation of energy. Neglect the mass of the bar and assume that in each case the mass of the weight W is concentrated in its center.

Solution. If φ is the angle of inclination of the pendulum, Fig. 20a, and l its length, the kinetic energy of the pendulum is $W\dot{\varphi}^2l^2/2g$. The change in potential energy of the pendulum is due to vertical displacement $l(1 - \cos\varphi) \approx l\varphi^2/2$ of the weight W and the equation of energy becomes

$$\frac{W\dot{\varphi}^2 l^2}{2g} + \frac{Wl\varphi^2}{2} = \text{const.} \tag{r}$$

Assuming motion $\varphi = \varphi_0 \sin pt$ and writing an equation, similar to eq. (14), we obtain the angular frequency

$$p = \sqrt{\frac{g}{l}}.$$

In the case shown in Fig. 20b the strain energy of the springs must be added to the potential energy of the weight W in writing the equation of energy. If k is the spring

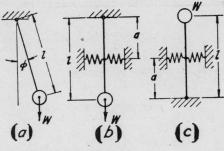

FIG. 20

constant, by taking into consideration both springs, the strain energy of springs is $k(a\varphi)^2/2$ and, instead of eq. (r), we obtain

$$\frac{W\dot{\varphi}^2 l^2}{2g} + (Wl + ka^2)\frac{\varphi^2}{2} = \text{const} \tag{s}$$

and the frequency of vibrations becomes

$$p = \sqrt{\frac{g}{l}\left(1 + \frac{ka^2}{Wl}\right)}.$$

In the case shown in Fig. 20c, the potential energy of the weight W, at any lateral displacement of the pendulum from a vertical position, decreases and by using the same reasoning as before we obtain

$$p = \sqrt{\frac{g}{l}\left(\frac{ka^2}{Wl} - 1\right)}.$$

It is seen that we obtain a real value for p only if

$$\frac{ka^2}{Wl} > 1 \quad \text{and} \quad W < \frac{ka^2}{l}.$$

If this condition is not satisfied the vertical position of equilibrium of the pendulum is not stable.

2. For recording of ship vibrations a device shown in Fig. 21 is used.[*] Determine the frequency of vertical vibrations of the weight W if the moment of inertia I of this weight, together with the bar BD about the fulcrum B is known.

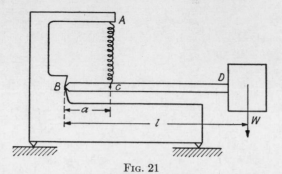

FIG. 21

Solution. Let φ be the angular displacement of the bar BD from its horizontal position of equilibrium and k the constant of the spring, then the energy stored during this displacement is $ka^2\varphi^2/2$ and the kinetic energy of the system is $I\dot\varphi^2/2$. The energy equation becomes

$$\frac{I\dot\varphi^2}{2} + \frac{ka^2\varphi^2}{2} = \text{const.}$$

Proceeding as in the case of eq. (*d*) we get for angular frequency the expression

$$p = \sqrt{\frac{ka^2}{I}}.$$

If we neglect the mass of the bar BD and assume the mass of the weight W concentrated in its center, $I = Wl^2/g$ and the frequency becomes

$$p = \sqrt{\frac{ka^2g}{Wl^2}} = \sqrt{\frac{a}{l}\frac{g}{\delta_{st}}},$$

where $\delta_{st} = Wl/ak$ is the statical elongation of the spring. Comparing this with eq. (4) it can be concluded that for the same elongation of the spring the horizontal pendulum has a much lower frequency than the device shown in Fig. 1, provided that the ratio a/l is sufficiently small. A low frequency of the vibration recorder is required in this case since the frequency of natural vibration of a large ship may be comparatively low, and the frequency of the instrument must be several times smaller than the frequency of vibrations which we are studying (see Art. 8).

3. Fig. 22 represents a heavy pendulum the axis of rotation of which makes a small angle α with the vertical. Determine the frequency of small vibration considering only the weight W which is assumed to be concentrated at its mass center C.

[*] This is O. Schlick's pallograph, see *Trans. Inst. Nav. Architects* (London), Vol. 34, p. 167, 1893.

Solution. If φ denotes a small angle of rotation of the pendulum about the inclined axis measured from the position of equilibrium, the corresponding elevation of the center C is

$$l(1 - \cos \varphi) \sin \alpha \approx \frac{l\varphi^2}{2} \alpha$$

and the equation of energy becomes

$$\frac{W}{2g} l^2 \dot{\varphi}^2 + \frac{W l \varphi^2 \alpha}{2} = \text{const.}$$

and the angular frequency of the pendulum is

$$p = \sqrt{\frac{g\alpha}{l}}.$$

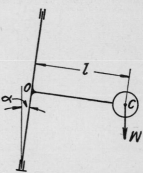

FIG. 22

It is seen that by choosing a small angle α the frequency of the pendulum may be made very low. This kind of pendulum is used sometimes in recording earthquake vibrations. To get two components of horizontal vibrations two instruments such as shown in Fig. 22 are used, one for the N.–S. component and the other for the E.–W. component.

PROBLEMS

1. Calculate the natural frequency of free vibration of the system in Fig. 18, for the following numerical data: $W = 5$ lb, $k_1 = 2$ lb/in., $k_2 = 10$ lb/in., $b = 4$ in., $c = 2$ in. Treat the arm BOA as a uniform slender rod of total weight $W' = 0.4$ lb and assume OA to be 12 in. long.

Answer. $f = 3.52$ osc. per sec.

2. When the system in Fig. 20c carries a weight $W_1 = 2$ lb at the top end of the vertical bar, the observed frequency is 90 osc. per min. With a weight $W_2 = 4$ lb, the observed frequency is 45 osc. per min. What weight W_3 at the top will just bring the system to a condition of unstable equilibrium? Neglect the weight of the bar.

Answer. $W_3 = 6$ lb.

3. Determine the angular frequency p for the system in Fig. 20c if the vertical bar has total weight wl uniformly distributed along its length.

Answer. $p = \sqrt{\dfrac{g}{l} \left[\dfrac{3ka^2/l}{3W + wl} - \dfrac{3}{4} \left(\dfrac{4W + 2wl}{3W + wl} \right) \right]}.$

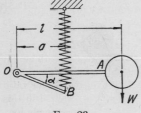

FIG. 23

4. For recording vertical vibrations the instrument shown in Fig. 23 is used, in which a rigid frame AOB carrying the weight W can rotate about an axis through O perpendicular to the plane of the figure. Determine the frequency of small vertical vibrations of the weight if the moment of inertia I of the frame together with the weight about the axis through O and the spring constant k are known and all dimensions are given.

Answer. $p = \sqrt{\dfrac{ka^2}{J}}.$

5. A prismatical bar AB suspended on two equal vertical wires, Fig. 24, performs small rotatory oscillations in the horizontal plane about the axis oo. Determine the frequency of these vibrations.

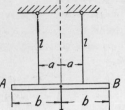

$$\textit{Answer.} \quad p = \sqrt{\frac{3ga^2}{lb^2}}.$$

6. What frequency will be produced if the wires in the previous problem will be placed at an angle β to the axis oo?

$$\textit{Answer.} \quad p = \sqrt{\sec \beta + \frac{l}{a}\tan \beta}\sqrt{\frac{3ga^2}{lb^2}}.$$

7. The journals of a rotor are supported by rails curved to a radius R, Fig. 25. Determine the frequency of small oscillations which the rotor performs when rolling without sliding on the rails. The rotor has moment of inertia I.

Fig. 24

Hint. If φ is the angle defining the position of the journals during oscillations and r is the radius of the journals, the angular velocity of the rotor during vibrations is

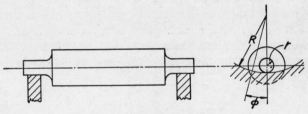

Fig. 25

$\varphi(R - r)/r$, the velocity of its center of gravity is $(R - r)\dot\varphi$ and the vertical elevation of this center is $(R - r)\varphi^2/2$.

$$\textit{Answer.} \quad p^2 = \frac{Wr^2}{\left(I + W\dfrac{r^2}{g}\right)(R - r)}.$$

8. A semicircular segment of a cylinder oscillates by rolling without sliding on a horizontal plane, Fig. 26. Determine the angular frequency of small vibrations if r is the radius of the cylinder, $c = \overline{OC}$ is the distance of center of gravity and $i^2 = Ig/W$, the square of the radius of gyration about centroidal axis.

$$\textit{Answer.} \quad p = \sqrt{\frac{cg}{i^2 + (r - c)^2}}.$$

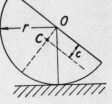

4. Rayleigh Method.—In all the previously considered cases, such as shown in Figs. 1, 4 and 11, by using certain simplifications the problem was

Fig. 26

reduced to the simplest case of vibration of a system with one degree of freedom. For instance, in the arrangement shown in Fig. 1, the mass of the spring was neglected in comparison with the mass of the weight W, while in the arrangement shown in Fig. 4 the mass of the beam was neglected and again in the case shown in Fig. 11 the moment of inertia of the shaft was neglected in comparison with the moment of inertia of the disc. Although these simplifications are accurate enough in many practical cases, there are technical problems in which a more detailed consideration of the accuracy of such approximations becomes necessary.

In order to determine the effect of such simplifications on the frequency of vibration an approximate method developed by Lord Rayleigh * will now be discussed. In applying this method some assumption regarding the configuration of the system during vibration has to be made. The frequency of vibration will then be found from a consideration of the energy of the system. As a simple example of the application of Rayleigh's method we take the case shown in Fig. 1 and discussed in Art. 3.

Assuming that the mass of the spring is small in comparison with the mass of the load W, the *type of vibration* will not be substantially affected by the mass of the spring and with a sufficient accuracy it can be assumed that the displacement of any cross section of the spring at a distance c from the fixed end is the same as in the case of a massless spring, i.e., equal to

$$\frac{xc}{l}, \tag{a}$$

where l is the length of the spring.

If the displacements, as assumed above, are not affected by the mass of the spring, the expression for the potential energy of the system will be the same as in the case of a massless spring (see eq. c, p. 16) and only the kinetic energy of the system has to be reconsidered. Let w denote the weight of the spring per unit length. Then the mass of an element of the spring of length dc will be wdc/g and the corresponding kinetic energy, by using eq. (a), becomes

$$\frac{w}{2g} \left(\frac{\dot{x}c}{l} \right)^2 dc.$$

The complete kinetic energy of the spring will be

$$\frac{w}{2g} \int_0^l \left(\frac{\dot{x}c}{l} \right)^2 dc = \frac{\dot{x}^2}{2g} \frac{wl}{3}. \tag{15}$$

* See his *Theory of Sound*, 2d Ed., Vol. 1, pp. 111 and 287, 1894.

This must be added to the kinetic energy of the weight W; so that the equation of energy becomes

$$\frac{\dot{x}^2}{2g}\left(W + \frac{wl}{3}\right) + \frac{kx^2}{2} = \frac{kx_0{}^2}{2}. \qquad (b)$$

Comparing this with eq. (e) of the previous article it can be concluded that in order to estimate the effect of the mass of the spring on the period of natural vibration it is only necessary to add one-third of the weight of the spring to the weight W.

This conclusion, obtained on the assumption that the weight of the spring is very small in comparison with that of the load, can be used with sufficient accuracy even in cases where the weight of the spring is of the same order as W. For instance, for $wl = 0.5W$, the error of the approximate solution is about $\frac{1}{2}\%$. For $wl = W$, the error is about $\frac{3}{4}\%$. For $wl = 2W$, the error is about 3%.*

As a second example consider the case of vibration of a beam of uniform cross section loaded at the middle (see Fig. 27). If the weight wl of the beam is small in comparison with the load W, it can be assumed with sufficient accuracy that the deflection curve of the beam during vibration has the same shape as the statical deflection curve. Then, denoting by x the displacement of the load W during vibration, the displacement of any element

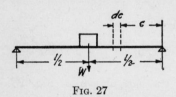

FIG. 27

wdc of the beam, distant c from the support, will be,

$$x \cdot \frac{3cl^2 - 4c^3}{l^3}.$$

The kinetic energy of the beam itself will be,

$$2\int_0^{l/2} \frac{w}{2g}\left(\dot{x}\,\frac{3cl^2 - 4c^3}{l^3}\right)^2 dc = \frac{17}{35}\,wl\,\frac{\dot{x}^2}{2g}. \qquad (16)$$

This kinetic energy of the vibrating beam must be added to the energy $W\dot{x}^2/2g$ of the load concentrated at the middle in order to estimate the effect of the weight of the beam on the period of vibration, i.e., the period of vibration will be the same as for a massless beam loaded at the middle by the load

$$W + (17/35)wl.$$

* A more detailed consideration of this problem is given in Art. 49.

It must be noted that eq. (16) obtained on the assumption that the weight of the beam is small in comparison with that of the load W, can be used in all practical cases. Even in the extreme case where $W = 0$ and where the assumption is made that $(17/35)wl$ is concentrated at the middle of the beam, the accuracy of the approximate method is sufficiently close for all practical cases. The deflection of the beam under the action of the load $(17/35)wl$ applied at the middle is,

$$\delta_{st} = \frac{17}{35} wl \cdot \frac{l^3}{48EI}.$$

Substituting this in eq. (3) (see p. 3) the period of the natural vibration is

$$\tau = 2\pi \sqrt{\frac{\delta_{st}}{g}} = 0.632 \sqrt{\frac{wl^4}{EIg}}.$$

The exact solution for this case * is

$$\tau = \frac{2}{\pi} \sqrt{\frac{wl^4}{EIg}} = 0.637 \sqrt{\frac{wl^4}{EIg}}.$$

It is seen that the error of the approximate solution for this limiting case is less than 1%.

The same method can be applied also in the case shown in Fig. 28. Assuming that during vibration the shape of the deflection curve of the beam is the same as the one produced by a load statically applied at the end and denoting by x the vertical displacement of the load W the kinetic energy of the cantilever beam of uniform cross section will be,

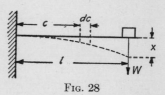

FIG. 28

$$\int_0^l \frac{w}{2g} \left(\dot{x} \frac{3c^2l - c^3}{2l^3} \right)^2 dc = \frac{33}{140} wl \frac{\dot{x}^2}{2g}. \tag{17}$$

The period of vibration will be the same as for a massless cantilever beam loaded at the end by the weight,

$$W + (33/140)wl.$$

This result was obtained on the assumption that the weight wl of the

* See Art. 52.

beam is small in comparison with W, but it is also accurate enough for cases where wl is not small. Applying the result to the extreme case where $W = 0$ we obtain

$$\delta_{st} = \frac{33}{140}\, wl\, \frac{l^3}{3EI}.$$

The corresponding period of vibration will be

$$\tau = 2\pi \sqrt{\frac{\delta_{st}}{g}} = \frac{2\pi}{3.567} \sqrt{\frac{wl^4}{EIg}}. \qquad (c)$$

The exact solution for the same case is *

$$\tau = \frac{2\pi}{3.515} \sqrt{\frac{wl^4}{EIg}}. \qquad (d)$$

It is seen that the error of the approximate solution is about $1\frac{1}{2}\%$. For the case $W = 0$ a better approximation can be obtained. It is only necessary to assume that during the vibration the shape of the deflection curve of the beam is the same as the one produced by a uniformly distributed load. The deflection y_0 at any cross section distant c from the built-in section will then be given by the following equation,

$$y_0 = x_0 \left[-\frac{1}{3} + \left(\frac{4c}{3l}\right) + \frac{1}{3}\left(1 - \frac{c}{l}\right)^4 \right], \qquad (e)$$

in which

$$x_0 = \frac{wl^4}{8EI}$$

represents the deflection of the end of the cantilever.

The potential energy of bending will be

$$V = \frac{w}{2} \int_0^l y_0\, dc = \frac{8}{5} \cdot \frac{EIx_0^2}{l^3}.$$

The kinetic energy of the vibrating beam is

$$T = \frac{1}{2} \int_0^l \frac{w}{g}\, \dot{y}^2\, dc.$$

Taking

$$y = y_0 \cos pt \quad \text{and} \quad (\dot{y})_{\max} = y_0 p,$$

* See Art 53.

eq. (14) for determining p becomes

$$\frac{1}{2} \int_0^l \frac{w}{g} (y_0 p)^2 \, dc = \frac{8}{5} \frac{EIx_0^2}{l^3}.$$

Substituting (e) for y_0 and performing the integration, we obtain

$$p = 3.530 \sqrt{\frac{EIg}{wl^4}}.$$

The corresponding period of vibration is

$$\tau = \frac{2\pi}{3.530} \sqrt{\frac{wl^4}{EIg}}. \qquad (f)$$

Comparing this result with the exact solution (d) it can be concluded that in this case the error of the approximate solution is only about $\frac{1}{2}\%$.

It must be noted that an elastic beam represents a system with an infinitely large number of degrees of freedom. It can, like a string, perform vibrations of various types. The choosing of a definite shape for the deflection curve in using Rayleigh's method is equivalent to introducing some additional constraints which reduce the system to one having one degree of freedom. Such additional constraints can only increase the rigidity of the system, i.e., increase the frequency of vibration. In all cases considered above the approximate values of the frequencies as obtained by Rayleigh's method are somewhat higher than their exact values.*

In the case of torsional vibrations (see Fig. 11) the same approximate method can be used in order to calculate the effect of the inertia of the shaft on the frequency of the torsional vibrations. Let i denote the moment of inertia of the shaft per unit length. Then assuming that the type of vibration is the same as in the case of a massless shaft, the angle of rotation of a cross section at a distance c from the fixed end of the shaft is $c\varphi/l$ and the kinetic energy of one element of the shaft will be

$$\frac{i \, dc}{2} \left(\frac{c\dot{\varphi}}{l} \right)^2.$$

---

* A complete discussion of Rayleigh's method can be found in G. Temple and W. G. Bickley, *Rayleigh's Principle*, Oxford University Press, 1933; see also Collatz, Z. angew. Math. u. Mech., Vol. 19, p. 224, 1939.

The kinetic energy of the entire shaft will be

$$\frac{i}{2} \int_0^l \left(\frac{c\dot{\varphi}}{l}\right)^2 dc = \frac{\dot{\varphi}^2}{2} \frac{il}{3}. \tag{18}$$

This kinetic energy must be added to the kinetic energy of the disc in order to estimate the effect of the mass of the shaft on the frequency of vibration, i.e., the period of vibration will be the same as for a massless shaft having at the end a disc, the moment of inertia of which is equal to

$$I + il/3.$$

The application of Rayleigh's method for calculating the critical speed of a rotating shaft will be shown in the following article.

EXAMPLES

1. Determine the frequency of natural vibrations of the load W supported by a beam AB, Fig. 29, of constant cross section (1) assuming that the weight of the beam can be neglected; (2) taking the weight of the beam into consideration and using Rayleigh's method.

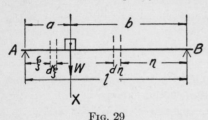

FIG. 29

Solution. If a and b are the distances of the load from the ends of the beam the static deflection of the beam under the load is $\delta = Wa^2b^2/3lEI$. Taking for the spring constant the expression $k = 3lEI/a^2b^2$ and neglecting the mass of the beam the angular frequency of vibration is obtained from the equation of energy

$$\frac{W}{2g} \dot{x}^2{}_{\max} = \frac{kx_0}{2} \frac{1}{} \tag{g}$$

in which $\dot{x}_{\max} = x_0 p$. Hence

$$p = \sqrt{\frac{kg}{W}} = \sqrt{\frac{3lEIg}{Wa^2b^2}}. \tag{h}$$

To take the mass of the beam into account, we consider the deflection curve of the beam under static action of the load W. The deflection at any point of the left portion of the beam at the distance ξ from the support A is

$$x_1 = \frac{W\xi b}{6lEI} [a(l + b) - \xi^2]. \tag{i}$$

For the deflection at any point to the right of the load W and at a distance η from the support B we have

$$x_2 = \frac{Wa\eta}{6lEI} [b(l + a) - \eta^2]. \tag{j}$$

Applying Rayleigh's method and assuming that during vibration the maximum velocity of any point of the left portion of the beam at a distance ξ from the support A is given by the equation

$$(\dot{x}_1)_{max} = \dot{x}_{max}\frac{x_1}{\delta} = \dot{x}_{max}\frac{\xi}{2a^2b}[a(l+b)-\xi^2]$$

in which $\dot{x}_{max}$ is the maximum velocity of the load W, we find that to take into account the mass of the left portion of the beam we must add to the left side of eq. (g) the quantity

$$\frac{w\dot{x}^2_{max}}{2g}\int_0^a\left(\frac{x_1}{\delta}\right)^2 d\xi = \frac{w\dot{x}^2_{max}}{2g}\int_0^a\frac{\xi^2}{4a^4b^2}[a(l+b)-\xi^2]^2 d\xi$$

$$= \dot{x}^2_{max}\frac{wa}{2g}\left[\frac{1}{3}\frac{l^2}{b^2}+\frac{23}{105}\frac{a^2}{b^2}-\frac{8}{15}\frac{al}{b^2}\right]. \qquad (k)$$

In the same manner, considering the right portion of the beam, we find that we must add to the left side of eq. (g) the expression

$$\frac{\dot{x}^2_{max}wb}{2g}\left[\frac{1}{12}\frac{(l+a)^2}{a^2}+\frac{1}{28}\frac{b^2}{a^2}-\frac{1}{10}\frac{b(l+a)}{a^2}\right]. \qquad (l)$$

The equation of energy becomes

$$\frac{(W+\alpha wa+\beta wb)}{2g}\dot{x}^2_{max} = \frac{kx_0^2}{2},$$

where α and β denote the quantities in the brackets of expressions (k) and (l) and we obtain for the angular frequency of vibration the following formula:

$$p = \sqrt{\frac{3lEIg}{(W+\alpha aw+\beta bw)a^2b^2}}. \qquad (m)$$

2. Determine the frequency of the natural vertical vibrations of the load W supported by a frame hinged at A and B, Fig. 30a, assuming that the three bars of the frame have the same length and the same cross section and the load is applied at the middle of the bar CD. In the calculation (1) neglect the mass of the frame; (2) consider the mass of the frame by using Rayleigh's method.

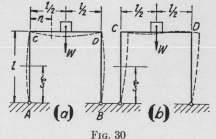

FIG. 30

Solution. By using the known formulas for deflections of beams, we find that the bending moments at the joints C and D are equal to $3Wl/40$. The deflections of vertical bars at a distance ξ from the bottom is

$$x_1 = \frac{3Wl^2\xi}{240EI}\left(1-\frac{\xi^2}{l^2}\right). \qquad (n)$$

The deflections of the horizontal bar to the left of the load is

$$x_2 = \frac{W\eta}{48EI}(3l^2 - 4\eta^2) - \frac{3}{80}\frac{Wl}{EI}\eta(l - \eta). \tag{o}$$

The deflection under the load W is

$$\delta = (x_2)_{\eta = \frac{l}{2}} = \frac{11}{960}\frac{Wl^3}{EI}. \tag{p}$$

By neglecting the mass of the frame we find the angular frequency

$$p = \sqrt{\frac{g}{\delta}} = \sqrt{\frac{960EIg}{11Wl^3}}. \tag{q}$$

In calculating the effect of this mass on the frequency, let us denote by $\dot{x}_{max}$ the maximum velocity of the vibrating body W. Then the maximum velocity of any point of the vertical bars at a distance ξ from the bottom is

$$(\dot{x}_1)_{max} = \dot{x}_{max}\frac{x_1}{\delta} = \dot{x}_{max}\frac{12}{11}\frac{\xi}{l}\left(1 - \frac{\xi^2}{l^2}\right) \tag{r}$$

and the maximum velocity at any point of the left portion of the horizontal bar CD,

$$(\dot{x}_2)_{max} = \dot{x}_{max}\frac{x_2}{\delta} = \dot{x}_{max}\left[\frac{20}{11}\frac{\eta}{l}\left(3 - \frac{4\eta^2}{l^2}\right) - \frac{36}{11}\frac{\eta}{l}\left(1 - \frac{\eta}{l}\right)\right]. \tag{s}$$

The kinetic energy of the frame which must be added to the kinetic energy of the load W is

$$2\int_0^l \frac{w\dot{x}^2_{max}}{2g}\left(\frac{x_1}{\delta}\right)^2 d\xi + 2\int_0^{l/2}\frac{w\dot{x}^2_{max}}{2g}\left(\frac{x_2}{\delta}\right)^2 d\eta.$$

Substituting for the ratios x_1/δ and x_2/δ their expressions from (r) and (s) and integrating, the additional kinetic energy can be represented in the following form

$$\frac{w\alpha l}{2g}(\dot{x})^2_{max}$$

where α is a constant factor.

The equation for angular frequency of vibration now becomes

$$p = \sqrt{\frac{960EIg}{11(W + \alpha wl)l^3}}. \tag{t}$$

3. Determine the frequency of lateral vibrations of the frame shown in Fig. 30b.

Solution. The frequency of these vibrations, if the mass of the frame is neglected, can be calculated by using the formulas of Ex. 4, p. 7. To take into account the mass of the frame, the bending of the frame must be considered. If x is the lateral displacement of the load W together with the horizontal bar CD, the horizontal displacement of any point of the vertical bars at a distance ξ from the bottom, from consideration of the bending of the frame, is

$$x_1 = x - \frac{x}{3}\left(1 - \frac{\xi}{l}\right) - \frac{2}{3}x\left[\frac{3}{2}\left(1 - \frac{\xi}{l}\right)^2 - \frac{1}{2}\left(1 - \frac{\xi}{l}\right)^3\right]. \qquad u)$$

The kinetic energy of the vertical bars is

$$2\int_0^l \frac{w\dot{x}_1^2}{2g}\,d\xi = \frac{\alpha wl}{g}\dot{x}^2,$$

where α is a constant factor which is obtained after substituting for x_1 its expression from (u) and integrating. In considering the kinetic energy of the horizontal bar, we use only the horizontal component $\dot{x}$ of the velocities of the particles of the bar. Then the total kinetic energy of the entire system is

$$\frac{W\dot{x}^2}{2g} + \frac{(1 + 2\alpha)wl\dot{x}^2}{2g},$$

and the frequency is obtained from the equation (see Ex. 4, p. 7).

$$f = \frac{1}{2\pi}\sqrt{\frac{4EIg}{[W + (1 + 2\alpha)wl]l^3}}. \qquad (v)$$

PROBLEMS

1. What portion of the uniformly distributed weight of the simply supported beam in Fig. 27 should be added to the weight W at the middle if, during lateral vibration, the beam is assumed to have the configuration of a half sine wave instead of a static deflection curve?

Answer. 1/2 instead of 17/35.

2. If the beam in Fig. 27 has both ends built in, instead of simply supported, what portion of its total weight should be added to the weight W at the mid-span in calculating the natural period of lateral vibration? Assume a configuration of the beam during vibration similar to a static deflection curve under the load W.

Answer. 13/35.

3. Repeat the preceding problem, assuming that during vibration the beam maintains a configuration identical in shape with a full wave of a cosine curve.

Hint. With the left end of the beam as an origin, the equation of the deflection curve will be

$$y = \frac{\Delta}{2}\left(1 - \cos\frac{2\pi x}{l}\right),$$

where Δ is the displacement under the load W.

Answer. 3/8.

4. For the frame shown in Fig. 10, p. 9, assume that each vertical member has a weight of 20 lb per ft and is pinned at the bottom. Find the natural frequency of lateral vibration of the frame corrected for the mass effect of the vertical members. Use the same data as given in Prob. 6, p. 9.

Answer. $\tau = 1.73$ sec.

5. What portion of the uniformly distributed weight of the beam ABC in Fig. 31 should be added to the weight W at the free end in calculating the natural frequency of lateral vibration? Assume a static deflection curve.

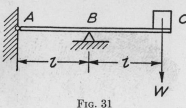

Answer. $239/1680 \approx 1/7$.

6. Referring to Ex. 3, p. 14, recalculate the frequency of torsional vibration of the wheel in Fig. 13 corrected for the mass effect of the radial spokes. Assume each spoke

Fig. 31

to have a mass wr/g uniformly distributed along its length.

Answer. $f = \dfrac{1}{2\pi} \sqrt{\dfrac{16gB}{(W + {}^{116}\!/_{105}wr)r^3}}$.

5. Critical Speed of a Rotating Shaft.—It is well known that rotating shafts at certain speeds become dynamically unstable and large vibrations are likely to develop. This phenomenon is due to resonance effects and a simple example will show that the *critical speed* for a shaft is that speed at which the number of revolutions per second of the shaft is equal to the frequency of its natural lateral vibration.*

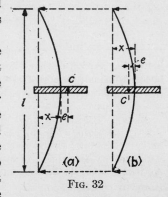

Fig. 32

Shaft with One Disc.—In order to exclude from our consideration the effect of the weight of the shaft and so make the problem as simple as possible, a vertical shaft with one circular disc will be taken (Fig. 32a). Let C be the center of gravity of the disc and e a small eccentricity, i.e., the distance of C from the axis of the shaft. During rotation, due to the eccentricity e, a centrifugal force will act on the shaft, and will produce deflection. The magnitude of the deflection x can easily be obtained from the condition of equilibrium of the centrifugal force and the reactive force P of the deflected shaft. This latter force is proportional to the deflection x, and can be represented in the following form:

$$P = kx.$$

The magnitude of the factor k can be calculated provided the dimensions of the shaft and the conditions at the supports be known. Assuming, for instance, that the shaft has a uniform section and the disc is in the middle between the supports, we have

---

* A more detailed discussion of lateral vibrations of a shaft is given in Arts. 36 and 45.

$$k = \frac{48EI}{l^3}.$$

Now from the condition of equilibrium the following equation for determining x will be obtained

$$\frac{W}{g}(x + e)\omega^2 = kx, \qquad (a)$$

in which W/g is the mass of the disc, ω is the angular velocity of the shaft. From eq. (a) we have,

$$x = \frac{e}{\dfrac{k}{\omega^2}\dfrac{g}{W} - 1}. \qquad (b)$$

Remembering (see eq. c, p. 2) that

$$\frac{kg}{W} = p^2,$$

it can be concluded from (b) that the deflection x tends to increase rapidly as ω approaches p, i.e., when the number of revolutions per second of the shaft approaches the frequency of the lateral vibrations of the shaft and disc. The critical value of the speed will be

$$\omega_{cr} = \sqrt{\frac{kg}{W}}. \qquad (19)$$

At this speed the denominator of (b) becomes zero and large lateral vibrations in the shaft occur. It is interesting to note that at speeds higher than the critical, quiet running conditions will again prevail. Experiments show that in this case the center of gravity C will be situated between the line joining the supports and the deflected axis of the shaft as shown in Fig. 32b. The equation for determining the deflection will be

$$\frac{W}{g}(x - e)\omega^2 = kx,$$

from which

$$x = \frac{e}{1 - \dfrac{kg}{\omega^2 W}}. \qquad (c)$$

It is seen that now with increasing ω the deflection x decreases and approaches the limit e, i.e., at very high speeds the center of gravity of the disc approaches the line joining the supports and the deflected shaft rotates about the center of gravity C.

Shaft Loaded with Several Discs.—It has been shown above in a simple example that the critical number of revolutions per second of a shaft is equal to the frequency of the natural lateral vibration of this shaft. Determining this frequency by using Rayleigh's method the critical speed for a shaft with many discs (Fig. 33) can easily be established. Let W_1, W_2, W_3 denote the loads and x_1, x_2, x_3 denote the corresponding statical deflections. Then the potential energy of deformation stored in the beam during bending will be

$$V = \frac{W_1 x_1}{2} + \frac{W_2 x_2}{2} + \frac{W_3 x_3}{2}. \qquad (d)$$

In calculating the period of the slowest type of vibration the static deflection curve shown in Fig. 33 can be taken as a good approximation for the deflection curve of the beam during vibration. The vertical displacements of the loads W_1, W_2 and W_3 during vibration can be written as:

$$x_1 \cos pt, \quad x_2 \cos pt, \quad x_3 \cos pt. \qquad (e)$$

Then the maximum deflections of the shaft from the position of equilibrium are the same as those given in Fig. 33; therefore, the increase in

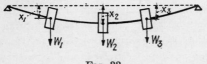

FIG. 33

the potential energy of the vibrating shaft during its deflection from the position of equilibrium to the extreme position will be given by eq. (d). On the other hand the kinetic energy of the system becomes a maximum at the moment when the shaft, during vibration, passes through its middle position. It will be noted, from expressions (e), that the velocities of the loads corresponding to this position are:

$$px_1, \quad px_2, \quad px_3$$

and the kinetic energy of the system becomes

$$\frac{p^2}{2g} \left(W_1 x_1^2 + W_2 x_2^2 + W_3 x_3^2 \right). \qquad (f)$$

Equating (d) and (f), the following expression for p^2 will be obtained:

$$p^2 = \frac{g(W_1x_1 + W_2x_2 + W_3x_3)}{W_1x_1{}^2 + W_2x_2{}^2 + W_3x_3{}^2}.$$ (20)

The period of vibration is

$$\tau = \frac{2\pi}{p} = 2\pi \sqrt{\frac{W_1x_1{}^2 + W_2x_2{}^2 + W_3x_3{}^2}{g(W_1x_1 + W_2x_2 + W_3x_3)}}.$$ (21)

In general, when n loads are acting on the shaft the period of the lowest type of vibration will be

$$\tau = 2\pi \sqrt{\frac{\sum_1^n W_ix_i{}^2}{g\sum_1^n W_ix_i}}.$$ (22

It is seen that for calculating τ the statical deflections x_1, x_2, $\cdots$ of the shaft alone are necessary. These quantities can easily be obtained by the usual methods. If the shaft has a variable cross section a graphical method for obtaining the deflections has to be used. The effect of the weight of the shaft itself also can be taken into account. It is necessary for this purpose to divide the shaft into several parts, the weights of which, applied to their respective centers of gravity, must be considered as concentrated loads.

Take, for instance, the shaft shown in Fig. 34a, the diameters of which and the loads acting on it are shown in the figure. By constructing the polygon of forces (Fig. 34b) and the corresponding funicular polygon (Fig. 34c) the bending moment diagram will be obtained. In order to calculate the numerical value of the bending moment at any cross section of the shaft it is only necessary to measure the corresponding ordinate e of the moment diagram to the same scale as used for the length of the shaft and multiply it with the pole distance h measured to the scale of forces in the polygon of forces (in our case $h = 80,000$ lb). In order to obtain the deflection curve a construction of the second funicular polygon is necessary in which construction the bending moment diagram obtained above must be considered as an imaginary loading diagram. In order to take into account the variation in cross section of the shaft, the intensity of this imaginary loading at every section should be multiplied by I_0/I where $I_0 = $ moment of inertia of the largest cross section of the shaft and

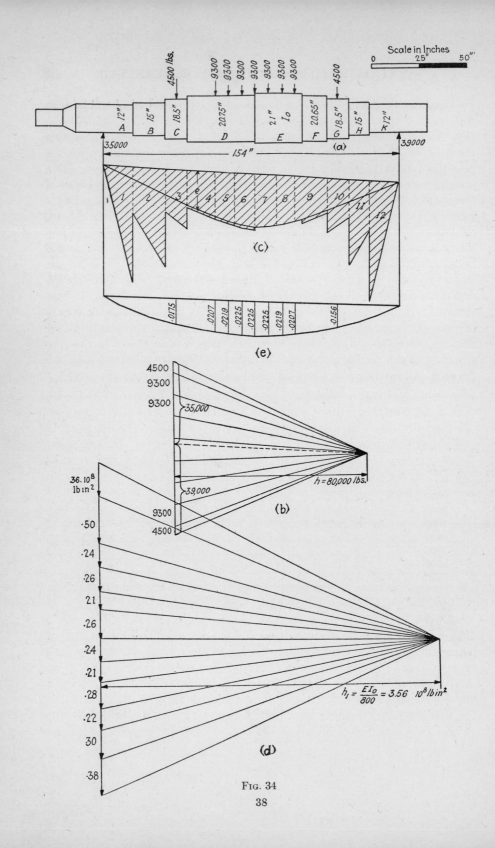

FIG. 34

38

I = moment of inertia of the portion of the shaft under consideration. In this manner the final imaginary loading represented by the shaded area (Fig. 34c) is obtained. Subdividing this area into several parts, measuring the areas of these parts in square inches and multiplying them with the pole distance h measured in pounds, the imaginary loads measured in pounds-inches [2] will be obtained. For these loads, the second polygon of forces (Fig. 34d) is constructed by taking a pole distance h_1 equal to EI_0/n where EI_0 is the largest flexural rigidity of the shaft and n is an integer (in our case $n = 800$). It should be noted that the imaginary loads and the pole distances EI/n have the same dimension, i.e., in.^{2}-lb, and should be represented in the polygon of forces to the same scale. By using the second polygon of forces the second funicular polygon (Fig. 34e) and the deflection curve of the shaft tangent to this polygon can easily be constructed. In order to get the numerical values of the deflections it is only necessary to measure them to the same scale to which the length of the shaft is drawn and divide them by the number n used above in the construction of the second polygon. All numerical results obtained from the drawing and necessary in using eq. (22) are given in the following table.

W lb	$x_i \times 10^2$ in.	$x_i^2 \times 10^4$ in.^{2}	Wx_i lb $\times$ in.	Wx_i^2 lb $\times$ in.^{2}
4500	1.75	3.05	79	1.37
9300	2.07	4.28	193	3.98
9300	2.19	4.80	204	4.47
9300	2.25	5.06	209	4.71
9300	2.25	5.06	209	4.71
9300	2.25	5.36	209	4.71
9800	2.19	4.88	204	4.47
9300	2.07	4.28	193	3.98
4500	1.56	2.43	70	1.09

$$\Sigma Wx_i = 1570 \qquad \Sigma Wx_i^2 = 33.09$$

The critical number of revolutions per minute will be obtained now as follows:

$$N_{cr} = \frac{60}{\tau} = \frac{30}{\pi} \sqrt{\frac{g \sum_{1}^{n} W_i x_i}{\sum_{1}^{n} W_i x_i^2}} = \frac{30}{\pi} \sqrt{\frac{386 \times 1570}{33.09}} = 1290 \text{ r.p.m.}$$

It should be noted that the hubs of spiders or flywheels shrunk on the shaft increase the stiffness of the shaft and may raise its critical speed considerably.   In considering this phenomenon it can be assumed that the stresses due to vibration are small and the shrink fit pressure between the hub and the shaft is sufficient to prevent any relative motion between these two parts, so that the hub can be considered as a portion of shaft of an enlarged diameter.   Therefore the effect of the hub on the critical speed will be obtained by introducing this enlarged diameter in the graphical construction developed above.*

In the case of a grooved rotor (Fig. 35) if the distances between the grooves are of the same order as the depth of the groove, the material

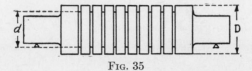

FIG. 35

between two grooves does not take any bending stresses and the flexibility of such a rotor is near to one of the diameter d measured at the bottom of the grooves.†

It must be noted also that in Fig. 33 rigid supports were assumed.   In certain cases the rigidity of the supports is small enough so as to produce a substantial effect on the magnitude of the critical speed.   If the additional flexibility, due to deformation of the supports, is the same in a vertical and in a horizontal direction the effect of this flexibility can be easily taken into account.   It is only necessary to add to the deflections x_1, x_2 and x_3 of the previous calculations the vertical displacement due to the deformation of the supports under the action of the loads W_1, W_2 and W_3.   Such additional deflections will lower the critical speed of the shaft.‡

6. Forced Vibrations: Steady State.—In all previous articles free vibrations of systems with one degree of freedom have been discussed.   Let us consider now the case when in addition to the force of gravity and to the

* Prof. A. Stodola in his book, *Dampf- und Gasturbinen*, 6th Ed., Berlin, p. 383, 1924, gives an example where such a consideration of the stiffening effect of shrunk on parts gave a satisfactory result and the calculated critical speed was in good agreement with the experiment.   See also B. Eck, "Versteifender Einfluss der Turbinenscheiben," *Z. Ver. deut. Ing.*, Vol. 72, p. 51, 1928.

† B. Eck, *loc. cit.*

‡ The case when the rigidities of the supports in two perpendicular directions are different is discussed on p. 287.

force in the spring (Fig. 1) there is acting on the load W a periodical *disturbing force* $P \sin \omega t$. The period of this force is $\tau_1 = 2\pi/\omega$ and its frequency is $f_1 = \omega/2\pi$. Proceeding as before (see Art. 1) we obtain the following differential equation of motion:

$$\frac{W}{g} \ddot{x} = W - (W + kx) + P \sin \omega t, \tag{a}$$

or, by using the notations

$$q = \frac{Pg}{W}, \quad p^2 = \frac{kg}{W}, \tag{b}$$

we obtain

$$\ddot{x} + p^2 x = q \sin \omega t. \tag{23}$$

A particular solution of this equation is obtained by assuming that x is proportional to $\sin \omega t$, i.e., by taking

$$x = A \sin \omega t, \tag{c}$$

where A is a constant, the magnitude of which must be chosen so as to satisfy eq. (23). Substituting (c) in that equation, we find

$$A = \frac{q}{p^2 - \omega^2}.$$

Thus the required particular solution is

$$x = \frac{q \sin \omega t}{p^2 - \omega^2}. \tag{24}$$

Adding to this particular solution expression (2), representing the solution of eq. (1) for free vibration, we obtain

$$x = C_1 \cos pt + C_2 \sin pt + \frac{q \sin \omega t}{p^2 - \omega^2}. \tag{25}$$

This expression contains two constants of integration and represents the general solution of the eq. (23). It is seen that this solution consists of two parts; the first two terms represent free vibrations which were discussed before and the third term, depending on the disturbing force, represents the *forced vibration* of the system. It is seen that this later vibration has the same period $\tau_1 = 2\pi/\omega$ as the disturbing force has. Using the first of notations (*b*) for *q* in eq. (24) and ignoring the free vibrations,* we get so-called *steady state* forced vibrations defined by the equation

$$x = \frac{P}{k}\left(\frac{1}{1 - \omega^2/p^2}\right) \sin \omega t. \tag{26}$$

The factor P/k is the deflection which the maximum disturbing force P would produce if acting statically and the factor $1/(1 - \omega^2/p^2)$ takes care of the dynamical action of this force. The absolute value of this factor is usually called the *magnification factor*. We see that it depends only on the

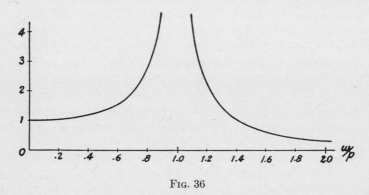

Fig. 36

ratio ω/p which is obtained by dividing the frequency of the disturbing force by the frequency of free vibration of the system. In Fig. 36 the values of the magnification factor are plotted against the ratio ω/p.

It is seen that for small values of the ratio ω/p, i.e., for the case when the frequency of the disturbing force is small in comparison with the frequency of free vibration, the magnification factor is approximately unity, and deflections are about the same as in the case of a statical action of the force $P \sin \omega t$.

When the ratio ω/p approaches unity the magnification factor and the amplitude of forced vibration rapidly increase and become infinite for $\omega = p$, i.e., for the case when the frequency of the disturbing force exactly coincides with the frequency of free vibration of the system. This is the *condition of resonance*. The infinite value obtained for the amplitude of forced vibrations indicates that if the pulsating force acts on the vibrating system always at a proper time and in a proper direction the amplitude of

* The effect of free vibrations in combination with forced vibrations will be discussed in the next article.

vibration increases indefinitely provided there is no damping. In practical problems we always have damping, the effect of which on the amplitude of forced vibration will be discussed later (see Art. 13).

When the frequency of the disturbing force increases beyond the frequency of free vibration the magnification factor again becomes finite. Its absolute value diminishes with the increase of the ratio ω/p and approaches zero when this ratio becomes very large. This means that when a pulsating force of high frequency (ω/p is large) acts on the vibrating body it produces vibrations of very small amplitude and in many cases the body may be considered as remaining immovable in space. The practical significance of this fact will be discussed in the next article.

Considering the sign of the expression $1/(1 - \omega^2/p^2)$ it is seen that for the case $\omega < p$ this expression is positive and for $\omega > p$ it becomes negative. This indicates that when the frequency of the disturbing force is less than that of the natural vibration of the system the forced vibrations and the disturbing force are always in the same *phase*, i.e., the vibrating mass (Fig. 1) reaches its lowest position at the same moment that the disturbing force assumes its maximum value in a downward direction. When $\omega > p$ the difference in phase between the forced vibration and the disturbing force becomes equal to π. This means that at the moment when the force is a maximum in a downward direction the vibrating mass reaches its upper position. This phenomenon can be illustrated by the following simple experiment. In the case of a simple pendulum AB (Fig. 37) forced vibrations can be produced by giving an oscillating motion in the horizontal direction to the point A. If this oscillating motion has a frequency lower than that of the pendulum the extreme positions of the pendulum during such vibrations will be as shown in Fig. 37a, the motions of the points A and B will be in the same phase. If the oscillatory motion of the point A has a higher frequency than that of the pendulum the extreme positions of the pendulum during vibration will be as shown in Fig. 37b. The phase difference of the motions of the points A and B in this case is equal to π.

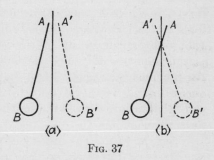

(a)   (b)

Fig. 37

In the above discussion the disturbing force was taken proportional to $\sin \omega t$. The same conclusions will be obtained if $\cos \omega t$, instead of $\sin \omega t$, be taken in the expression for the disturbing force.

Forced vibrations of the spring suspended weight in Fig. 1 can be produced also in another way slightly different from that discussed above. Suppose, for example, that the upper end of the spring will be given a simple harmonic motion

$$x_1 = a \sin \omega t \qquad (d)$$

in the vertical direction. Then measuring displacement x of the suspended weight W from its equilibrium position when $x_1 = 0$, the elongation of the spring at any instant t will be $x - x_1 + \delta_{st}$ and the corresponding force in the spring is $k(x - x_1) + W$. Thus the equation of motion of the suspended weight becomes

$$\frac{W}{g} \ddot{x} = W - k(x - x_1) - W.$$

Substituting for x_1 its expression (d) and using the notations

$$q = \frac{akg}{W}, \quad p^2 = \frac{kg}{W}, \qquad (e)$$

we obtain

$$\ddot{x} + p^2 x = q \sin \omega t \qquad (23')$$

This is identical with eq. (23) obtained before. Thus it may be concluded that giving the upper end of the spring a simple harmonic motion $a \sin \omega t$ is equivalent to the direct application of a disturbing force $(ak) \sin \omega t$. All previous conclusions attached to the solution of eq. (23) hold also in this case and we conclude finally that we will again obtain steady state forced vibrations defined by the equation

$$x = a \left(\frac{1}{1 - \omega^2/p^2} \right) \sin \omega t. \qquad (26')$$

EXAMPLES

1. Determine the amplitude of forced torsional vibration of a shaft in Fig. 11 produced by a pulsating torque $M \sin \omega t$ if the free torsional vibration of the same shaft has the frequency $f = 10 \ \sec^{-1}$, $\omega = 10\pi \ \sec^{-1}$ and the angle of twist produced by torque M, if acting on the shaft statically, is equal to 0.01 of a radian.

Solution. The equation of motion in this case is (see Art. 2)

$$\ddot{\varphi} + p^2\varphi = \frac{M}{I}\sin \omega t,$$

where φ is the angle of twist and $p^2 = k/I$. The forced vibration is

$$\varphi = \frac{M}{I(p^2 - \omega^2)}\sin \omega t = \frac{M}{k(1 - \omega^2/p^2)}\sin \omega t.$$

Noting that the statical deflection is $M/k = 0.01$ and $p = 2\pi \cdot 10$ we obtain the required amplitude equal to

$$\frac{0.01}{(1 - \frac{1}{4})} = 0.0133 \text{ radian.}$$

2. A wheel is rolling along a wavy surface with a constant horizontal speed v, Fig. 38. Determine the amplitude of the forced vertical vibrations of the load W attached to

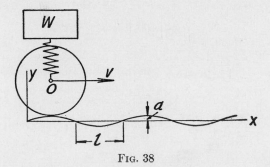

Fig. 38

the axle of the wheel by a spring if the statical deflection of the spring under the action of the load W is $\delta_{st} = 3.86$ in., $v = 60$ ft per sec and the wavy surface is given by the equation $y = a \sin\dfrac{\pi x}{l}$ in which $a = 1$ in. and $l = 36$ in.

Solution. Considering vertical vibrations of the load W on the spring we find that the square of the angular frequency of these vibrations is $p^2 = g/\delta_{st} = 100$. Due to the wavy surface the center O of the rolling wheel makes vertical oscillations. Assuming that at the initial moment $t = 0$ the point of contact of the wheel is at $x = 0$ and putting $x = vt$, these vertical oscillations are given by the equation $y = a \sin\dfrac{\pi vt}{l}$. The forced vibration of the load W is now obtained from equation (26′) by substituting in it $a = 1$ in., $\omega = \dfrac{\pi v}{l} = 20\pi$, $p^2 = 100$. Then the amplitude of forced vibration is $1/(4\pi^2 - 1) = 0.026$ in. At the given speed v the vertical oscillations of the wheel are transmitted to the load W only in a very small proportion. If we take the speed v of the wheel $\frac{1}{4}$ as great we get $\omega = 5\pi$ and the amplitude of forced vibration becomes $1/(\pi^2/4 - 1) = 0.68$ in. By further decrease in speed v we finally come to the condition of resonance when $\pi v/l = p$ at which condition heavy vibration of the load W will be produced. The mass of the wheel is neglected in this discussion.

PROBLEMS

1. If the upper end of the spring in Fig. 1 has a vertical simple harmonic motion with amplitude $a = 1$ in. and angular frequency $\omega = 180$ sec^{-1}, find the amplitude of forced vibration of the suspended load W. Assume that this weight has a static deflection $\delta_{st} = 3$ in.

Answer.   0.004 in.

2. In Fig. 1, the suspended load W has a static deflection $\delta_{st} = 1$ in. What amplitude of forced vibration will be produced by a disturbing force $P \cos \omega t$ if $P = 2$ lb, $\omega = 10\pi$ sec^{-1}, and $W = 10$ lb?

Answer.   0.128 in.

3. A standard 8″ I-beam (18.4 lb per ft) with clear span $l = 12$ ft is simply supported at its ends. At mid-span it carries an electric motor of weight $W = 1000$ lb that runs at 1800 r.p.m. Due to unbalance, the rotor sets up a rotating centrifugal force $Q = 500$ lb. What amplitude of steady state forced vibrations will be produced?

Answer.   0.0077 in.

7. Forced Vibrations: Transient State.—In the preceding article only the last term in eq. (25) representing forced vibrations was considered. In general, the application of a disturbing force produces also some free vibrations of the system as represented by the first two terms of eq. (25). Thus the actual motion is a superposition of two simple harmonic motions having, in general, different amplitudes, different frequencies and different phase. This results in a very complicated motion. However, owing to damping, not considered in the derivation of eq. (25), the free vibration disappears after a short time and we are left only with the steady state forced vibrations which are constantly maintained by the action of the disturbing force. A particular case is represented graphically by the displacement-time curve in Fig. 39. On the dotted curve, representing forced vibrations with the angular frequency ω, are superimposed free vibrations with a higher angular frequency p and with decreasing amplitude due to damping. Thus the complete motion is represented by the solid curve which gradually approaches the dotted curve as a steady state condition. The early part of this motion, i.e., the first few cycles in which free vibrations are present is generally referred to as the *transient state*. It is sometimes of practical interest to study this motion in detail.

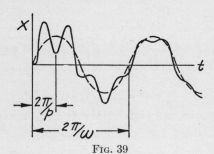

Fig. 39

The amplitude of the free vibration can be found from the general solution (25) by taking into consideration the initial conditions. Let us assume that at the initial instant $(t = 0)$ the displacement and the velocity of the vibrating body are equal to zero. The arbitrary constants of the solution (25) must then be determined in such a manner that for $t = 0$

$$x = 0 \quad \text{and} \quad \dot{x} = 0. \tag{a}$$

These conditions will be satisfied by taking

$$C_1 = 0, \quad C_2 = -\frac{q\omega/p}{p^2 - \omega^2}.$$

Substituting in expression (25), we obtain

$$x = \frac{q}{p^2 - \omega^2}\left(\sin \omega t - \frac{\omega}{p}\sin pt\right). \tag{27}$$

Thus the motion consists of two parts, free vibration proportional to $\sin pt$ and forced vibration proportional to $\sin \omega t$.

Let us consider the case when the frequency of the disturbing force is very close to the frequency of free vibrations of the system, i.e., ω is close to p. Using the notation

$$p - \omega = 2\Delta,$$

where Δ is a small quantity, and neglecting a small term with the factor $2\Delta/p$, we represent expression (27) in the following form:

$$x = \frac{q}{p^2 - \omega^2}(\sin \omega t - \sin pt) = \frac{2q}{p^2 - \omega^2}\cos\frac{(\omega + p)t}{2}\sin\frac{(\omega - p)t}{2}$$

$$= -\frac{2q\sin \Delta t}{p^2 - \omega^2}\cos\frac{(\omega + p)t}{2} \approx -\frac{q\sin \Delta t}{2\omega\Delta}\cos \omega t. \tag{28}$$

Since Δ is a small quantity the function $\sin \Delta t$ varies slowly and its period, equal to $2\pi/\Delta$, is large. In such a case expression (28) can be considered as representing vibrations with period $2\pi/\omega$ and of variable amplitude equal to $q\sin \Delta t/2\omega\Delta$. This kind of vibration is called *beating* and is shown in

Fig. 40. The period of beating, equal to π/Δ, increases as ω approaches p, i.e., as we approach the condition of resonance.

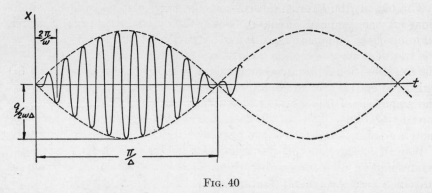

FIG. 40

For the limiting condition $\omega = p$ we can put in expression (28) Δt, instead of sin Δt and we obtain

$$x = -\frac{qt}{2\omega}\cos \omega t. \tag{29}$$

The amplitude of vibration in eq. (29) increases indefinitely with time as shown in Fig. 41. This shows that, while we theoretically obtain infinite

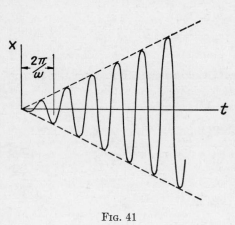

FIG. 41

amplitude of forced vibration at resonance in the absence of damping, it also takes time to build up these large amplitudes. Thus in the case of a machine designed to operate above resonance, no great difficulty will be experienced in passing through the resonance condition, providing this transition is made fairly rapidly. However, experiments show that if any vibrating system is once allowed to reach a steady state just below resonance, it then becomes difficult to accelerate the machine through the resonance condition. Additional power supplied for this purpose is simply used up in increasing the amplitude of vibration rather than the running speed of the machine.

This applies particularly to the case of passing through the critical speed of a rotating shaft with unbalanced discs as discussed in Art. 5.

Throughout the foregoing discussion, the particular set of initial conditions (a) were assumed for convenience. While initial conditions of motion have no effect on steady state forced vibrations, they naturally influence the transient state of motion greatly, since they determine to what extent the free vibrations enter into combination with the forced vibrations. Referring to eq. (27) for example, we see that for the initial conditions (a), the amplitude of free vibrations are in the ratio ω/p to the amplitude of forced vibrations. Thus, in this case, free vibrations influence the transient motion to a greater extent above resonance than they do below resonance.

We can consider another particular case in which, with the same initial conditions (a), we assume a disturbing force $P \cos \omega t$ instead of $P \sin \omega t$. In such a case the general solution of eq. (23) will again be given by eq. (25) except that the last term representing forced vibrations will now be proportional to $\cos \omega t$ instead of $\sin \omega t$. Then proceeding as before, we find the constants of integration in this case to be

$$C_1 = - \frac{q}{p^2 - \omega^2}, \quad C_2 = 0,$$

and the complete solution becomes

$$x = \frac{q}{p^2 - \omega^2} (\cos \omega t - \cos pt). \tag{30}$$

We see that in this case the free vibrations have the same amplitude as the forced vibrations regardless of the ratio ω/p.

EXAMPLE

1. The upper end of the spring in Fig. 1 has a uniform downward velocity v_0 which, at a certain instant $t = 0$, becomes a simple harmonic motion

$$x_1 = \frac{v_0}{\omega} \sin \omega t.$$

Determine the complete expression for the subsequent motion of the suspended weight W.

Solution. In this case the initial conditions of motion will be

$$t = 0, \quad x = 0, \quad \dot{x} = v_0. \tag{b}$$

Substituting these into the general solution (25) and its first time-derivative, we find

$$C_1 = 0, \quad C_2 = \frac{v_0}{p} - \frac{q\omega/p}{p^2 - \omega^2}.$$

Substituting back into (25) and noting that in this case

$$q = \frac{akg}{W} = ap^2 = \frac{v_0 p^2}{\omega},$$

we get

$$x = \frac{v_0/\omega}{1 - \dfrac{\omega^2}{p^2}} \left(\sin \omega t - \frac{\omega^3}{p^3} \sin pt \right).$$

PROBLEMS

1. For the system shown in Fig. 1, the weight $W = 10$ lb and the spring constant $k = 10$ lb per in. Assuming a disturbing force $P \sin \omega t$, where $P = 2$ lb and $\omega = 10\pi$ sec^{-1}, and initial conditions $x = \dot{x} = 0$ when $t = 0$, find the velocity and displacement of the weight W at time $t = 1$ sec.

Answer. $x_1 = +0.14$ in.; $\dot{x}_1 = -1.11$ in. per sec.

2. What displacement and velocity will the weight W of the preceding problem have at time $t = 1$ sec if the disturbing force is $P \cos \omega t$ instead of $P \sin \omega t$? Assume all other data to be the same as in Prob. 1.

Answer. $x_1 = -0.035$ in.; $\dot{x}_1 = -1.73$ in. per sec.

3. Calculate the maximum displacement of the weight W in Ex. 1 above for the particular case where $\omega/p = 0.9$.

Answer. $x_{\max} = 9.1 v_0/\omega$.

8. Technical Applications of Forced Vibrations.—

(*a*) *Spring Mounting of Machines.*—Rotating machines with some unbalance produce on their foundations periodic disturbing forces as a result of which undesirable vibrations of foundations and noise may occur. To

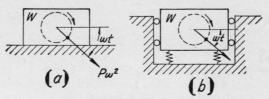

(*a*)   (*b*)

Fig. 42

reduce these bad effects a spring mounting of machines is sometimes used. Let a block of weight W in Fig. 42 represent the machine and P denote the centrifugal force due to unbalance when the angular velocity of the machine is one radian per second. Then at any angular velocity ω the centrifugal force is $P\omega^2$ and, measuring the angle of rotation as shown in the figure, we obtain the vertical and the horizontal components of the disturbing force equal to $P\omega^2 \sin \omega t$ and $P\omega^2 \cos \omega t$ respectively. If the machine is rigidly attached to a rigid foundation, as shown in Fig. 42a, there will be no motion of the block W and the total centrifugal force will be transmitted to the foundation. To diminish the force acting on the foundation, let us introduce a spring mounting, as shown in Fig. 42b, and assume that there is a constraint preventing lateral movement of the machine. In this way a vibrating system consisting of the block W on vertical springs, analogous to the system shown in Fig. 1, is obtained. To determine the pulsating vertical force transmitted through the springs to the foundation the vertical vibration of the block under the action of the disturbing force $P\omega^2 \sin \omega t$ must be investigated.* Using expression (26) for forced vibrations given in Art. 6 and substituting $P\omega^2$ for P, we find that the amplitude of forced vibration is equal to the numerical value of the expression

$$\frac{Pp^2}{k} \cdot \frac{\omega^2/p^2}{1 - \omega^2/p^2},\qquad(a)$$

where k is the spring constant, i.e., the force required to produce vertical

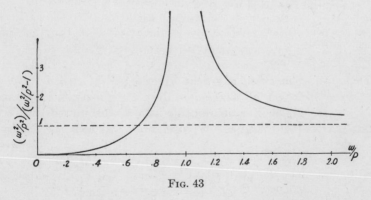

FIG. 43

deflection of the block equal to unity, and p is the natural angular frequency of the system. It is seen that for a given value of the ratio Pp^2/k the amplitude of forced vibration depends only on the value of the ratio ω/p. The absolute values of the second factor in expression (a) are plotted against the values of ω/p in Fig. 43. It is seen that for large values of ω/p these

---

* It is assumed here that vibrations are small and do not affect appreciably the magnitude of the disturbing force calculated on the assumption that the unbalanced weight is rotating about a fixed axis.

quantities approach unity and the absolute value of expression (a) approaches Pp^2/k. Having the amplitude of forced vibration of the block W and multiplying it by the spring constant k, we obtain the maximum pulsating force in the spring which will be transmitted to the foundation. Keeping in mind that $P\omega^2$ is the maximum vertical disturbing force when the machine is rigidly attached to the foundation, Fig. 42a, it can be concluded from (a) that the spring mounting reduces the disturbing force only if $1 - \omega^2/p^2$ is numerically larger than one, i.e., when $\omega > p\sqrt{2}$. When ω is very large in comparison with p, i.e., when the machine is mounted on soft springs, expression (a) approaches numerically the value Pp^2/k and we have, due to spring mounting, a reduction of the vertical disturbing force in the ratio p^2/ω^2. From this discussion we see that to reduce disturbing forces transmitted to the foundation, the machine must be mounted on soft springs such that the frequency of free vibration of the block W is small in comparison with the number of revolutions per second of the machine. The effect of damping in supporting springs will be discussed later (see Art. 14). To simplify the problem, we have discussed here only vertical vibrations of the block. To reduce the horizontal disturbing force, horizontal springs must be introduced and horizontal vibrations must be investigated. We will again come to the conclusion that the frequency of vibration must be small in comparison with the number of revolutions per second of the machine in order to reduce horizontal disturbing forces.

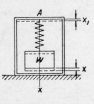

FIG. 44

(b) *Instruments for Investigating Vibrations.*—For measuring vertical vibrations a weight W suspended on a spring can be used (Fig. 44). If the point of suspension A is immovable and a vibration in the vertical direction of the weight is produced, the equation of motion (1) can be applied, in which x denotes displacement of W from the position of equilibrium. Assume now that the box, containing the suspended weight W, is attached to a body performing vertical vibration. In such case the point of suspension A vibrates also and due to this fact forced vibration of the weight will be produced. Let us assume that vertical vibrations of the box are given by the equation

$$x_1 = a \sin \omega t, \tag{b}$$

so that the point of suspension A performs simple harmonic motion of amplitude a. Then we have the second case of forced vibration discussed in Art. 6 and conclude accordingly that motion of the suspended weight W is given by eq. (26'), i.e.,

$$x = \frac{a \sin \omega t}{1 - \omega^2/p^2}. \tag{c}$$

It is seen that in the case when ω is small in comparison with p, i.e., the frequency of oscillation of the point of suspension A is small in comparison with the frequency of free vibration of the system, the displacement x is approximately equal to x_1 and the load W performs practically the same oscillatory motion as the point of suspension A does. When ω approaches p the denominator in expression (c) approaches zero and we approach the resonance condition at which heavy forced vibrations are produced.

Considering now the case when ω is very large in comparison with p, i.e., the frequency of vibration of the body to which the instrument is attached is very high in comparison with frequency of free vibrations of the load W, the amplitude of forced vibrations (c) becomes small and the weight W can be considered as immovable in space. Taking, for instance, $\omega = 10p$ we find that the amplitude of forced vibrations is only $a/99$, i.e., in this case vibrations of the point of suspension A will scarcely be transmitted to the load W.

This fact is utilized in various instruments used for measuring and recording vibrations. Assume that a dial is attached to the box with its plunger pressing against the load W (Fig. 44). During vibration the hand of the dial, moving back and forth, gives the double amplitude of relative motion of the weight W with respect to the box. This amplitude is equal to the maximum value of the expression

$$x - x_1 = a \sin \omega t \left(\frac{1}{1 - \omega^2/p^2} - 1 \right) = a \sin \omega t \cdot \frac{\omega^2/p^2}{1 - \omega^2/p^2}. \tag{d}$$

When p is small in comparison with ω this value is very close to the amplitude a of the vibrating body to which the instrument is attached. The numerical values of the last factor in expression (d) are plotted against the ratio ω/p in Fig. 43.

The instrument described has proved very useful in power plants for studying vibrations of turbo-generators. Introducing in addition to vertical also horizontal springs, horizontal vibrations also can be measured by the same instrument. The springs of the instrument are usually chosen in such a manner that the frequencies of free vibrations of the weight W in both vertical and horizontal directions are about 200 per minute. If a turbogenerator makes 1800 r.p.m. it can be expected that, owing to some unbalance, vibrations of the foundation and of the bearings of the same frequency will be produced. Then the dials of the instrument attached to the foundation or to a bearing will give the amplitudes of vertical and horizontal vibrations with sufficient accuracy since in this case $\omega/p = 9$ and the difference between the motion in which we are interested and the relative motion (d) is a small one.

To get a record of vibrations a cylindrical drum rotating with constant speed can be used. If such a drum with vertical axis is attached to the box, Fig. 44, and a pencil attached to the weight presses against the drum, a complete record of the relative motion (d) during vibration will be recorded. On this principle various vibrographs are built. A simple arrangement for recording vibrations in a ship hulls is shown

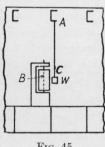

FIG. 45

in Fig. 45. A weight W is attached at point A to a beam by a rubber band AC. During vertical vibrations of the hull this weight remains practically immovable provided the period of free vibrations of the weight is sufficiently large. Then the pencil attached to it will record the vibrations of the hull on a rotating drum B. To get a satisfactory result the frequency of free vibrations of the weight must be small in comparison with that of the hull of the ship. This requires that the statical elongation of the string AC must be large. For instance, to get a frequency of ½ of an oscillation per second the elongation of the string under the statical action of the weight W must be nearly 3 ft. The requirement of large extensions is a defect in this type of instrument.

A device analogous to that shown in Fig. 44 can be applied also for measuring accelerations. In such a case a rigid spring must be used and the frequency of natural vibrations of the weight W must be made very large in comparison with the frequency of the vibrating body to which the instrument is attached. Then p is large in comparison with ω in expression (d) and the relative motion of the load W is approximately equal to $a\omega^2 \sin \omega t/p^2$ and proportional to the acceleration $\ddot{x}_1$ of the body to which the instrument is attached. Due to the rigidity of the spring the relative displacements of the load W are usually small and require special devices for recording them.

EXAMPLES

1. A machine of weight $W = 1000$ lb and making 1800 r.p.m. is supported by four helical springs (Fig. 42b) made of steel wire of diameter $d = \frac{1}{2}$ in. The diameter corresponding to the center line of the helix is $D = 4$ in. and the number of coils $n = 10$. Determine the maximum vertical disturbing force transmitted to the foundation if th·

centrifugal force of unbalance for the angular speed equal to 1 radian per sec is $P = 1$ lb.

Solution. The statical deflection of the springs under the action of the load W is

$$\delta_{st} = \frac{2nD^3W}{d^4G} = \frac{2 \cdot 10 \cdot 4^3 \cdot 1000}{(\frac{1}{2})^4 \cdot 12 \cdot 10^6} = 1.71 \text{ in.}$$

from which the spring constant $k = 1000/1.71 = 585$ lb per in. and the square of the angular frequency of free vibration $p^2 = g/\delta_{st} = 225$ are obtained. By using eq. (a) we obtain the maximum force transmitted to foundation

$$1 \cdot \frac{(60\pi)^2}{(60\pi)^2/(225) - 1} = 227 \text{ lb.}$$

2. For measuring vertical vibrations of a foundation the instrument shown in Fig. 44 is used. What is the amplitude of these vibrations if their frequency is 1800 per minute, the hand of the dial fluctuates between readings giving deflections 0.100 in. and 0.120 in. and the springs are chosen so that the statical deflection of the weight W is equal to 1 in.?

Solution. From the dial reading we conclude that the amplitude of relative motion, see eq. (d), is 0.01 in. The frequency of free vibrations of the weight W, from eq. (4), is $f = 3.14$ per sec. Hence $\omega/p = 30/3.14$. The amplitude of vibration of the foundation, from eq. (d), is

$$a = 0.01 \frac{(30/3.14)^2 - 1}{(30/3.14)^2} = 0.00989 \text{ in.}$$

3. A device such as shown in Fig. 44 is used for measuring vertical acceleration of a cab of a locomotive which makes, by moving up and down, 3 vertical osc. per sec. The spring of the instrument is so rigid that the frequency of free vibrations of the weight W is 60 per sec. What is the maximum acceleration of the cab if the vibrations recorded by the instrument representing the relative motion of the weight W with respect to the box have an amplitude $a_1 = 0.001$ in.? What is the amplitude a of vibration of the cab?

Solution. From eq. (d) we have

$$a_1 = \frac{a\omega^2}{p^2 - \omega^2}.$$

Hence the maximum vertical acceleration of the cab is

$$a\omega^2 = a_1(p^2 - \omega^2).$$

Noting that $p = 2\pi \cdot 60$ and $\omega = 2\pi \cdot 3$, we obtain

$$a\omega^2 = 0.001 \cdot 4\pi^2(60^2 - 3^2) = 142 \text{ in. sec}^{-2}$$

and

$$a = \frac{142}{36\pi^2} = 0.4 \text{ in.}$$

PROBLEMS

1. In what proportion will the vertical disturbing force exerted on the foundation by the unbalanced machine discussed in Ex. 1 above be increased if there are 8 supporting springs instead of 4? Assume all other data the same.

Answer. Approx. doubled.

2. Calculate the required spring constant k for the spring mounting of an electric motor weighing 200 lb and operating at 1800 r.p.m. if the maximum force transmitted to the foundation is to be only $\frac{1}{10}$ of the centrifugal force due to unbalance.

Answer. $k = 1680$ lb per in.

3. The instrument shown in Fig. 46 is to be used to record vertical vibrations of a bridge which has a natural frequency in the neighborhood of 90 osc. per min. The

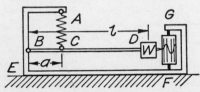

weight $W = 0.67$ lb; the bar BD weighs 1 lb; the spring AC has a constant $k_2 = 1$ lb per in. Find the proper ratio a/l so that the record left on the rotating drum FG will represent the motion of the bridge within $\pm 2\%$.

Answer. $a/l \approx 1/15$.

Fig. 46

4. The record taken with an accelerometer attached to the reciprocating cross-head of a steam engine shows an amplitude of 0.25 in. Find the maximum acceleration of the cross-head if the spring constant for the instrument is $k = 10$ lb per in. and the suspended weight $W = 0.2$ lb.

Answer. $\ddot{x}_1 = 4825$ in. per sec².

5. Referring again to Fig. 46, assume that $a/l = 1/10$ and $W = 10$ lb. Find the proper spring constant k_2 to make the instrument record ship vibrations of 90 osc. per min. with only 1% error. Neglect the weight of the bar BD in this case.

Answer. $k_s = 2.3$ lb per in.

6. An electric motor and bed-plate together weigh 10,000 lb. The motor operates at 1800 r.p.m. Find the spring constant k for a spring mounting that will reduce the force transmitted to the foundation to 10% of the centrifugal force due to unbalance.

Answer. $k = 83,700$ lb per in.

9. Other Technical Applications.—*Oscillator.*—For determining the frequency of free vibrations of structures a special device called the *Oscillator* * is sometimes used. It consists of two discs rotating in a vertical plane with constant speed in opposite directions, as shown in Fig. 47. The bearings of the discs are housed in a rigid frame

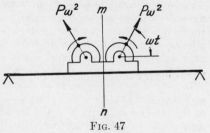

Fig. 47

which must be rigidly attached to the structure, the vibrations of which are studied. By attaching to the discs the unbalanced weights symmetrically situated with respect to the vertical axis mn, the centrifugal forces $P\omega^2$ which are produced during rotation of

* Such an oscillator is described in a paper by W. Späth, *Z. Ver. deut. Ing.*, Vol. 73, p. 963, 1929.

the discs have a resultant $2P\omega^2 \sin \omega t$ acting along the axis mn.* Such a pulsating force produces forced vibrations of the structure which can be recorded by a vibrograph. By gradually changing the speed of the discs the number of revolutions per second at which the amplitude of forced vibrations of the structure becomes a maximum can be established. Assuming that this occurs at resonance,† the frequency of free vibration of the structure is equal to the above-found number of revolutions per second of the discs.

Frahm's Vibration Tachometer.‡ An instrument widely used for measuring the frequency of vibrations is known as Frahm's tachometer. This consists of a system of steel strips built in at their lower ends as shown in Fig. 48. To the upper ends of the strips small masses are attached, the magnitudes of which are adjusted in such a manner

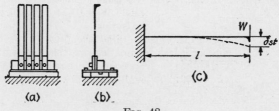

FIG. 48

that the system of strips represents a definite series of frequencies. The difference between the frequencies of any two consecutive strips is usually equal to half a vibration per second.

In figuring the frequency, a strip can be considered as a cantilever beam (Fig. 48c). In order to take into consideration the effect of the mass of the strip on the vibration it is necessary to imagine that one quarter of the weight W_1 of the strip is added to the weight W, the latter being concentrated at the end. Then,

$$\delta_{st} = \frac{(W + W_1/4)l^3}{3EI}.$$

This statical deflection must be substituted in eq. (4) in order to obtain the period of natural vibration of the strip. In service the instrument is attached to the machine, the vibrational frequency of which is to be measured. The strip whose period of natural vibration is nearest to the period of one revolution of the machine will be in a condition near resonance and a heavy vibration of this strip will be built up. From the frequency of the strip, which is known, the speed of the machine can be obtained.

Instead of a series of strips of different lengths and having different masses at the ends, one strip can be used having an adjustable length. The frequency of vibration of the machine can then be found by adjusting the length of the strip in this instrument so as to obtain resonance. On this latter principle the well-known Fullarton vibrometer is built.

* It is assumed that the effect of vibrations on the inertia forces of the unbalanced weights can be neglected.

† For a more accurate discussion of this question the effect of damping must be considered (see Art. 13).

‡ This instrument is described by F. Lux, *Elektrotech. Z.*, pp. 264–387, 1905.

Indicator of Steam Engines. Steam engine indicators are used for measuring the variation of steam pressure in the engine cylinder. The accuracy of the records of such indicators will depend on the ability of the indicator system, consisting of piston, spring and pencil, to follow exactly the variation of the steam pressure. From the general discussion of Art. 6 it is known that this condition will be satisfied if the frequency of free vibrations of the indicator system is very high in comparison with that of the steam pressure variation in the cylinder.

Let $A = 0.20$ sq in. be the area of the indicator piston,

$W = 0.133$ lb the weight of the piston, piston rod and modified weight of other parts connected with the piston,

$s = 0.1$ in. the displacement of the pencil produced by a pressure of one atmosphere (15 lb per sq in.) and

$n = 4$, the ratio of the displacement of the pencil to that of the piston.

From the condition that the pressure on the piston equal to $15 \times 0.2 = 3.00$ lb produces a compression of the spring equal to $\frac{1}{4} \times 0.1 = 0.025$ in., we find that the spring constant is:

$$k = 3.00 : 0.025 = 120 \text{ lb per in.}$$

The frequency of the free vibrations of the indicator is

$$f = \frac{1}{2\pi} \sqrt{\frac{g}{\delta_{st}}} = \frac{1}{2\pi} \sqrt{\frac{gk}{W}} = \frac{1}{2\pi} \sqrt{\frac{386.120}{0.133}} = 94 \text{ per sec.}$$

This frequency can be considered as sufficiently high in comparison with the usual frequency of steam engines and the indicator's record of steam pressure will be sufficiently accurate. In the case of high speed engines, however, such an instrument may give completely unreliable records * under certain conditions.

Locomotive Wheel Pressure on the Rail. It is well known that inertia forces of counterweights in locomotive wheels produce additional pressure on the track. This effect of counterweights can easily be obtained by using the theory of forced vibrations. Let W be the weight of the wheel and of all parts rigidly connected to the wheel, Q, the spring borne weight, P, the centrifugal force due to unbalance, ω, the angular velocity of the wheel. Considering then the problem as one of statics, the vertical pressure of the wheel on the rail, Fig. 49, will be equal to

$$Q + W + P \cos \omega t. \tag{a}$$

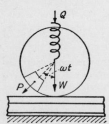

FIG. 49

At slow speed this expression represents a good approximation for the wheel pressure. In order to get this pressure with greater accuracy, forced vibrations of the wheel on the rail produced by the periodical vertical force $P \cos \omega t$ must be considered. Let k denote the vertical load on the rail necessary to produce a deflection of the rail equal to unity directly under the load and δ_{st}, the deflection produced by the weight W, then,

* The description of an indicator for high-frequency engines (Collins Micro-Indicator) is given in *Engineering*, Vol. 113, p. 716, 1922. Symposium of papers on indicators, see *Proc. Inst. Mech. Engrs.* (London), Jan. 1923.

$$\delta_{st} = \frac{W}{k}.$$

The period of free vibrations of the wheel on the rail is given by the equation *

$$\tau = 2\pi \sqrt{\frac{W}{kg}}. \qquad (b)$$

The period of one revolution of the wheel, i.e., the period of the disturbing force $P \cos \omega t$, is

$$\tau_1 = \frac{2\pi}{\omega}.$$

Now, by using eq. (26), it can be concluded that the dynamical deflection of the rail produced by the force P will be larger than the corresponding statical deflection in the ratio,

$$\frac{1}{1 - \left(\dfrac{\tau}{\tau_1}\right)^2}. \qquad (c)$$

The pressure on the rail produced by the centrifugal force P will also increase in the same ratio and the maximum wheel pressure will be given by

$$Q + W + \frac{P}{1 - \left(\dfrac{\tau}{\tau_1}\right)^2}. \qquad (d)$$

For a 100-lb rail, a modulus of the elastic foundation equal to 1500 lb per sq in. and $W = 6000$ lb we will have

$$\tau = 0.068 \text{ sec.}$$

Assuming that the wheel performs five revolutions per sec we obtain

$$\tau_1 = 0.2 \text{ sec.}$$

Substituting the values of τ and τ_1 in the expression (c) it can be concluded that the dynamical effect of the counterbalance will be about 11% larger than that calculated statically.

10. Balancing of Rotating Machines.—One of the most important applications of the theory of vibrations is in the solution of balancing problems. It is known that a rotating body does not exert any variable

* In this calculation the mass of the rail is neglected and the compressive force Q in the spring is considered as constant. This latter assumption is justified by the fact that the period of vibration of the engine cab on its spring is usually very large in comparison with the period of vibration of the wheel on the rail, therefore vibrations of the wheel will not be transmitted to the cab and variations in the compression of the spring will be very small (see Art. 8).

disturbing action on the supports when the axis of rotation coincides with one of the principal axes of inertia of the body. It is difficult to satisfy this condition exactly in the process of manufacturing because, due to errors in geometrical dimensions and non-homogeneity of the material, some irregularities in the mass distribution are always present. As a result of this, variable disturbing forces occur which produce vibrations. In order to remove these vibrations in machines and establish quiet running conditions, balancing becomes necessary. The importance of balancing becomes especially great in the case of high speed machines. In such cases the slightest unbalance may produce a very large disturbing force. For

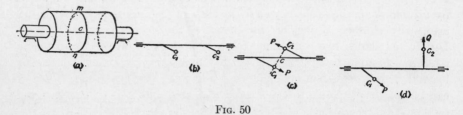

Fig. 50

instance, at 1800 r.p.m. an unbalance equal to one pound at a radius of 30 in. produces a disturbing force equal to 2760 lb.

In order to explain the various conditions of unbalance a rotor shown in Fig. 50a will now be considered.* Imagine the rotating body divided into two parts by any cross section mn. The three following typical cases of unbalance may arise:

1. The centers of gravity of both parts may be in the same axial plane and on the same side of the axis of rotation as shown in Fig. 50b. The center of gravity C of the whole body will consequently be in the same plane at a certain distance from the axis of rotation. This is called *static unbalance*, because it can be detected by a statical test. A statical balancing test consists of putting the rotor with the two ends of its shaft on absolutely horizontal, parallel rails. If the center of gravity of the whole rotor is on the axis (Fig. 50c) the rotor will be in static equilibrium in any position; if the center is slightly off the shaft, as in Fig. 50b, it will roll on the rails until the center of gravity reaches its lowest position.

2. The centers of gravity of both parts may be in the same axial plane but on opposite sides of the axis of rotation as shown in Fig. 50c, and at such radial distances that the center of gravity C of the whole body will be

* The rotor is considered as an absolutely rigid body and vibrations due to elastic deflections of it are neglected.

exactly on the axis of rotation. In this case the body will be in balance under static conditions, but during rotation a disturbing couple of centrifugal forces P will act on the rotor. This couple rotates with the body and produces vibrations in the foundation. Such a case is called *dynamic unbalance.*

3. In the most general case the centers of gravity, C_1 and C_2, may lie in different axial sections and during rotation a system of two forces formed by the centrifugal forces P and Q will act on the body (see Fig. 50d). This system of forces can always be reduced to a couple acting in an axial section and a radial force, i.e., static and dynamic unbalance will occur together.

It can be shown that in all cases complete balancing can be obtained by attaching to the rotor a weight in each of two cross-sectional planes arbitrarily chosen. Consider, for instance, the case shown in Fig. 51. Due to unbalance two centrifugal forces P and Q act on the rotor during motion. Assume now that the weights necessary for balance must be located in the cross-sectional planes I and II. The centrifugal force P can be balanced by two forces P_1 and P_2, lying with P in the same axial section. The magnitude of these forces will be determined from the following equations of statics,

$$P_1 + P_2 = P,$$

$$P_1a = P_2b.$$

In the same manner the force Q can be balanced by the forces Q_1 and Q_2. The resultant of P_1 and Q_1 in plane I, and the resultant of P_2 and Q_2 in plane II will then determine the magnitudes and the positions of the correction weights necessary for complete balancing of the rotor. It is seen from this discussion that balancing can be made without any difficulty if the position and magnitude of the unbalance is known.   For determining this unbalance various types of balancing machines are used and the fundamentals of these machines will now be discussed.

A balancing machine represents usually an arrangement in which the effects of any unbalance in the rotor which is under test may be magnified by resonance.   There are three principal types of balancing machines: (1) machines where the rotor rests on two independent pedestals such as the machines of Lawaczeck-Heymann, or the Westinghouse machine; (2)

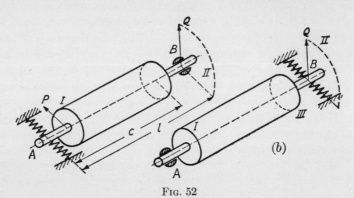

Fig. 52

machines in which the rotor rests on a vibrating table with an immovable fulcrum; (3) balancing machines with a movable fulcrum.

The *Lawaczeck-Heymann machine* consists mainly of two independent pedestals.   The two bearings supporting the rotor are attached to springs, which allow vibrations of the ends of the rotor in a horizontal axial plane. One of the bearings is locked with the balancing being performed on the other end (see Fig. 52).   Any unbalance will produce vibration of the rotor about the locked bearing as a fulcrum.   In order to magnify these vibrations all records are taken at *resonance condition*.   By a special motor the rotor is brought to a speed above the *critical* and then the motor power is shut off.   Due to friction the speed of the rotor gradually decreases and, as it passes through its *critical value*, pronounced forced vibrations of the unlocked bearing of the rotor will be produced by any unbalance.   The process of balancing then consists of removing these vibrations by attaching suitable correction weights.   The most suitable planes for placing these weights are the ends of the rotor body, where special holes for such weights are usually provided along the circumference.   By such an arrangement the largest distance between the correction weights is obtained; therefore the magnitude of these weights is brought to a minimum. When the plane for such correction weight has been chosen there still remain two questions to be answered, (1) the location of the correction weight and (2) its magnitude. Both these questions can be solved by trial. In order to determine the location, some arbitrary correction weight should be put in the plane of balancing and several runs should be made with the weight in different positions along the circumference of the rotor. A curve representing the variation in amplitude of vibrations, with the angle of location of the weight, can be obtained. The minimum amplitude will then indicate the true location for the correction weight. In the same manner, by gradually changing the magnitude of the weight, the true magnitude of the correction weight can be established.

The procedure for balancing a rotor AB (see Fig. 52) will now be described. Assume first that the bearing B is locked and the end A of the rotor is free to vibrate in a horizontal axial plane. It has been shown already that in the most general case the unbalance can be represented by two centrifugal forces acting in two arbitrarily chosen planes perpendicular to the axis of the shaft. Let the force P in the plane I (see Fig. 52a) and the force Q in the plane II through the center of the locked bearing B represent the unbalance in the rotor. In the case under consideration the force P only will produce vibrations. Proceeding as described above, the force P can be determined and the vibrations can be annihilated by a suitable choice of correction weight. In order to balance the force Q, the bearing A must be locked and the bearing B made free to vibrate (see Fig. 52b). Taking the plane III, for placing the correction weight and proceeding as before, the magnitude and the location of this weight can be determined. Let G denote the centrifugal force corresponding to this weight. Then from the equation of statics,

$$G \cdot c = Q \cdot l$$

and

$$Q = \frac{Gc}{l}. \qquad (a)$$

It is easy to see that by putting the correction weight in the plane III, we annihilate vibrations produced by Q only under the condition that the bearing A is locked. Otherwise there will be vibrations due to the fact that the force Q and the force G are acting in two different planes II and III. In order to obtain complete balance one correction weight must be placed in each of the two planes I and III, such that the corresponding centrifugal forces G_1 and G_2 will have as their resultant the force $-Q$

equal and opposite to the force Q (Fig. 53). Then, from statics, we have

$$G_1 - G_2 = Q,$$

$$G_2 \cdot b = Q \cdot a,$$

from which, by using eq. (a),

$$G_2 = \frac{Qa}{b} = \frac{Gac}{bl}, \tag{b}$$

$$G_1 = Q + G_2 = \frac{Gcd}{bl}. \tag{c}$$

It is seen from this that by balancing at the end B and determining in this manner the quantity G, the true correction weight for the plane III

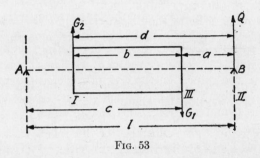

Fig. 53

and the additional correction weight for the plane I can be found from eqs. (b) and (c) and complete balancing of the rotor will be obtained.

The large *Westinghouse machine* * having a capacity of rotors weighing up to 300,000 pounds consists essentially of two pedestals mounted on a rigid bed-plate, together with a driving motor and special magnetic clutch for rotating the rotor. A cross section of the pedestal consists of a solid part bolted to the rails of the bed-plate and a pendulum part held in place by strong springs. The vertical load of the rotor is carried by a flexible, thin vertical plate, making a frictionless hinge. The rotor is brought to a speed above the critical speed of the bearing which can be controlled by changing the springs according to the weight of the rotor, and the magnetic clutch is disengaged. The rotor drifts slowly through this critical speed when observations of the oscillations produced by magnified effect of the unbalance are made.

* L. C. Fletcher, "Balancing Large Rotating Apparatus," *Elec. J.*, Vol. 21, p. 5.

The balancing is done by locking first one bearing and balancing the opposite end, and then locking the second end and balancing the corresponding opposite end. The balancing is done by a cut-and-try method, the time of balancing proper of large rotors being small when compared with the time of setting up and preparations for balancing. The additional correction weights are put into the balancing rings, the same as described with the Lawaczeck-Heymann machine.

Akimoff's Balancing Machine, * consists of a rigid table on which the rotor and the compensating device are mounted. The table is secured to the pedestals in such a way that it is free to vibrate, either about an axis parallel to the axis of the rotor or about an axis perpendicular to the axis of the rotor. In the first case static unbalance alone produces vibrations; in the second, both static and dynamic unbalance will cause vibration. Beginning with checking for static unbalance, the table must be supported in such a way as to obtain vibration about the axis parallel to the axis of rotation of the rotor. The method for determining the location and magnitude of unbalance consists in creating an artificial unbalance in some moving part of the machine to counteract the unbalance of the body to be tested. When this artificial unbalance becomes the exact counterpart of the unbalance in the body being tested, the whole unit ceases to vibrate and the magnitude and the angular plane of unbalance are indicated on the machine.

After removing the static unbalance of the rotor, testing for dynamic unbalance can be made by rearranging the supports of the table in such a manner as to have the axis of vibration perpendicular to the axis of rotation. The magnitude and the angular plane of dynamic unbalance will then be easily found in the same manner as explained above by introducing an artificial couple of unbalance in the moving part of the machine. It is important to note that all the static unbalance must be removed before checking for dynamic unbalance.

The *Soderberg-Trumpler machine* is an example of the third type. When mass production balancing of small units is performed, the time per unit necessary for balancing is of great importance. The additional correction weights necessary with the previously described types cause a loss of time. In order to eliminate these corrections, the fulcrum of the balancing table is movable in this machine. The body to be balanced is mounted in bearing blocks on a vibrating table supported by two spring members and a movable fulcrum. By placing the fulcrum axis in the plane of one of the balancing rings, say *BB*, the action of the theoretical unbalance weight in this plane is

* *Trans. A.S.M.E.*, Vol. 38, p. 367, 1916.

eliminated as far as its effect upon the motion of the vibrating table is concerned. This will now be produced by the unbalance in the other plane only. Then the force at AA is balanced, after which the fulcrum is moved to the position in the plane AA; then BB is balanced. It is evident that this balancing is final and does not require any correction. These machines are used mostly when small rotors are balanced.

On this principle, an automatic machine is built by the Westinghouse Company for their small motor works.* In order to eliminate harmful damping in friction joints, knife edges were replaced by flexible spring members. The table oscillates horizontally, being carried on a vertical stem presenting a torsionally flexible axis. The table proper is moved in guides in such a way that one weight correction plane can be brought for balancing in line with the axis of the vertical stem.

For *automatic* balancing, the table is supplied with an unbalance compensating head coupled to the rotor. The counter-balancing is done by two electrically operated small clutches. The movable weights in the head produce a counter-balancing couple. One clutch shifts the weights apart, increasing the magnitude of this couple; another clutch changes the angular position of the counter-balancing couple with respect to the rotor. Two switches mounted in front of the machine actuate the clutches. It is easy in a very short time, a fraction of a minute, to adjust the counter-balancing weights in a way that the vibration of the table is brought to zero. Indicators on the balancing head show then the amount and location of unbalance, and the necessary correction weights are inserted into the armature. †

11. Damping.—In the previous discussion of free and forced vibrations it was assumed that there are no resisting forces acting on the vibrating body. As a result of this assumption it was found that in the case of free vibrations the amplitude of vibrations remains constant, while experience shows that the amplitude diminishes with time, and vibrations are gradually damped out. In the case of forced vibrations at resonance it was found that the amplitude of vibration can be indefinitely built up, but, as we know, due to damping, there is always a certain upper limit below

* W. E. Trumpler, "The Dynamic Balance of Small High Speed Armatures," *Elec. J.*, Vol. 22, p. 34, 1925.

† Recently several new types of balancing machines have been developed which reduce considerably the time required for balancing. It should be mentioned here the Leblanc-Thearle balancing machine described by E. L. Thearle, *Trans. A.S.M.E.*, Vol. 54, p. APM-131, 1932; the Automatic Balancing Machine of Spaeth-Losenhausen and the method of balancing rotors by means of electrical networks recently developed by J. G. Baker and F. C. Rushing, *J. Franklin Inst.*, Vol. 222, p. 183, 1936.

which the amplitude always remains. To bring an analytical discussion of vibration problems in better agreement with actual conditions *damping forces* must be taken into consideration. These damping forces may arise from several different sources such as friction between the dry sliding surfaces of the bodies, friction between lubricated surfaces, air or fluid resistance, electric damping, internal friction due to imperfect elasticity of materials, etc.

In the case of friction between dry surfaces the Coulomb-Morin law is usually applied.* It is assumed that in the case of dry surfaces the friction force F is proportional to the normal component N of the pressure acting between the surfaces, so that

$$F = \mu N, \tag{a}$$

where μ is the *coefficient of friction*, the magnitude of which depends on the materials of the bodies in contact and on the roughness of their surfaces.

Experiments show that the force F required to overcome friction and start motion is larger than the force necessary to maintain uniform motion. Thus usually larger values are assumed for the coefficients of friction at rest than for the coefficients of friction during motion. It is usually assumed also that the coefficient of friction during motion is independent of the velocity so that Coulomb's law can be represented by a line BC, parallel to abscissa axis, as shown in Fig. 54. By the position of the point A in the same figure the coefficient of friction at rest is given. This law agrees satisfactorily with experiments in the

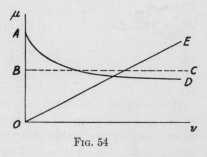

Fig. 54

case of smooth surfaces. When the surfaces are rough the coefficient of friction depends on velocity and diminishes with increase of the velocity as shown in Fig. 54 by the curve AD.†

If, instead of sliding, we have rolling as in ball bearings, the coefficient of friction is independent of velocity and decreases with the normal load on the

---

* C. A. Coulomb, *Mémoires de mathématique et de physique*, Paris, 1785; see also his *Théorie des machines simples*, Paris, 1821; A. Morin, *Mémoires présentés par divers savants*, Vol. 4, 1833, and Vol. 6, 1835. For references to new literature on the same subject, see *Handbuch der physikalischen, und technischen Mechik*, Vol. 1, p. 751, 1929.

† The coefficient of friction between a locomotive wheel and rail were investigated by Douglas Galton, see *Engineering*, Vols. 25 and 26, 1878; and Vol. 27, 1879.

bearing. It is very small in comparison with the coefficient of sliding friction. For example, in the case of steel sliding on steel, the coefficient of friction is of the order of $\mu = 0.15$ to $\mu = 0.20$ while in the case of ball or roller bearings this coefficient varies from 0.001 to 0.002.

In the case of friction between lubricated surfaces the friction force does not depend on materials of the bodies in contact but on the *viscosity* of lubricant and on the velocity of motion. In the case of perfectly lubricated surfaces in which there exists a continuous lubricating film between the sliding surfaces it can be assumed that friction forces are proportional both to the viscosity of the lubricant and to the velocity. The coefficient of friction, as a function of velocity, is represented for this case, in Fig. 54 by the straight line OE.

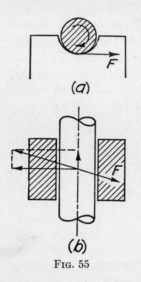

(a)

(b)

Fig. 55

We obtain also resisting forces proportional to the velocity if a body is moving in a viscous fluid with a small velocity or if a moving body causes fluid to be forced through narrow passages as in the case of dash pots.* In further discussion of all cases in which friction forces are proportional to velocity we will call these forces *viscous damping*.

In the case of motion of bodies in air or in liquid with larger velocities, a resistance proportional to the square of velocity can be assumed with sufficient accuracy.

It should be noted that friction forces always act so as to oppose the relative velocity between sliding bodies. In the case of a shaft, rotating in bearings (Fig. 55) the friction force F is perpendicular to the axis of the shaft. Imagine now that by the application of an axial force some movement of the rotating shaft in the longitudinal direction is produced. In such a case, the relative velocity will have not only a circumferential but also an axial component and the friction force F will be inclined to the axis of the shaft as shown in Fig. 55b. It is seen that the resisting force in the axial direction will be small; thus it is very much easier to slide a shaft longitudinally in its bearings when it is rotating than when it is at rest. This means that a rotating shaft can oscillate axially practically without damping.

Another example of negligible damping occurs when a shaft, rotating at high speed, performs torsional vibrations. Since the amplitude of torsional

* See experiments by A. Stodola, *Schweiz. Bauzeitung*, Vol. 23, p. 113, 1893.

vibrations and the corresponding circumferential velocity on the surface of the shaft is small in comparison with the velocity due to rotation of the shaft as a rigid body, the relative velocity at the points of contact with the bearing remains practically constant so that the friction forces retain their direction and magnitude during torsional vibration. Such forces produce a constant twist of the shaft, but have no damping effect on torsional vibrations. Damping in this case depends almost entirely upon *internal friction* of the material of the shaft. This internal friction is principally of thermal origin.* The temperature changes produced by deformation of a poly-crystalline metal specimen vary from grain to grain depending on their crystallographic orientation and there will be some energy dissipation due to the heat flow between the individual crystals. If cycles of loading and unloading are produced, the corresponding test diagrams will show hysteresis loops the areas of which measure the energy dissipated per cycle. Since the heat generated in any one grain is proportional to its volume, while the heat exchange depends on the magnitude of its surface area, it is evident that the temperature equilization will be facilitated and the losses of mechanical energy increased by diminution of the grain size. Thus to increase damping due to internal friction, materials having small grain size should be used.

In our further study, we will see that the problem of vibration is much simplified if damping forces are proportional to velocity. For this reason resisting forces of a complicated nature are very often replaced, for purposes of analysis, by an *equivalent viscous damping*. This equivalent damping is determined in such a manner as to produce the same dissipation of energy per cycle as that produced by the actual resisting forces. In this manner, for example, damping due to internal friction can be treated. In the following articles, various examples of vibrations with damping will be discussed in detail.

12. Free Vibration with Viscous Damping.—Consider again the vibration of the system shown in Fig. 1 and assume that the vibrating body W encounters in its motion a resistance proportional to the velocity. In such case, instead of eq. (b), p. 2, we obtain

$$\frac{W}{g}\ddot{x} = W - (W + kx) - c\dot{x}. \qquad (a)$$

The last term on the right side of this equation represents the damping force, proportional to velocity $\dot{x}$. The minus sign shows that the force is

* See C. M. Zener, *Elasticity and Anelasticity of Metals*, Chicago, 1948.

acting in the direction opposite to the velocity. The coefficient c is a constant depending on the kind of damping device and numerically is equal to the magnitude of the damping force when the velocity is equal to unity. Dividing eq. (a) by W/g and using notations

$$p^2 = kg/W \quad \text{and} \quad cg/W = 2n, \tag{b}$$

we obtain for free vibrations with viscous damping the following equation

$$\ddot{x} + 2n\dot{x} + p^2 x = 0. \tag{31}$$

In discussing this equation we apply the usual method of solving linear differential equations with constant coefficients, and assume a solution of it in the form

$$x = e^{rt}, \tag{c}$$

in which e is the base of natural logarithms, t is time and r is a constant which must be determined from the condition that expression (c) satisfies eq. (31). Substituting (c) in eq. (31) we obtain

$$r^2 + 2nr + p^2 = 0,$$

from which

$$r = -n \pm \sqrt{n^2 - p^2}. \tag{d}$$

Let us consider first the case when the quantity n^2, depending on damping, is smaller than the quantity p^2. In such case the quantity

$$p_1{}^2 = p^2 - n^2 \tag{e}$$

is positive and we get for r two complex roots:

$$r_1 = -n + p_1 i \quad \text{and} \quad r_2 = -n - p_1 i.$$

Substituting these roots in expression (c) we obtain two particular solutions of eq. (31). The sum or the difference of these two solutions multiplied by any constant will be also a solution. In this manner we get solutions

$$x_1 = \frac{C_1}{2} (e^{r_1 t} + e^{r_2 t}) = C_1 e^{-nt} \cos p_1 t,$$

$$x_2 = \frac{C_2}{2i} (e^{r_1 t} - e^{r_2 t}) = C_2 e^{-nt} \sin p_1 t.$$

Adding these together the general solution of eq. (31) is obtained in the following form:

$$x = e^{-nt}(C_1 \cos p_1 t + C_2 \sin p_1 t), \tag{32}$$

in which C_1 and C_2 are constants which in each particular case must be determined from the initial conditions.

The expression in the parenthesis of solution (32) is of the same form as we had before for vibrations without damping (see eq. 2). It represents a periodic function with the period

$$\tau = \frac{2\pi}{p_1} = \frac{2\pi}{p} \frac{1}{\sqrt{1 - n^2/p^2}}. \tag{33}$$

Comparing this with the period $2\pi/p$, obtained before for vibrations without damping, we see that due to damping the period of vibration increases, but if n is small in comparison with p, this increase is a small quantity of second order. Therefore, in practical problems, it can be assumed with sufficient accuracy that a small viscous damping does not affect the period of vibration.

The factor e^{-nt} in solution (32) gradually decreases with the time and the vibrations, originally generated, will be gradually damped out.

To determine the constants C_1 and C_2 in solution (32) let us assume that at the initial instant $t = 0$ the vibrating body is displaced from its position of equilibrium by the amount x_0 and has an initial velocity $\dot{x}_0$. Substituting $t = 0$ in expression (32) we then obtain

$$x_0 = C_1. \tag{f}$$

Differentiating the same expression with respect to time and equating it to $\dot{x}_0$, for $t = 0$, we obtain

$$C_2 = (\dot{x}_0 + nx_0)/p_1. \tag{g}$$

Substituting (f) and (g) into solution (32) we obtain

$$x = e^{-nt}\left(x_0 \cos p_1 t + \frac{\dot{x}_0 + nx_0}{p_1} \sin p_1 t\right). \tag{34}$$

The first term in this expression proportional to $\cos p_1 t$, depends only on the initial displacement x_0 and the second term, proportional to $\sin p_1 t$ depends on both, initial displacement x_0 and initial velocity $\dot{x}_0$. Each term can be readily represented by a curve. The wavy curve in Fig. 56 represents the first term. This curve is tangent to the curve $x = x_0 e^{-nt}$ at the points m_1, m_2, m_3, where $t = 0, t = \tau, t = 2\tau, \cdots$; and to the curve $x = -x_0 e^{-nt}$ at the points $m_1', m_2', \cdots$ where $t = \tau/2, t = 3\tau/2, \cdots$. These points do not coincide with the points of extreme displacements of the body from the position of equilibrium and it is easy to see that due to damping, the time interval necessary for displacement of the body from a middle position to the subsequent extreme position is less than that necessary to return from an extreme position to the subsequent middle position.

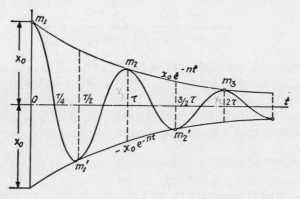

Fig. 56

The rate of damping depends on the magnitude of the constant n (see eq. b). It is seen from the general solution (34) that the amplitude of the vibration diminishes after every cycle in the ratio

$$e^{-n\tau}:1, \tag{h}$$

i.e., it decreases following the law of geometrical progression. Eq. (h) can be used for an experimental determination of the coefficient of damping n. It is only necessary to determine by experiment in what proportion the amplitude of vibration is diminished after a given number of cycles.

The quantity

$$n\tau = \frac{2\pi}{p} \frac{n}{\sqrt{1 - n^2/p^2}}, \tag{35}$$

on which the rate of damping depends, is usually called the *logarithmic decrement*. It is equal to the difference between the logarithms of the two consecutive amplitudes measured at the instants t and $t + \tau$.

In discussing vibrations without damping the use of a rotating vector for representing motion was shown. Such a vector can be used also in the case of vibrations with damping. Imagine a vector $\overline{OA}$, Fig. 57, of variable magnitude $x_0 e^{-nt}$ rotating with a constant angular velocity p_1. Measuring the angle of rotation in the counter-clockwise direction from the x-axis, the projection OA_1 of the vector is equal to $x_0 e^{-nt} \cos p_1 t$ and represents the first term of expression (34). In the same manner, by taking a vector $\overline{OB}$ equal to $e^{-nt}(\dot{x}_0 + nx_0)/p_1$ and perpendicular to $\overline{OA}$ and projecting it on the axis, we get the second term of solution (34). The total expression

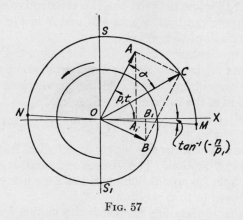

FIG. 57

will be obtained by projecting on the x-axis the vector $\overline{OC}$ which is the geometrical sum of the vectors $\overline{OA}$ and $\overline{OB}$. The magnitude of this vector is

$$\overline{OC} = \sqrt{\overline{OA}^2 + \overline{OB}^2} = e^{-nt}\sqrt{x_0^2 + (\dot{x}_0 + nx_0)^2/p_1^2}, \qquad (i)$$

and the angle which it makes with x-axis is $p_1 t - \alpha$ where

$$\alpha = \arctan \frac{\dot{x}_0 + nx_0}{p_1 x_0}. \qquad (j)$$

From this discussion it follows that expression (34) can be put in the following form:

$$x = e^{-nt}\sqrt{x_0^2 + (\dot{x}_0 + nx_0)^2/p_1^2} \cos (p_1 t - \alpha). \qquad (36)$$

During rotation of the vector $\overline{OC}$, in Fig. 57, the point C describes a logarithmic spiral the tangent to which makes a constant angle equal to $\arctan (-n/p_1)$ with the perpendicular to the radius vector $\overline{OC}$. The extreme positions of the vibrating body correspond to the points at which the spiral has vertical tangents. These points are defined by the intersections of the spiral with the straight line MN, Fig. 57. The points of intersection of the spiral with the vertical axis define the instants when the vibrating body is passing through the equilibrium position. It is clearly seen that the time interval required for the displacement of the body from the equilibrium position to the extreme position, say the time given by the angle SON, in Fig. 57, is less than that necessary to return from the extreme position to the subsequent equilibrium position, as given by the angle NOS_1. But the time between the two consecutive extreme positions of the body, such as given by the points M and N in Fig. 57 is always the same and equal to half of the period τ.

In the foregoing discussion of eq. (31) we assumed that $p^2 > n^2$. If $p^2 < n^2$ both roots (d) become real and are negative. Substituting them in expression (c) we obtain the two particular solutions of eq. (31) and the general solution of the same equation becomes

$$x = C_1 e^{r_1 t} + C_2 e^{r_2 t}. \qquad (k)$$

The solution does not contain any longer a periodical factor and does not represent a vibratory motion. The viscous resistance is so large that the body, displaced from its equilibrium position does not vibrate and only creeps gradually back to that position.

The *critical value* of damping at which the motion loses its vibratory character is given by the condition $n = p$, and by using notations (b) we obtain for this case:

$$c_{cr} = 2 \sqrt{\frac{kW}{g}}. \qquad (l)$$

In the foregoing discussion, we always considered n as a positive quantity, i.e., damping represented a resisting force. Thus due to its action energy is dissipated and the amplitude of vibration gradually diminishes and the motion dies out. There are cases * however in which energy is brought into the system during motion and as a result of this the amplitude of vibration grows with time. In such cases, the notion of *negative damping* is sometimes used. From the solution (32), we see that if n is negative the factor e^{-nt} grows with time and the vibrations are gradually building up. The case of positive n in which vibrations are dying out, represents a *stable motion;* the case of negative n, an *unstable motion*. Various cases in which

* Some of these cases are discussed in Art. 20.

it is necessary to distinguish between stable and unstable motion will be discussed later.

EXAMPLES

1. A body vibrating with viscous damping (Fig. 1) makes 10 complete oscillations per sec. Determine n if after an elapse of 10 seconds the amplitude of vibration is reduced to 0.9 of the initial amplitude. Determine in what proportion the period of vibration decreases if damping is removed. Calculate the logarithmic decrement.

Solution. Assuming that motion is given by the equation

$$x = x_0 e^{-nt} \cos p_1 t,$$

and substituting in this equation $x = 0.9x_0$, $t = 10$, $p_1 = 20\pi$ we obtain

$$e^{10n} = \frac{1}{0.9} = 1.111,$$

from which $n = 0.01054$.

The effect of damping on the period of vibration is given, in eq. (33), by the factor $1/\sqrt{1 - n^2/p^2} = p/\sqrt{p^2 - n^2} = p/p_1$. Substituting $p = \sqrt{p_1^2 + n^2} = p_1\sqrt{1 + n^2/p_1^2}$ we see that by removing damping the period of vibration decreases in the ratio $1/\sqrt{1 + n^2/p_1^2} \approx 1 - \frac{1}{2}\frac{n^2}{p_1^2}$, in which n and p_1 have the values calculated above. The logarithmic decrement is $n\tau = 0.01054 \cdot 0.1 = 0.001054$.

2. Determine the general nature of the displacement-time curve for the motion of a spring suspended mass released with initial displacement x_0 and without initial velocity, if the damping is greater than critical, i.e., $n > p$.

Solution. Substituting the initial conditions $x = x_0$ and $\dot{x} = 0$, when $t = 0$ into eq. (k) and its first time-derivative, we find

$$C_1 + C_2 = x_0, \quad C_1 r_1 + C_2 r_2 = 0,$$

from which

$$C_1 = -\frac{r_2 x_0}{r_1 - r_2}, \quad C_2 = +\frac{r_1 x_0}{r_1 - r_2}.$$

Thus eq. (k) becomes, in this case,

$$x = \frac{x_0}{r_1 - r_2} (r_1 e^{r_2 t} - r_2 e^{r_1 t}). \qquad m)$$

Differentiating this expression twice with respect to time, we find, for velocity and acceleration, the following expressions:

$$\dot{x} = \frac{r_1 r_2 x_0}{r_1 - r_2} (e^{r_2 t} - e^{r_1 t}), \qquad (n)$$

$$\ddot{x} = \frac{r_1 r_2 x_0}{r_1 - r_2} (r_2 e^{r_2 t} - r_1 e^{r_1 t}). \qquad (o)$$

From expression (n), we see that the velocity is zero at $t = 0$ and at $t = \infty$, and that it is negative for all intermediate values of t since both r_1 and r_2 are negative. To find the time t_1 at which this negative velocity is a maximum, we set expression (o) equal to zero and find

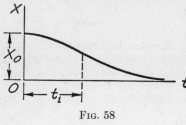

$$t_1 = \frac{\ln\left(\dfrac{r_2}{r_1}\right)}{r_1 - r_2}. \qquad (p)$$

From expressions (m) through (p), we conclude that the displacement-time curve has the general shape shown in Fig. 58. For any particular system with a given damping coefficient c, the exact details of Fig. 58 can be established by remembering that

Fig. 58

$$r_1 = -n + \sqrt{n^2 - p^2},$$

$$r_2 = -n - \sqrt{n^2 - p^2},$$

where n and p are defined by expressions (b).

PROBLEMS

1. A body of weight $W = 10$ lb is supported by a spring with constant $k = 10$ lb per in. and has connected to it a dash-pot damper that is so adjusted as to produce a resistance of 0.01 lb at a velocity of 1 in. per sec. In what ratio will the amplitude of vibration be reduced after 10 cycles?

Answer. 0.539:1.

2. A weight $W = 2$ lb hangs by a spring for which $k = 1$ lb per in. and is subject to damping such that $n = \sqrt{5}\,p/2$. If released from rest with an initial displacement $x_0 = 2$ in., what maximum negative velocity will it attain in its return to the equilibrium position?

Answer. $\dot{x}_{\max} = -9.45$ in. per sec.

13. Forced Vibrations with Viscous Damping.—In discussing forced vibration with viscous damping, we assume that in addition to forces considered in the previous article a disturbing force $P \sin \omega t$ is acting on the vibrating body, Fig. 1. Then instead of eq. (a) of the previous article, we obtain

$$\frac{W}{g}\ddot{x} = W - (W + kx) - c\dot{x} + P \sin \omega t.$$

By using notations (b) on p. 70), this equation becomes

$$\ddot{x} + 2n\dot{x} + p^2 x = \frac{Pg}{W} \sin \omega t. \qquad (37)$$

The general solution of this equation is obtained by adding to the solution of the corresponding homogeneous eq. (31), p. 70 a particular solution of eq. (37). This later solution will have the form

$$x_1 = M \sin \omega t + N \cos \omega t, \tag{a}$$

in which M and N are constants. Substituting this expression into eq. (37) we find that it is satisfied if the constants M and N satisfy the following linear equations

$$-N\omega^2 + 2M\omega n + Np^2 = 0,$$

$$-M\omega^2 - 2N\omega n + Mp^2 = \frac{Pg}{W},$$

from which

$$M = \frac{Pg}{W} \cdot \frac{p^2 - \omega^2}{(p^2 - \omega^2)^2 + 4n^2\omega^2}, \quad N = -\frac{Pg}{W}\frac{2n\omega}{(p^2 - \omega^2)^2 + 4n^2\omega^2}. \tag{b}$$

Substituting these expressions in (a), we obtain the required particular solution. Adding it to the general solution (32) of the homogeneous equation the general solution of eq. (37) becomes

$$x = e^{-nt}(C_1 \cos p_1 t + C_2 \sin p_1 t) + M \sin \omega t + N \cos \omega t. \tag{c}$$

The first member on the right side, having the factor e^{-nt}, represents the free damped vibration discussed in the previous article. The two other terms, having the same frequency as the disturbing force, represent *forced vibration*.

The expression for the forced vibration can be simplified by using rotating vectors as before, see p. 73. Take a vector $\overline{OD}$ of magnitude M rotating with a constant angular velocity ω in the counter-clockwise direction. Then measuring angles as shown in Fig. 59, the projection of this vector on the x-axis gives us the first term of expression (a) for the forced vibration. The second term of the same expression is obtained by taking the projection on the x-axis of the vector $\overline{OB}$ perpendicular to $\overline{OD}$ the magnitude of which is

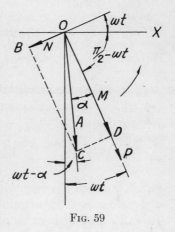

Fig. 59

equal to the absolute value of N and which is directed so as to take care of the negative sign of N in the second of expressions (b). The algebraic sum of the projections of the two vectors $\overline{OD}$ and $\overline{OB}$ can be replaced by the projection of their geometrical sum represented by the vector $\overline{OC}$. The magnitude of this vector, which we denote by A, is obtained from the triangle ODC and, by using expressions (b), is

$$A = \sqrt{M^2 + N^2} = \frac{Pg}{W} \frac{1}{\sqrt{(p^2 - \omega^2)^2 + 4n^2\omega^2}},$$

from which, by taking p^2 out of the radical and substituting for it its value kg/W, we obtain

$$A = \frac{P}{k} \cdot \frac{1}{\sqrt{\left(1 - \dfrac{\omega^2}{p^2}\right)^2 + \dfrac{4n^2\omega^2}{p^4}}} = x_{st} \cdot \frac{1}{\sqrt{\left(1 - \dfrac{\omega^2}{p^2}\right)^2 + \dfrac{4n^2\omega^2}{p^4}}}, \quad (38)$$

in which x_{st} denotes the deflection of the spring, in Fig. 1, when a vertical forced P is acting statically. The angle α between the vectors $\overline{OD}$ and $\overline{OC}$ is determined from the equation

$$\tan \alpha = \frac{-N}{M} = \frac{2n\omega}{p^2 - \omega^2}. \quad (39)$$

Projecting now vector $\overline{OC}$ on the x-axis we obtain the following expression for the forced vibration

$$x_1 = x_{st} \frac{1}{\sqrt{\left(1 - \dfrac{\omega^2}{p^2}\right)^2 + \dfrac{4n^2\omega^2}{p^4}}} \sin(\omega t - \alpha). \quad (40)$$

It is seen that the amplitude of the forced vibration is obtained by multiplying the statical deflection x_{st} by the absolute value of the factor

$$1 \Big/ \sqrt{\left(1 - \frac{\omega^2}{p^2}\right)^2 + \frac{4n^2\omega^2}{p^4}},$$

which is called the *magnification factor*. The magnitude of it depends on the ratio ω/p of the angular frequencies of the disturbing force and of the free vibration without damping, and also on the ratio n/p which, in most practical cases, is a small quantity. By taking this latter ratio equal to zero, we obtain for the amplitude of forced vibration the value found before in discussing vibrations without damping, see eq. (26), p. 42.

In Fig. 60 the values of the magnification factor for various values of the ratio $2n/p$ are plotted against the values of ω/p. From this figure it is seen that in the cases when the frequency of the disturbing force is small in comparison with that of free vibration of the system, the magnification

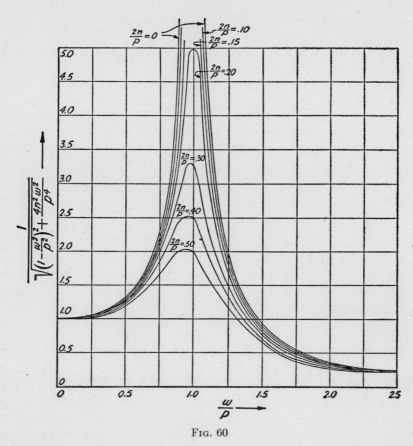

Fig. 60

factor approaches the value of unity, hence the amplitude of forced vibration is approximately equal to x_{st}. This means that in such cases the deflection of the spring at any instant can be calculated with sufficient accuracy by assuming that the disturbing force $P \sin \omega t$ is acting statically.

We have another extreme case when ω is large in comparison with p, i.e., when the frequency of the disturbing force is large in comparison with the frequency of free vibration of the system. In such a case the magnification factor becomes very small and the amplitude of forced vibration is small also.

The curves shown in Fig. 60 are very close together for both extreme cases mentioned above. This indicates that for these cases the effect of damping is of no practical importance in calculating the amplitudes of forced vibrations and the amplitude calculated before by neglecting damping, see Art. (6), can be used with sufficient accuracy.

When the frequency of the disturbing force approaches the frequency of free vibration of the system the magnification factor increases rapidly and, as we see from the figure, its value is very sensitive to changes in the magnitude of damping especially when this damping is small. It is seen also that the maximum values of the magnification factor occur at values of the ratio ω/p which are somewhat smaller than unity. By equating to zero the derivative of the magnification factor with respect to ω/p it can be shown that this maximum occurs when

$$\frac{\omega^2}{p^2} = 1 - \frac{2n^2}{p^2}. \tag{d}$$

Since n is usually very small in comparison with p, the values of the frequency ω at which the amplitude of forced vibration becomes a maximum differ only very little from the frequency p of the free vibration of the system without damping and it is usual practice to take, in calculating maximum amplitudes, $\omega = p$, in which case, from eq. (38),

$$A_{\max} = \frac{x_{st}p}{2n}. \tag{41}$$

We have discussed thus far the magnitude of the amplitude of forced vibration given in Fig. 59 by the magnitude of the vector $\overline{OC}$. Let us consider now the significance of the angle α defining the direction of the vector $\overline{OC}$. For this purpose we use a rotating vector for representation of the disturbing force. Since this force is proportional to $\sin \omega t$ the vector $\overline{OP}$, representing the force, coincides in Fig. 59 with the direction of the vector $\overline{OD}$, and its projection on the x-axis gives at any instant the magnitude of the disturbing force. Due to the angle α between the vectors $\overline{OP}$ and $\overline{OC}$ the forced vibration always lags behind the disturbing force. When the vector $\overline{OP}$ coincides with the x-axis and the disturbing force is a maximum, the displacement of the body, given by the projection of $\overline{OC}$ on the x-axis, has not yet reached its maximum value and becomes a maximum only after an interval of time equal to α/ω when $\overline{OC}$ coincides with the x-axis. The angle α represents the *phase difference* between the disturbing force and the forced vibration. From eq. (39) we see that when $\omega < p$, i.e., when the frequency of the disturbing force is less than the frequency of the natural undamped vibration, tan α is positive and α is less than $\pi/2$. For $\omega > p$, tan α is negative and $\alpha > \pi/2$. When $\omega = p$, tan α becomes infinite and the difference in phase α becomes equal to $\pi/2$. This means that

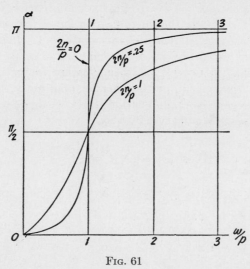

Fig. 61

during such motion the vibrating body passes through the middle position at the instant when the disturbing force attains its maximum value. In Fig. 61 the values of α are plotted against the values of the ratio ω/p for various values of damping. It is seen that in the region of resonance ($\omega = p$) a very sharp variation in the phase difference α takes place when damping is small. Under the limiting condition when $n = 0$, an abrupt change in the phase difference from $\alpha = 0$ to $\alpha = \pi$ occurs at resonance and instead of a curve we obtain in Fig. 61 a broken line 0113. This later condition corresponds to the case of undamped forced vibration as discussed before (see p. 42).

Let us consider now the work per cycle produced by the disturbing force during steady forced vibration.* The force acting at any instant is $P \sin \omega t$

* Due to presence of the factor e^{-nt} in the first term on the right side of eq. (c) (see p. **77**) the free vibrations will be gradually damped out and steady forced vibrations will be established.

and the velocity of its point of application is $\dot{x}_1 = A\omega \cos (\omega t - \alpha)$, hence the work produced in an infinitely small interval of time is

$$P \sin \omega t \, A\omega \cos (\omega t - \alpha) \, dt,$$

and the work per cycle will be

$$\int_0^\tau P \sin \omega t \, A\omega \cos (\omega t - \alpha) \, dt = \frac{A\omega P}{2} \int_0^\tau [\sin (2\omega t - \alpha) + \sin \alpha] \, dt$$

$$= \frac{A\omega P\tau \sin \alpha}{2} = \pi A P \sin \alpha. \tag{42}$$

This work must be equal to the energy dissipated during one cycle due to the damping force. The magnitude of this force is $-c\dot{x}_1 = -cA\omega \cos (\omega t - \alpha)$. Multiplying it by $\dot{x}_1 \, dt$ and integrating in the interval from 0 to τ we get for the energy dissipated per cycle the expression

$$\int_0^\tau cA^2\omega^2 \cos^2 (\omega t - \alpha) \, dt = \frac{cA^2\omega^2\tau}{2} = \pi cA^2\omega. \tag{43}$$

Thus the energy dissipated per cycle increases as the square of the amplitude.

Expressions (42) and (43) can be used for calculating the maximum amplitude which a given disturbing force may produce when damping is known. It may be assumed with sufficient accuracy that this amplitude occurs at resonance, when $\omega = p$ and $\alpha = \pi/2$. Substituting $\sin \alpha = 1$ in eq. (42) and equating the work done by the disturbing force to the energy dissipated, we obtain

$$\pi A P = \pi cA^2\omega,$$

from which

$$A_{max} = \frac{P}{c\omega}. \tag{44}$$

This expression can be easily brought in coincidence with the expression (41) by using notations (b), p. 70.

From Fig. 59 it is seen that the quantity $A \sin \alpha$ is equal to the absolute value of N given by expression (b). Substituting this value into formula (42) we obtain for the work per cycle of the disturbing force the following expression:

$$\frac{\pi P^2 g}{W} \frac{2n\omega}{(p^2 - \omega^2)^2 + 4n^2\omega^2} = \frac{2\pi}{\omega} \frac{P^2 g}{W} \frac{2n/p}{2p[(p/\omega - \omega/p)^2 + (2n/p)^2]}.$$

Using notations

$$2n/p = \gamma, \quad p/\omega = 1 + z,$$
(e)

we represent this work in the form:

$$\frac{2\pi}{\omega} \frac{P^2 g}{W} \frac{\gamma}{2p \left[\left(1 + z - \dfrac{1}{1 + z} \right)^2 + \gamma^2 \right]},$$

and since $2\pi/\omega$ is the period of vibration, the *average work* per second is

$$\frac{P^2 g}{W} \frac{\gamma}{2p \left[\left(1 + z - \dfrac{1}{1 + z} \right)^2 + \gamma^2 \right]}.$$
(f)

Assuming that all quantities in this expression, except z, are given we conclude that the average work per second becomes a maximum at resonance $(p = \omega)$ when z is zero.

In studying the variation of the average work per second near the point of resonance the quantity z can be considered as small and expression (f) can be replaced by the following approximate expression

$$\frac{P^2 g}{2pW} \cdot \frac{\gamma}{4z^2 + \gamma^2}.$$

The second factor of this expression is plotted against z in Fig. 62 for three different values of γ. It may be seen that with diminishing of damping the curves in the figure acquire a more and more pronounced peak at resonance $(z = 0)$ and also that only near the resonance point the dissipated energy increases with decreasing damping. For points at a distance from resonance $(z = 0)$ the dissipated energy decreases with the decrease of damping.

We have discussed thus far only the second part of the general expression (c) for motion of the body in Fig. 1, which represents the *steady* forced vibrations and which will be established only after the interval of time required to damp out the free vibration, produced at the beginning of the action of the disturbing force. If we are interested in motion which the body performs at the beginning of the action of the disturbing force the general expression for motion,

$$x = e^{-nt}(C_1 \cos p_1 t + C_2 \sin p_1 t) + A \sin (\omega t - \alpha),$$
(g)

must be used and the constants of integration C_1 and C_2 must be determined

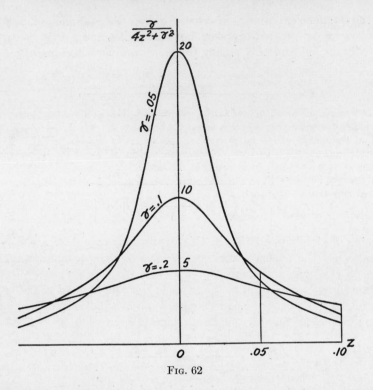

FIG. 62

from the initial conditions. Assume, for instance, that for $t = 0$, $x = 0$ and $\dot{x} = 0$, i.e., the body is at rest at the instant when the disturbing force $P \sin \omega t$ begins to act. Then by using expression (g) and its derivative with respect to time we obtain

$$C_1 = A \sin \alpha, \quad C_2 = \frac{nA \sin \alpha - \omega A \cos \alpha}{p_1}.$$

Substituting these in eq. (g), the general expression for the motion of the body is obtained. For the case of a small damping and far from resonance the phase-angle α is small and we can take $C_1 = 0$, $C_2 = -\omega A/p_1$. The motion (g) is represented then by the following approximate expression:

$$x = -\frac{\omega A e^{-nt}}{p_1} \sin p_1 t + A \sin \omega t. \tag{h}$$

Thus on steady forced vibrations of amplitude A and with angular frequency ω, free vibrations, sometimes called *transient*, with a frequency p_1 and with a gradually damped out amplitude are superposed.

If the frequencies ω and p_1 are close together the phenomenon of beating, discussed in Art. 6, will appear, but due to damping this beating will gradually die out and only steady forced vibrations will remain.

EXAMPLES

1. Determine the amplitude of forced vibrations produced by an oscillator, fixed at the middle of a beam, Fig. 47, at a speed 600 r.p.m. if $2P = 1$ lb, the weight concentrated at the middle of the beam is $W = 1000$ lb and produces statical deflection of the beam equal to $\delta_{st} = 0.01$ in.   Neglect the weight of the beam and assume that damping is equivalent to a force acting at the middle of the beam, proportional to the velocity and equal to 100 lb at a velocity of 1 in. per sec.   Determine also the amplitude of forced vibration at resonance ($\omega = p$).

Solution. $\omega^2 = 400\pi^2;\quad c = 100$

$$p^2 = 38,600,$$

$$n = \frac{cg}{2W} = \frac{100 \times 386}{2 \times 1000} = 19.3$$

$$2P\omega^2 = 1 \cdot \omega^2 = 400\pi^2 \text{ lb,}$$

$$A = \frac{2Pg\omega^2}{W} \frac{1}{\sqrt{(p^2 - \omega^2)^2 + 4n^2\omega^2}}$$

$$= \frac{400\pi^2 \times 386}{1000\sqrt{(38,600 - 400\pi^2)^2 + 4 \times \overline{19.3}^2 \times 400\pi^2}} = 0.0439 \text{ in.,}$$

if $\omega = p$,

$$A = \frac{2Pg\omega^2}{W} \frac{1}{2n\omega} = \frac{400\pi^2 \times 386}{1000 \times 2 \times 19.3 \times 20\pi} = 0.629 \text{ in.}$$

2. Investigate the effect of damping on the readings of the instrument shown in Fig. 44.
   Solution.   Assuming that the vibratory motion of the point of suspension A is given by $x_1 = a \sin \omega t$, the equation of motion of the suspended weight is

$$\ddot{x} + 2n\dot{x} + p^2x = \frac{akg}{W} \sin \omega t.$$

Substituting ak for P in expression (38), the forced vibration becomes

$$x = \frac{a}{\sqrt{\left(1 - \frac{\omega^2}{p^2}\right)^2 + \frac{4n^2\omega^2}{p^4}}} \sin (\omega t - \alpha) = a\beta \sin (\omega t - \alpha), \tag{i}$$

where β is the magnification factor.
   The instrument measures the difference of the displacements x_1 and x and we obtain

$$x_1 - x = a \sin \omega t - \beta a \sin (\omega t - \alpha).$$

The two terms on the right side of this equation can be added together by using rotating vectors $\overline{OC}$ of magnitude a and OD of magnitude βa as shown in Fig. 63. The geometrical sum OE of these two vectors gives us the amplitude of the relative motion $x_1 - x$. From the triangle OCE this amplitude is

$$A = a\sqrt{\beta^2 - 2\beta\cos\alpha + 1}. \tag{j}$$

It depends not only on the magnification factor β but also on the phase-angle α.

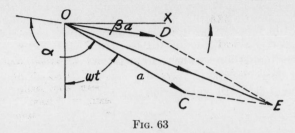

Fig. 63

In the case of instruments used for measuring amplitudes of vibrations (see Art. 8) the frequency ω is large in comparison with p, β is small, α approaches the value π and the amplitude, given by expression (j), is approximately equal to $a(1 + \beta)$. Substituting for β its value from eq. (i) and neglecting damping we find

$$A = a\left(1 + \frac{1}{\frac{\omega^2}{p^2} - 1}\right) = \frac{a}{1 - \frac{p^2}{\omega^2}},$$

which is approximately equal to a.

In the case of instruments used for measuring accelerations ω is small in comparison with p, α is small also and expression (j) approaches the value $a(\beta - 1)$. Substituting again for β its value and neglecting damping,* we get in this case

$$A = a\left(\frac{1}{1 - \frac{\omega^2}{p^2}} - 1\right) = \frac{a}{\frac{p^2}{\omega^2} - 1},$$

which is approximately equal to $a\omega^2/p^2$ and proportional to the maximum acceleration.

14. Spring Mounting of Machines with Damping Considered.—In our previous discussion of spring mounting of machines, Art. 8, it was assumed that there is no damping and the supporting springs are perfectly elastic. Such conditions are approximately realized in the case of helical steel

---

* Since the impressed motion is often not a simple sine motion and may contain higher harmonics with frequencies in the vicinity of the resonance of the instrument, it is usual practice to have in accelerometers a considerable viscous damping, say taking $0.5 < n/p < 1$.

springs, but if leaf springs or rubber and cork padding are used damping is considerable and cannot any longer be neglected. In the case of such imperfect springs it can be assumed that the spring force consists of two parts: one, proportional to the spring elongation, is an elastic force and the other, proportional to the velocity, is a damping force. This condition can be realized, for instance, by taking a combination of perfect springs and a dash pot as shown in Fig. 64. Considering the case discussed in Art. 8 and calculating what portion of the disturbing force is transmitted to the foundation, we have now to take into

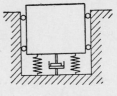

Fig. 64

account not only the elastic force but also the force of damping. Since these two forces act with a phase difference of 90 degrees their resultant is

$$A\sqrt{k^2 + c^2\omega^2} = Ak\sqrt{1 + \frac{4n^2\omega^2}{p^4}}, \qquad (a)$$

where A is the amplitude of forced vibration, k is the spring constant and $c = 2nW/g$ is the damping force when the velocity is equal to unity. Substituting for A its value from formula (38) and taking, as in Art. 8, the disturbing force $P\omega^2 \sin \omega t$, we find that the maximum force transmitted to the foundation is

$$\frac{P\omega^2\sqrt{1 + \dfrac{4n^2\omega^2}{p^4}}}{\sqrt{\left(1 - \dfrac{\omega^2}{p^2}\right)^2 + \dfrac{4n^2\omega^2}{p^4}}}. \qquad (b)$$

Assuming that ω is large in comparison with p and at the same time the ratio n/p is small, we find that the result (b) differs from what was found in Art. 8 principally by the presence of the term $4n^2\omega^2/p^4$ under the radical of the numerator.

Taking, as in Ex. 1, p. 54, $\omega = 60\pi$, $p^2 = 225$, $P = 1$ lb and assuming $2n = 1$, we find

$$\sqrt{1 + 4n^2\omega^2/p^4} = 1.305, \qquad \sqrt{\left(1 - \frac{\omega^2}{p^2}\right)^2 + \frac{4n^2\omega^2}{p^4}} = 156.9,$$

and the force transmitted to the foundation is

$$\frac{(60\pi)^2 1.305}{156.9} = 296 \text{ lb}$$

which is about 30% larger than we obtained before by neglecting damping.

The ratio of the force transmitted to the foundation (b) to the disturbing force $P\omega^2$ determines the *transmissibility*. It is equal to

$$\sqrt{1 + 4n^2\omega^2/p^4} : \sqrt{(1 - \omega^2/p^2)^2 + 4n^2\omega^2/p^4}, \qquad (c)$$

and its magnitude depends not only on the ratio ω/p but also on the ratio n/p.

As a second example let us consider a single-phase electric generator. In this case the electric forces acting between the rotor and stator produce on the stator a pulsating torque which is represented by the equation

$$M_t = M_0 + M_1 \sin \omega t, \qquad (d)$$

where ω is the double angular velocity of the rotor and M_0 and M_1 are constants.

If the stator is rigidly attached to the foundation the variable reactions due to pulsating torque may produce very undesirable vibrations. To reduce these reactions the stator is supported by springs as shown in Fig. 65.* The constant portion M_0 of the torque is directly transmitted to the foundation and produces constant reactions which can be readily obtained from equations of statics. We have to consider only the variable portion $M_1 \sin \omega t$. Under the action of this variable moment the stator is subjected to rotatory vibrations with respect to the torque axis. If φ denotes the angle of rotation during these vibrations and k the spring constant which in this case represents the torque which, if applied statically, produces an angle of rotation of the stator equal to one radian, the moment of the reactions acting on the stator during vibration will be $-k\varphi$ and the equation of motion is

$$I\ddot{\varphi} + c\dot{\varphi} + k\varphi = M_1 \sin \omega t, \qquad (e)$$

in which I is moment on inertia of the stator with respect to the torque axis and c is the magnitude of the damping couple for an angular velocity equal to unity. Using notations

$$\frac{c}{I} = 2n, \quad \frac{k}{I} = p^2, \qquad (f)$$

we bring eq. (e) to the form of eq. (37) and we can use the general expression (38) for the amplitude of forced vibration, it being only necessary to sub-

* See C. R. Soderberg, *Elec. J.*, Vol. 21, p. 160, 1924.

stitute in this expression M_1 instead of P. Multiplying this amplitude with the spring constant k we obtain the maximum value of the variable torque due to deformation of the springs. To this torque we must add the variable torque due to damping. Using the same reasoning as in the previous problem we finally obtain the maximum variable torque transmitted to the foundation from expression (b) by substituting in it M_1 instead of $P\omega^2$.

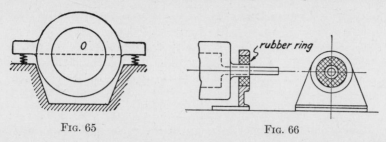

FIG. 65   FIG. 66

The use of elastic supports in the case of single-phase electric motors and generators has proved very successful. In the case of large machines the springs usually consist of steel beams. In small motors such as used in domestic appliances the required elasticity of supports is obtained by placing rubber rings between the rigid supports and the rotor bearings which are in this case rigidly built into the stator as shown in Fig. 66. The rubber ring firmly resists any lateral movement of the bearing since any radial compression of the rubber ring requires a circumferential expansion which is prevented by friction forces between the ring and the rigid support. At the same time any rotation of the stator produces in the rubber ring only shearing deformations which do not require a change in volume and the rubber in such case is very flexible and has on the transmission of the pulsating torque the same effect as the springs shown in Fig. 65.

We have another example of the use of elastic supports in the case of automobile internal-combustion engines. Here again we deal with a pulsating torque which in the case of a rigidly mounted engine will be transmitted to the car. By introducing an elastic mounting, such that the engine may have low frequency rotary vibrations about the torque axis, a considerable improvement can be obtained.

15. Free Vibrations with Coulomb Damping.—As an example of vibrations with constant damping let us consider the case shown in Fig. 67. A body W attached by a spring to a fixed point A slides along the horizontal dry surface with a vibratory motion. To write the equation of motion let us assume that the body is brought to its extreme right position and released. Then under the action of the tensile force in the spring it begins to move towards the left as shown. The forces which it is necessary to consider are: (1) the force in the spring, and (2) the friction force. Denoting by x the displacement of the body from the position at which the spring is unstretched and taking the positive direction of the x-axis, as shown in the

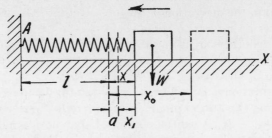

FIG. 67

figure, the spring force is $-kx$. The friction force in the case of a dry surface is constant. It acts in the direction opposite to the motion, i.e., in this case, in the positive direction of the x-axis. Denoting this force by F, the equation of motion becomes

$$\frac{W}{g}\ddot{x} = -kx + F, \tag{a}$$

or, by introducing notations

$$\frac{kg}{W} = p^2, \quad \frac{F}{k} = a, \tag{b}$$

we obtain

$$\ddot{x} + p^2(x - a) = 0, \tag{c}$$

where a has a simple physical meaning, namely, it represents the statical elongation of the spring which would be produced by the friction force F. Eq. (c) can be brought in complete agreement with the eq. (1) (p. 2) for free vibrations without damping by introducing a new variable

$$x_1 = x - a, \tag{d}$$

which means that the distances will now be measured not from the position when the spring is unstretched but from the position when it has an elongation equal to a. Then, substituting x from eq. (d) into eq. (c) we obtain

$$\ddot{x}_1 + p^2 x_1 = 0. \tag{e}$$

The solution of this equation, satisfying the initial conditions, is

$$x_1 = (x_0 - a) \cos pt, \qquad\qquad (f)$$

where x_0 denotes the initial displacement of the body from the unstressed position. This solution is applicable as long as the body is moving to the left as assumed in the derivation of eq. (a). The extreme left position will be reached after an interval of time equal to π/p, when $x_1 = -(x_0 - a)$ and the distance of the body from the unstressed position is $x_0 - 2a$. From this discussion it is seen that the time required for half a cycle of vibration is the same as in the case of free vibration without damping, thus the frequency of vibration is not affected by a constant damping. At the same time, considering the two extreme positions of the body defined by distances x_0 and $x_0 - 2a$, it can be concluded that during half a cycle the amplitude of vibrations is diminished by $2a$.

Considering now the motion of the body from the extreme left position to the right, and applying the same reasoning, it can be shown that during the second half of the cycle a further diminishing of the amplitude by the quantity $2a$ will occur. Thus the decrease of the amplitude follows the law of arithmetical progression. Finally, the load W will remain in one of its extreme positions as soon as the amplitude becomes less than a, since at such a position the friction force will be sufficient to balance the tensile force of the spring.

This vibratory motion again can be visualized by using rotating vectors. To obtain the motion corresponding to the first half of a cycle, eq. (f), we use vector O_1B_1, Fig. 68, of magnitude $x_0 - a$ rotating with a constant

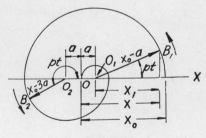

FIG. 68

angular velocity p about the center O_1, which is displaced to the right with respect to the unstressed position O by the amount a. For the second half of the cycle we use the vector O_2B_2 of magnitude $x_0 - 3a$ and rotating with constant speed p around the center O_2, which is displaced from O to the left by the amount a, and so on. In this way we get a kind of spiral, and the intersection point of this spiral with the x-axis in the interval O_1O_2 gives the final position of the body.

EXAMPLES

1. The body in Fig. 67 is displaced from the unstressed position by the amount $x_0 = 10$ in., with the tensile force in the spring at this displacement, equal to $5W = 10$ lb, and then released without initial velocity. How long will the body vibrate and at what distance from the unstressed position will it stop if the coefficient of friction is $\frac{1}{4}$?

Solution. The friction force in this case is $F = W/4 = 0.5$ lb, spring constant $k = 1$ lb per in., $a = \frac{1}{2}$ in. Hence the amplitude diminishes by 1 in. per each half a cycle and the body will stop after 5 cycles at the unstressed position. The period of one oscillation is $\tau = 2\pi\sqrt{\delta_{st}/g} = 2\pi\sqrt{2/386}$ and the total time of oscillation is $10\pi\sqrt{2/386} = 2.26$ sec.

2. Determine the coefficient of friction for the case shown in Fig. 67 if a tensile force equal to W produces an elongation of the spring equal to $\frac{1}{4}$ in. and the initial amplitude $x_0 = 25$ in. is reduced to 0.90 of its value after 10 complete cycles.

Solution. The amplitude of vibration due to friction is reduced after each cycle by

$$4a = \frac{4F}{k}$$ and since after 10 cycles it is reduced by 2.5 in. we have

$$10\,\frac{4F}{k} = \frac{10F}{W} = 2.5 \text{ in.}$$

Hence $F = \frac{1}{4}W$ and the coefficient of friction is equal to $\frac{1}{4}$.

16. Forced Vibrations with Coulomb Damping and Other Kinds of Damping.

—From the discussion of the previous article it is seen that to take care of the change in direction of the constant friction force F it is necessary to consider each half cycle separately. The fact complicates a rigorous treatment of the problem of forced vibration, but an approximate solution can be obtained without much difficulty.* In practical applications we are principally interested in the magnitude of steady forced vibrations and this magnitude can be obtained with sufficient accuracy by assuming that the forced vibration in the case of a constant damping force F is a simple harmonic motion, as in the case of viscous damping, and by replacing the constant damping force by an *equivalent viscous damping*, such that the amount of energy dissipated per cycle will be the same for both kinds of damping.

* This approximate method has been developed by L. S. Jacobsen, *Trans. A.S.M.E.*, Vol. 52, p. APM-169, 1930. See also A. L. Kimball, *ibid.*, Vol. 51, p. APM-227, 1929. A rigorous solution of the problem has been given by J. P. Den Hartog, *ibid.*, Vol. 53, p. APM-107, 1931. See also *Phil. Mag.*, Vol. 9, p. 801, 1930.

Let $P \sin \omega t$ be the disturbing force and assume that the steady forced vibration is given by the equation

$$x = A \sin(\omega t - \alpha). \tag{a}$$

Between two consecutive extreme positions the vibrating body travels a distance $2A$, thus the work done per cycle against the constant friction force, representing the dissipated energy, is

$$4AF. \tag{b}$$

If instead of constant friction we have a viscous damping the corresponding value of the dissipated energy is given by formula (43), p. 82, and the magnitude of the equivalent viscous damping is determined from the equation

$$\pi c A^2 \omega = 4AF, \tag{c}$$

from which

$$c = \frac{4F}{\pi A \omega}. \tag{d}$$

Thus the magnitude of the equivalent viscous damping depends not only on F but also on the amplitude A and the frequency ω of the vibration. Using notations (b), p. 70, and substituting in expression (38)

$$\frac{2n}{p^2} = \frac{c}{k} = \frac{4F}{\pi A k \omega},$$

we obtain for the amplitude of the forced vibration with equivalent viscous damping the following expression

$$\frac{P}{k} \frac{1}{\sqrt{\left(1 - \dfrac{\omega^2}{p^2}\right)^2 + \left(\dfrac{4F}{\pi A k}\right)^2}}.$$

This expression represents the amplitude A in eq. (a), hence the equation for determining A is

$$\frac{P}{k} \frac{1}{\sqrt{\left(1 - \dfrac{\omega^2}{p^2}\right)^2 + \left(\dfrac{4F}{\pi A k}\right)^2}} = A,$$

from which

$$A = \pm \frac{P}{k} \cdot \frac{\sqrt{1 - (4F/\pi P)^2}}{1 - \omega^2/p^2}. \tag{45}$$

The first factor on the right side represents *static deflection* and the second is the *magnification factor*. We see that this factor has a real value only if

$$F/P < \pi/4. \tag{e}$$

In practical applications, where we are usually dealing with small frictional force, this condition is satisfied and we find that the magnification factor depends on the value of the ratio ω/p. Values of this factor, for various values of the ratio F/P, are plotted against ω/p in Fig. 69.* It

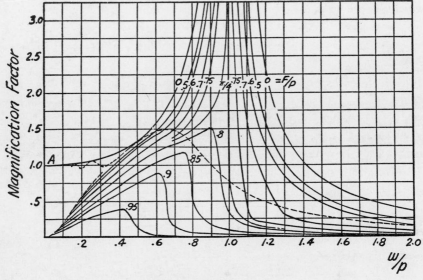

Fig. 69

is seen that in all cases in which condition (e) is satisfied the magnification factor becomes infinite at resonance $(p = \omega)$, which means that in this case even with considerable friction the amplitude at resonance tends to infinity. This fact can be explained if we consider the dissipation of energy and the work produced by the disturbing force. In the case of viscous damping the energy dissipated per cycle, eq. (43), increases as the square of the amplitude. At the same time the work produced per cycle by the disturbing force (eq. 42) increases in proportion to the amplitude.

* This figure and the two following are taken from the above-mentioned Den Hartog's exact solution. By the dotted line the limit is indicated above which a non-stop oscillatory motion occurs. Below that limit the motion is more complicated and the curves shown in the figure can be obtained only by using the exact solution.

Thus the finite amplitude is obtained by intersection of the parabola with a straight line as shown in Fig. 70. In the case of constant friction the dissipated energy is proportional to A, eq. (b), and in Fig. 70 it will be represented by a straight line the slope of which is smaller than the slope of the line OE, if condition (e) is satisfied, hence there will always be an excess of input and the amplitude increases indefinitely.

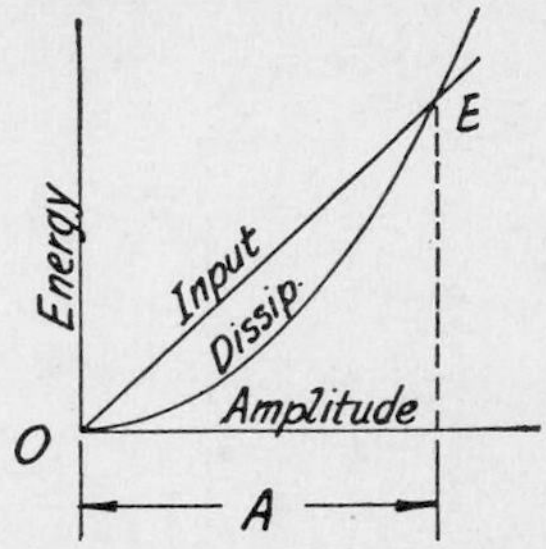

By substituting the value of the equivalent damping (eq. d) into eq. (39) and using eq. (45) we obtain the equation

$$\tan \alpha = \pm \frac{4F}{\pi P} \frac{1}{\sqrt{1 - \left(\frac{4F}{\pi P}\right)^2}}, \qquad (f)$$

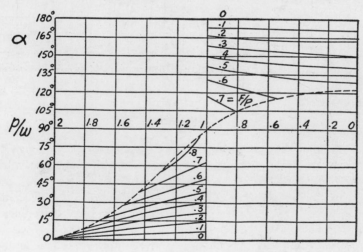

Fig. 70

from which the phase-angle α can be calculated. The angle does not vary with the ratio ω/p and only at resonance ($\omega = p$) it changes its value abruptly. The exact solution shows that the phase angle varies somewhat with the ratio ω/p as shown in Fig. 71.

Fig. 71

The described approximate method of investigating forced vibrations can be used also in general, when the friction force is any function of the velocity. In each particular case it is only necessary to calculate the corresponding equivalent damping by using an equation similar to eq. (c). Assuming for example that the friction force is represented by a function $f(\dot{x})$, this equation becomes

$$\pi c A^2 \omega = \int_0^\tau f(\dot{x})\dot{x}\,dt. \tag{g}$$

Substituting for x its expression from eq. (a) the value of c can always be calculated.

Take, as an example, a combination of Coulomb friction and viscous friction. Then

$$f(\dot{x}) = \pm F + c_1 \dot{x}.$$

Substituting in eq. (g) we find

$$\pi c A^2 \omega = 4AF + \pi c_1 A^2 \omega,$$

from which

$$c = \frac{4F}{\pi A \omega} + c_1.$$

Proceeding with this value of c as before, we obtain for determining the amplitude A the equation

$$A^2\left[\left(1 - \frac{\omega^2}{p^2}\right)^2 + \frac{c_1^2 \omega^2}{k^2}\right] + 2A\frac{4F c_1 \omega}{\pi k^2} + \left(\frac{4F}{\pi k}\right)^2 - \frac{P^2}{k^2} = 0. \tag{h}$$

When $c_1 = 0$ this equation gives for A expression (45). When $F = 0$ we get for A expression (38). For any given values of F and c_1, the amplitude of forced vibrations can be readily obtained from eq. (h).

EXAMPLE

1. Develop an approximate equation for the amplitude of steady forced vibration if the damping force is proportional to the square of velocity.*

Solution. Assuming that the damping force is given by the expression $c_1(\dot{x})^2$ and taking one quarter of a cycle, starting from the middle position, the dissipated energy is

$$c_1 \omega^3 A^3 \int_0^{\pi/2\omega} \cos^3 \omega t\,dt = \tfrac{2}{3}c_1 \omega^2 A^3$$

---

* Free vibrations with damping proportional to the square of velocity were studied by W. E. Milne, *Univ. Oregon Publ. Math. Ser.*, Vol. 1, No. 1, 1923; and Vol. 2, No. 2, 1929. The tables attached to these papers will be found useful in application to such vibrations. For forced vibrations, we have the approximate solution given by L. S. Jacobsen, *loc. cit.*, p. 92.

and eq. (g) becomes

$$\pi c A^2 \omega = \tfrac{8}{3} c_1 \omega^2 A^3,$$

from which

$$c = \frac{8}{3\pi} c_1 \omega A.$$

The equation for calculating A becomes

$$A^4 + A^2 \frac{P^2}{k^2} \cdot \frac{\left(1 - \dfrac{\omega^2}{p^2}\right)^2}{\dfrac{\omega^4}{p^4} \cdot c_1{}^2 \left(\dfrac{8}{3\pi}\right)^2 \dfrac{p^4}{k^4} P^2} - \frac{\dfrac{P^4}{k^4}}{\dfrac{\omega^4}{p^4} \cdot c_1{}^2 \left(\dfrac{8}{3\pi}\right)^2 \dfrac{p^4}{k^4} P^2} = 0$$

or

$$A^4 + A^2 k^2 \frac{\left(1 - \dfrac{\omega^2}{p^2}\right)^2}{c_1{}^2 \omega^4 \left(\dfrac{8}{3\pi}\right)^2} - \frac{P^2}{\omega^4 c_1{}^2 \left(\dfrac{8}{3\pi}\right)^2} = 0.$$

17. General Case of Periodic Disturbing Force.—In previous discussions of forced vibration (see Arts. 6 and 13) we always assumed a simple harmonic disturbing force proportional to sin ωt or cos ωt. In general, it is possible to have a disturbing force that is a more complicated function of time.

Consider, for example, the horizontal one-cylinder engine mounted on a table as shown in Fig. 72. When such an engine, whose reciprocating parts

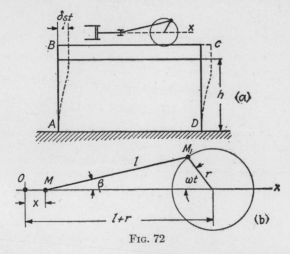

Fig. 72

are not balanced, is running, it will exert a periodic disturbing force producing forced horizontal vibrations of the rigid bed-plate BC supported on flexible columns AB and CD. In studying such forced vibrations, it will be important to know the exact nature of the disturbing force; in particular its period in relation to the natural period of free lateral vibration of the system.

In the analysis of the disturbing force, the mass of the connecting rod can be replaced with sufficient accuracy by two masses, one at the crankpin and the second at the corsshead. To the same two points all other unbalanced masses in motion can readily be reduced, so that finally only two masses M_1 and M have to be taken into consideration (Fig. 72b). The horizontal component of the inertia force of the mass M_1 is

$$-M_1\omega^2 r \cos \omega t, \qquad (a)$$

in which ω is angular velocity of the engine,
   r is the radius of the crank,
   ωt is the angle of the crank to the horizontal axis.

The motion of the reciprocating mass M is more complicated. Let x denote the displacement of M from the dead position and β, the angle between the connecting rod and the x-axis. From the figure we have,

$$x = l(1 - \cos \beta) + r(1 - \cos \omega t) \qquad (b)$$

and

$$r \sin \omega t = l \sin \beta. \qquad (c)$$

From (c),

$$\sin \beta = \frac{r}{l} \sin \omega t.$$

The length l is usually several times larger than r so that with sufficient accuracy it can be assumed that

$$\cos \beta = \sqrt{1 - \frac{r^2}{l^2} \sin^2 \omega t} \approx 1 - \frac{r^2}{2l^2} \sin^2 \omega t.$$

Substituting in eq. (b),

$$x = r(1 - \cos \omega t) + \frac{r^2}{2l} \sin^2 \omega t. \qquad (d)$$

From this equation the velocity of the reciprocating masses will be

$$\dot{x} = r\omega \sin \omega t + \frac{r^2\omega}{2l} \sin 2\omega t$$

and the corresponding inertia forces will be

$$-M\ddot{x} = -M\omega^2 r \left(\cos \omega t + \frac{r}{l} \cos 2\omega t \right). \qquad (e)$$

Combining this with (a), the complete expression for the disturbing force will be obtained. It will be noted that this expression consists of two terms, one having a frequency equal to the number of revolutions of the machine and another having twice as high a frequency. From this it can be concluded that in the case under consideration we have two critical speeds of the engine: the first when the number of revolutions of the machine per second is equal to the frequency $1/\tau$ of the natural vibrations of the system, and the second when the number of revolutions of the machine is half of the above value. By a suitable choice of the rigidity of the columns AB and CD it is always possible to ascertain conditions sufficiently far away from such critical speeds and to remove in this manner the possibility of large vibrations. It must be noted that expression (e) for the inertia force of the reciprocating masses was obtained by making several approximations. A more accurate solution will also contain harmonics of a higher order. This means that there will be critical speeds of an order lower than those considered above, but usually these are of no practical importance because the corresponding forces are too small to produce substantial vibrations of the system.

In general, a periodic disturbing force of any kind can be represented in the form of a trigonometric series such as

$$f(t) = a_0 + a_1 \cos \omega t + a_2 \cos 2\omega t + \cdots$$

$$+ b_1 \sin \omega t + b_2 \sin 2\omega t + \cdots, \quad (f)$$

in which $f_1 = \dfrac{\omega}{2\pi}$ is the frequency of the disturbing force,

$$\tau_1 = \frac{2\pi}{\omega} \text{ is the period of the disturbing force.}$$

In order to calculate any one of the coefficients of eq. (f), provided $f(t)$ be known, the following procedure may be followed. Assume that any coefficient a_i is desired, then both sides of the equation can be multiplied by $\cos i\omega t \, dt$ and integrated from $t = 0$ to $t = \tau_1$. It can be shown that

$$\int_0^{\tau_1} a_0 \cos i\omega t \, dt = 0, \quad \int_0^{\tau_1} a_k \cos k\omega t \cos i\omega t \, dt = 0,$$

$$\int_0^{\tau_1} b_k \sin k\omega t \cos i\omega t \, dt = 0, \quad \int_0^{\tau_1} a_i \cos^2 i\omega t \, dt = \frac{a_i}{2} \tau_1,$$

where i and k denote integer numbers 1, 2, 3, $\cdots$. By using these formulas we obtain, from eq. (f),

$$a_i = \frac{2}{\tau_1} \int_0^{\tau_1} f(t) \cos i\omega t \, dt. \qquad (g)$$

In the same manner, by multiplying eq. (f) by $\sin i\omega t \, dt$, we obtain

$$b_i = \frac{2}{\tau_1} \int_0^{\tau_1} f(t) \sin i\omega t \, dt. \qquad (h)$$

Finally, multiplying eq. (f) by dt and integrating from $t = 0$ to $t = \tau_1$, we have

$$a_0 = \frac{1}{\tau_1} \int_0^{\tau_1} f(t) \, dt. \qquad (i)$$

It is seen that by using formulas (g), (h) and (i), the coefficients of eq. (f) can be calculated if $f(t)$ be known analytically. If $f(t)$ be given graphically, while no analytical expression is available, some approximate numerical method for calculating the integrals (i), (h) and (g) must be used or they can be obtained mechanically by using one of the instruments for analyzing curves in a trigonometric series.*

Assuming that the disturbing force is represented in the form of a trigonometric series, the equation for forced vibrations will be (see eq. 37, p. 76).

$$\ddot{x} + 2n\dot{x} + p^2 x + a_0 + a_1 \cos \omega t + a_2 \cos 2\omega t + \cdots$$

$$+ b_1 \sin \omega t + b_2 \sin 2\omega t + \cdots. \quad (j)$$

The general solution of this equation will consist of two parts, one of free vibrations (see eq. 31, p. 70) and one of forced vibrations. The free vibrations will be gradually damped due to friction. In considering the forced vibration it must be noted that in the case of a linear equation, such as eq. (j), the forced vibrations will be obtained by superimposing the forced vibrations produced by every term of the series (f). These latter vibrations can be found in the same manner as explained in article (13) and on the basis of solution (40) (see p. 78) it can be concluded that large forced vibrations may occur when the period of one of the terms

---

* A discussion of various methods of analyzing curves in a trigonometric series and a description of the instruments for harmonic analysis can be found in H. von Sanden, *Practical Mathematical Analysis*, New York, 1926.

of series (f) coincides with the period τ of the natural vibrations of the system, i.e., if the period τ_1 of the disturbing force is equal to, or a multiple of, the period τ.

EXAMPLES

1. For the system shown in Fig. 72, the following numerical data are given:

> weight of piston, $W_p = 6.00$ lb,
> weight of connecting rod, $W_c = 3.00$ lb,
> $Mg = W_p + \frac{1}{3}W_c = 7.00$ lb,
> $M_1g = \frac{2}{3}W_c = 2.00$ lb,
> total weight of engine and platform, $W = 500$ lb,
> r.p.m. of engine $= 600$,
> crank radius $r = 8$ in.,
> length of connecting rod, $l = 24$ in.,
> flexural rigidity of each column, $EI = 22.35(10)^6$ lb-in.^{2},
> length of each column, $h = 3$ ft.

Neglecting damping, find the maximum horizontal displacement of the platform during steady-state forced vibrations of the system. Assume that the crankshaft and flywheels are perfectly balanced.

Solution. We begin with a calculation of the natural frequency of lateral vibration of the system. Noting that each column has an inflection point at its mid-height, we easily can write

$$\delta_{st} = 2\left(\frac{\frac{1}{2}W(\frac{1}{2}h)^3}{3EI}\right) = \frac{2 \times 250 \times 5832}{3 \times 22.35(10)^6} = 0.0435 \text{ in.}$$

Then the natural angular frequency

$$p = \sqrt{\frac{g}{\delta_{st}}} = \sqrt{\frac{386}{0.0435}} = \sqrt{8880} = 94.3 \text{ sec}^{-1}.$$

$32.2\,(12) = 3\,86$

Also

$$\omega = {}^{600}\!\!/_{60} \times 2\pi = 20\pi = 62.83 \text{ sec}^{-1},$$

and we find

$$\frac{\omega}{p} = \frac{62.83}{94.3} = \frac{2}{3}, \quad \frac{2\omega}{p} = \frac{4}{3}.$$

From these ratios, we see that the disturbing force proportional to $\cos \omega t$ will be working below resonance while that proportional to $\cos 2\omega t$ will be working above resonance. Neglecting higher frequency components of the disturbing force, we have only to superimpose the effects of the inertia forces represented by eqs. (a) and (e) above. Writing these in the form

$$\left.\begin{array}{l} P_1 \cos \omega t = (M + M_1)\omega^2 r \cos \omega t, \\[2mm] P_2 \cos 2\omega t = M\omega^2 r \left(\dfrac{r}{l}\right) \cos 2\omega t, \end{array}\right\} \tag{k}$$

we have

$$P_1 = (M + M_1)\omega^2 r = \left(\frac{7+2}{386}\right)400\pi^2 \times 8 = 736 \text{ lb},$$

$$P_2 = M\omega^2 r\left(\frac{r}{l}\right) = \left(\frac{7}{386}\right)400\pi^2 \times 8 \times \frac{1}{3} = 191 \text{ lb}.$$

Returning now to eq. (26), p. 42, and noting that

$$k = \frac{W}{\delta_{st}} = \frac{500}{0.0435} = 11,500 \text{ lb per in.,}$$

we find that the forced vibrations produced separately by the two disturbing forces (k) are

$$x_1 = \frac{P_1}{k}\left(\frac{1}{1 - \dfrac{\omega^2}{p^2}}\right)\cos \omega t = \frac{736}{11,500}\left(\frac{1}{1 - \tfrac{4}{9}}\right)\cos \omega t = 0.115 \cos \omega t,$$

$$x_2 = \frac{P_2}{k}\left(\frac{1}{1 - \dfrac{4\omega^2}{p^2}}\right)\cos 2\omega t = \frac{191}{11,500}\left(\frac{1}{1 - \tfrac{16}{9}}\right)\cos 2\omega t = -0.0214 \cos 2\omega t.$$

To get a maximum displacement, we take $\omega t = \pi$; then

$$(x_1 + x_2)_{\max} = -0.115 - 0.0214 = -0.1364 \text{ in.}$$

2. The system shown in Fig. 73a is subjected to a vertical disturbing force $F(t)$ which varies with time according to the diagram shown in Fig. 73b. Neglecting damping, find

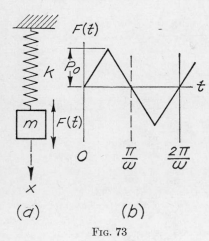

Fig. 73

the steady state forced vibrations $x = f(t)$ that will be produced if the mass m and the spring constant k are such that $\omega/p = 0.9$.

Solution. We begin by making a harmonic analysis of the given $F(t)$ which we assume can be represented by the trigonometric series (f). For this purpose, we have eqs. (g), (h) and (i), defining the coefficients a_0, a_i, and b_i of the series.

Considering first eq. (i), we see that $\int_0^{2\pi/\omega} F(t)\,dt$ is simply the area under the given saw-tooth diagram in Fig. 73b between the ordinates $t = 0$ and $t = 2\pi/\omega$. Clearly this area is zero and hence $a_0 = 0$.

Considering next the eq. (g), we see that each ordinate of the diagram in Fig. 73b must be multiplied by $\cos i\omega t$ and then integrated from $t = 0$ to $t = 2\pi/\omega$. Now from the anti-symmetry of $F(t)$ about the ordinate $t = \pi/\omega$, together with the symmetry of $\cos i\omega t$ about the same ordinate, we conclude again that the integral in eq. (g) vanishes and $a_i = 0$.

Finally, considering eq. (h), we see that each ordinate of $F(t)$ in Fig. 73b must be multiplied by $\sin i\omega t$ and integrated from $t = 0$ to $t = 2\pi/\omega$. In this case $F(t)$ from

$t = 0$ to $t = \pi/\omega$ is symmetrical about $t = \pi/2\omega$. Likewise when i is an even integer, corresponding parts of $\sin i\omega t$ are antisymmetrical about $t = \pi/2\omega$ and $t = 3\pi/2\omega$, respectively. Thus for $i = 2, 4, 6, \cdots$, we conclude that $b_i = 0$.

When i is an odd integer, both $F(t)$ and $\sin i\omega t$ are antisymmetrical about the ordinate $t = \pi/\omega$ and eq. (h) gives

$$b_i = \frac{\omega}{\pi} \int_0^{2\pi/\omega} F(t) \sin i\omega t\, dt = \frac{4\omega}{\pi} \int_0^{\pi/2\omega} F(t) \sin i\omega t\, dt \qquad (l)$$

Referring to Fig. 73b, we see that in the interval from $t = 0$ to $t = \pi/2\omega$

$$F(t) = \frac{2P_0\omega}{\pi} \cdot t.$$

Substituting this in expression (l), we obtain

$$b_i = \frac{8P_0\omega^2}{\pi^2} \int_0^{\pi/2\omega} t \cdot \sin i\omega t \cdot dt = \frac{8P_0}{i^2\pi^2} \int_0^{i\pi/2} u \cdot \sin u \cdot du.$$

Integrating and substituting limits,

$$b_i = \frac{8P_0}{i^2\pi^2} \sin \frac{i\pi}{2} = \frac{8P_0}{i^2\pi^2}(-1)^{\frac{i-1}{2}}, \qquad (m)$$

where, of course, $i = 1, 3, 5, 7, \cdots$.

Using $a_0 = 0$, $a_i = 0$, and expression (m) for b_i, the trigonometric series (f) becomes

$$F(t) = \frac{8P_0}{\pi^2} \left(\sin \omega t - \frac{1}{3^2} \sin 3\omega t + \frac{1}{5^2} \sin 5\omega t - \cdots \right). \qquad (n)$$

We see that to represent the saw-tooth diagram in Fig. 73b by a trigonometric series, we need only to superimpose sine curves with an odd number of full waves in the interval $t = 0$ to $t = 2\pi/\omega$. This is quite logical since only in this way can we preserve the antisymmetrical shape of the given diagram. Further, we see that the series (n) converges rapidly so that only the first term is of practical importance. This simply means that the saw-tooth disturbing force produces practically the same effect as a true simple harmonic disturbing force of slightly smaller amplitude, i.e.,

$$F(t) \approx \tfrac{8}{10}P_0 \sin \omega t \qquad (o)$$

To judge the insignificance of the second term, we note that for $\omega/p = 0.9$,

$$\frac{1}{1 - \left(\dfrac{3\omega}{p}\right)^2} = -0.159.$$

Thus the amplitude of forced vibration produced by the second term is only $0.159/3^2 = 0.0177$ times that produced statically by the force $8P_0/\pi^2$ while the amplitude produced by the first term is

$$\frac{1}{1 - \dfrac{\omega^2}{p^2}} = 5.26 \text{ times.}$$

We conclude that using the approximate expression (o) results in an error of less than 1.2%.

PROBLEMS

1. Using data from Ex. 1 above, construct the displacement-time curve $x = f(t)$ for steady-state forced vibrations of the system in Fig. 72.

2. Expand the disturbing force $F(t)$ represented graphically in Fig. 74a into a trigonometric series.

Answer. $F(t) = \dfrac{4P_0}{\pi} \left(\sin \omega t + \dfrac{1}{3} \sin 3\omega t + \cdots \right).$

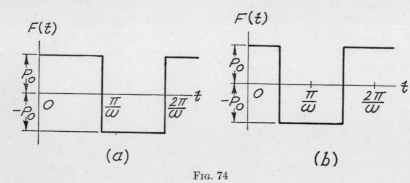

(a) (b)

FIG. 74

3. Expand the disturbing force $F(t)$ represented graphically in Fig. 74b into a trigonometric series.

Answer. $F(t) = \dfrac{4P_0}{\pi} \left(\cos \omega t - \dfrac{1}{3} \cos 3\omega t + \cdots \right).$

4. Expand the disturbing force $F(t)$ represented graphically in Fig. 75 into a trigonometric series.

Answer. $F(t) = \dfrac{2P_0}{\pi} \left(\sin \omega t - \dfrac{1}{2} \sin 2\omega t + \dfrac{1}{3} \sin 3\omega t - \cdots \right).$

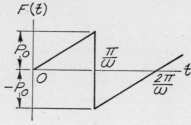

FIG. 75

18. General Case of Disturbing Force: Transient State.—In the preceding article consideration of the transient state was excluded. It was assumed that the free vibrations of the system generated at the beginning of motion would be damped out by friction and steady-state forced vibrations alone were considered. It was also assumed that the disturbing force was periodic in nature so that it could be represented with good accuracy by only a few terms of a trigonometric series. When we are interested in the exact nature of the motion of a system before free vibrations have been dissipated or when the acting force cannot be accurately represented by a few terms of the trigonometric series (f), p. 99, another way of calculating displacements of a vibrating system, based on solution (5) (see p. 4) of the equation of free harmonic vibration, has certain advantages. To explain the method let us consider the system shown in Fig. 1. We assume that at the initial instant ($t = 0$) the body is at rest in its position of static equilibrium. A vertical disturbing force of magnitude q per unit mass of the body W is applied at the initial instant and it is required to find the displacement of the body at any instant $t = t_1$. The variation of the force with time is represented by the curve MN in Fig. 76. To calculate the required displacement we imagine the continuous action of the force divided into small intervals dt.* The

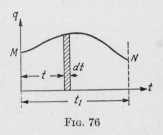

FIG. 76

impulse $q\,dt$ of the force during one of these elemental intervals is shown in Fig. 76 by the shaded strip. Let us now calculate the displacement of the body at the instant t_1 produced by this elemental impulse. As a result of this impulse an increase in the velocity of the body will be generated at the instant t. The magnitude of the velocity increase is found from the equation

$$\frac{d\dot{x}}{dt} = q,$$

from which

$$d\dot{x} = q\,dt. \tag{a}$$

The displacement of the body at the instant t_1 corresponding to the velocity $d\dot{x}$ which was communicated to it at the instant t may be calculated by the use of solution (5). It is seen from this solution that by reason of the initial velocity $\dot{x}_0$ the displacement at any instant t is $(\dot{x}_0 \sin pt)/p$. Hence the velocity $d\dot{x}$ communicated at the instant t to the body produces a displacement of the body at the instant t_1 given by

$$dx = \frac{q\,dt}{p} \sin p(t_1 - t). \tag{b}$$

---

* This method has been used by Lord Rayleigh, p. 74, *loc. cit.*

This is the displacement due to one elemental impulse only. In order to obtain the total displacement of the body produced by the continuous action of the force q, it is necessary to make a summation of all the elemental displacements given by expression (b). The summation yields:

$$x = \frac{1}{p} \int_0^{t_1} q \sin p(t_1 - t) \, dt. \tag{46}$$

This expression represents the complete displacement produced by the force q acting during the interval from $t = 0$ to $t = t_1$. It includes both forced and free vibrations and may become useful in studying the motion of the system at starting. It can be used also in cases where an analytical expression for the disturbing force is not known and where the force q is given graphically or numerically. It is only necessary in such a case to determine the magnitude of the integral (46) by using one of the approximate methods of integration.*

As an example of the application of this method, vibration under the action of a disturbing force $q = u \sin \omega t$ will now be considered. Substituting this expression of q in eq. (46) and observing that

$$\sin \omega t \sin p(t - t_1) = \tfrac{1}{2} \{ \cos (\omega t + pt - pt_1) - \cos (\omega t - pt + pt_1) \},$$

we obtain

$$x = \frac{u}{p^2 - \omega^2} \left(\sin \omega t_1 - \frac{\omega}{p} \sin p t_1 \right)$$

which coincides with solution (27) for $t = t_1$.

Eq. (46) can be used also in cases where it is necessary to find the displacement of the load W (see Fig. 1) resulting from several impulses. Assume, for instance, that due to impulses received by the load W at the moments t', t'', t''', $\cdots$ increments of the speed $\Delta_1 \dot{x}$, $\Delta_2 \dot{x}$, $\Delta_3 \dot{x}$, $\cdots$ be produced. Then from eqs. (b) and (46) the displacement at any moment t_1 will be,

$$x = \frac{1}{p} [\Delta_1 \dot{x} \sin p(t_1 - t') + \Delta_2 \dot{x} \sin p(t_1 - t'')$$
$$+ \Delta_3 \dot{x} \sin p(t_1 - t''') + \cdots]. \quad (c)$$

This displacement can be obtained very easily graphically by considering $\Delta_1 \dot{x}$, $\Delta_2 \dot{x}$, $\cdots$ as vectors inclined to the horizontal axis at angles $p(t_1 - t')$, $p(t_1 - t'')$, $\cdots$ Fig. 77). The vertical projection OC_1 of the geometrical

---

* See von Sanden, *loc. cit.*, p. 100.

sum OC of these vectors, divided by p, will then represent the displacement x given by the above equation.

In cases where a constant force q is applied at the moment $t = 0$ to the load W (Fig. 1) the displacement of the load at any moment t_1 becomes from eq. (46):

$$x = \frac{q}{p} \int_0^{t_1} \sin p(t_1 - t) \, dt = \frac{q}{p^2} (1 - \cos pt_1), \tag{d}$$

where q/p^2 is statical deflection due to the force q (see p. 42). It is seen, from (d), that the maximum deflection during vibrations produced by a suddenly applied force is equal to twice the statical deflection corresponding to the same force.

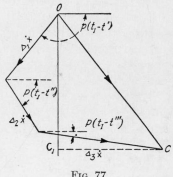

FIG. 77

It was assumed that the suddenly applied, constant force q is acting all the time from $t = 0$ to $t = t_1$. If the force q acts only during a certain interval Δ of that time and then is suddenly removed, the motion of the body, after removal of the force, can also be obtained from eq. (46). We write this equation in the following form

$$x = \frac{1}{p} \int_0^{\Delta} q \sin p(t_1 - t) \, dt + \frac{1}{p} \int_{\Delta}^{t_1} q \sin p(t_1 - t) \, dt.$$

Observing that q is zero for $\Delta < t < t_1$, the second integral on the right side vanishes and we obtain

$$x = \frac{1}{p} \int_0^{\Delta} q \sin p(t_1 - t) \, dt = \frac{q}{p^2} |\cos p(t_1 - t) |_0^{\Delta}$$

$$= \frac{q}{p^2} [\cos p(t_1 - \Delta) - \cos pt_1] = \frac{2q}{p^2} \sin \frac{p\Delta}{2} \sin p \left(t_1 - \frac{\Delta}{2} \right). \tag{e}$$

Thus a constant force acting during an interval of time Δ produces a simple sinusoidal motion the amplitude of which depends on the ratio of the interval Δ to the period $\tau = 2\pi/p$ of the free vibration of the system. Taking, for instance, $\Delta/\tau = \frac{1}{2}$ we find $\sin (p\Delta/2) = 1$ and the amplitude of vibration (e) is twice as large as the statical deflection q/p^2. If we take $\Delta = \tau$, $\sin (p\Delta/2) = 0$ and there will be no vibration at all after removal of the force. Considering the system in Fig. 1 we have in the first case the force q removed when the weight W is in its lowest position. In the second case the force is removed when the body is in its highest position, which is its position of static equilibrium.

If the loading and unloading of the system is repeated several times and τ_1 is the constant interval of time between two consecutive applications of the force, the resulting motion is

$$x = \frac{2q}{p^2} \sin \frac{p\Delta}{2} \left[\sin p \left(t_1 - \frac{\Delta}{2} \right) + \sin p \left(t_1 - \tau_1 - \frac{\Delta}{2} \right) \right.$$
$$\left. + \sin p \left(t_1 - 2\tau_1 - \frac{\Delta}{2} \right) + \cdots \right].$$

We see that by taking $\tau_1 = 2\pi/p$ the phenomenon of resonance takes place and the amplitude of vibration will be gradually built up.

It was assumed in the derivation of eq. (46) that the system is at rest initially. If there is some initial displacement x_0 and an initial velocity $\dot{x}_0$, the total displacement at an instant t_1 will be obtained by superposing on the displacement given by expression (46) the displacement due to the initial conditions. In this case we obtain

$$x = x_0 \cos pt_1 + \frac{\dot{x}_0}{p} \sin pt_1 + \frac{1}{p} \int_0^{t_1} q \sin p(t_1 - t) \, dt. \tag{47}$$

If there is a viscous damping a similar method can be used in studying forced vibrations. From solution (34) we see that an initial velocity $\dot{x}_0$ produces a displacement of the body (Fig. 1) at an instant t which is given by

$$\frac{1}{p_1} \dot{x}_0 e^{-nt} \sin p_1 t. \tag{f}$$

The quantity n defines the damping and $p_1 = \sqrt{p^2 - n^2}$. From this we conclude that a velocity $d\dot{x} = q \, dt$ communicated at an instant t produces a displacement at the instant t_1 equal to

$$dx = \frac{q}{p_1} e^{-n(t_1 - t)} \sin p_1(t_1 - t) \, dt. \tag{g}$$

The complete displacement of the body resulting from the action of the force q from $t = 0$ to $t = t_1$, will be obtained by a summation of expressions (g). Thus we have

$$x = \frac{1}{p_1} \int_0^{t_1} q e^{-n(t_1 - t)} \sin p_1(t_1 - t) \, dt. \tag{48}$$

As an application of the solution (48), let us consider the case when the frequency of a pulsating disturbing force is not constant but increases uniformly with time, so that we can express the force per unit of vibrating mass in the form

$$q = q_0 \sin \left(\tfrac{1}{2}at^2 + \alpha\right), \tag{h}$$

where a denotes the angular acceleration and α, the initial phase angle of the disturbing force. In such case it will be of special interest to consider vibrations produced by this force when its frequency passes through the natural frequency of the system. The displacement at any time t_1 is obtained by substituting expression (h) into the general solution (48), which gives

$$x = \frac{q_0}{p_1} \int_0^{t_1} e^{-n(t_1 - t)} \sin p_1(t_1 - t) \sin \left(\tfrac{1}{2}at^2 + \alpha\right) dt. \tag{i}$$

This rather complicated integral has been evaluated by F. M. Lewis.[*] The result of this calculation for the particular case of no damping is shown in Fig. 78. The wavy line represents the motion for the particular case when $p^2/2\pi a = 10$ and initially $(t = 0)$ the mass is at rest and the spring force is balanced by the initial value of the disturbing force. Varying the phase-angle α in expression (h), a family of such curves can be produced. The envelope to this family, shown in the figure by a solid line, defines the maximum amplitude obtainable. It is seen that in this particular case, the maximum amplitude is about $11\delta_{st}$ and that it occurs when the instantaneous frequency at of the disturbing force is about 25% above the natural frequency p of the system. There are three more curves in the figure for smaller values of the acceleration a, and we see that the greater the acceleration a, the smaller the maximum amplitude and the greater the shift of this maximum from true resonance $(at = p)$. A similar conclusion was obtained also when damping was taken into account. It was found also [†] "that unless the acceleration through resonance is extremely rapid, or there is little damping, the amplitudes are not a great deal smaller than the constant frequency amplitudes" shown in Fig. 60.

Curves similar to those in Fig. 78 were obtained also for the case of deceleration. The maximum amplitudes occur now at speeds below critical and are slightly larger for decreasing speed than for increasing.

It was assumed in the above discussion that the amplitude of the pulsating force (h) remains constant and that only its frequency changes with

[*] See his paper, "Vibration during Acceleration through a Critical Speed," *Trans. A.S.M.E.*, Vol. 54, p. APM-253, 1932.

[†] See Lewis, *loc. cit.*

time.   In practical cases such as we have in the starting or stopping of rotating machinery that normally operates above resonance and must pass through this critical speed in starting (or stopping), the amplitude of the pulsating force, due to unbalance, will not remain constant but will contain

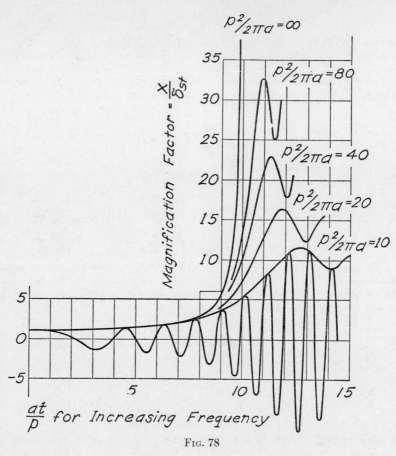

Fig. 78

a term proportional to t^2. The calculation of the integral in eq. (48) for this case * has been made with the aid of a differential analyzer.† This analysis showed that vibrations of large amplitude can be built up while passing through critical speed and sometimes special damping devices

* See paper by J. G. Baker, *J. Appl. Mech.*, Vol. 6, pp. 145–150, 1939.

† For a description of this machine, see V. Bush, *J. Franklin Inst.*, Vol. 212, p. 447, 1931.

may be required to prevent damage. It was shown also that the amplitude of such vibrations can be considerably reduced by the introduction of spring mountings so as to reduce the critical speed of the system.

EXAMPLE

1. As an example of an application of eq. (46) let us consider the effect of low spots on deflection of rails. Due to the presence of a low spot on the rail some vertical displacement of a rolling wheel occurs which results in an additional vertical pressure on the rail. This additional pressure depends on the velocity of rolling and on the profile of the low spot. Taking the coordinate axes as shown in Fig. 79 we denote by l the length

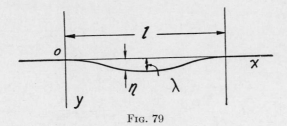

FIG. 79

of the low spot and by η the variable depth of the spot. The rail we consider as a beam on a uniform elastic foundation and we denote by k the concentrated vertical pressure which is required to produce a vertical deflection of the rail equal to one inch. If W denotes the weight of the wheel together with the weights of other parts rigidly connected with the wheel, the static deflection of the rail under the action of this weight is

$$\delta_{st} = \frac{W}{k}.\qquad\qquad (j)$$

If the rail be considered an elastic spring, the period of free vibration of the wheel supported by the rail will be

$$\tau = 2\pi \sqrt{\frac{\delta_{st}}{g}}.\qquad\qquad (k)$$

For a 100-lb rail, with $EI = 44 \times 30 \times 10^6$ lb in.^{2}, and with $W = 3000$ lb, we will find, for a usual rigidity of the track, that the wheel performs about 20 osc. per sec. Since this frequency is large in comparison with the frequency of oscillation of a locomotive cab on its springs, we can assume that the vibrations of the wheel are not transmitted to the cab and that the vertical pressure of the springs on the axle remains constant and equal to the spring-borne weight. Let us now consider the forced vibrations of the wheel due to the low spot. We denote the dynamic deflection of the rail under the wheel by y during this vibration.* Then the vertical displacement of the wheel

* This deflection is measured from the position of static equilibrium which the wheel has under the action of the weight W and of the spring-borne weight.

traveling along the spot of variable depth η is $y + \eta$ and the vertical inertia force of the wheel will be

$$-\frac{W}{g}\frac{d^2(y + \eta)}{dt^2}.$$

The reaction of the rail is $-ky$ and the equation of motion of the wheel in the vertical direction becomes:

$$\frac{W}{g}\frac{d^2(y + \eta)}{dt^2} + ky = 0,$$

from which

$$\frac{W}{g}\frac{d^2y}{dt^2} + ky = -\frac{W}{g}\frac{d^2\eta}{dt^2}. \tag{l}$$

If the shape of the low spot and the speed of the locomotive are known, the depth η and consequently the right side of eq. (l) can be expressed as functions of time. Thus we obtain the equation of forced vibration of the wheel produced by the low spot.

Let us consider a case when the shape of the low spot (Fig. 79) is given by the equation

$$\eta = \frac{\lambda}{2}\left(1 - \cos\frac{2\pi x}{l}\right), \tag{m}$$

in which λ denotes the depth of the low spot at the middle of its length.

If we begin to reckon time from the instant when the point of contact of the wheel and the rail coincides with the beginning of the low spot, Fig. 79, and if we denote the speed of the locomotive by v, we have $x = vt$, and we find, from eq. (m), that

$$\eta = \frac{\lambda}{2}\left(1 - \cos\frac{2\pi vt}{l}\right). \tag{n}$$

Substituting this into eq. (l) we obtain

$$\frac{W}{g}\frac{d^2y}{dt^2} + ky = -\frac{W}{g}\frac{\lambda}{2}\frac{4\pi^2v^2}{l^2}\cos\frac{2\pi vt}{l}.$$

Dividing by W/g, and using our previous notations this becomes:

$$\ddot{y} + p^2 y = -\frac{2\lambda\pi^2 v^2}{l^2}\cos\frac{2\pi vt}{l}. \tag{o}$$

If the right side of this equation be substituted into eq. (46) we find that the additional deflection of the rail caused by the dynamical effect of the low spot is

$$y = -\frac{2\pi^2\lambda v^2}{pl^2}\int_0^{t_1}\cos\frac{2\pi vt}{l}\sin p(t_1 - t)\,dt. \tag{p}$$

Performing the integration and denoting by τ_1 the time l/v required for the wheel to pass over the low spot, we obtain

$$y = \frac{\lambda}{2(1 - \tau_1^2/\tau^2)}\left(\cos\frac{2\pi t_1}{\tau_1} - \cos\frac{2\pi t_1}{\tau}\right). \tag{q}$$

It is seen that the additional deflection of the rail, produced by the low spot, is proportional to the depth λ of the spot and depends also on the ratio τ_1/τ. As the wheel is traveling along the low spot, the variation of the additional deflection is represented for several values of the ratio τ_1/τ by the curves in Fig. 80. The abscissas give the position of the wheel along the low spot, and the ordinates give the additional deflection expressed in terms of λ. As soon as the wheel enters the low spot the pressure on the rail and consequently the deflection of the rail begin to diminish (y is negative) while the wheel begins to accelerate in a downward direction. Then follows a retardation of this movement with corresponding increases in pressure and in deflection. From the figure

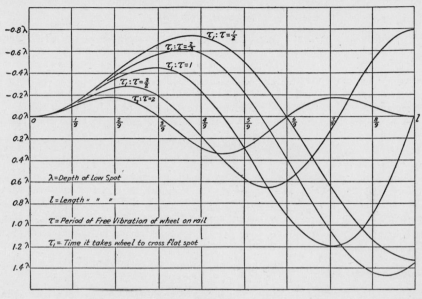

FIG. 80

we see that for $\tau_1 < \tau$ the maximum pressure occurs when the wheel is approaching the other end of the low spot. The ratios of the maximum additional deflection to the depth λ of the low spot calculated from formula (q) are given in the table:

$\tau_1/\tau =$	2	3/2	1	4/5	2/3	3/5	1/2
$y_{max}/\lambda =$	0.33	0.65	1.21	1.41	1.47	1.45	1.33.

It is seen that the maximum value is about equal to 1.47. This ratio occurs when the speed of the locomotive is such that $(\tau_1/\tau) \approx 2/3$.

Similar calculations can be readily made if some other expression than eq. (n) is taken for the shape of the low spot, provided that the assumed curve is tangent to the rail surface at the ends of the spot. If this condition is not fulfilled an impact at the ends of the low spot must be considered.*

* See author's papers in *Trans. Inst. Engrs. of Ways of Communication, St. Petersburg*, 1915; and in *Génie civil*, p. 551, 1921. See also doctoral dissertation by B. K. Hovey, Göttingen, 1933. For stresses at the surface of contact, see *J. Appl. Mech.*, Vol. 17, p. 466–467, 1950.

PROBLEMS

1. A mass m suspended by a spring having a constant k (Fig. 1) is subjected to the action of a vertical disturbing force $F(t) = \alpha t$, i.e., a force that increases linearly with time. Assuming that when $t = 0$, $x_0 = \dot{x}_0 = 0$, derive the general displacement-time equation for the induced motion of the suspended mass.

Answer. $x = \dfrac{\alpha}{k}\left(t - \dfrac{1}{p}\sin pt\right)$, where $p = \sqrt{k/m}$.

2. A rigid ball of mass m rolls to the right along the flat vertical curve OBC, which has the shape of a half sine wave, with constant horizontal speed v, Fig. 81. Assuming

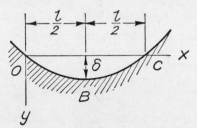

Fig. 81

that OBC is an elastic foundation with modulus k, develop a general expression for the deformation y of the foundation, over and above that due to the weight of the ball. Follow the general procedure used in Ex. 1 above.

Answer. $y = \delta\left(\dfrac{1}{p^2/\omega^2 - 1}\right)\left(\sin \omega t - \dfrac{\omega}{p}\sin pt\right)$; $\omega = \dfrac{\pi v}{l}$, $p = \sqrt{\dfrac{k}{m}}$.

3. A weight W constrained to move vertically is actuated by a rigid cam moving horizontally with constant velocity v as shown in Fig. 82. Neglecting friction and the

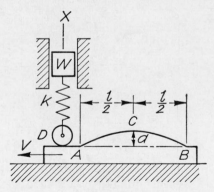

Fig. 82

mass of the spring k and cam follower D, find the displacement x of the weight W measured from its normal position, for any time $0 < t_1 < v/l$ if point A on the cam comes to the roller D at the instant $t_1 = 0$. ACB has the shape of a half sine wave.

Answer. $\quad x = \dfrac{a}{1 - \dfrac{\omega^2}{p^2}} \left(\sin \omega t - \dfrac{\omega}{p} \sin pt \right);\quad \omega = \dfrac{\pi v}{l},\quad p = \sqrt{\dfrac{kg}{W}}.$

4. A mine cage of weight W suspended by a flexible cable of cross-sectional area A and modulus E is being lowered into a vertical shaft with constant velocity v_0 (Fig. 83). At a certain instant $t_1 = 0$ when the length of free cable is l, brakes are applied to the drum which is stopped with constant angular deceleration a/r. Find the displacement x of the cage for any instant $0 < t_1 < \dfrac{2v_0}{a}$ thereafter. Neglect the small increase in l due to further unwinding of cable after the instant $t_1 = 0$. What amplitude of free vibration will the cage have after the drum has stopped?

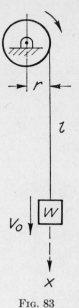

FIG. 83

Answer. $\quad x = v_0 t_1 - \frac{1}{2} a t_1{}^2 + \dfrac{a}{p^2}(1 - \cos p t_1);\quad p = \sqrt{\dfrac{AEg}{Wl}}.$

19. General Case of Disturbing Force: Graphical Solution.—In the two preceding articles, we have considered only cases of forced vibration for which the disturbing force $F(t)$ could be handled analytically, either by expansion into a trigonometric series or by direct integration of eq. (46). In many practical cases the disturbing force may not be readily expressible by any simple analytic function of time. Such is the case, for example, if we wish to investigate vibrations produced by a blast or other type of pulse loading as shown in Fig. 84.

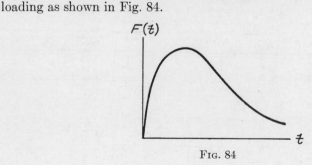

FIG. 84

In all such cases, we can obtain an approximate solution for the transient state * by a graphical treatment of eq. (47), assuming that the influence of damping can be neglected. To do this, let us assume that the disturbing

* When the disturbing force is not periodic, there is, of course, no such thing as a steady-state motion.

force $F(t)$ is any function of time as represented graphically in Fig. 85, and that we approximate this curve by a suitable step-curve having constant ordinates $F_1, F_2, F_3, \cdots$ over equal intervals of time Δ. That is, we assume that the continuous action of the force $F(t)$ is replaced by a series of constant forces $F_1, F_2, F_3, \cdots$, each acting for a time interval Δ.

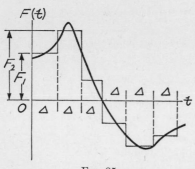

FIG. 85

Let us consider now any one such time interval Δ during which the disturbing force has the constant magnitude F_i. Then due to the action of this constant force, the displacement x of the disturbed spring-suspended mass at any instant $t_1 < \Delta$ measured from the beginning of that interval will be given by eq. (d) of the preceding article. This becomes

$$x = \frac{q}{p^2}(1 - \cos pt_1) = \frac{F_i}{k}(1 - \cos pt_1) \qquad (a)$$

and the complete displacement, represented by eq. (47), becomes

$$x_i = x_{i-1} \cos pt_1 + \frac{\dot{x}_{i-1}}{p} \sin pt_1 + \frac{F_i}{k}(1 - \cos pt_1), \qquad (b)$$

where x_{i-1} and $\dot{x}_{i-1}$ are the displacement and velocity of the disturbed mass at the beginning of the interval in question. Expression (b) is easily rewritten in the following form:

$$x_i = \frac{F_i}{k} + \left(x_{i-1} - \frac{F_i}{k}\right) \cos pt_1 + \frac{\dot{x}_{i-1}}{p} \sin pt_1. \qquad (49)$$

Differentiating eq. (49) once with respect to time, we obtain

$$\frac{\dot{x}_i}{p} = -\left(x_{i-1} - \frac{F_i}{k}\right) \sin pt_1 + \frac{\dot{x}_{i-1}}{p} \cos pt_1. \qquad (50)$$

Setting $t_1 = \Delta$ in eqs. (49) and (50), we obtain the displacement x_i and velocity $\dot{x}_i$ at the end of the interval in question.

Beginning now with x_0 and $\dot{x}_0$ as known initial displacement and velocity at time $t = 0$ and using eqs. (49) and (50) for the first interval, we find

x_1 and $\dot{x}_1$ at the end of this interval. Then using these values as new initial displacement and velocity for the second interval, we find x_2 and $\dot{x}_2$ and so on. In this way, the approximate solution can be carried as far as we like on the basis of a suitable step-curve in place of the true disturbing force $F(t)$.

The step-by-step procedure as outlined above can be carried out graphically in a very simple way.* To show this, we square both eqs. (49) and (50) and add them together, obtaining

$$\left(x_i - \frac{F_i}{k}\right)^2 + \left(\frac{\dot{x}_i}{p}\right)^2 = \left(x_{i-1} - \frac{F_i}{k}\right)^2 + \left(\frac{\dot{x}_{i-1}}{p}\right)^2. \tag{c}$$

This, we recognize as the equation of a circle of radius

$$R = \sqrt{\left(x_{i-1} - \frac{F_i}{k}\right)^2 + \left(\frac{\dot{x}_{i-1}}{p}\right)^2}$$

and with center coordinates $\left(\dfrac{F_i}{k}, 0\right)$ in the phase plane x vs. $\dot{x}/p$. Thus during each time interval Δ, the motion of the vibrating mass is represented in the phase plane by the arc of a circle the center of which is defined by the corresponding value of F_i/k.

To make this phase-plane construction, we proceed as follows: Referring to Fig. 86a, let point A with coordinates $(x_0, \dot{x}_0/p)$ represent the given initial conditions of motion at time $t = 0$. Then with C_1, having the ordinate F_1/k, as a center, we draw the circular arc AB with central angle $p\Delta$ as shown. Point B, obtained in this way represents the displacement x_1 and velocity $\dot{x}_1$ of the disturbed mass at the end of the first time interval Δ. Then with C_2, defined by the ordinate F_2/k, as a center, we make the next circular arc BC again having the central angle $p\Delta$ and obtain point C defining displacement x_2 and velocity $\dot{x}_2$ at the end of the second interval, i.e., at time $t = 2\Delta$. Proceding in this way, the construction in Fig. 86a has been carried out to time $t = 5\Delta$ on the basis of the assumed $F(t)$ curve in Fig. 85.

Having completed the phase-plane construction in Fig. 86a, the points A, B, C, D, $\cdots$ may be readily projected onto a displacement-time plane

* The construction to be described is due to J. Lamoën. See his paper, "Etude graphique des vibrations de systèmes à un seul degré de liberté," *Rev. universelle mines*, May 1935.

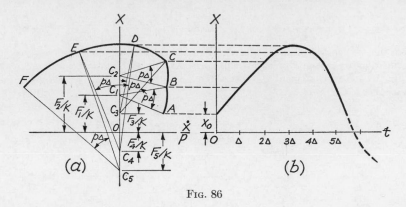

Fig. 86

and the displacement-time curve $x = f(t)$ constructed as shown in Fig. 86b. A velocity-time curve $\dot{x} = \phi(t)$ can be obtained in the same way, if desired.

The described procedure will give good accuracy if reasonable care is taken in choosing the step-curve to approximate the given disturbing force $F(t)$. In choosing the time interval Δ, we must be guided not only by variations in the given $F(t)$ curve but also by the natural period $\tau = 2\pi/p$ of the spring-suspended mass. In general Δ should be a small fraction of this period. If the disturbing force $F(t)$ exhibits rapid variation over part of its duration and is fairly constant over another part, it may be expedient to vary the time intervals Δ accordingly. There is no fundamental reason for the time intervals to be equal.

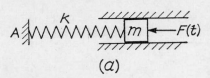

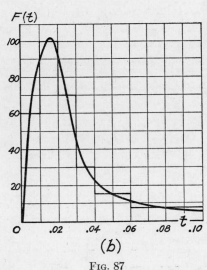

Fig. 87

EXAMPLES

1. A piston weighing 0.978 lb is supported by a spring having a constant $k = 10$ lb per in. (Fig. 87a). Initially at rest in its equilibrium position, the piston is acted upon by an explosion which creates the disturbing force $F(t)$ shown in Fig. 87b. What amplitude of free vibrations will be set up by the explosion? Neglect damping.

Solution. The natural period of the system is $\tau = 2\pi \sqrt{\dfrac{m}{k}} = \dfrac{2\pi}{\sqrt{3940}} = 0.1$ sec.

From this we conclude that the step-curve in Fig. 87*b* will represent a satisfactory approximation to the true $F(t)$ curve. The corresponding phase-plane trajectory is shown in Fig. 88 and ends at point G. Thereafter the piston performs free vibrations with the amplitude $OH = 11.7$ in.

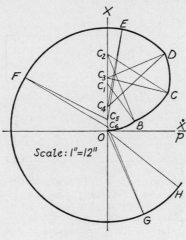

FIG. 88

2. Investigate the response of the system in Fig. 87*a* to a horizontal movement of point A represented by the displacement-time curve shown in Fig. 89.

Solution. If x represents the displacement of the piston and x_1 that of point A at any instant t, then the equation of motion becomes

$$m\ddot{x} = -k(x - x_1).$$

Writing this in the form

$$m\ddot{x} + kx = kx_1,$$

we conclude that the piston behaves as if subjected to an external disturbing force $F(t) = kx_1$. Thus replacing the displacement-time curve in Fig. 89 by a suitable step-curve, we may proceed exactly as before with the construction of the phase-plane trajectory.

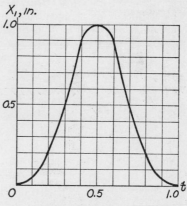

FIG. 89

PROBLEMS

1. Investigate the response of the piston in Fig. 87a to the disturbing force represented in Fig. 87b if the spring constant $k = 100$ lb per in. and all other data are the same as given in Ex. 1 above.

2. Investigate the response of the system in Fig. 87a and described in Ex. 2 to the disturbing force represented graphically in Fig. 90.

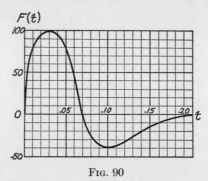

FIG. 90

3. What maximum horizontal displacement of the top of the portal frame in Fig. 10 will be produced by a horizontal ground motion represented by the displacement-time curve in Fig. 89? Assume complete bending restraint at A and B.

20. Self-excited Vibration.—In discussing various problems of forced vibration we always assumed that the force producing vibration is independent of the vibratory motion. There are cases, however, in which a steady forced vibration is sustained by forces created by the vibratory motion itself and disappearing when the motion stops. Such vibrations are called *self-excited* or *self-induced* vibrations.

As a simple example of such vibration, let us consider the case shown in Fig. 91. A mass m, attached by a spring to a fixed point A, rests on a horizontal plane ss which is gradually brought to a uniform speed v_0 directed as shown. Neglecting the initial disturbance, we might assume that the mass m would take a position of equilibrium determined by the friction force F and the equal but opposite tensile force in the spring. However, experiment shows that equilibrium in this position is unstable and that horizontal vibrations of the mass will be built up.

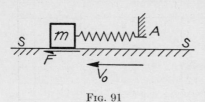

FIG. 91

To explain such vibrations, we have to take into consideration the fact that ordinary Coulomb friction is not constant, but diminishes slightly as the velocity of relative sliding increases. If, due to some slight disturbance, vibrations of the mass are started, the friction force F, always having the direction of v_0,* will not remain constant but will be larger when the mass moves in the direction of v_0 than when it moves in the

* We assume that the velocity of vibratory motion is always less than v_0.

direction opposite to v_0. Observing that in the first case the force F produces positive work on the mass m while in the second case it produces negative work, we conclude that over one complete cycle of vibration a net positive work on the mass will be produced. Thus energy is added to the mass and its amplitude of vibration will be gradually increased. This phenomenon is called self-induced vibration because the disturbing force, superimposed on the constant average friction, is created by the motion of the mass and vanishes if the mass is at rest.

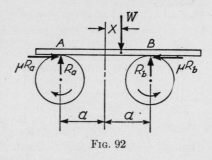

FIG. 92

A similar phenomenon can be observed in the case of the system shown in Fig. 92. Here we have two circular discs in a vertical plane with slightly grooved rims which support a bar AB of weight W. The distance between the axes of the discs is $2a$ and they rotate with the same constant angular velocity but in opposite directions as shown. Now assuming a constant coefficient of dry friction μ at each point of contact, let the bar be displaced from its middle position by an amount x. Then the reactions at points A and B will be

$$R_a = W(a - x)/2a, \brace R_b = W(a + x)/2a, \qquad (a)$$

and the corresponding friction forces are μR_a and μR_b, respectively. The resultant force acting on the bar is

$$X = \mu(R_a - R_b) = -\frac{\mu W x}{a}, \qquad (b)$$

and the equation of motion for the bar becomes

$$\frac{W}{g} \ddot{x} = -\frac{\mu W x}{a},$$

which reduces to

$$\ddot{x} + \frac{\mu g}{a} x = 0. \qquad (c)$$

From this we conclude that, if displaced from its middle position ($x = 0$), the bar will perform simple harmonic motion with the period

$$\tau = \frac{2\pi}{p} = 2\pi \sqrt{\frac{a}{\mu g}}. \qquad (d)$$

Now let us consider the effect of a slight variation of coefficient of friction with relative velocity of sliding as mentioned before. Observing that the disc whose rotation opposes the motion of the bar has a higher relative velocity of slip and consequently a smaller coefficient of friction than the disc assisting the motion, we conclude that, superimposed on the constant average friction that produces the simple harmonic motion represented by eq. (c), there is a secondary disturbing force that always acts in the direction of motion. This does positive work on the bar and gradually builds up the amplitude of oscillation, so that we have the phenomenon of self-induced oscillations. This is easily demonstrated by experiment; in fact the device can be used to study the law of variation of coefficient of friction with relative velocity of sliding by running the discs at different angular velocities and noting the corresponding periods of oscillation of the bar. The coefficient of friction μ for each run can then be computed from eq. (d).

One of the earliest experiments with self-excited mechanical vibration was made by W. Froude,* who found that the vibrations of a pendulum swinging from a shaft, Fig.

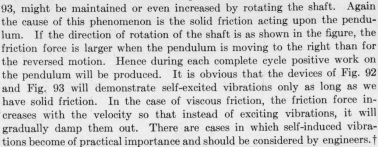

93, might be maintained or even increased by rotating the shaft. Again the cause of this phenomenon is the solid friction acting upon the pendulum. If the direction of rotation of the shaft is as shown in the figure, the friction force is larger when the pendulum is moving to the right than for the reversed motion. Hence during each complete cycle positive work on the pendulum will be produced. It is obvious that the devices of Fig. 92 and Fig. 93 will demonstrate self-excited vibrations only as long as we have solid friction. In the case of viscous friction, the friction force increases with the velocity so that instead of exciting vibrations, it will gradually damp them out. There are cases in which self-induced vibrations become of practical importance and should be considered by engineers.†

Fig. 93

An example of self-excited vibration has been experienced with a vertical machine, Fig. 94, consisting of a mass A driven by a motor B. There is considerable clearance between the shaft and the guide C, and the shaft can be considered a cantilever built in at the bottom and loaded at the top. The frequency of the natural lateral vibration of the shaft, which is also its critical or whirling speed, can be readily calculated in the usual way (see Art. 5). Experience shows that the machine is running smoothly as long as the shaft remains straight and does not touch the guide, but if for one reason or another the shaft strikes the guide, a violent whirling starts and is maintained indefinitely. This type of whirling may occur at any speed of the shaft, and it has the same frequency as the critical speed or frequency of the shaft mentioned above. In order to explain this type of whirling, let us consider the horizontal cross sections of the shaft and of the guide represented in Fig. 94b. As soon as the shaft touches the guide a solid friction force F will be exerted on the shaft which tends to displace the shaft and thereby produces the whirl in the direction opposite to the rotation

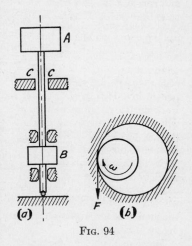

Fig. 94

of the shaft. The pressure necessary for the existence of a friction force is provided by the centrifugal force of the mass A acting through the shaft against the guide.

Vibration of Electric Transmission Lines.—A wire stretched between two towers at a considerable distance apart, say about 300 ft, may, under certain conditions, vibrate

---

* Lord Rayleigh, p. 212, *loc. cit.*

† Several cases of such vibrations are described and explained by J. G. Baker, *Trans. A.S.M.E.*, Vol. 55, p. APM-5, 1933; also J. P. Den Hartog, *Proc. 4th Intern. Congr. Appl. Mech.*, p. 36, 1934.

violently at a low frequency, say one cycle per second. It happens usually when a rather strong transverse wind is blowing and the temperature is around 32°F, i.e., when the weather is favorable for formation of sleet on the wire. This phenomenon can be considered as a self-excited vibration.* If a transverse wind is blowing on a wire of a circular cross section (Fig. 95a), the force exerted on the wire has the same direction as the wind. But in the case of an elongated cross section resulting from sleet formation (Fig. 95b), the condition is different and the force acting on the wire has usually a direction different from that of the wind. A familiar example of this occurs on an airplane wing on which not only a *drag* in the direction of the wind but also a *lift*

FIG. 95   FIG. 96

in a perpendicular direction is exerted. Let us now assume a vibration of the wire and consider the half cycle when the wire is moving downwards. In the case of a circular wire we shall have, owing to this motion, some air pressure in an upward direction. This force together with the horizontal wind pressure give an inclined force F (Fig. 96a), which has an upward component opposing the motion of the wire. Thus we have a damping action which will arrest the vibration. In the case of an elongated cross section (Fig. 96b) it may happen, as it was explained above, that due to the action of horizontal wind together with downward motion of the wire a force F having a component in a downward direction may be exerted on the wire so that it produces positive work during the downward motion of the wire. During the second half of the cycle, when the wire is moving upwards, the direction of the air pressure due to wire motion changes sign so that the combined effect of this pressure and the horizontal wind may produce a force with vertical component directed upwards. Thus again we have positive work produced during the motion of the wire resulting in a building up of vibrations.

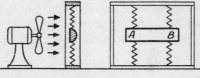

FIG. 97

The above type of vibration can be demonstrated by using the device shown in Fig. 97. A light wooden bar suspended on flexible springs and with its flat side turned perpendicular to the wind of a fan, may be brought into violent vibrations in a vertical plane. The explanation of this vibration follows from the fact that a semicircular cross section satisfies the condition discussed above, so that the combined effect of the wind and of the vertical motion of the bar results in a force on the bar having always a vertical component in the direction of the vertical motion. Thus positive work is produced during the vibration.

* J. P. Den Hartog, *Trans. Am. Inst. Elec. Engrs.*, p. 1074, 1932.

CHAPTER II

SYSTEMS WITH NON-LINEAR AND VARIABLE SPRING CHARACTERISTICS

21. Examples of Non-linear Systems.—In discussing vibration problems of the previous chapter it was always assumed that the force in a spring is proportional to the deformation. It was assumed also that in the case of damping the resisting force is a linear function of the velocity of motion. As a result of these assumptions we always had vibrations of a system represented by a linear differential equation with constant coefficients. There are many practical problems in which these assumptions represent satisfactory actual conditions, however there are also systems in which a linear differential equation with constant coefficients is no longer sufficient to describe the actual notion, so that a general investigation of vibrations requires a discussion of non-linear differential equations. Such systems are called *systems with non-linear characteristics*. One kind of such systems we have when the restoring force of a spring is not proportional to the displacement of the system from its position of equilibrium.

Sometimes, for instance, an organic material such as rubber or leather is used in couplings and vibration absorbers. The tensile test diagram for these materials has the shape shown in Fig. 98a; thus the modulus of elasticity increases with the elongation. For small amplitudes of vibration this variation in modulus may be negligible, but with increasing amplitude the increase in modulus may result in a substantial increase in the frequency of vibration.

Another example of variable flexibility is met with in the case of structures made of such materials as cast iron or concrete. In both cases the tensile test diagram has the shape shown in Fig. 98b, i.e., the modulus of elasticity decreases with the deformation. Therefore some decrease in the frequency with increase of amplitude of vibration must be expected.

Sometimes special types of steel springs are used, such that their elastic characteristics vary with the displacement. The natural frequency of systems involving such springs depends on the amplitude. By using such types of springs the unfavorable effect of resonance can be diminished. If, due to resonance, the amplitude of vibration begins to increase, the frequency of the vibration changes, i.e., the resonance condition disappears.

A simple example of such a spring is shown in Fig. 99. The flat spring, supporting the weight W, is built in at the end A. During vibration the spring is partially in contact with one of two cylindrical surfaces AB or AC.

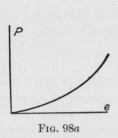

Fig. 98a

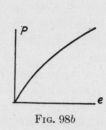

Fig. 98b

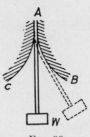

Fig. 99

Due to this fact the free length of the cantilever varies with the amplitude so that the rigidity of the spring increases with increasing deflection. The conditions are the same as in the case represented in Fig. 98a, i.e., the frequency of vibration increases with an increase in amplitude.

If the dimensions of the spring and the shape of the curves AB and AC are known, a curve representing the restoring force as a function of the deflection of the end of the spring can easily be obtained.

Another example of a non-linear system is the vibration along the x-axis of a mass m attached to a stretched wire AB (Fig. 100). Assume

S is initial tensile force in the wire,
x is small displacement of the mass m in a hori-
    zontal direction,
A is cross-sectional area of the wire,
E is modulus of elasticity of the wire.

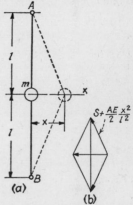

Fig. 100

The unit elongation of the wire, due to a displacement x, is

$$\frac{\sqrt{l^2 + x^2} - l}{l} \approx \frac{x^2}{2l^2}.$$

The corresponding tensile force in the wire is

$$S + AE\frac{x^2}{2l^2},$$

and the restoring force acting on the mass m (Fig. 100b) will be

$$\left(S + AE\,\frac{x^2}{2l^2}\right)\frac{2x}{\sqrt{l^2 + x^2}} \approx \frac{2Sx}{l} + AE\,\frac{x^3}{l^3}.$$

The differential equation of motion of the mass m thus becomes

$$m\ddot{x} + \frac{2Sx}{l} + AE\,\frac{x^3}{l^3} = 0. \tag{a}$$

It is seen that in the case of very small displacements and when the initial tensile force S is sufficiently large, the last term on the left side of eq. (a) can be neglected and a simple harmonic vibration of the mass m in a horizontal direction will be obtained. Otherwise, all three terms of eq. (a) must be taken into consideration. In such a case the restoring force will increase in greater proportion than the displacement and the frequency of vibration will increase with the amplitude.

In the case of a simple mathematical pendulum (Fig. 101), by applying d'Alembert's principle and by projecting the weight W and the inertia force on the direction of the tangent mn the following equation of motion will be obtained:

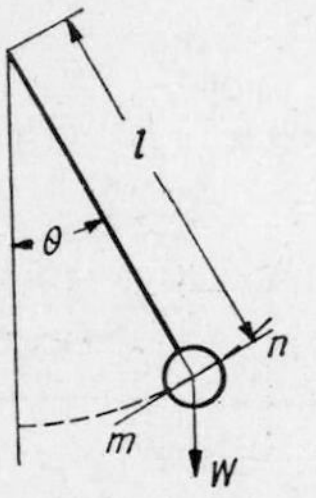

$$\frac{Wl}{g}\ddot{\theta} + W\sin\theta = 0$$

or

$$\ddot{\theta} + \frac{g}{l}\sin\theta = 0, \tag{b}$$

Fig. 101

in which l is length of the pendulum, and θ is angle between the pendulum and the vertical.

It is seen that only in the case of small amplitudes, when $\sin\theta \approx \theta$, the oscillations of such a pendulum can be considered as simple harmonic. If the amplitudes are not small a more complicated motion takes place and the period of oscillation will depend on the magnitude of the amplitude. It is clear that the restoring force is not proportional to the displacement but increases at a lesser rate so that the frequency will decrease with an increase in amplitude of vibration. Expanding $\sin\theta$ in a power series and taking only the two first terms of the series, the following equation, instead of eq. (b), will be obtained

$$\ddot{\theta} + \frac{g}{l}\,(\theta - \theta^3/6) = 0. \tag{c}$$

Comparing this equation with eq. (*a*) it is easy to see that the non-linear terms have opposite signs.   Hence by combining the pendulum with a horizontal stretched string (Fig. 102) attached to the bar of the pendulum at B and perpendicular to the plane of oscillation, a better approximation to isochronic oscillations may be obtained.

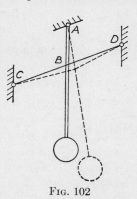

In Fig. 103*a* another example is given of a system in which the period of vibration depends on the amplitude.   A mass m performs vibrations between two springs by sliding without friction along the bar AB. Measuring the displacements from the middle position of the mass m, the variation of the restoring force with the displacement can be represented graphically as shown in Fig. 103*b*.   The frequency of the vibrations will depend not only

Fig. 102

on the spring constant but also on the magnitude of the clearance a and on the initial conditions.   Assume, for instance, that at the initial moment ($t = 0$) the mass m is in its middle position and has an initial velocity v in the x direction.   Then the time necessary to cross the clearance a will be

$$t_1 = \frac{a}{v}. \tag{d}$$

After crossing the clearance, the mass m comes in contact with the spring and further motion in the x direction will be simple harmonic.   The time

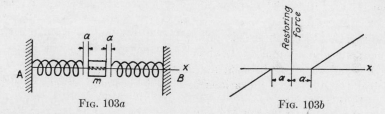

Fig. 103*a*   Fig. 103*b*

during which the velocity of the mass is changing from v to 0 (quarter period of the simple harmonic motion) will be (see eq. 3, p. 3)

$$t_2 = \frac{\pi}{2}\sqrt{\frac{m}{k}}, \tag{e}$$

where k is the spring constant for one spring.   The complete period of vibration of the mass m is

$$\tau = 4(t_1 + t_2) = \frac{4a}{v} + 2\pi \sqrt{\frac{m}{k}}. \qquad (f)$$

For a given magnitude of clearance, a given mass m and a given spring constant k, the period of vibration depends only on the initial velocity v. The period becomes very large for small values of v and decreases with increase of v, approaching the limit $\tau_0 = 2\pi \sqrt{m/k}$ (see Fig. 104) when

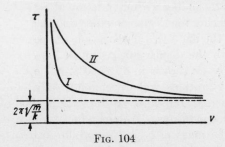

FIG. 104

$v = \infty$. Such conditions always are obtained if there are clearances in the system between the vibrating mass and the spring.

If the clearances are very small, the period τ remains practically constant for the larger part of the range of the speed v, as shown in Fig. 104 by curve I. With increase in clearance for a considerable part of the range of speed v a pronounced variation in period of vibration takes place (curve II, Fig. 104). The period of vibration of such a system may have any value between $\tau = \infty$ and $\tau = \tau_0$. If a periodic disturbing force having a period larger than τ_0 is acting, it will always be possible to give to the mass m such an impulse that the corresponding period of vibration will become equal to τ and in such manner resonance conditions will be established. Some heavy vibrations in electric locomotives have been explained in this manner.*

We may have another kind of non-linear system when the damping forces are not represented by a linear function of the velocity. For instance, the resistance of air or of liquid, at considerable speed, can be taken proportional to the square of the velocity and the equation for the vibratory motion of a body in such a resisting medium will no longer be a linear one, although the spring of the system may have a linear characteristic.

* See A. Wichert, "Schüttelerscheinungen in elektrischen Lokomotiven," *Forschungsarbeiten*, No. 277, 1924.

22. Free Vibrations of Systems with Non-linear Restoring Force.—If damping be neglected, the general equation of motion in this case has the form

$$\frac{W}{g}\ddot{x} + cf(x) = 0 \tag{a}$$

or

$$\ddot{x} + p^2 f(x) = 0, \tag{51}$$

in which $p^2 f(x)$ represents the restoring force per unit mass as a function of the displacement x. Observing that

$$\ddot{x} = \frac{d\dot{x}}{dt} = \frac{d\dot{x}}{dx}\dot{x} = \frac{1}{2}\frac{d(\dot{x})^2}{dx},$$

eq. (51) becomes

$$\frac{1}{2}\frac{d(\dot{x})^2}{dx} + p^2 f(x) = 0. \tag{b}$$

Assuming that the restoring force $p^2 f(x)$ is given by the curve *om* (Fig. 105) and that at time $t = 0$ the mass is at rest in its extreme position $[(x)_{t=0} = x_0, (\dot{x})_{t=0} = 0]$, we obtain, by integrating eq. (*b*),

$$\tfrac{1}{2}(\dot{x})^2 = -p^2\int_{x_0}^{x} f(x)\,dx = p^2\int_{x}^{x_0} f(x)\,dx, \tag{c}$$

which means that for any position of the vibrating mass its kinetic energy is equal to the difference of the potential energy which was stored in the spring initially, due to deflection x_0, and the potential energy at the moment under consideration. In Fig. 105 this decrease in potential energy is shown by the shaded area. If an analytical expression for the restoring force is given, the velocity $\dot{x}$ of the vibrating mass in any position is obtained by calculating the integral on the right side of eq. (*c*). If $f(x)$ is

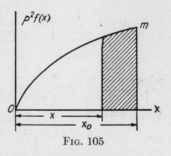

Fig. 105

given by a curve, graphical or numerical integration should be used.

Observing now that $\dot{x} = dx/dt$, we obtain from eq. (*c*)

$$dt = -\frac{dx}{\sqrt{2p^2\int_{x}^{x_0} f(x)\,dx}}. \tag{d}$$

The minus sign is taken since for the assumed initial condition x decreases with increase in time.

Integrating eq. (d), we obtain

$$t = -\int_{x_0}^{x} \frac{dx}{\sqrt{2p^2 \int_{x}^{x_0} f(x)\,dx}}, \qquad (e)$$

from which the time required for the mass to reach any position can be calculated. We are usually interested in the period of vibration τ. If the spring arrangement is symmetrical with respect to the middle position of the system, the time it takes the mass to move from the extreme position $(x = x_0)$ to the middle position $(x = 0)$ is equal to $\tau/4$ and we obtain, from eq. (e),

$$\tau = -4\int_{x_0}^{0} \frac{dx}{\sqrt{2p^2 \int_{x}^{x_0} f(x)\,dx}} = 4\int_{0}^{x_0} \frac{dx}{\sqrt{2p^2 \int_{x}^{x_0} f(x)\,dx}}. \qquad (f)$$

Let us consider now some particular cases. Assume first that the restoring force is given by the equation

$$p^2 f(x) = p^2 x^{2n-1}.$$

Substituting this into eq. (f), we obtain

$$\tau = \frac{4\sqrt{n}}{p}\frac{1}{x_0^{n-1}}\int_{0}^{x_0} \frac{d\left(\dfrac{x}{x_0}\right)}{\sqrt{1 - \left(\dfrac{x}{x_0}\right)^{2n}}} = \frac{4\sqrt{n}}{p}\frac{1}{x_0^{n-1}}\int_{0}^{1} \frac{du}{\sqrt{1 - u^{2n}}}, \qquad (52)$$

where $u = x/x_0$.

In the particular case, where $n = 1$ (linear spring), the integral of eq. (52) becomes

$$\int_{0}^{1} \frac{du}{\sqrt{1 - u^2}} = \mid \text{arc cos } u \mid_{1}^{0} = \frac{\pi}{2}$$

and we obtain

$$\tau = \frac{2\pi}{p}. \qquad (g)$$

When $n = 2$, i.e., the restoring force is proportional to x^3, eq. (52) gives

$$\tau = \frac{4\sqrt{2}}{p}\frac{1}{x_0}\int_{0}^{1} \frac{du}{\sqrt{1 - u^4}}. \qquad (h)$$

The numerical value of this integral is known * and is equal to $1.8541/\sqrt{2}$, so that

$$\tau = \frac{4}{px_0}\,(1.8541).$$

We see that in this case the period of vibration is inversely proportional to the amplitude. We have such vibrations, for example, in the case represented in Fig. 100, if the initial tension S in the wire be equal to zero.

If the tension S in Fig. 100 is not zero, we obtain a more general case of vibration in which the restoring force has the form

$$p^2 f(x) = p^2(x + \alpha x^3); \quad (\alpha > 0). \tag{i}$$

In such case, we have

$$\int_x^{x_0} f(x)\,dx = \frac{1}{2}\left(x_0^2 + \frac{\alpha x_0^4}{2}\right) - \frac{1}{2}\left(x^2 + \frac{\alpha x^4}{2}\right)$$

and eq. (f) gives

$$\tau = \frac{4}{p}\int_0^{x_0} \frac{dx}{\sqrt{\left(\dfrac{\alpha}{2}x_0^4 + x_0^2\right) - \left(\dfrac{\alpha x^4}{2} + x^2\right)}}$$

$$= \frac{4}{p}\int_0^{x_0} \frac{dx}{\sqrt{(x_0^2 - x^2)\left(1 + \dfrac{\alpha}{2}x_0^2 + \dfrac{\alpha}{2}x^2\right)}}.$$

To bring the elliptic integral on the right-hand side of this equation to standard form, we introduce the notations

$$x/x_0 = z, \quad \theta = \alpha x_0^2.$$

Then

$$\tau = \frac{4}{p}\int_0^1 \frac{dz}{\sqrt{(1 - z^2)(1 + \tfrac{1}{2}\theta + \tfrac{1}{2}\theta z^2)}}$$

$$= \frac{4}{p}\sqrt{\frac{2}{\theta}}\int_0^1 \frac{dz}{\sqrt{(1 - z^2)\left(\dfrac{2 + \theta}{\theta} + z^2\right)}}. \tag{j}$$

* See Jahnke-Emde, *Tables of Functions*, Berlin, p. 131, 1933.

In the tables we find *

$$\int_0^x \frac{dt}{\sqrt{(a^2 - t^2)(b^2 + t^2)}} = \frac{1}{c} F\left(\frac{a}{c}, \phi\right), \tag{k}$$

where $F(a/c, \phi)$ is the eliptic integral of the first kind, the values of which, for various values of a/c and ϕ, are given in the tables and

$$c^2 = a^2 + b^2, \quad \sin^2 \phi = \frac{c^2 x^2}{a^2(b^2 + x^2)}.$$

Comparing the integrals (j) and (k), we conclude that

$$a^2 = 1, \quad b^2 = \frac{2 + \theta}{\theta}, \quad c^2 = 1 + \frac{2 + \theta}{\theta} = \frac{2(1 + \theta)}{\theta},$$

$$x = 1, \quad \sin^2 \phi = 1, \quad \phi = \frac{\pi}{2}$$

and eq. (h) gives

$$\tau = \frac{4}{p} \frac{1}{\sqrt{1 + \theta}} F\left(\sqrt{\frac{\theta}{2(1 + \theta)}}, \frac{\pi}{2}\right). \tag{53}$$

If the deviation of the spring characteristic from linearity is very small we put $\theta = 0$ in eq. (i). Then we obtain for τ the value (g), found for the case of a linear spring. On the other hand if, in the expression (i), the first term is negligible in comparison with the second, α and θ become very large and, omitting unity in comparison with the terms containing θ in eq. (j), we obtain for τ expression (h).† For any intermediate condition, we obtain the period τ from eq. (53). It is necessary, in each particular case to calculate the numerical value of $\sqrt{\theta/2(1 + \theta)}$ and take from the tables the corresponding value of the elliptic integral.

In our derivation we assumed that with the increase of deflections the restoring force is increasing in a larger proportion than the deflection (eq. i). In the reversed case, we take for the restoring force the expression

$$p^2 f(x) = p^2(x - \alpha x^3); \quad (\alpha > 0). \tag{l}$$

---

* See above-mentioned tables, p. 130.

† The term $p\sqrt{\alpha}$ instead of p, appears here, since the restoring force, from eq. (i), is $p^2 \alpha x^3$, instead of $p^2 x^3$, used in the derivation of eq. (h).

Proceeding then in the same manner as before, we obtain

$$\tau = \frac{4}{p} \int_0^1 \frac{dz}{\sqrt{(1 - z^2)(1 - \frac{1}{2}\theta - \frac{1}{2}\theta z^2)}}$$

$$= \frac{4}{p} \sqrt{\frac{2}{\theta}} \int_0^1 \frac{dz}{(1 - z^2)\left(\dfrac{2 - \theta}{\theta} - z^2\right)}. \qquad (m)$$

In the tables we find for this case

$$\int_0^x \frac{dt}{\sqrt{a^2 - t^2}\sqrt{c^2 - t^2}} = \frac{1}{c} F\left(\frac{a}{c}, \phi\right), \qquad (n)$$

where $\sin \phi = \dfrac{x}{a}$.

Comparing the integrals (m) and (n), we conclude that

$$a^2 = 1, \quad c^2 = \frac{2 - \theta}{\theta}, \quad \sin \phi = x = 1$$

and obtain

$$\tau = \frac{4}{p} \sqrt{\frac{2}{2 - \theta}} F\left(\sqrt{\frac{\theta}{2 - \theta}}, \frac{\pi}{2}\right). \qquad (54)$$

Again, for any value of $\theta = \alpha x_0^2$, we can readily calculate τ by using tables of elliptic integrals.

Eqs. (i) and (l) for the restoring force with a proper selection of α can be used for an approximate calculation of τ in various cases of symmetrical springs. In a more general case, when the restoring force is given by a polynomial

$$f(x) = \alpha x + \beta x^2 + \gamma x^3,$$

the problem can be discussed also by using elliptic integrals.*

Another case of non-linear restoring force, in which a rigorous solution can be obtained, is represented by the theoretical pendulum in which case the differential equation is

$$\ddot{\phi} + p^2 \sin \phi = 0.$$

* See George Duffing, *Erzwungene Schwingungen bei veränderlicher Eigenfrequenz ...*, Braunschweig, 1918; also paper by A. Weigand, *Forsch. Gebiete Ingenieurw.*, Vol. 12, p. 274, 1941.

Proceeding as before, we obtain

$$\tfrac{1}{2}(\dot{\phi})^2 = p^2 \int_{\phi}^{\phi_0} \sin \phi \, d\phi = p^2(\cos \phi - \cos \phi_0)$$

and

$$\tau = \frac{4}{p\sqrt{2}} \int_0^{\phi_0} \frac{d\phi}{\sqrt{\cos \phi - \cos \phi_0}} = \frac{2}{p} \int_0^{\phi_0} \frac{d\phi}{\sqrt{\sin^2 \dfrac{\phi_0}{2} - \sin^2 \dfrac{\phi}{2}}}. \qquad (o)$$

Using the notation $k = \sin \dfrac{\phi_0}{2}$ and introducing a new variable θ in such a manner that

$$\sin \frac{\phi}{2} = k \sin \theta = \sin \frac{\phi_0}{2} \sin \theta, \qquad (p)$$

we find

$$d\phi = \frac{2k \cos \theta \, d\theta}{\sqrt{1 - k^2 \sin^2 \theta}}.$$

Substituting into eq. (o) and observing from eq. (p), that θ varies from 0 to $\pi/2$ while ϕ varies from 0 to ϕ_0, we obtain

$$\tau = \frac{4}{p} \int_0^{\frac{\pi}{2}} \frac{d\theta}{\sqrt{1 - k^2 \sin^2 \theta}}. \qquad (q)$$

We have again an elliptic integral of the first kind, the numerical values of which for any value of k can be taken from the tables. When the initial angle ϕ_0 is small, the quantity k is also small and we can neglect the term $k^2 \sin^2\theta$ in comparison with unity in eq. (q). The integral then becomes equal to $\pi/2$ and we obtain $\tau = 2\pi/p$.

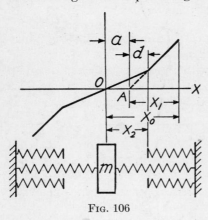

FIG. 106

In conclusion let us consider the case where the spring constant changes abruptly, as in Fig. 106. If the mass M is displaced by x_0 from the middle position and released without initial velocity, the equation of motion for the interval $x_2 < x < x_0$ represents simple harmonic motion with the center at A and is

$$x = a + x_1 \cos p_1 t, \qquad (r)$$

where $p_1{}^2$ is the spring constant per unit mass in the interval $x_2 < x < x_0$.

The time t_1 taken to pass from $x = x_0$ to $x = x_2$ is obtained from eq. (r) by substituting x_2 for x. Then

$$x_1 \cos p_1 t_1 = x_2 - a = d$$

and

$$t_1 = \frac{1}{p_1} \operatorname{arc} \cos \frac{d}{x_1}. \qquad (s)$$

In the interval $0 < x < x_2$ the mass M has a harmonic motion with the center at 0 and with the initial conditions (from eq. r)

$$(x)_{t=0} = x_2 \quad \text{and} \quad (\dot{x})_{t=0} = -x_1 p_1 \sin p_1 t_1.$$

Denoting by $p_2{}^2$ the spring constant for this interval, the equation of motion becomes

$$x = x_2 \cos p_2 t - \frac{x_1 p_1 \sin p_1 t_1}{p_2} \sin p_2 t.$$

The time t_2 taken to reach point O is found from the equation

$$0 = x_2 \cos p_2 t_2 - \frac{x_1 p_1 \sin p_1 t_1}{p_2} \sin p_2 t_2,$$

from which

$$t_2 = \frac{1}{p_2} \arctan \left(\frac{x_2 p_2}{x_1 p_1 \sin p_1 t_1} \right). \qquad (t)$$

Knowing t_1 and t_2, from eqs. (s) and (t), we obtain the period of oscillation

$$\tau = 4(t_1 + t_2).$$

We can proceed in a similar manner if there are more than two discontinuities in the spring constant, as represented by the polygon in Fig. 107. In a general case, when the spring characteristic is given by a curve, this curve can be replaced by a polygon and the above-described method can be used for the approximate calculation of the period of vibration.* Other approximate methods of investigation of free non-linear vibrations will be discussed in the following two articles.

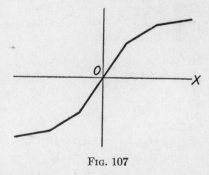

Fig. 107

* See K. Klotter, *Ing.-Arch.*, Vol. 7, p. 87, 1936.

23. Non-linear Vibrations: Graphical Method.—Let us consider again the differential equation for free non-linear vibrations of a single degree of freedom system in the form:

$$\ddot{x} + p^2 f(x) = 0. \tag{a}$$

We have seen in the preceding article that an analytical solution of this equation is likely to be cumbersome, or even impossible. In many practical cases, particularly where the restoring force $p^2 f(x)$ per unit mass is defined only by a graph, it may be necessary to resort to some kind of approximate step-by-step method of solution. Various approximate graphical methods of solution of differential equations have been developed and we shall discuss first a method proposed by Lord Kelvin,* which historically was perhaps one of the first.

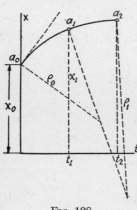

To show the wider possibilities of the method, we consider eq. (a) in the more general form:

$$\ddot{x} = f(x, t, \dot{x}). \tag{b}$$

The solution of this equation will represent the displacement x as a function of the time t. This function can be represented graphically by a time-displacement curve (Fig. 108). In order to obtain a definite solution the initial conditions, i.e., the initial displacement and initial velocity of the system must be known.

FIG. 108

Let $x = x_0$ and $\dot{x} = \dot{x}_0$ for $t = 0$.

Then the initial ordinate and initial slope of the time-displacement curve are known. Substituting the initial values of x and $\dot{x}$ in eq. (b), the initial value of $\ddot{x}$ can be calculated. Now from the known equation,

$$\rho = \frac{\sqrt{(1 + \dot{x}^2)^3}}{\ddot{x}}, \tag{c}$$

the radius of curvature ρ_0 at the beginning of the time-displacement curve can be found. By using this radius a small element $a_0 a_1$ of the time-

* See, Lord Kelvin, "On Graphic Solution of Dynamical Problems," *Phil. Mag.*, Vol. 34, 1892. The description of this and several other graphical methods of integrating differential equations can be found in W. Hort, *Die Differentialgleichungen des Ingenieurs*, Berlin, 2d Ed., 1925, which contains applications of these methods to the

displacement curve can be traced as an arc of a circle (Fig. 108) and the values of the ordinate $x = x_1$ and of the slope $\dot{x} = \dot{x}_1$ at the new point a_1 can be taken from the drawing and the corresponding value of $\ddot{x}$ calculated from eq. (b). Now from eq. (c) the magnitude of $\rho = \rho_1$ will be obtained by the use of which the next element a_1a_2 of the curve can be traced. Continuing this construction, as described, the time-displacement curve will be obtained graphically. The calculations involved can be somewhat simplified by using the angle of inclination of a tangent to the time-displacement curve. Let θ denote this angle, then

$$\dot{x} = \tan\theta \quad \text{and} \quad \ddot{x} = f(x, t, \tan\theta).$$

Substituting in eq. (c)

$$\rho = \frac{\sqrt{(1 + \tan^2\theta)^3}}{f(x, t, \tan\theta)} = \frac{1}{\cos^3\theta f(x, t, \tan\theta)}. \qquad (d)$$

In this calculation the square root is taken with positive sign so that the sign of ρ is the same as the sign of $\ddot{x}$. If $\ddot{x}$ is negative the center of curvature must be taken in such a manner as to obtain the curve convex up (see Fig. 108).

In the case of free vibration and by neglecting damping, eq. (b) assumes the form given in eq. (a) and the graphical integration described above becomes very simple, because the function f depends in this case only on the magnitude of displacement x. Taking for the initial conditions $x = x_0$ and $\dot{x} = 0$ for $t = 0$, the time-displacement curve will have the general form shown in Fig. 109. In the case of a system symmetrical about the middle position the intersection of this curve with the t axis will determine the period τ of the free vibration of the system. The magnitude of τ can always be de-

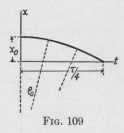

Fig. 109

termined in this manner with an accuracy sufficient for practical applications. In Fig. 109 for instance, the case of a simple harmonic vibration was taken for which the differential equation is

$$\ddot{x} + p^2x = 0$$

solution of technical problems. See also H. von Sanden, *op. cit.*, p. 100. Further development of such graphical methods, with applications to the solution of vibration problems, is due to Dr. E. Meissner. See his papers, "Graphische Analyse vermittels des Linienbildes einer Funktion," Kommissions verlag Rascher & Co., Zürich, 1932; *Schweiz. Bauzeitung*, Vol. 104, p. 35, 1934; *Z. angew. Math. u. Mech.*, Vol. 15, p. 62, 1935.

and the exact solution gives

$$\tau = \frac{2\pi}{p}.$$

Eq. (d) for this case becomes

$$\rho = \frac{1}{\cos^3 \theta p^2 x}. \tag{d'}$$

The initial displacement x_0 in Fig. 109 is taken equal to 20 units of length and ρ_0 equal to 100 units of length. Then from eq. (d') for $\theta = 0$, we obtain

$$\frac{1}{p} = \sqrt{20 \cdot 100} = 44.7 \text{ units.} \tag{e}$$

The quantity $1/p$ has the dimension of time and the length given by eq. (e) should be used in determining the period from Fig. 109. By measuring $\frac{\tau}{4}$ to the scale used for x_0 and ρ, we obtain from this figure

$$\frac{\tau}{4} = 69.5 \text{ units}$$

or by using (e)

$$\tau = 1/p \cdot \frac{4 \times 69.5}{44.7} = \frac{6 \cdot 22}{p}.$$

In this graphical solution only 7 intervals have been taken in drawing the quarter period of the time-displacement curve and the result obtained is accurate within 1%.

As another graphical way of solving eq. (b), we shall now describe an adaptation of the phase-plane method of Lamoën already discussed in Art. 19.* Taking the differential equation of motion in the general form of eq. (b), we assume only that the restoring force contains a term proportional to x and write, instead of eq. (b),

$$\ddot{x} + p^2[x + g(x, \dot{x}, t)]. \tag{f}$$

Now let us assume that during any small interval of time Δt, the function $g(x, \dot{x}, t)$ remains constant and equal to its value at the beginning of that

---

* This adaptation of the phase-plane construction to non-linear problems is due to L. S. Jacobsen and is discussed in more detail in his paper, "On a General Method of Solving Second Order Ordinary Differential Equations by Phase-Plane Displacements," *J. Appl. Mech.*, Dec. 1952.

interval.   Then introducing the notation

$$\delta_i = g(x, \dot{x}, t), \tag{g}$$

eq. (f) may be written in the simplified form:

$$\ddot{x} + p^2(x + \delta_i) = 0. \tag{55}$$

This equation, of course, is valid only for the interval of time t to $t + \Delta t$ for which δ_i has been calculated from expression (g).

We now take the general solution of eq. (55) in the form:

$$x = C_1 \cos pt_1 + C_2 \sin pt_1 - \delta_i, \tag{h}$$

where C_1 and C_2 are constants of integration, t_1 is the time from the beginning of the interval Δt under consideration, and δ_i has been treated as constant.   Differentiating expression (h) with respect to time gives

$$\dot{x} = -pC_1 \sin pt_1 + pC_2 \cos pt_1. \tag{i}$$

Denoting by x_i and $\dot{x}_i$ the displacement and velocity of the vibrating mass when $t_1 = 0$, we find from eqs. (h) and (i) that

$$C_1 = x_i + \delta_i \quad \text{and} \quad C_2 = \frac{\dot{x}_i}{p}. \tag{j}$$

Substituting these values back into expressions (h) and (i), we obtain

$$\left. \begin{array}{l} x = (x_i + \delta_i) \cos pt_1 + \dfrac{\dot{x}_i}{p} \sin pt_1 - \delta_i, \\[2mm] \dfrac{\dot{x}}{p} = -(\dot{x}_i + \delta_i) \sin pt_1 + \dfrac{\dot{x}_i}{p} \cos pt_1. \end{array} \right\} \tag{k}$$

Finally, squaring each of these equations and adding together, gives

$$(x + \delta_i)^2 + \left(\frac{\dot{x}}{p}\right)^2 = (x_i + \delta_i)^2 + \left(\frac{\dot{x}_i}{p}\right)^2. \tag{56}$$

Eq. (56) shows that the solution of eq. (55) is represented in the phase plane x vs. $\dot{x}/p$ by the arc of a circle, the center of which lies on the x-axis with coordinate $-\delta_i$.

To construct this phase-plane trajectory, we must know the initial values x_0 and $\dot{x}_0$ of the displacement and velocity of the vibrating mass when

$t = 0$. This determines the starting point A_0 in Fig. 110a and from expression (g) we find

$$\delta_0 = g(x_0, \dot{x}_0, 0),$$

which locates the first center C_0 in Fig. 110a. Now with C_0 as a center and C_0A_0 as a radius we draw the arc A_0A_1, subtending a small central angle $p \cdot \Delta t_1$ as shown. The coordinates $x_1, \dot{x}_1/p$ of point A_1 may now be used as new initial values for the second time interval Δt_2 and from eq. (g) we can find

$$\delta_1 = g(x_1, \dot{x}_1, \Delta t_1),$$

which locates the center C_1 in Fig. 110a. With this center and the radius C_1A_1, we make a second arc A_1A_2, again with a small central angle $p \cdot \Delta t_2$.[*]

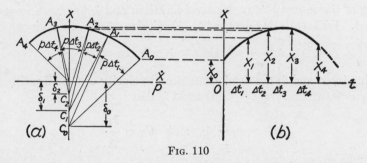

FIG. 110

The coordinates $x_2, \dot{x}_2/p$ may now be used as new initial conditions for the third step, and so on. In this way the phase-plane trajectory $A_0A_1A_2 \cdots$ may be carried as far as we like, after which the displacement-time curve $x = f(t)$ may be constructed as shown in Fig. 110b.

Reviewing the construction in Fig. 110a, it will be clear that a better approximate solution would have been obtained if a center C_0' somewhere between C_0 and C_1 has been used to construct the first arc A_0A_1, etc. This additional refinement of the method can be introduced as follows: with C_0 as a center, we make first a tentative estimate as to where point A_1 will fall and then use the average values $(x_0 + x_1)/2$ and $(\dot{x}_0 + \dot{x}_1)/2$ in eq. (g) to locate the improved center C_0' after which the arc A_0A_1' will be constructed. Repeating this step and half-step procedure for each arc, we can avoid the cumulative errors resulting from the use of δ_i at the beginning of each interval instead of the more appropriate use of the average δ_i through-

---

[*] Although convenient, it is not necessary that the time intervals Δt_i be the same for each step.

out the interval. This refinement will also allow the use of somewhat larger time intervals.

EXAMPLE

1. A mass m suspended from a spring having the characteristic

$$k(x) = k_0 + k_1 x^2$$

as shown in Fig. 111b is set in free vertical vibration with initial displacement $x_0 = 1$ in. and no initial velocity. Find the period of vibration for this particular amplitude, if

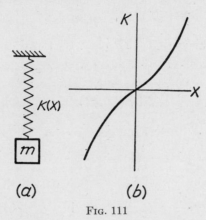

Fig. 111

the following numerical data are given: $mg = 1$ lb, $k_0 = 2$ lb per in., $k_1 = 4$ lb per in.[3].

Solution. Measuring displacement x from the equilibrium position, the equation of motion becomes

$$m\ddot{x} = -(k_0 + k_1 x^2)x. \qquad (l)$$

Introducing the notation $p = \sqrt{k_0/m} = 27.8$ sec^{-1}, we write eq. (l) as

$$\ddot{x} + p^2 \left[x + \frac{k_1}{k_0} x^3 \right] = 0, \qquad (m)$$

to agree with the general form of eq. (55).

We see that in this case the term

$$\delta_i = \frac{k_1}{k_0} x^3 = 2x^3 \qquad (n)$$

is a function of x only and this fact can be used to somewhat expedite the graphical solution of eq. (m) by the phase-plane method. We proceed as follows: from eq. (n), we construct the curve $\delta = 2x^3$ and superimpose it onto the phase plane in such a way that the x-axis of the δ-curve coincides with the x-axis of the phase plane (Fig. 112). We choose next a series of points a_0, a_1, a_2, $\cdots$ on this δ-curve, which define the steps in x that we propose to take, and draw through them the horizontal lines a_0A_0, a_1A_1, a_2A_2, $\cdots$, as shown. The mid-points of the segments a_0a_1, a_1a_2, a_2a_3, $\cdots$ are now projected onto the δ-axis and then carried around to the negative x-axis, giving us the centers C_0', C_1', C_2', $\cdots$, as shown. It will be noted that in this way we obtain centers corresponding to average values of δ_i for each step rather than initial values and hence improve the accuracy of the approximate solution. Now with A_0 as a starting point ($x_0 = 1$ in., $\dot{x}_0 = 0$), C_0' as a center and $C_0'A_0$ as a radius, we swing the arc A_0A_1 to its

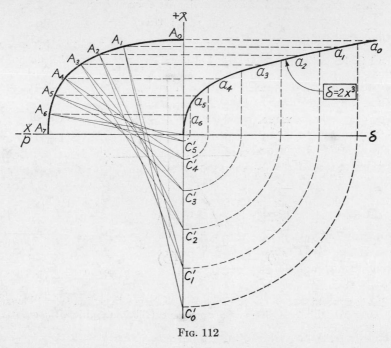

Fig. 112

intersection A_1 with the previously drawn horizontal through a_1. This completes the first step and the coordinates of A_1 in the phase plane define the displacement x_1 and the velocity $\dot{x}_1$ at the end of this step.

Next, with C_1' as a center and $C_1'A_1$ as a radius, we swing the arc A_1A_2 until it cuts the horizontal line through a_1, etc., etc. This procedure is continued until we reach point A_7 in the phase plane, which indicates that the motion has completed a quarter cycle since the system is symmetrical about the origin.

Measuring the angles $A_0C_0'A_1$, $A_1C_1'A_2$, etc., with a protractor and adding them together, we obtain

$$13\overset{\circ}{.}0 + 6\overset{\circ}{.}33 + 6\overset{\circ}{.}33 + 7\overset{\circ}{.}5 + 8\overset{\circ}{.}0 + 8\overset{\circ}{.}5 + 8\overset{\circ}{.}25 = 57\overset{\circ}{.}9 = 1.01 \text{ rad.}$$

Hence the period
$$\tau = \frac{4.04}{27.8} = 0.1452 \text{ sec.}$$

Using eq. (53) of Art. 22 and a table of elliptic functions, we find that the exact period in this case is $\tau = 0.1447$ sec. Thus the error in the graphical solution is $\frac{1}{3}\%$.

24. Free Non-linear Vibrations: Numerical Solution.—Non-harmonic vibrations as given by eq. (51) can also be solved in a numerical way. Consider as an example free vibration without damping. The corresponding differential equation is

$$\ddot{x} + p^2 f(x) = 0. \tag{a}$$

Let the initial conditions be

$$x = x_0, \quad \dot{x} = 0, \quad \text{for} \quad t = 0. \tag{b}$$

By substituting x_0 for x in eq. (a) the magnitude of $\ddot{x}_0$ can be calculated. By using the value $\ddot{x}_0$ of the acceleration at $t = 0$ the magnitude of $\dot{x}_1$ and x_1, i.e., the velocity and displacement at any moment t_1 chosen very close to the time $t = 0$ can be calculated. Let Δt denote the small interval of time between the instant $t = 0$ and the instant $t = t_1$. The approximate value of $\dot{x}_1$ and x_1 will then be obtained from the following equations:

$$\dot{x}_1 = \dot{x}_0 + \ddot{x}_0 \Delta t, \quad x_1 = x_0 + \frac{\dot{x}_0 + \dot{x}_1}{2} \Delta t. \tag{c}$$

Substituting the value x_1 for x in eq. (a), the value of $\ddot{x}_1$ will be obtained. By using this latter value better approximations for $\dot{x}_1$ and x_1 can be calculated from the following equations:

$$\dot{x}_1 = \dot{x}_0 + \frac{\ddot{x}_0 + \ddot{x}_1}{2} \Delta t \quad \text{and} \quad x_1 = x_0 + \frac{\dot{x}_0 + \dot{x}_1}{2} \Delta t. \tag{d}$$

A still better approximation for $\ddot{x}_1$ will now be obtained by substituting the second approximation of x_1 (eq. d in eq. a). Now, taking the second step, by using x_1, $\dot{x}_1$ and $\ddot{x}_1$ the magnitude of x_2, $\dot{x}_2$, $\ddot{x}_2$ for the time $t = t_2 = 2 \Delta t$ can be calculated exactly in the same manner as explained above. By taking the intervals Δt small enough and making the calculations for every value of t twice as explained above in order to obtain the second approximation, this method of numerical integration can always be made sufficiently accurate for practical applications.

In order to show this procedure of calculation and to give some idea of the accuracy of the method we will consider the case of simple harmonic vibration, for which the equation of motion is

$$\ddot{x} + p^2 x = 0.$$

The exact solution of this equation for the initial conditions (b) is

$$x = x_0 \cos pt, \quad \dot{x} = -x_0 p \sin pt. \tag{e}$$

The results of the numerical integration are given in Table I below. The length of the time intervals was taken equal to $\Delta t = 1/4p$. Remembering that the period of vibration in this case is $\tau = 2\pi/p$ it is seen that Δt, the inteval chosen, is equal approximately to $1/6$ of a quarter of the period τ. The second line of the table expresses the initial conditions. Now, for obtaining first approximations for $\dot{x}_1$ and x_1, at the time $t = \Delta t = 1/4p$, eqs. (c) were used. The results obtained are given in the third line of the table. For getting better approximations for $\dot{x}_1$ and x_1, eqs. (d) were used and the results are put in the fourth line of the table. Proceeding in this manner the complete table was calculated. In the last two columns the corresponding values of sin pt and cos pt proportional to the exact solutions (e) are given, so that the accuracy of the numerical integration can be seen directly from the table. We see that the velocities obtained by calculation always have a high accuracy. The largest error in the displacement is seen from the last line of the table and amounts to about 1% of the initial displacement x_0.

These results were obtained by taking only 6 intervals in a quarter of a period. By increasing the number of intervals the accuracy can be increased, but at the same time the number of necessary calculations becomes larger.

TABLE I

NUMERICAL INTEGRATION

t	x	$\dot{x}$	$\ddot{x}$	cos pt	sin pt
0	x_0	0	$-p^2x_0$	1	0
Δt	$0.9687x_0$	$-0.2500px_0$	$-0.9687p^2x_0$		
Δt	0.9692 "	-0.2461 "	-0.9692 "	0.9689	0.2474
$2\Delta t$	0.8774 "	-0.4884 "	-0.8774 "		
$2\Delta t$	0.8788 "	-0.4769 "	-0.8788 "	0.8776	0.4794
$3\Delta t$	0.7321 "	-0.6966 "	-0.7321 "		
$3\Delta t$	0.7344 "	-0.6783 "	-0.7344 "	0.7317	0.6816
$4\Delta t$	0.5419 "	-0.8619 "	-0.5419 "		
$4\Delta t$	0.5449 "	-0.8378 "	-0.5449 "	0.5403	0.8415
$5\Delta t$	0.3184 "	-0.9740 "	-0.3184 "		
$5\Delta t$	0.3220 "	-0.9457 "	-0.3220 "	0.3153	0.9490
$6\Delta t$	0.0755 "	-1.0262 "	-0.0755 "		
$6\Delta t$	0.0794 "	-0.9954 "	-0.0794 "	0.0707	0.9975
$7\Delta t$	-0.1719 "	-1.0153 "	-0.1719 "		
$7\Delta t$	-0.1680 "	-0.9838 "	-0.1680 "	-0.1792	0.9840

By using the table the period of vibration also can be calculated. It is seen from the first and second columns that for $t = 6\,\Delta t$ the time-displacement curve has a positive ordinate equal to $0.0794x_0$. For $t = 7\,\Delta t$ the ordinate of the same curve is negative and equal to $0.1680x_0$. The point of intersection of the time-displacement curve with the t-axis determines the time equal to a quarter of the period of vibration. By using linear interpolation this time will be found from the equation

$$\frac{1}{4}\,\tau = 6\,\Delta t + \Delta t\,\frac{0.0794}{0.0794 + 0.1680} = 6.32\,\Delta t = \frac{6.32}{4p} = \frac{1.58}{4p}.$$

The exact value of the quarter of a period of vibration is $\pi/2p \approx 1.57/p$. It is seen that by the calculation indicated the period of vibration is obtained with an error less than 1%. From this example it is easy to see that the numerical method described can be very useful for calculating the period of vibration of systems having a flexibility which varies with the displacement.*

A more general approach to the numerical solution of eq. (a) when initial conditions (b) are given is to write the solution $x = f(t)$ as a power series.† To show this, we take the differential equation of motion again in the more general form

$$\ddot{x} = \phi(x, \dot{x}, t). \tag{f}$$

Then by simple differentiation, we can easily obtain all higher derivatives:

$$\left.\begin{aligned}
\overset{\text{III}}{x} &= \phi'(x, \dot{x}, t), \\
\overset{\text{IV}}{x} &= \phi''(x, \dot{x}, t), \\
\overset{\text{V}}{x} &= \phi'''(x, \dot{x}, t).
\end{aligned}\right\} \tag{g}$$

Substituting the given initial values x_0 and $\dot{x}_0$, together with $t = 0$, in eqs. (f) and (g) and using Maclauren's formula

$$f(t) = f(0) + t \cdot f'(0) + \frac{t^2}{2!}f''(0) + \frac{t^3}{3!}f'''(0) + \cdots, \tag{h}$$

---

*A discussion of more elaborate methods of numerical integration of differential equations can be found in the previously mentioned books by W. Hort and by H. von Sanden (p. 124). See also, Runge-König, *Vorlesungen über numerisches Rechnen*, Berlin, 1924; and A. N. Krylov, *Approximate Numerical Integration of Ordinary Differential Equations*, Berlin, 1923.

† The method to be described is due to Viktor Blaess, "Zur angenäherten Lösung gewöhnlicher Differentialgleichungen," *Z. Ver. deut. Ing.* Vol. 81, pp. 587–596, 1937.

we may write the solution $x = f(t)$ in the following form:

$$x = x_0 + \dot{x}_0 t + \ddot{x}_0 \frac{t^2}{2} + \overset{\text{III}}{x_0} \frac{t^3}{6} + \overset{\text{IV}}{x_0} \frac{t^4}{24} + \overset{\text{V}}{x_0} \frac{t^5}{120} + \overset{\text{VI}}{x_0} \frac{t^6}{720} + \cdots. \quad (57)$$

We assume now that for very small values of t the series (57) converges rapidly, and take only the first three terms. Thus, for very small values of t,

$$\left. \begin{aligned} x &\approx x_0 + \dot{x}_0 t + \ddot{x}_0 \frac{t^2}{2}, \\ \dot{x} &\approx \dot{x}_0 + \ddot{x}_0 t. \end{aligned} \right\} \quad (i)$$

It will be noted that the use of these expressions amounts to approximating the actual motion by a fictitious one with constant acceleration

$$\ddot{x}_0 = \phi(x_0, \dot{x}_0, 0), \quad (j)$$

found by substituting the given initial values $x = x_0$, $\dot{x} = \dot{x}_0$, $t = 0$, into eq. (f). In this respect, the use of eqs. (i) would be identical with the use of eqs. (c) on p. 143. However, from this point on, we proceed in a slightly different manner. Instead of immediately seeking a better second approximation for x_1 and $\dot{x}_1$ at the end of the first small time interval Δt, as represented by eqs. (d) on p. 143, we use eqs. (i) as they stand and write

$$\left. \begin{aligned} x_1 &= x_0 + \dot{x}_0 \, \Delta t + \ddot{x}_0 \frac{(\Delta t)^2}{2}, \\ \dot{x}_1 &= \frac{1}{\Delta t} \left(\dot{x}_0 \, \Delta t + 2\ddot{x}_0 \frac{(\Delta t)^2}{2} \right). \end{aligned} \right\} \quad (k)$$

Now substituting these values together with $t = \Delta t$ into eq. (f), we find for the acceleration, at the end of the first interval,

$$\ddot{x}_1 = \phi(x_1, \dot{x}_1, \Delta t). \quad (l)$$

Then, using x_1, $\dot{x}_1$ and $\ddot{x}_1$ as new initial values in eqs. (i) we find for displacement and velocity at the end of the second interval Δt,

$$\left. \begin{aligned} x_2 &= x_1 + \dot{x}_1 \, \Delta t + \ddot{x}_1 \frac{(\Delta t)^2}{2}, \\ \dot{x}_2 &= \frac{1}{\Delta t} \left(\dot{x}_1 \, \Delta t + 2\ddot{x}_1 \frac{(\Delta t)^2}{2} \right) \end{aligned} \right\} \quad (m)$$

and so on. Such calculations lend themselves to very simple tabulations, as shown in Table II below.

TABLE II

NUMERICAL INTEGRATION

Step	Time	x_i	$\dot{x}_i \, \Delta t$	$\ddot{x}_i \dfrac{(\Delta t)^2}{2}$
0	0	x_0	$\dot{x}_0 \, \Delta t$	$\ddot{x}_0 \dfrac{(\Delta t)^2}{2}$
1	Δt	$x_1 = x_0 + \dot{x}_0 \, \Delta t + \ddot{x}_0 \dfrac{(\Delta t)^2}{2}$	$\dot{x}_1 \, \Delta t = \dot{x}_0 \, \Delta t + 2\ddot{x}_0 \dfrac{(\Delta t)^2}{2}$	$\ddot{x}_1 \dfrac{(\Delta t)^2}{2}$
2	$2 \, \Delta t$	$x_2 = x_1 + \dot{x}_1 \, \Delta t + \ddot{x}_1 \dfrac{(\Delta t)^2}{2}$	$\dot{x}_2 \, \Delta t = \dot{x}_1 \, \Delta t + 2\ddot{x}_1 \dfrac{(\Delta t)^2}{2}$	$\ddot{x}_2 \dfrac{(\Delta t)^2}{2}$
3	$3 \, \Delta t$	$x_3 = x_2 + \dot{x}_2 \, \Delta t + \ddot{x}_2 \dfrac{(\Delta t)^2}{2}$	$\dot{x}_3 \, \Delta t = \dot{x}_2 \, \Delta t + 2\ddot{x}_2 \dfrac{(\Delta t)^2}{2}$	$\ddot{x}_3 \dfrac{(\Delta t)^2}{2}$
4	$4 \, \Delta t$	$x_4 = x_3 + \dot{x}_3 \, \Delta t + \ddot{x}_3 \dfrac{(\Delta t)^2}{2}$	$\dot{x}_4 \, \Delta t = \dot{x}_3 \, \Delta t + 2\ddot{x}_3 \dfrac{(\Delta t)^2}{2}$	$\ddot{x}_4 \dfrac{(\Delta t)^2}{2}$
5	$5 \, \Delta t$	$x_5 = x_4 + \dot{x}_4 \, \Delta t + \ddot{x}_4 \dfrac{(\Delta t)^2}{2}$	$\dot{x}_5 \, \Delta t = \dot{x}_4 \, \Delta t + 2\ddot{x}_4 \dfrac{(\Delta t)^2}{2}$	$\ddot{x}_5 \dfrac{(\Delta t)^2}{2}$
—	Correction	$X_5 - x_5$	$\dot{X}_5 \, \Delta t - \dot{x}_5 \, \Delta t$	—
5c	$5 \, \Delta t$	X_5	$\dot{X}_5 \, \Delta t$	$\ddot{X}_5 \dfrac{(\Delta t)^2}{2}$
6	$6 \, \Delta t$	$x_6 = X_5 + \dot{X}_5 \, \Delta t + \ddot{X}_5 \dfrac{(\Delta t)^2}{2}$	$\dot{x}_6 \, \Delta t = \dot{X}_5 \, \Delta t + 2\ddot{X}_5 \dfrac{(\Delta t)^2}{2}$	$\ddot{x}_6 \dfrac{(\Delta t)^2}{2}$
7	$7 \, \Delta t$	$x_7 = x_6 + \dot{x}_6 \, \Delta t + \ddot{x}_6 \dfrac{(\Delta t)^2}{2}$	$\dot{x}_7 \, \Delta t = \dot{x}_6 \, \Delta t + 2\ddot{x}_6 \dfrac{(\Delta t)^2}{2}$	$\ddot{x}_7 \dfrac{(\Delta t)^2}{2}$
8	$8 \, \Delta t$	$x_8 = \cdots$	$\cdots$	$\cdots$

Having chosen a suitable time interval Δt, the table is built up line by line from left to right exactly as one reads the page of a book. With the exception of the values in the last column, each entry involves only simple addition (or subtraction) of previous items. At the end of each step, the entry in the last column is computed from formula (f) and this is often a simple operation also.

The procedure is continued for five steps as shown. Since the errors involved in the approximations represented by eqs. (i) are cumulative, it is not permissible to continue further without correcting these errors. This correction is made in the following manner: let X_5 and $\dot{X}_5$ denote more exact values of x_5 and $\dot{x}_5$ as obtained by inserting $t = 5\,\Delta t$ in the first seven terms of the series (57) and its first derivative with respect to time. Then, on the basis of the values already obtained in the first five steps, Blaess shows that the corresponding corrections are very nearly represented by the formulas: *

$$
\left.
\begin{aligned}
X_5 - x_5 &= \frac{45}{24}\ddot{x}_4\frac{(\Delta t)^2}{2} + \frac{100}{24}\ddot{x}_1\frac{(\Delta t)^2}{2} - \frac{145}{24}\ddot{x}_0\frac{(\Delta t)^2}{2}, \\
\Delta t\,(\dot{X}_5 - \dot{x}_5) &= \frac{11}{12}\ddot{x}_5\frac{(\Delta t)^2}{2} + \frac{5}{12}\ddot{x}_1\frac{(\Delta t)^2}{2} - \frac{16}{12}\ddot{x}_0\frac{(\Delta t)^2}{2}.
\end{aligned}
\right\}
\tag{58}
$$

Using these two correction formulas, we get a new set of starting values X_5 and $\dot{X}_5\,\Delta t$, as shown in line 5c of Table II, and then proceed with another five steps after which corrections are again made by using formulas (58) and so on.

Regarding the size of steps, we see that they must be small enough so that the series (57) still converges rapidly for a value of $t = 5\,\Delta t$. In discussing this matter, Blaess recommends, as a criterion, that Δt be so chosen that

$$
\left| \frac{\dfrac{\Delta t^2}{2}\ddot{x}_{n+1} - \dfrac{\Delta t^2}{2}\ddot{x}_n}{x_{n+1} - x_n} \right| < 0.01.
\tag{n}
$$

The significance of this criterion has the following basis. In making any one step from $t_n = n\,\Delta t$ to $t_{n+1} = (n+1)\,\Delta t$, we assume the initial acceleration $\ddot{x}_n$ to prevail over this interval. The displacement resulting from this acceleration alone is $\ddot{x}_n\dfrac{(\Delta t)^2}{2}$. At the end of the interval, we use eq. (f) and find $\ddot{x}_{n+1}$ which, in general, is different from $\ddot{x}_n$. If we use this final acceleration $\ddot{x}_{n+1}$ throughout the interval, the displacement due to acceleration alone is $\ddot{x}_{n+1}\dfrac{(\Delta t)^2}{2}$. Since the average acceleration for the interval lies somewhere between these two extreme values, it seems reasonable that the numerator of expression (n) represents the greatest possible error in displacement, due to using the initial acceleration throughout the interval. At the same tine, the denominator of expression (n) is approximately the amount of displacement that takes place. Thus, by using expression (n) as a criterion for selecting Δt, we are holding our calculations

* See the paper, *loc. cit.*, p. 145, for development of these formulas.

to something less than 1% error in each step, which is sufficient to obtain a high degree of accuracy from the correction formulas (58).

To illustrate the use of the Blaess method and to judge its accuracy, let us again consider the free vibrations of the system in Fig. 111 and discussed in Ex. 1 of the preceding article. Using the same numerical data as before, we have, from eq. (m) on p. 141,

$$\ddot{x} = -772(x + 2x^3). \tag{o}$$

Arbitrarily taking $\Delta t = 0.005$ sec, we have

$$\ddot{x}\frac{(\Delta t)^2}{2} = -0.00965(x + 2x^3). \tag{p}$$

Beginning now with $x_0 = 1$ in. and $\dot{x}_0 = 0$, we proceed according to Table II, as shown below in Table III.

TABLE III

NUMERICAL INTEGRATION

Step	Time	x_i	x_i^3	$x_i + 2x_i^3$	$\dot{x}_i\,\Delta t$	$\ddot{x}_i\dfrac{(\Delta t)^2}{2}$
0	0.000	1.000	1.000	3.000	0.000	−0.0290
1	0.005	0.978	0.935	2.848	−0.058	−0.0275
2	0.010	0.893	0.712	2.317	−0.113	−0.0224
3	0.015	0.758	0.436	1.630	−0.158	−0.0157
4	0.020	0.584	0.199	0.982	−0.189	−0.0095
5	0.025	0.385	0.057	0.499	−0.208	−0.0048
—	Corr.	+0.043	—	—	+0.023	—
5c	0.025	0.428	0.078	0.584	−0.185	−0.0056
6	0.030	0.237	0.013	0.263	−0.196	−0.0025
7	0.035	0.038	—	0.038	−0.201	−0.0004

The columns for x_i^3 and $x_i + 2x_i^3$ have been inserted as an aid to calculating values in the last column from eq. (p). At the end of step 5, corrections are made in accordance with formulas (58) and new starting values entered in line 5c. Noting that step 7 brings us almost to $x = 0$, we find by linear extrapolation and without further correction that $x = 0$ at $t = 0.036$ sec. Thus the period $\tau = 4 \times 0.036 = 0.144$ sec. Recalling again that the exact period given by eq. (53) is $\tau = 0.1447$, we see that the error by numerical integration is less than $\frac{1}{2}\%$.

25. Method of Successive Approximations Applied to Free Vibrations.—We begin with problems in which the non-linearity of the equation of motion is due to the non-linear characteristic of the spring. If the deviation of the spring characteristic from a linear law is comparatively small, the differential equation of the motion can be represented in the following form:

$$\ddot{x} + p^2 x + \alpha f(x) = 0, \qquad (59)$$

in which α is a small factor and $f(x)$ is a polynomial of x with the lowest power of x not smaller than 2. In the cases when the arrangement of the system is symmetrical with respect to the configuration of static equilibrium, i.e., for $x = 0$, the numerical value of $f(x)$ must remain unchanged when x is replaced by $-x$, and $f(x)$ must contain odd powers of x only. The simplest equation of this kind is obtained by keeping only the first term in the expression for $f(x)$. Then the equation of motion becomes

$$\ddot{x} + p^2 x + \alpha x^3 = 0. \qquad (60)$$

A system of this kind is shown in Fig. 100. Since there are important problems in astronomy which require studies of eqs. (59) and (60), several methods of handling them have been developed.* In the following, a general method is discussed for obtaining periodical solutions of eq. (60) by calculating successive approximations.

We begin with the calculation of the second approximation of the solution of eq. (60).† Since α is small it is logical to assume, as a first approximation, for x a simple harmonic motion with a circular frequency p_1, which differs only little from the frequency p. We then put

$$p^2 = p_1{}^2 + (p^2 - p_1{}^2), \qquad (a)$$

where $p^2 - p_1{}^2$ is a small quantity. Substituting (a) in eq. (60) we obtain:

$$\ddot{x} + p_1{}^2 x + (p^2 - p_1{}^2)x + \alpha x^3 = 0. \qquad (b)$$

Assuming that at the initial instant, $t = 0$, we have $x = a$, $\dot{x} = 0$, the harmonic motion satisfying these initial conditions is given by

$$x = a \cos p_1 t. \qquad (c)$$

This represents the first approximation to the solution of eq. (60) for the given initial conditions.

* These methods are discussed in a paper by A. N. Krylov, *Bull. Russian Acad. Sci.*, No. 1, p. 1, 1933. The method which is described in the following discussion is developed principally by A. Lindsted, *Mém. acad. sci. (St. Petersburg)*, Ser. 7, Vol. 31, 1883; and by A. M. Liapounoff in his doctoral thesis (Russian), 1892, dealing with the general problem on stability of motion, Kharkov, 1892.

† Such an approximation was obtained first by M. V. Ostrogradsky, *Mém. acad. sci. (St. Petersburg)*, Ser. 6, Vol. 3, 1840. A similar solution was given also by Lord Rayleigh in his *Theory of Sound*, Vol. 1, p. 77, 1894. The incompleteness of both these solutions is discussed in the above-mentioned paper by Krylov.

Substituting this expression for x into the last two terms of eq. (b), which are small, we obtain

$$\ddot{x} + p_1{}^2 x = -a(p^2 - p_1{}^2) \cos p_1 t - \alpha a^3 \cos^3 p_1 t$$

or, by using the relation

$$4 \cos^3 p_1 t = \cos 3p_1 t + 3 \cos p_1 t,$$

we find

$$\ddot{x} + p_1{}^2 x = - \left[a(p^2 - p_1{}^2) + \frac{3\alpha a^3}{4} \right] \cos p_1 t - \frac{\alpha a}{4} \cos 3p_1 t. \tag{d}$$

Thus we obtain apparently an equation of forced vibration for the case of harmonic motion without damping. The first term on the right side of the equation represents a disturbing element which has the same frequency as the frequency of the natural vibrations of the system. To eliminate the possibility of resonance we employ an artifice that consists in choosing a value of p_1 that will make,[*]

$$a(p^2 - p_1{}^2) + \frac{3\alpha a^3}{4} = 0.$$

From this equation we obtain

$$p_1{}^2 = p^2 + \frac{3\alpha a^2}{4}. \tag{e}$$

Combining eqs. (d) and (e) we find the following general solution for x:

$$x = C_1 \cos p_1 t + C_2 \sin p_1 t + \frac{\alpha a^3}{32 p_1{}^2} \cos 3p_1 t$$

To satisfy the assumed initial conditions we must put

$$C_1 = a - \frac{\alpha a^3}{32 p_1{}^2}$$

and

$$C_2 = 0$$

in this solution. From this it follows that the second approximation for x is

$$x = \left(a - \frac{\alpha a^3}{32 p_1{}^2} \right) \cos p_1 t + \frac{\alpha a^3}{32 p_1{}^2} \cos 3p_1 t. \tag{61}$$

It is seen that due to presence in eq. (60) of the term involving x^3, the solution is no longer a simple harmonic motion proportional to $\cos p_1 t$. A higher harmonic proportional to $\cos 3p_1 t$ appears, so that the actual time-displacement curve is not a cosine curve. The magnitude of the deviation from the simple harmonic curve depends on the magnitude of the factor α. Moreover, the fundamental frequency of the vibration, as we see from eq. (e), is no longer constant. It depends on the amplitude of vibrations a, and it increases with the amplitude in the case when α is positive. Such conditions prevail in the case represented by Fig. 100.

* This manner of calculating p_1 represents an essential feature of the method of successive approximation. If the factor before $\cos p_1 t$ in eq. (d) is not eliminated, a term in the expression for x will be obtained which increases indefinitely with the time t.

Expressions (e) and (61) can be put into the following forms:

$$p^2 = p_1{}^2 + c_1\alpha,$$

$$x = \varphi_0 + \alpha\varphi_1,$$

$$(f)$$

where

$$c_1 = -\frac{3a^2}{4}, \quad \varphi_0 = a \cos p_1 t,$$

$$\varphi_1 = \frac{a^3}{32 p_1{}^2} (\cos 3p_1 t - \cos p_1 t).$$

Thus the approximate expressions (f) for the frequency and for the displacement contain the small quantity α to the first power. If we wish to get further approximations, we take instead of expressions (f) the series:

$$x = \varphi_0 + \alpha\varphi_1 + \alpha^2\varphi_2 + \alpha^3\varphi_3 + \cdots$$

$$p^2 = p_1{}^2 + c_1\alpha + c_2\alpha^2 + c_3\alpha^3 + \cdots$$

$$(g)$$

which contain higher powers of the small quantity α. In these series φ_0, φ_1, φ_2, $\cdots$ are unknown functions of time t, p_1 is the frequency, which will be determined later, and c_1, c_2, $\cdots$ are constants which will be chosen so as to eliminate condition of resonance, as was explained above in the calculation of the second approximation. By increasing the number of terms in expressions (g) we can calculate as many successive approximations as we desire. In the following discussion we limit our calculations by omitting all the terms containing α in a power higher than the third. Substituting expressions (g) into eq. (60) we obtain:

$$\ddot{\varphi}_0 + \alpha\ddot{\varphi}_1 + \alpha^2\ddot{\varphi}_2 + \alpha^3\ddot{\varphi}_3 + (p_1{}^2 + c_1\alpha + c_2\alpha^2 + c_3\alpha^3)(\varphi_0 + \alpha\varphi_1 + \alpha^2\varphi_2 + \alpha^3\varphi_3)$$

$$+ \alpha(\varphi_0 + \alpha\varphi_1 + \alpha^2\varphi_2 + \alpha^3\varphi_3)^3 = 0. \quad (h)$$

After making the indicated algebraic operations and neglecting all the terms containing α to a power higher than the third, we can represent eq. (h) in the following form:

$$\ddot{\varphi}_0 + p_1{}^2\varphi_0 + \alpha(\ddot{\varphi}_1 + p_1{}^2\varphi_1 + c_1\varphi_0 + \varphi_0{}^3) + \alpha^2(\ddot{\varphi}_2 + p_1{}^2\varphi_2 + c_2\varphi_0 + c_1\varphi_1 + 3\varphi_0{}^2\varphi_1)$$

$$+ \alpha^3(\ddot{\varphi}_3 + p_1{}^2\varphi_3 + c_3\varphi_0 + c_2\varphi_1 + c_1\varphi_2 + 3\varphi_0{}^2\varphi_2 + 3\varphi_0\varphi_1{}^2) = 0. \quad (i)$$

This equation must hold for any value of the small quantity α which means that each factor for each of the three powers of α must be zero. Thus eq. (i) will split in the following system of equations:

$$\ddot{\varphi}_0 + p_1{}^2\varphi_0 = 0,$$

$$\ddot{\varphi}_1 + p_1{}^2\varphi_1 = -c_1\varphi_0 - \varphi_0{}^3,$$

$$\ddot{\varphi}_2 + p_1{}^2\varphi_2 = -c_2\varphi_0 - c_1\varphi_1 - 3\varphi_0{}^2\varphi_1,$$

$$\ddot{\varphi}_3 + p_1{}^2\varphi_3 = -c_3\varphi_0 - c_2\varphi_1 - c_1\varphi_2 - 3\varphi_0{}^2\varphi_2 - 3\varphi_0\varphi_1{}^2. \quad (j)$$

Taking the same initial conditions as before, i.e., for $t = 0$,

$$x = a \quad \text{and} \quad \dot{x} = 0$$

and substituting for x from eq. (g), we obtain:

$$\varphi_0(0) + \alpha\varphi_1(0) + \alpha^2\varphi_2(0) + \alpha^3\varphi_3(0) = a,$$

$$\dot{\varphi}_0(0) + \alpha\dot{\varphi}_1(0) + \alpha^2\dot{\varphi}_2(0) + \alpha^3\dot{\varphi}_3(0) = 0.$$

Again, since these equations must hold for any magnitude of α, we have:

$$\varphi_0(0) = a, \qquad \dot{\varphi}_0(0) = 0,$$

$$\varphi_1(0) = 0, \qquad \dot{\varphi}_1(0) = 0,$$

$$\varphi_2(0) = 0, \qquad \dot{\varphi}_2(0) = 0,$$

$$\varphi_3(0) = 0, \qquad \dot{\varphi}_3(0) = 0.$$

$$(k)$$

Considering the first of eqs. (j) and the corresponding initial conditions represented by the first row of the system (k) we find as before

$$\varphi_0 = a \cos p_1 t. \tag{l}$$

Substituting this first approximation into the right side of the second of eqs. (j) we obtain

$$\ddot{\varphi}_1 + p_1^2\varphi_1 = -c_1 a \cos p_1 t - a^3 \cos^3 p_1 t = -(c_1 a + \tfrac{3}{4}a^3) \cos p_1 t - \tfrac{1}{4}a^3 \cos 3p_1 t.$$

To eliminate the condition of resonance we will choose the constant c_1 so as to make the first term on the right side of the equation equal to zero.   Then

$$c_1 a + \tfrac{3}{4}a^3 = 0$$

and we find

$$c_1 = -\tfrac{3}{4}a^2. \tag{m}$$

The general solution for φ_1 then becomes

$$\varphi_1 = C_1 \cos p_1 t + C_2 \sin p_1 t + \frac{1}{32}\frac{a^3}{p_1^2} \cos 3p_1 t.$$

To satisfy the initial conditions given by the second row of the system (k), we put

$$C_1 + \frac{a^3}{32p_1^2} = 0,$$

$$C_2 = 0.$$

Thus

$$\varphi_1 = \frac{a^3}{32p_1^2} (\cos 3p_1 t - \cos p_1 t). \tag{n}$$

If we limit our calculations to the second approximation and substitute expressions (l), (m) and (n) into expressions (g), we obtain

$$x = a \cos p_1 t + \frac{\alpha a^3}{32 p_1^2} (\cos 3 p_1 t - \cos p_1 t), \qquad (o)$$

where

$$p_1^2 = p^2 + \tfrac{3}{4} a^2 \alpha. \qquad (p)$$

These results coincide entirely with expressions (f) which were previously obtained (see p. 152).

To obtain the third approximation we substitute the expressions (l), (m) and (n) into the right side of the third of eqs. (j) and obtain

$$\ddot{\varphi}_2 + p_1^2 \varphi_2 = -c_2 a \cos p_1 t + \tfrac{3}{4} a^2 \cdot \frac{a^3}{32 p_1^2} (\cos 3 p_1 t - \cos p_1 t)$$
$$-3a^2 \cos^2 p_1 t \cdot \frac{a^3}{32 p_1^2} (\cos 3 p_1 t - \cos p_1 t).$$

By using formulas for trigonometric functions of multiple angles we can write this equation in the following form:

$$\ddot{\varphi}_2 + p_1^2 \varphi_2 = -a \left(c_2 - \frac{3}{128} \frac{a^4}{p_1^2} \right) \cos p_1 t - \frac{3}{128} \frac{a^5}{p_1^2} \cos 5 p_1 t.$$

Again, to eliminate the condition of resonance, we put

$$c_2 = + \frac{3}{128} \frac{a^4}{p_1^2}. \qquad (q)$$

Then the general solution for φ_2 becomes

$$\varphi_2 = C_1 \cos p_1 t + C_2 \sin p_1 t + \frac{1}{1024} \frac{a^5}{p_1^4} \cos 5 p_1 t.$$

By using the third row of the system (k), the constants of integration are

$$C_1 = - \frac{1}{1024} \frac{a^5}{p_1^4},$$

$$C_2 = 0.$$

Thus we obtain

$$\varphi_2 = \frac{1}{1024} \frac{a^5}{p_1^4} (\cos 5 p_1 t - \cos p_1 t). \qquad (r)$$

If we limit the series (g) to terms containing α and α^2, we obtain the third approximation by using the above results for φ_0, φ_1, φ_2, c_1 and c_2:

$$x = a \cos p_1 t + \frac{\alpha a^3}{32 p_1^2} (\cos 3 p_1 t - \cos p_1 t) + \frac{\alpha^2 a^5}{1024 p_1^4} (\cos 5 p_1 t - \cos p_1 t) \qquad (s)$$

where p_1 is now determined by the equation

$$p_1^2 = p^2 + \frac{3}{4} a^2 \alpha - \frac{3}{128} \frac{a^4 \alpha^2}{p_1^2}. \qquad (t)$$

Substituting the expressions for φ_0, φ_1, φ_2, c_1 and c_2 in the last of eqs. (j), and proceeding as before, we finally obtain the fourth approximation

$$x = a \cos p_1 t + \frac{\alpha}{32} \frac{a^3}{p_1^2} (\cos 3p_1 t - \cos p_1 t) + \frac{\alpha^2}{1024} \frac{a^5}{p_1^4} (\cos 5p_1 t - \cos p_1 t)$$

$$+ \frac{\alpha^3}{32{,}768} \frac{a^7}{p_1^6} (\cos 7p_1 t - 6 \cos 3p_1 t + 5 \cos p_1 t), \quad (u)$$

in which

$$p_1^2 = p^2 + \frac{3}{4} \alpha a^2 - \frac{3}{128} \alpha^2 \frac{a^4}{p_1^2}. \quad (v)$$

Using expression (p), this becomes

$$p_1^2 = p^2 + \frac{3}{4} \alpha a^2 - \frac{3}{128} \alpha^2 \frac{a^4}{p^2} + \frac{9}{512} \alpha^3 \frac{a^6}{p^4}.$$

We see that the frequency p_1 depends on the amplitude a of the vibration. The time-displacement curve is not a simple cosine curve; it contains, according to expression (u), higher harmonics, the amplitudes of which, for small values of α, are rapidly diminishing as the order of the harmonic increases.

Let us apply the method to the case of vibration of a theoretical pendulum. Equation of motion in this case (see p. 126) is

$$\ddot{\theta} + \frac{g}{l} \sin \theta = 0.$$

Developing $\sin \theta$ in the series and using only the two first terms of this series we obtain

$$\ddot{\theta} + \frac{g}{l} \theta - \frac{g}{6l} \theta^3 = 0.$$

Taking for the frequency the second approximation (e) and denoting by θ_0 the angular amplitude, we find

$$p_1^2 = \frac{g}{l} - \frac{g}{8l} \theta_0^2.$$

Thus the period of oscillation is

$$\tau = \frac{2\pi}{p_1} = 2\pi \sqrt{\frac{l}{g}} \frac{1}{\sqrt{1 - \frac{1}{8}\theta_0^2}} \approx 2\pi \sqrt{\frac{l}{g}} \left(1 + \frac{1}{16} \theta_0^2\right).$$

This formula is a very satisfactory one for angles of swing smaller than one radian.

The method of successive approximations, applied to solutions of eq. (60), can be used also in the more general case of eq. (59).

The same method can be employed also in studying non-harmonic vibrations in which the non-linearity of the equation of motion is due to a non-linear expression for the damping force.* As an example let us consider the case when the damping force is proportional to the square of the velocity. The equation of motion is then

$$\ddot{x} + p^2 x \mp \alpha \dot{x}^2 = 0.$$

* Another method of solution of this problem is given by R. von Mises, *Elemente der Technischen Hydromechanik*, Berlin, p. 188, 1914.

The minus sign must be taken when the velocity is in the direction of the negative x-axis and the plus sign for the velocity in the direction of the positive x-axis. Taking $x = a$ and $\dot{x} = 0$ at the initial instant ($t = 0$), we have for the first half of the oscillation the equation

$$\ddot{x} + p^2 x - \alpha \dot{x}^2 = 0. \tag{a'}$$

Limiting our calculations to terms containing α^2, we put, as before,

$$x = \varphi_0 + \alpha \varphi_1 + \alpha^2 \varphi_2, \tag{b'}$$
$$p^2 = p_1{}^2 + c_1 \alpha + c_2 \alpha^2.$$

Substituting in eq. (a') and neglecting all terms containing α to powers higher than the second, we obtain the equation

$$\ddot{\varphi}_0 + p_1{}^2 \varphi_0 + \alpha(\ddot{\varphi}_1 + p_1{}^2 \varphi_1 - \dot{\varphi}_0{}^2) + \alpha^2(\ddot{\varphi}_2 + p_1{}^2 \varphi_2 + c_1 \varphi_1 + c_2 \varphi_0 - 2\dot{\varphi}_0 \dot{\varphi}_1) = 0$$

from which it follows that:

$$\begin{aligned}
\ddot{\varphi}_0 + p_1{}^2 \varphi_0 &= 0_0, \\
\ddot{\varphi}_1 + p_1{}^2 \varphi_1 &= \dot{\varphi}_0{}^2, \\
\ddot{\varphi}_2 + p_1{}^2 \varphi_2 &= -c_1 \varphi_1 - c_2 \varphi_0 + 2\dot{\varphi}_0 \dot{\varphi}_1.
\end{aligned} \tag{c'}$$

The initial conditions give

$$\begin{aligned}
\varphi_0(0) &= a, & \dot{\varphi}_0(0) &= 0, \\
\varphi_1(0) &= 0, & \dot{\varphi}_1(0) &= 0, \\
\varphi_2(0) &= 0, & \dot{\varphi}_2(0) &= 0.
\end{aligned} \tag{d'}$$

From the first of eqs. (c') and by using the first row of conditions (d'), we obtain the first approximation

$$\varphi_0 = a \cos p_1 t.$$

Substituting this into the right side of the second of eqs. (c'), we obtain:

$$\ddot{\varphi}_1 + p_1{}^2 \varphi_1 = a^2 p_1{}^2 \sin^2 pt = \tfrac{1}{2} a^2 p_1{}^2 (1 - \cos 2p_1 t).$$

The solution of this equation, satisfying the initial conditions, is then

$$\varphi_1 = \tfrac{1}{2} a^2 - \tfrac{2}{3} a^2 \cos p_1 t + \tfrac{1}{6} a^2 \cos 2p_1 t.$$

Substituting φ_0 and φ_1 in the right side of the third of eqs. (c') we obtain

$$\ddot{\varphi}_2 + p_1{}^2 \varphi_2 = -c_2 a \cos p_1 t - c_1(\tfrac{1}{2} a^2 - \tfrac{2}{3} a^2 \cos p_1 t + \tfrac{1}{6} a^2 \cos 2p_1 t)$$
$$- 2a^3 p_1{}^2 \sin p_1 t(\tfrac{2}{3} \sin p_1 t - \tfrac{1}{3} \sin 2p_1 t). \tag{e'}$$

We have on the right side of this equation two constants c_1 and c_2 and since there will be only one condition for the elimination of the possibility resonance, one of these constants can be taken arbitrarily. The simplest assumption is that $c_1 = 0$. Then eq. (e') can be represented in the following form:

$$\ddot{\varphi}_2 + p_1{}^2 \varphi_2 = (-c_2 a + \tfrac{1}{3} p_1{}^2 a^3) \cos p_1 t - \tfrac{2}{3} a^3 p_1{}^2$$
$$+ \tfrac{2}{3} a^3 p_1{}^2 \cos 2p_1 t - \tfrac{1}{3} a^3 p_1{}^2 \cos 3p_1 t. \tag{f'}$$

To eliminate the resonance condition we put

$$-c_2 a + \tfrac{1}{3} p_1{}^2 a^3 = 0$$

or

$$c_2 = \tfrac{1}{3} p_1{}^2 a^2. \tag{g'}$$

Then the general solution of eq. (f') is

$$\varphi_2 = C_1 \cos p_1 t + C_2 \sin p_1 t - \tfrac{2}{3} a^3 - \tfrac{2}{9} a^3 \cos 2 p_1 t + \tfrac{1}{24} a^3 \cos 3 p_1 t.$$

To satisfy the initial conditions represented by the third row of the system (d') we must put

$$C_1 = {}^{61}\!/_{72} a^3, \quad C_2 = 0,$$

and finally we obtain

$$\varphi_2 = -\tfrac{2}{3} a^3 + \frac{a^3}{72} (61 \cos p_1 t - 16 \cos 2 p_1 t + 3 \cos 3 p_1 t).$$

Substituting φ_0, φ_1, φ_2, c_1 and c_2 in expressions (b'), we obtain

$$x = a \cos p_1 t + \frac{\alpha a^2}{6} (3 - 4 \cos p_1 t + \cos 2 p_1 t)$$
$$- \frac{\alpha^2 a^3}{72} (48 - 61 \cos p_1 t + 16 \cos 2 p_1 t - 3 \cos 3 p_1 t) \tag{h'}$$

and

$$p^2 = p_1{}^2 + c_1 \alpha + c_2 \alpha^2 = p_1{}^2 + \tfrac{1}{3} p_1{}^2 a^2 \alpha^2,$$

from which

$$p_1 = \frac{p}{\sqrt{1 + \tfrac{1}{3} a^2 \alpha^2}}. \tag{i'}$$

The time required for half a cycle is

$$\frac{\tau_1}{2} = \frac{\pi}{p_1} = \frac{\pi}{p} \sqrt{1 + \tfrac{1}{3} a^2 \alpha^2} \approx \frac{\pi}{p} (1 + \tfrac{1}{6} a^2 \alpha^2) \tag{j'}$$

and the displacement of the system at the end of the half cycle is obtained from expression (h') by substituting $p_1 t = \pi$ into it. Then

$$(x)_{t = \pi/p_1} = a_1 = -a + \tfrac{4}{3} \alpha a^2 - {}^{16}\!/_9 \alpha^2 a^3. \tag{k'}$$

Beginning now with the initial conditions $x = a_1$, $\dot{x} = 0$ and using formulas (j') and (k'), we will find that the time required for the second half of the cycle is

$$\frac{\tau_2}{2} \approx \frac{\pi}{p} (1 + \tfrac{1}{6} a_1{}^2 \alpha^2)$$

and the displacement of the system at the end of the cycle is

$$a_2 = -a_1 + \tfrac{4}{3} \alpha a_1{}^2 - {}^{16}\!/_9 \alpha^2 a_1{}^3.$$

Thus we obtain oscillations with gradually decreasing amplitudes.*

* Another method of solving the problem on vibrations with damping proportional to the square of velocity is given by H. Burkhardt, *Z. Math. u. Phys.*, Vol. 63, p. 303, 1914. Tables for handling vibration problems with non-linear damping containing a term proportional to the square of velocity have been calculated by W. E. Milne, *loc. cit.*, p. 96.

26. Forced Non-linear Vibrations: Steady State.—In preceding articles, we have considered only free vibrations of systems with non-linear characteristics. We shall now consider an approximate method of studying the steady-state response of such a system to an external disturbing force.

Using the non-linear system in Fig. 100 as an example, and assuming a viscous damping together with a simple harmonic disturbing force, we may take the equation of motion in the form

$$\ddot{x} + \mu\dot{x} + p^2(x + \beta x^3) = q \cos(\omega t + \alpha) \qquad (a)$$

The general solution of this equation is not known and we must resort to an approximate investigation. From the non-linear character of the equation, we must realize that the method of superposition of vibrations which was always applicable in problems discussed in the first chapter is no longer valid. That is, even if the free vibrations of the system as well as its forced vibrations can be found, the sum of these two motions does not give the resultant vibrations. Also if there are several harmonics in the disturbing force, the resultant forced vibrations cannot be obtained by summing up vibrations due to each harmonic alone as was done in Art. 17.

To simplify the problem, we will discuss here only steady-state forced vibrations and will disregard the free vibrations depending on initial conditions. It will be assumed also that β is small, i.e., that the restoring force does not deviate greatly from a linear law. Then for an approximate particular solution of eq. (a), we can try

$$x = a \cos \omega t. \qquad (b)$$

This assumes that the steady-state forced vibrations will have the same angular frequency as the disturbing force that produces them, but leaves the amplitude a and the phase relation α to the disturbing force to be determined.

Substituting expression (b) into eq. (a) and noting that $\cos(\omega t + \alpha) = \cos \omega t \cos \alpha - \sin \omega t \sin \alpha$, we obtain

$$-a\omega^2 \cos \omega t - \mu a\omega \sin \omega t + p^2 a \cos \omega t + p^2\beta a^3 \cos^3 \omega t$$
$$= q \cos \alpha \cos \omega t - q \sin \alpha \sin \omega t \cdots. \qquad (c)$$

We see at once that this equation cannot be satisfied for all values of t but only for $t = n\pi/2\omega$, if n is limited to either odd or even integers. This means that by proper choice of amplitude a and phase-angle α, the assumed solution (b) can be made to satisfy the equation of motion for extreme or middle positions of the vibrating mass. Taking n as an even integer, we have $\cos \omega t = \pm 1$ and $\sin \omega t = 0$ and eq. (c) reduces to

$$p^2 a + p^2 \beta a^3 = q \cos \alpha + a \omega^2. \tag{d}$$

Taking n as an odd integer, we have $\cos \omega t = 0$ and $\sin \omega t = \pm 1$ and eq. (c) reduces to

$$\mu a \omega = q \sin \alpha. \tag{e}$$

For any value of ω, eqs. (d) and (e) may now be used to determine the approximate amplitude a and phase-angle α of the steady-state forced vibrations. From eq. (e) we have

$$\sin \alpha = \frac{\mu a \omega}{q} \tag{f}$$

and

$$\cos \alpha = \pm \sqrt{1 - \frac{\mu^2}{q^2} (a\omega)^2}. \tag{g}$$

Substituting expression (g) for $\cos \alpha$ into eq. (d), we obtain

$$p^2 a + p^2 \beta a^3 = \pm q \sqrt{1 - \frac{\mu^2}{q^2} (a\omega)^2} + a \omega^2. \tag{62}$$

For any given system, i.e., for given values of p^2, β, q, and μ, this algebraic equation defines approximately the relation between the amplitude a and the impressed frequency ω for steady-state forced vibrations. Its solution can be obtained graphically as follows:

The left-hand side of eq. (62) is seen to represent the restoring force per unit mass for an extreme position and, knowing the spring characteristics, this can be plotted as a function of a as shown by the curve OA in Fig. 113. For a chosen value of ω, the right-hand side of eq. (62) may also be considered as a function of a and we see that it consists of two branches DC and EC in Fig. 113 having, respectively, the intercepts $\pm q$ on the $f(a)$-axis and the common asymptote OCB with a slope equal to the chosen ω^2. Furthermore, we see that these two branches join the asymptote at a point C defined by

$$a_{cr} = q/\mu\omega \tag{h}$$

and that they are imaginary for $a > q/\mu\omega$. The points of intersection F, G and H determine, in general, three values of a which, for the chosen value of ω, can satisfy eq. (62).

If we make the constructions in Fig. 113 for a series of values of ω and determine the intersections with the curve OA, we can construct, for a given system, a so-called *response diagram* showing possible amplitudes of steady-state forced vibrations of the system for all values of the impressed frequency ω of the disturbing force. A little study of Fig. 113 will show that for small values of ω, the lower branch EC of the curve representing the right-hand side of eq. (62) will miss the curve OA completely and we get only the intersection F defining the value a_1. Also from eq. (h), we see that as we take larger values of ω the point C, beyond which the right-hand side

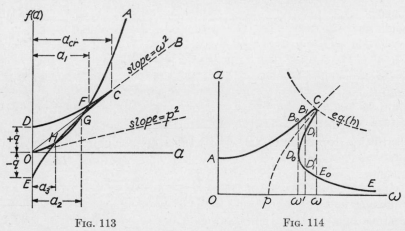

FIG. 113   FIG. 114

of eq. (62) becomes imaginary, may fall inside the curve OA, in which case we again get only one intersection H defining the value a_3. Thus the response diagram will have the general form shown in Fig. 114. Starting with $\omega = 0$, we find that for each chosen ω up to a certain value ω', we get only one intersection F of the upper branch with the curve OA in Fig. 113, and in this way the portion AB_0 of the response curve in Fig. 114 is established. For the value $\omega = \omega'$ the lower branch just touches the curve OA in Fig. 113 for the first time, and we get simultaneously with point B_0 in Fig. 114 a point D_0. Thereafter for each value $\omega' < \omega < \omega_{cr}$ we get three intersections in Fig. 113 as shown by F, G and H, and three points such as B_1, D_1, D_1' in Fig. 114. Finally, we reach a value of $\omega = \omega_{cr}$ for which the point C in Fig. 113 falls on the curve OA and we get only two intersections defining amplitudes represented by points C and E_0 in Fig. 114. For each chosen value of $\omega > \omega_{cr}$ the point C falls inside the curve OA in Fig. 113 and we get only intersections H of the lower branch defining points along the portion E_0E of the response curve in Fig. 114. In this way the response diagram in Fig. 114 is completed for one chosen value of the ratio q/μ. Taking a series of values of q/μ, a family of response curves can be constructed similar to those shown in Fig. 60 for a linear system.

If we take $q = 0$ in eq. (62), we get the case of *free vibrations* of the system with non-linear restoring force. In such case, eq. (62) reduces to

$$p^2a + p^2\beta a^3 = a\omega^2 \qquad (62')$$

and we see that an approximate relation between amplitude a and angular frequency ω of free vibrations is easily obtained by intersections of the straight line OB with the curve OA in Fig. 113. In this way the dotted curve in Fig. 114 is obtained. If we plot the hyperbola represented by eq. (h) in Fig. 114, we see that its intersection with the free vibration curve also determines the point C at which the response curve crosses the free vibration curve. Thus for any chosen ratio q/μ, the maximum possible amplitude of steady-state forced vibration can easily be found without the necessity to construct the entire response curve.

Returning to eq. (f), we see that for small values of ω the phase-angle α is small and that it gradually grows to $\pi/2$ as ω approaches ω_{cr}. Thus at resonance the disturbing force leads the forced motion by a full quarter cycle as in the case of a linear system. Remembering that for $\omega > \omega_{cr}$ we get intersections in Fig. 113 only from the lower branch corresponding to the minus sign in eq. (62), we conclude from eq. (g) that $\cos \alpha$ is negative and therefore that $\alpha > \pi/2$ for large values of ω.

Referring to Fig. 114, we may now describe what may be expected to happen in the case of damped non-linear forced vibrations if, starting with $\omega = 0$, we gradually increase the frequency of the disturbing force. At first both the amplitude a and the phase-angle α will grow with ω until we reach the value ω_{cr}. Here, as we have already observed, the disturbing force leads the motion by a full quarter cycle and no further increase in amplitude can occur. As soon as ω is increased slightly beyond ω_{cr}, the motion changes form completely; the amplitude falls to E_0 and the disturbing force leads the new motion by something more than a quarter cycle. With further increase in ω, the amplitude gradually falls along the curve E_0E and the phase-angle α approaches π. Now if we reverse the procedure and begin gradually to decrease ω, the amplitude grows according to the curve ED_0 until we reach the value ω'. Since there is only one solution of eq. (62) for values of $\omega < \omega'$, a further decrease in ω will be accompanied by a sudden jump in amplitude to B_0 and a change in the phase angle from something greater than $\pi/2$ to something less than $\pi/2$. Then with further decrease in ω, the amplitude gradually falls according to the curve B_0A. Experiments * verify this general prediction of behavior and show that conditions represented by points along the portion CD_0 of the response curve cannot be

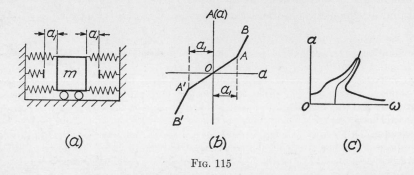

(a)   (b)   (c)

Fig. 115

realized in a true physical system. It has recently been shown by K. Klotter that solutions of eq. (62) represented by points on the portion CD_0

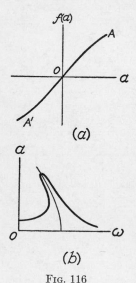

(a)

(b)

Fig. 116

of the response curve in Fig. 114 represent dynamically unstable conditions and this explains the failure to observe them in actual physical systems.†

To apply the graphical method discussed above, the restoring force need not necessarily be exactly the cubic parabola represented by the left-hand side of eq. (62). In general, if the curve OA in Fig. 113 is symmetrical about the origin and does not depart too greatly from a straight line, we may proceed with the graphical solution as described. The method is, of course, always approximate, except in the case of a true linear-restoring force.

For the arrangement shown in Fig. 115a, we have a so-called bilinear restoring force as shown in Fig. 115b. The graphical solution illustrated in Fig. 113 is applicable to this case also if the restoring force is symmetrical about the origin and if there is not too great a difference in the slopes of

* The first experiments of this kind were made by O. Martienssen working with analogous electric current vibrations, see *Phys. Z.* Vol. 11, p. 448, 1910. Similar experiments with mechanical systems were made by G. Duffing, p. 40, *loc. cit.*

† See K. Klotter and E. Pinney, "A Comprehensive Stability Criterion for the Forced Vibrations of Non-linear Systems," *J. Appl. Mech.*, Vol. 20, p. 9, 1953.

the lines OA and AB in Fig. 115b. In such case we obtain for a given case a response diagram as shown in Fig. 115c.

If a one degree of freedom system has a restoring force characteristic as shown in Fig. 116a, we may again proceed as illustrated in Fig. 113 and will find a response diagram of the type shown in Fig. 116b.

In the foregoing discussion of forced vibrations, we assumed that the frequency of this vibration is the same as the frequency of the disturbing force. In the case of non-linear spring characteristics, however, a harmonic force $q \cos \omega t$ may sometimes produce large vibrations of lower frequencies, such as $\frac{1}{2}\omega$, $\frac{1}{3}\omega$. This phenomenon is called *sub-harmonic resonance*. The theoretical investigation of this phenomenon is a complicated one * and we limit our discussion here to an elementary consideration which gives some explanation of the phenomenon. Let us take, as an example, the case of eq. (60) discussed in the previous article. It was shown that the free vibrations in this case do not represent a simple harmonic motion and that their approximate expression contains also a higher harmonic of the third order, so that for the displacement x we can take the expression

$$x = a \cos \omega t + b \cos 3\omega t. \qquad (i)$$

If there is no exciting force, this vibration, owing to unavoidable friction, will be gradually damped out. Assume now that a pulsating force $q \cos (3\omega t + \beta)$ is acting on the system. On the displacements (i) it will produce the following work per cycle $\tau = 2\pi/\omega$:

$$\int_0^\tau q \cos (3\omega t + \beta)\dot{x}\, dt = -a\omega q \int_0^\tau \sin \omega t \cos (3\omega t + \beta)\, dt - 3b\omega q \int_0^\tau \sin 3\omega t \cos (3\omega t + \beta)\, dt.$$

The first term on the right side of this expression vanishes while the second term gives $3\pi bq \sin \beta$. Thus, due to the presence of the higher harmonic in expression (i), the assumed pulsating force produces work depending on the phase difference β. By a proper choice of the phase angle we may get an amount of work compensating for the energy dissipated due to damping. Thus the assumed pulsating force of frequency 3ω may maintain vibrations (i) having frequency ω and we obtain the phenomenon of sub-harmonic resonance.†

27. Application of Ritz Method in Non-linear Vibrations.—Let us consider now a more general method of approximate solution of non-linear vibration problems based on the application of the Ritz method ‡ in

* The theory of non-linear vibrations has been considerably developed in recent years, principally in connection with radio engineering. We will mention here important publications by Dr. B. van der Pol, *Phil. Mag.*, Ser. 7, Vol. 3, p. 65, 1927; A. Andronov, *Comptes rend.*, Vol. 189, p. 559, 1929; A. Andronov and A. Witt, *ibid.*, Vol. 190, p. 256, 1930; L. Mandelstam and N. Papalexi, *Z. Physik*, Vol. 73, p. 233, 1931; A. N. Krylov and N. Bogoliubov, *Schweiz. Bauzeitung*, Vol. 103, 1934.

† The possibility of such a phenomenon in mechanical systems was indicated by J. G. Baker, *Trans. A.S.M.E.*, Vol. 54, p. APM-162, 1932.

‡ The first application of Ritz method in solving non-linear vibration problems is due to G. Duffing, p. 130, *loc. cit.* The application of the method to several particular cases

solving the corresponding non-linear equation of motion. In a general case this equation has the form

$$\ddot{x} + 2ng(\dot{x}) + p^2f(x) - F(t) = 0, \tag{63}$$

where $g(\dot{x})$ and $f(x)$ are some given functions of the velocity $\dot{x}$ and of the displacement x, and $F(t)$ is the disturbing force per unit mass, n and p^2 being constants defining, respectively, the magnitudes of the resisting force and restoring force per unit mass of the system.

Eq. (63) can be considered as an equation of equilibrium in which the inertia force is balanced by the resisting force, the spring force, and the disturbing force. The work done by this system of forces on any virtual displacement δx must vanish and we have

$$[\ddot{x} + 2ng(\dot{x}) + p^2f(x) - F(t)]\,\delta x = 0. \tag{64}$$

In applying the Ritz method, we assume as an approximate solution for the steady-state forced vibrations a series

$$x = a_1\phi_1(t) + a_2\phi_2(t) + a_3\phi_3(t) + \cdots, \tag{65}$$

in which $\phi_1(t)$, $\phi_2(t)$, $\cdots$ are properly selected functions of time and a_1, a_2, $\cdots$ parameters, which have to be determined in such a way as to make the series (65), with a limited number of terms, as good an approximation for x as possible. Virtual displacements then have the form

$$\delta x = \delta a_n\phi_n(t).$$

Substituting this for δx and the series (65) for x into eq. (64), we will usually find that the equation is not satisfied at every instant t and some work on the assumed virtual displacement is produced, since the series (65) is not an exact solution for x but only an approximation. To get the approximation as accurate as possible, we select now the parameters a_1, a_2, $\cdots$ so as to make the average value of the virtual work (64) per cycle vanish, which give us equations of the following form: *

$$\int_0^\tau [\ddot{x} + 2ng(\dot{x}) + p^2f(x) - F(t)]\phi_n(t)\,dt = 0, \tag{66}$$

in which we have to substitute the series (65) for x and make the integration

---

was made by A. Lourié and A. Tchekmarev, *Acad. Sci. Publ.*, Sect. Appl. Math. Mech. (Moscow), Vol. 1, No. 3, p. 307, 1938. In recent times the method was used in a variety of cases by K. Klotter; see his paper presented at the Chicago National Meeting of Applied Mechanics, 1951.

* We may come to the same equations by using Hamilton's principle. See Timoshenko and D. H. Young, *Advanced Dynamics*, New York, p. 234, 1948.

over the period τ of one cycle. In this way as many algebraic equations as the number of terms in the series (65) are obtained and by solving them we find the proper values of all the parameters $a_1, a_2, \cdots$. Comparing this method of approximate solution with that of the previous article, we see that in the latter case the amplitude of vibration was selected so as to satisfy the equation of motion only at the instants when the vibrating system is in an extreme or middle position. In applying the Ritz method, we select the amplitudes $a_1, a_2, \cdots$ so as to make the average value per cycle of the virtual work vanish. In this way we can expect to get a better approximate solution than before. Let us apply now this *averaging method* to some examples.

As a first example we consider the case in which there is no damping and the equation of motion is

$$\ddot{x} + p^2(x + \beta x^3) = q \cos \omega t.$$

Forced vibrations will be symmetrical with respect to the middle position $(x = 0)$, and without damping will be either in phase or completely out of phase with the disturbing force. As a first approximation we can assume

$$x = a_1 \phi_1(t) = \pm a_1 \cos \omega t \tag{67}$$

and eq. (66) becomes

$$\int_0^\tau [\ddot{x} + p^2(x + \beta x^3) - q \cos \omega t] \cos \omega t \, dt = 0.$$

Substituting expression (67) in this and observing that

$$\int_0^\tau \cos^2 \omega t \, dt = \frac{1}{\omega} \int_0^{2\pi} \cos^2 \omega t \, d(\omega t) = \frac{\pi}{\omega}$$

and

$$\int_0^\tau \cos^4 \omega t \, dt = \frac{1}{\omega} \int_0^{2\pi} \cos^4 \omega t \, d(\omega t) = \frac{3}{4} \frac{\pi}{\omega},$$

we obtain

$$p^2 a_1 + \tfrac{3}{4}\beta p^2 a_1{}^3 = \mp q + a_1 \omega^2. \tag{68}$$

Comparing this with eq. (62) of the preceding article for the case of no damping ($\mu = 0$), we see that they differ only slightly due to the appearance of $\tfrac{3}{4}\beta$ on the left side instead of β. This shows the improvement due to using the averaging method. As a second approximation satisfying the condition of symmetry we can take

$$x = a_1 \cos \omega t + a_2 \cos 3\omega t.$$

From eq. (66) we obtain then two algebraic cubic equations which can be numerically solved for a_1 and a_2 for any system of particular values of constants p^2, ω^2, β, q.

Another case, in which the averaging method can be used to advantage, we have when the spring characteristic is represented by two straight lines (Fig. 115a). The first approximation taken in the form (67) already gives a satisfactory agreement with the rigorous solution, which in this case is known.* Fig. 117 shows a typical set of response curves obtained for a

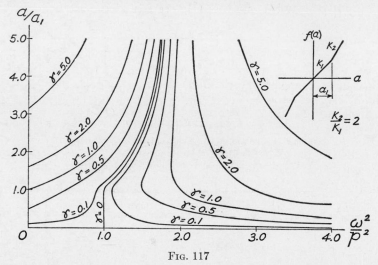

FIG. 117

bilinear system without damping by use of the one-term approximation and the averaging method.† To make the parameters dimensionless, values of a/a_1 are plotted against values of ω^2/p^2 for several values of $\gamma = Q/k_1 a_1$. The equation of motion is

$$\ddot{x} + p^2 f(x) = \frac{Q}{m} \sin \omega t,$$

where $p^2 = k_1/m$.

Let us consider now vibrations with damping and assume a damping force proportional to velocity and the spring characteristic, the same as in the first example, so that the differential equation of motion is

$$\ddot{x} + 2n\dot{x} + p^2(x + \beta x^3) = q \cos \omega t. \tag{69}$$

* See the paper by J. P. Den Hartog and R. M. Heiles, *J. Appl. Mech.*, Vol. 3, p. 127, 1936.

† These curves are taken from the paper by Klotter referred to on p. 164.

The steady forced vibration in this case will not be in phase with the disturbing force and we assume, as a first approximation,

$$x = c \cos(\omega t - \alpha) = a \cos \omega t + b \sin \omega t, \tag{70}$$

where $c^2 = a^2 + b^2$, $\tan \alpha = a/b$.

For determining the two constants a and b by the averaging method, we use two equations of the form (66), which in this case become

$$\int_0^\tau [\ddot{x} + 2n\dot{x} + p^2(x + \beta x^3) - q \cos \omega t] \cos \omega t \, dt = 0,$$

$$\int_0^\tau [\ddot{x} + 2n\dot{x} + p^2(x + \beta x^3) - q \cos \omega t] \sin \omega t \, dt = 0.$$

Substituting expression (70) for x and performing the indicated integrations, we obtain the following equations for calculating the amplitude and the phase of forced vibrations:

$$-a\omega^2 + 2n\omega b + p^2(a + \tfrac{3}{4}\beta ac^2) - q = 0,$$

$$-b\omega^2 - 2n\omega a + p^2(b + \tfrac{3}{4}\beta bc^2) = 0,$$

or, substituting $a = c \cos \omega t$, $b = c \sin \omega t$, we obtain

$$\left.\begin{aligned} -\omega^2 \cos \alpha + 2n\omega \sin \alpha + p^2(1 + \tfrac{3}{4}\beta c^2) \cos \alpha - \frac{q}{c} = 0, \\ -\omega^2 \sin \alpha - 2n\omega \cos \alpha + p^2(1 + \tfrac{3}{4}\beta c^2) \sin \alpha = 0. \end{aligned}\right\} \tag{71}$$

Multiplying the first of these equations by $\cos \alpha$ and the second by $\sin \alpha$ and adding them, we obtain

$$-\omega^2 + p^2(1 + \tfrac{3}{4}\beta c^2) = \frac{q}{c} \cos \alpha.$$

Multiplying the first equation by $\sin \alpha$ and the second by $\cos \alpha$ and subtracting the second from the first, we find

$$2n\omega = \frac{q}{c} \sin \alpha.$$

From the last two equations we find

$$\left.\begin{aligned} [-\omega^2 + p^2(1 + \tfrac{3}{4}\beta c^2)]^2 + 4n^2\omega^2 = \left(\frac{q}{c}\right)^2, \\ \tan \alpha = \frac{2n\omega}{-\omega^2 + p^2(1 + \tfrac{3}{4}\beta c^2)}. \end{aligned}\right\} \tag{72}$$

From these two equations the amplitude c and the phase-angle α can be calculated in each particular case. If there is no friction we find $\alpha = 0$ or π and the first of eqs. (72) coincides with the previously obtained eq. (68). Comparing the first of eqs. (72) with eq. (62) of the preceding article and noting that $\mu = 2n$, we see again that they differ only in the appearance of $\frac{3}{4}\beta$ in place of β.

It is seen from these examples that the first approximation in applying the *averaging method* can be readily obtained, and comparisons * with known rigorous solutions show that it already has a satisfactory accuracy. The discussion of the second approximation brings us to two non-linear equations, the solution of which may be cumbersome, but the difficulty is only an algebraic one.

28. Examples of Variable Spring Characteristics.—In the previous articles problems were considered in which the stiffness of springs was changing with displacement. Here we will discuss cases in which the spring characteristic is varying with time.

As a first example let us consider a string AB of a length $2l$ stretched vertically and carrying at the middle a particle of mass m, Fig. 118. If

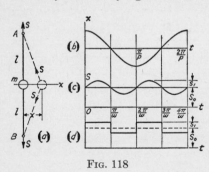

FIG. 118

x is a small displacement of the particle from its middle position, the tensile force in the string corresponding to this displacement is (see p. 125)

$$S' = S + AE\frac{x^2}{2l^2},\qquad (a)$$

where S is the tensile force in the string for static equilibrium position of the particle, A is the cross-sectional area of the string and E is the modulus of elasticity of the string. Let us assume that S is very large in comparison with the change in the tensile force represented by the second term in expression (a). In such a case this second term can be neglected, $S' = S$, and the equation for motion of the particle m becomes:

$$m\ddot{x} + \frac{2Sx}{l} = 0.\qquad (b)$$

The spring characteristic in this case is defined by the quantity $2S/l$ and as long as S remains constant, eq. (b) gives a simple harmonic motion of a

* See the above-mentioned Klotter paper.

frequency $p = \sqrt{2S/lm}$ and of an amplitude which depends on the initial conditions. If the initial displacement as well as the initial velocity of the particle are both zero, the particle remains in its middle position which is its position of stable equilibrium.

Assume now that by some device a small steady periodic fluctuation of the tensile force S is produced such that

$$S = S_0 + S_1 \sin \omega t. \qquad (c)$$

Since S always remains large enough, eq. (b) continues to hold also in this case and we obtain a system in which the spring characteristic $2S/l$ is a periodic function of time. Without going at present into a discussion of the differential eq. (b), it can be seen that by a proper choice of the frequency ω of the fluctuating tension, large vibrations of the particle m can be built up under proper conditions. Such a condition is represented in Fig. 118b and Fig. 118c. The first of these curves represents displacements of the particle m when it vibrates freely under the action of a constant tension $S = S_0$, so that a complete cycle requires the time $\tau = 2\pi/p = 2\pi\sqrt{lm/2S_0}$. The second curve represents the fluctuating tension of the string which is assumed to have an angular frequency $\omega = 2p$. It is seen that during the first quarter of the cycle, when the particle m is moving from the extreme position to its middle position and the resultant of the forces S produces positive work, the average value of S is larger than S_0. During the second quarter of the cycle, when the forces S oppose the motion of the particle, their average value is smaller than S_0. Thus during each half cycle there is a surplus of positive work produced by the tensile forces S. The result of this work is a gradual building up of the amplitude of vibration. This conclusion can be readily verified by experiment.* Furthermore, an experiment will also show that the middle position of the particle is no longer a position of stable equilibrium if a fluctuation in tensile force S of a frequency $\omega = 2p$ is maintained. A small accidental force producing an initial displacement or an initial velocity, may start vibrations which will be gradually built up as explained above.

In Fig. 118d a case is represented in which the tensile force in the string is changing abruptly so that

$$S = S_0 \pm S_1. \qquad (d)$$

---

* We have an example of such vibrations in Melde's experiment, see *Phil. Mag.*, Apr. 1883. In this experiment a fine string is maintained in transverse vibrations by attaching one of its ends to the vibrating tuning fork, the motion of the point of attachment being in the direction of the string. The period of transverse vibrations is double that of the fork.

By using the same reasoning as in the previous case, it can be shown that changing the tension S as indicated in Fig. 118d will result in the production of a large vibration of the particle.

In Fig. 119 another case of the same kind is represented. On a vertical shaft is mounted a circular disc AB. Rotation of the shaft is free but its bending is confined, by the use of guiding bars nn, to the plane xy of the figure. Along most of its length the shaft has non-circular cross section, as shown in the figure, so that its flexural rigidity in the xy-plane depends on

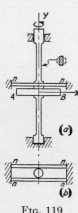

FIG. 119

the angle of rotation. Assume first that the shaft does not rotate and in some manner its lateral vibrations in the xy-plane are produced. The disc will perform a simple harmonic motion, the frequency of which depends on the flexural rigidity of the shaft in that plane. For the position of the shaft shown in the figure, flexural rigidity is a minimum and the lateral vibrations will therefore have the smallest frequency. By making the plane of maximum flexural rigidity of the shaft to coincide with the xy-plane, we will obtain the highest frequency of vibration. In our further discussion we will assume that the difference between the two principal rigidities is small, say not larger than 10%. Thus the difference between the maximum and minimum frequency of the lateral vibrations will be also small, not larger than say 5%.

Assume now that the shaft rotates during its lateral vibrations. In such a case we obtain a vibrating system the spring characteristic of which is changing with the time, making one complete cycle during half a revolution of the shaft. By using the same kind of reasoning as in the previous case, it can be shown that for a certain relation between the angular velocity ω of the shaft and the mean value p of the angular frequency of its lateral vibrations positive work will be done on the vibrating system, and this work will result in a gradual building up of the amplitude of the lateral vibrations. Such a condition is shown by the two curves in Fig. 120. The upper curve represents the displacement-time curve for the lateral vibration of the shaft with a mean frequency p. The lower curve represents the fluctuating flexural rigidity of the shaft, assuming that the shaft makes one complete revolution during one cycle of its lateral oscillations so that $\omega = p$. At the bottom of the figure the corresponding positions of rotating cross sections of the shaft with the neutral axis n are shown. It is seen that during the first quarter of a cycle when the disc is moving from the extreme position towards the middle position and the reaction of the shaft on the disc produces positive work, the flexural rigidity is larger than its average value, while during the second quarter of a cycle, when the reaction of the shaft opposes the motion of the disc, the flexural rigidity is smaller than its average value.   Observing that at any instant the reaction is proportional to the corresponding flexural rigidity, it can be concluded that the positive work done during the first quarter of the cycle is numerically larger than the negative work during the second quarter.   This results in a surplus of positive work during one revolution of the shaft which produces a gradual increase in the amplitude of the lateral vibrations of the shaft.

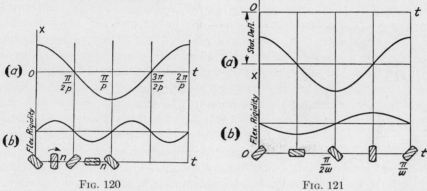

FIG. 120   FIG. 121

If the shaft shown in Fig. 119 is placed horizontally the action of gravity force must be taken into consideration.   Assuming that the deflections due to vibrations are smaller than the statical deflection of the shaft produced by the gravity force of the disc, the displacements of the disc from the unbent axis of the shaft will always be down and can be represented during one cycle by the ordinates of the upper curve measured from the t-axis in Fig. 121a.   There are two forces acting on the disc, (1) the constant gravity force and (2) the variable reaction of the shaft on the disc which in our case always has an upward direction.   The work of the gravity force during one cycle is zero, thus only the work of the reaction of the shaft should be considered.   During the first half of the cycle in which the disc is moving down, the reaction opposes the motion and negative work is produced.   During the second half of the cycle the reaction is acting in the direction of motion and produces positive work.   If we assume, as in the previous case, that the time of one revolution of the shaft is equal to the period of the lateral vibrations and take the same curve as in Fig. 120b for the fluctuating flexural rigidity, it can be seen that the total work per cycle is zero. A different conclusion will be reached if we take the angular velocity ω of the shaft two times smaller than the frequency of the lateral vibrations, so that the variation of the flexural rigidity can be represented by the lower curve in Fig. 121. It is seen that during the first half of the cycle, when the reaction is opposing the motion, the flexural rigidity is smaller that its average value, and during

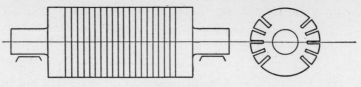

Fig. 122

the second half of the cycle, when the reaction is acting in the direction of motion, the flexural rigidity is larger than its average value. Thus a positive work during a cycle will be produced which will result in a building up of the amplitude of vibrations. We see that, owing to a combination of the gravity force and of the variable flexural rigidity, a large lateral vibration can be produced when the number of revolutions of the shaft per minute is only half the number of lateral free oscillations of the shaft per minute. Such types of vibration may occur in a rotor having a variable flexural rigidity, for instance in a two-pole rotor (Fig. 122) of a turbogenerator. The deflection of such a rotor under the action of its own weight varies during rotation and at a certain speed heavy vibration, due to this variable flexibility, may take place. The same kind of vibration may occur also when the non-uniformity of flexural rigidity of a rotor is due to a keyway cut in the shaft. By cutting two additional keyways, 120 degrees apart from the first, a cross section with constant moment of inertia in all directions will be obtained and in this way the cause of vibrations will be removed.

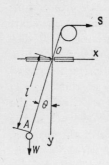

Fig. 123

As another example let us consider a simple pendulum of variable length l (Fig. 123). By pulling the string OA with a force S, a variation in the length l of the pendulum can be produced. In order to obtain the differential equation of motion the principle of angular momentum will be applied. The momentum of the moving mass W/g can be resolved into two components, one in the direction of the string OA and another in the direction perpendicular to OA. In calculating the angular momentum about the point O, only the second component equal to $(W/g)l\dot\theta$ must be taken into consideration. The derivative of this angular momentum with respect to the time t should be equal to the moment of the acting forces about the point O. Hence the equation

$$\frac{d}{dt}\left(\frac{W}{g}\,l^2\dot\theta\right) = -Wl\sin\theta,$$

or

$$\ddot\theta + \frac{2}{l}\frac{dl}{dt}\dot\theta + \frac{g}{l}\sin\theta = 0. \tag{73}$$

In the case of vibrations of small amplitude, θ can be substituted for $\sin\theta$ in eq. (73) and we obtain

$$\ddot\theta + \frac{2}{l}\frac{dl}{dt}\dot\theta + \frac{g}{l}\theta = 0. \tag{74}$$

When l is constant, the second term on the left side of this equation vanishes and we obtain a simple harmonic motion in which g/l takes the place of the spring constant divided by the mass in eq. (b), p. 168. The variation of the length l, owing to which the second term in eq. (74) appears, may have the same effect on the vibration as the fluctuating spring stiffness discussed in the previous examples. Comparing eq. (74) with eq. (31) (see p. 70) for damped vibration, we see that the term containing the derivative dl/dt takes the place of the term representing damping in eq. (31). By an appropriate variation of the length l with time the same effect can be produced as with *negative damping*. In such a case a progressive accumulation of energy in the system instead of a dissipation of energy takes place and the amplitude of the oscillation of the pendulum increases with the time. It is easy to see that such an accumulation of energy results from the work done by the tensile force S during the variation in the length l of the pendulum. Various methods of varying the length l can be imagined which will result in the accumulation of energy of the vibrating system.

As an example consider the case represented in Fig. 124 in which the angular velocity $d\theta/dt$ of the pendulum and the velocity dl/dt of variation in length of the pendulum are represented as functions of the time. The period of variation of the length of the pendulum is taken as half that of the vibration of the pendulum and the $d\theta/dt$ line is placed in such a manner with respect to the dl/dt line that the maximum negative damping effect coincides with the maximum speed. This means that a decrease in the length l has to be produced while the velocity $d\theta/dt$ is large and an increase in length l while the velocity is comparatively small. Remembering that

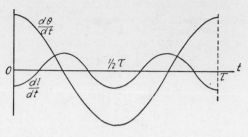

FIG. 124

the tensile force S is working against the radial component of the weight W together with the centrifugal force, it is easy to see that in the case represented in Fig. 124 the work done by the force S during any decrease in length l will be larger than that returned during the increase in length

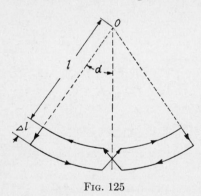

FIG. 125

l. The surplus of this work results in an increase in energy of vibration of the pendulum.

The calculation of the increase in energy of the oscillating pendulum becomes especially simple in the case shown in Fig. 125. It is assumed in this case that the length of the pendulum is suddenly decreased by the quantity Δl when the pendulum is in its middle position and is suddenly increased to the same amount when the pendulum is in its extreme positions. The trajectory of the mass W/g is shown in the figure by the full line. The mass performs two complete cycles during one oscillation of the pendulum. The work produced during the shortening of the length l of the pendulum will be

$$\left(W + \frac{W}{g}\frac{v^2}{l}\right)\Delta l.* \qquad (e)$$

Here v denotes the velocity of the mass W/g of the pendulum when in its

---

* In this calculation the variation in centrifugal force during the shortening of the pendulum is neglected.

middle position. The work returned at the extreme positions of the pendulum is

$$W \, \Delta l \cos \alpha. \tag{f}$$

The gain in energy during one complete oscillation of the pendulum will be

$$\Delta E = 2 \left\{ \left(W + \frac{W}{g} \frac{v^2}{l} \right) \Delta l - W \, \Delta l \cos \alpha \right\},$$

or by putting

$$v^2 = 2gl(1 - \cos \alpha),$$

we have

$$\Delta E = 6W \, \Delta l(1 - \cos \alpha). \tag{g}$$

Due to this increase in energy a progressive increase in amplitude of oscillation of the pendulum takes place.

In our discussion a variation of the length l of the pendulum was considered. But a similar result can be obtained if, instead of a variable length, a variable acceleration g is introduced. This can be accomplished by placing an electromagnet under the bob of the pendulum. If two cycles of the magnetic force per complete oscillation of the pendulum are produced, the surplus of energy will be put into the vibrating system during each oscillation and in this way large oscillations will be built up.

It is seen from the discussion that a vertically hanging pendulum at rest may become unstable under the action of a pulsating vertical magnetic force and vibrations, described above, can be produced if a proper timing of the magnetic action is used.* A similar effect can be produced also if a vibratory motion along the vertical axis is communicated to the suspension point of a hanging pendulum. The inertia forces of such a vertical motion are equivalent to the pulsating magnetic forces mentioned above.

If, instead of a variable spring characteristic, we have a variable oscillating mass or a variable moment of inertia of a body making torsional vibrations, the same phenomena of instability and of a gradual building up of vibrations may occur under certain conditions. Take, for example, a vertical shaft with a flywheel attached to its end (Fig. 126). The free torsional vibrations of this system will be represented by the equation

$$\frac{d}{dt} (I\dot{\theta}) + k\theta = 0, \tag{h}$$

in which I is the moment of inertia of the flywheel and k is the spring con-

* See Lord Rayleigh, p. 82, *loc. cit.*

stant. Let us assume now that the moment of inertia I does not remain constant but varies periodically with time due to the prescribed harmonic motion of two symmetrically situated masses m sliding along the spokes of the wheel (Fig. 126b). In such a case the moment of inertia can be represented by a formula.

$$I = I_0(1 + \alpha \sin \omega t), \tag{i}$$

in which ω is the angular frequency of the prescribed motion of the masses m and α is a factor which we assume to be small in comparison with unity, so that there is only a slight fluctuation in the magnitude of the moment of inertia I. Substituting expression (i) into eq. (h), we can write this equation in the following form:

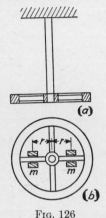

$$I_0\ddot{\theta} + \frac{I_0\alpha\omega \cos \omega t}{1 + \alpha \sin \omega t} \dot{\theta} + \frac{k}{1 + \alpha \sin \omega t} \theta = 0,$$

or, observing that α is a small quantity, we obtain

$$I_0\ddot{\theta} + I_0\alpha\omega \cos \omega t \, \dot{\theta} + k(1 - \alpha \sin \omega t)\theta = 0. \tag{j}$$

It is seen that on account of the fluctuation in the magnitude of the moment of inertia we obtain an eq. (j) similar to those which we had before for the case of systems with variable spring stiffnesses. From this it can be concluded that by a proper choice of the frequency ω of the radially oscillating masses m large torsional vibrations of the system in Fig. 126 can be built up. The necessary energy for these vibrations is supplied by forces producing the prescribed radial motion of the masses m. When the masses are moving toward the axis of the shaft a positive work against their centrifugal forces is produced. For a reversed motion the work is negative. If the masses be pulled towards the axis when the angular velocity of the torsional vibration and the consequent centrifugal forces are large and the motion be reversed when the centrifugal forces are small, a surplus of positive work, required for building up the torsional vibrations, will be

(a)

(b)

Fig. 126

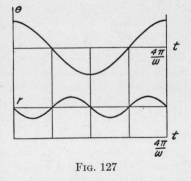

Fig. 127

provided. Such a condition is shown in Fig. 127 in which the upper curve represents angular velocity $\dot{\theta}$ of the vibrating wheel and the lower curve represents radial displacements r of the masses m. The frequency of oscillation of the masses m is twice as great as the frequency of the torsional vibrations of the shaft.

If the wheel of the shaft is connected to a reciprocating mass as shown in Fig. 128, conditions similar to those just described may take place. If the upper end of the shaft is fixed and the flywheel performs small torsional vibrations such that the configuration of the system changes very little, all the masses of the system can be replaced by an equivalent disc of a constant moment of inertia (see p. 18). But if the shaft is rotating, the configuration of the system is changing periodically and the equivalent

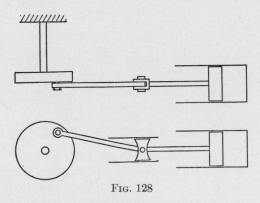

FIG. 128

disc must assume periodically varying moment of inertia. On the basis of the previous example it can be concluded that at certain angular velocities of the shaft heavy torsional vibrations in the system can be built up. These vibrations are of considerable practical importance in the case of engines with reciprocating masses.*

29. Conditions of Instability in Systems with Variable Spring Characteristics.—From the examples of the preceding article, it can be seen that large vibrations can be built up in systems with variable spring characteristics if the frequency ω of the stiffness fluctuation is properly chosen. In practical applications it is very important to know those values of ω at which such large vibrations may occur. This question can be answered on the basis of a discussion of the corresponding differential equation of motion,

* This problem is discussed in the following: E. Trefftz, *Aachener Vorträge aus dem Gebiete der Aerodynamik und verwandter Gebiete*, Berlin, 1930; F. Kluge, *Ing.-Arch.*, Vol. 2, p. 119, 1931; T. E. Schunk, *ibid.*, Vol. 2, p. 591, 1932; R. Grammel, *ibid.*, Vol. 6, p. 59, 1935, and *Z. angew. Math. u. Mech.*, Vol. 15, p. 47, 1935; N. Kotschin, *Appl. Math. and Mech.* (Russian), Vol. 2, p. 3, 1934. See also C. B. Biezeno and R. Grammel, *Technische Dynamik*, Berlin, p. 1037, 1939.

which in the general case of vibration without damping can be written in the form

$$\ddot{x} + [p^2 + \alpha f(t)]x = 0. \tag{a}$$

Here the term $\alpha f(t)$ represents a periodic function of time defining the fluctuation of the spring stiffness. In mechanical vibration problems, we usually have small fluctuations of the spring stiffness and this term can be considered as small in comparison with p^2. The form of the function $f(t)$ depends on the arrangement of the system. In Figs. 118c and 118d, the two important cases, so-called sinusoidal and rectangular ripples, are represented. The general solution of eq. (a) is unknown, but for our purpose it is not necessary to have it. We are interested to know only if the motion, described by (a), is stable or unstable in a given case. To answer this question, we can assume that the system is in its middle position ($x = 0$) and that, by application of some disturbing force, a small initial displacement x_0 and small velocity $\dot{x}_0$ are produced so that a small vibration ensues. If it can be shown that the amplitude of this vibration indefinitely grows with time, we have a case of instability. If the vibration gradually dies out with time, the motion is stable. Consider, for example, the case in Fig. 118a. Under the action of the vertical pulsating forces S, the mass m may remain in its middle position on the line of action of the forces S, but as we have seen, this position of equilibrium becomes unstable if the frequency ω of the pulsating force S is twice as large as the frequency p of lateral vibration of the mass m in a ripple-free spring system. From the fact that the expression in the brackets in eq. (a) is a periodic function, we can expect that with a proper selection of the initial conditions such a motion $x = F(t)$ can be produced that at the end of the first cycle ($t = \tau = 2\pi/\omega$) we will have

$$(x)_{t=\tau} = sx_0, \quad (\dot{x})_{t=\tau} = s\dot{x}_0, \tag{b}$$

i.e., the displacement and the velocity at the end of the cycle are obtained by multiplying the initial values x_0 and $\dot{x}_0$ by some constant s. Considering now the quantities (b) as the initial conditions for the second cycle, we conclude that the displacements in the second cycle are obtained by multiplying by s the corresponding displacements of the first cycle, i.e.,

$$(x)_{t+\tau} = s(x)_t. \tag{c}$$

At the end of the second cycle, we will then have

$$(x)_{2\tau} = s^2 x_0, \quad (\dot{x})_{2\tau} = s^2 \dot{x}_0. \tag{d}$$

Proceeding further in the same way, we conclude that displacements of any new cycle are obtained by multiplying by s the corresponding displacements of the preceding cycle. The character of motion depends therefore on the magnitude of the quantity s. If the absolute value of s is less than unity, the displacements will gradually die out and the motion is stable. If the absolute value of s is larger than unity, the tendency of displacements will be to grow with time. Thus in this case the motion is unstable.

In practical applications it is very important to know the regions in which instability takes place and a building up of large vibrations may occur. If the fluctuation of the spring stiffness consists only in a rectangular ripple superposed on the spring constant, the determination of the regions of instability can be made without much difficulty since for each half cycle the spring characteristic remains constant and the equation of simple harmonic motion can be used. Let Δ be the quantity defining the magnitude of the ripple, so that the equation of motion for the first half of a cycle, i.e., for $0 < t < \pi/\omega$, is

$$\ddot{x} + (p^2 + \Delta)x = 0, \tag{e}$$

and for the second half of the cycle when $\pi/\omega < t < 2\pi/\omega$, it is

$$\ddot{x} + (p^2 - \Delta)x = 0. \tag{f}$$

Using the notations

$$p_1 = \sqrt{p^2 + \Delta} \quad \text{and} \quad p_2 = \sqrt{p^2 - \Delta}, \tag{g}$$

the solutions of eqs. (e) and (f) are:

$$x_1 = C_1 \sin p_1 t + C_2 \cos p_1 t, \tag{h}$$

$$x_2 = C_3 \sin p_2 t + C_4 \cos p_2 t, \tag{i}$$

where $C_1 \cdots C_4$ are the constants of integration which must be determined from the following conditions:

(1) At the end of the first half cycle ($t = \pi/\omega$) solutions (h) and (i) must agree, i.e., at this instant both solutions must give the same value for the displacement and for the velocity.

(2) At the end of a full cycle ($t = 2\pi/\omega$) the displacement and the velocity, by virtue of condition (c) must be s times as large as at the beginning. Thus the equations for determining the four constants are

$$
\begin{aligned}
(x_1)_{t=\pi/\omega} &= (x_2)_{t=\pi/\omega}, \\
(\dot{x}_1)_{t=\pi/\omega} &= (\dot{x}_2)_{t=\pi/\omega}, \\
(x_2)_{t=2\pi/\omega} &= s(x_1)_{t=0}, \\
(\dot{x}_2)_{t=2\pi/\omega} &= s(\dot{x}_1)_{t=0}.
\end{aligned}
\tag{j}
$$

Substituting for x_1 and x_2 from (h) and (i) the first of eqs. (j) becomes

$$C_1 \sin \frac{\pi p_1}{\omega} + C_2 \cos \frac{\pi p_1}{\omega} - C_3 \sin \frac{\pi p_2}{\omega} - C_4 \cos \frac{\pi p_2}{\omega} = 0.$$

The remaining three equations of the system (j) will have a similar form so that we obtain altogether four linear homogeneous equations for determining $C_1 \cdots C_4$. These equations can give solutions for the C's different from zeros only if their determinant is zero. Evaluating this determinant and equating it to zero, we finally obtain the following quadratic equation for s:

$$s^2 - 2s \left(\cos \frac{\pi p_1}{\omega} \cos \frac{\pi p_2}{\omega} - \frac{p_1^2 + p_2^2}{2p_1 p_2} \sin \frac{\pi p_1}{\omega} \sin \frac{\pi p_2}{\omega} \right) + 1 = 0, \tag{k}$$

or using the notation

$$N = \cos \frac{\pi p_1}{\omega} \cos \frac{\pi p_2}{\omega} - \frac{p_1^2 + p_2^2}{2p_1 p_2} \sin \frac{\pi p_1}{\omega} \sin \frac{\pi p_2}{\omega}, \tag{l}$$

we obtain

$$s^2 - 2sN + 1 = 0$$

from which

$$s = N \pm \sqrt{N^2 - 1}. \tag{m}$$

It is seen that the magnitude of the factor s depends on the quantity N. If $N > 1$ one of the roots of eq. (m) is larger than unity and the vibrations will gradually build up. Hence the motion is unstable.

When N lies between $+1$ and -1 the roots of eq. (m) are complex with their moduli equal to unity. This means that there will be no tendency for the vibrations to grow, so that the motion is stable.

When $N < -1$ one of the roots of eq. (m) again becomes numerically larger than unity; consequently the motion becomes unstable.

Let us now consider the physical significance of the fact that multiplier s is positive when $N > 1$, and negative when $N < -1$. Considering the displacements of the vibrating system at the ends of several consecutive cycles of the spring fluctuations, we find, from eq. (c), that in the case of positive value of s these displacements will increase and will always have the same sign. This indicates that the vibrations of the system have the same frequency as the spring fluctuation frequency ω or they are a multiple of it. If we denote the frequency of these vibrations by ω_0 we conclude that for $N > 1$ we shall have $\omega_0 = \omega$ or $\omega_0 = 2\omega$, 3ω, etc. If s is negative the displacement at the ends of the consecutive cycles of the spring fluctuations have alternating signs, which indicates that $\omega_0 = \omega/2$, $3\omega/2$, etc.

The quantity N, given by expression (l), is a function of the ratios p_1/ω and p_2/ω. By using eqs. (g) we can also represent it as a function of the ratios Δ/p^2 and p/ω. The first of these ratios gives the relative fluctuation of the spring constant and the second is the ratio of the vibration frequency of a ripple-free spring system, to the frequency of the stiffness fluctuation. If we take $(p/\omega)^2$ as abscissas and $(\Delta/p^2)(p^2/\omega^2)$ as ordinates, a point in a plane for each set of values of the ratios Δ/p^2 and p/ω may be plotted and the corresponding value of N may be calculated. If such calculations have been made for a sufficient number of points, curves can be drawn that will define the transition from stable to unstable states of motion. Several curves of this kind are shown in Fig. 129,* in which the shaded areas represent the regions in which $-1 < N < 1$ (stability) and the blank area, the regions where $N > 1$ or $N < -1$ (instability). The full lines correspond to $N = +1$ and dotted lines to $N = -1$. The numbers in the regions indicate the number of oscillations of the system during one cycle, $\tau = 2\pi/\omega$, of the stiffness fluctuation.

For a given ratio Δ/p^2, i.e., for a known value of the relative fluctuation of the stiffness of the spring, the ordinates are in a constant ratio to the abscissas in Fig. 129 and we obtain an inclined line, say OA. Moving along this line we are crossing regions of stable and of unstable motions, indicating that the stability of motion varies as the frequency ω of the stiffness fluctuation is changed. When ω is small we get points on the line OA far away from the origin O. As ω is gradually increased, the system passes through an infinite number of instability regions. Finally, as p/ω approaches the origin, the last two regions of instability aa and bb are crossed, one in which the ratio p/ω is approximately unity and the other in which p/ω is approximately one-half. Experiences with such cases as are discussed in the previous article indicate that these two instability regions are practically the most important and that large vibrations can be expected if the frequency of the stiffness fluctuation coincides with that of the free

* See papers by B. van der Pol, *Phil. Mag.*, Ser. 7, Vol. 5, p. 18, 1928; and E. Schwerin, *Z. tech. Phys.*, Vol. 12, p. 104, 1931.

vibration * or is twice as large as that frequency. It is seen from the figure that the extents of the regions of instability such as are given by the distances $\overline{aa}$ or $\overline{bb}$ can be reduced by diminishing the slope of the line OA, i.e., by reducing the relative fluctuation of the spring stiffness. Practically such a reduction can be accomplished in the case of torsional vibrations by introducing flexible couplings. In this way the general flexibility of the system is increased and the relative spring fluctuation becomes smaller.

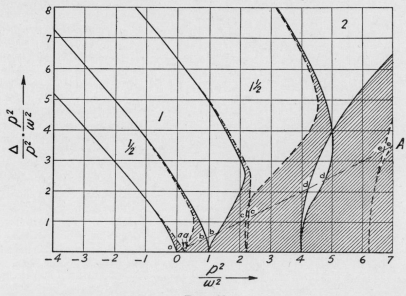

FIG. 129

Damping is, of course, another important factor. In all our discussions damping has been neglected, thus theoretically we do not get an upper limit for the amplitude of the gradually built-up vibrations. Practically this limit depends on the amount of damping, therefore, by introducing some additional friction into the flexible couplings considerable reduction in the vibrations can be effected.

In Fig. 130 the results of the investigation of eq. (a) for the case of a sinusoidal ripple $\Delta \sin \omega t$ are shown.† We see that the boundaries of stable and unstable regions are similar to those obtained for a rectangular ripple. Experimental results obtained by H. Neusinger ‡ who investigated the boundaries of instability regions by using a pendulum of special construction are indicated by small circles. We see that experimental results are in good agreement with the theory.

In a more general case where the ripple superimposed on the constant spring stiffness is of complicated form, a method of successive approximations can be used to calculate

---

* Calculated by assuming the average value per cycle for the stiffness of the spring.

† The first investigation of this case was made by B. van der Pol, *loc. cit.* (p. 163). See also E. L. Ince, *Proc. Roy. Soc., Edinburgh*, Vol. 52, pp. 355–433, 1931–32.

‡ See *Akust. Z.*, Vol. 5, pp. 11–26, 1940.

the extent of the instability regions. Taking one of the instability regions for a given stiffness fluctuation, say region aa in Fig. 129, we know that for any point in that region, the numerical value of the factor s in eq. (c) is larger than unity and that the amplitude

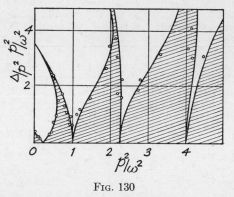

of vibration is growing. If we consider the limiting points a, we know also that at these points the numerical value of s becomes equal to unity and there is the possibility of having a steady vibratory motion. Thus the limiting points of an instability region are characterized by the fact that at these points steady vibrations of the system are possible. For the purpose of calculating the position of such points, we may assume some motion of the system and see for what values of the frequency ω this motion becomes a steady periodic motion. Those values then define the limits of the instability regions.

FIG. 130

Such a method was used in analyzing vibrations in electric locomotives with side-rod drive system,* Fig. 131. The rigidity of the elastic connection between the two rotating

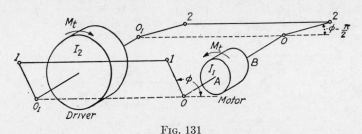

FIG. 131

masses consisting of driver and motor depends on the angular position of the cranks and the expression in the brackets of eq. (a) can be represented in the form

$$\frac{I_1 + I_2}{I_1 I_2} \left[\frac{a - b \cos 4\omega t}{c - d \cos 4\omega t} \right], \tag{n}$$

so that the flexibility of the drive goes through four cycles during one revolution of the driver. If a and c are large in comparison with b and d, we can neglect periodic terms

* This problem was of considerable practical importance in the early stage of the development of electric locomotive construction. Its solution was furnished principally by Prof. E. Meissner, *Schweiz. Bauzeitung*, Vol. 72, p. 95, 1918, and his pupil K. E. Müller, *ibid.*, Vol. 74, p. 141, 1919. See also the papers of L. Dreyfus, "A. Föppl zum siebzigsten Geburtstag," p. 89, 1924; A. Wichert, *Forschungsarbeiten*, No. 266, 1924; A. C. Couwenhoven, *ibid.*, No. 218, 1919; E. Schwerin, *Z. tech. Phys.*, Vol. 10, p. 37, 1929.

in expression (n) and obtain simple torsional vibrations as discussed in Art. 2. In the general case, we will get regions of instability which can be established by the above-described method.

The points to the left from the origin in Fig. 129 correspond to negative spring constants. Such spring characteristic we may have, for instance, in the case of a pendulum. For a hanging pendulum the spring characteristic is defined by the quantity g/l, where l is the equivalent length of the pendulum. In the case of the inverted pendulum, Fig. 132, the spring characteristic is given by $-g/l$. We know that this position of equilibrium is unstable. By giving a vertical vibratory motion to the point of support A, a fluctuation in the spring stiffness can be introduced (see p. 175). In such a case, as shown by the small shaded area to the left of the origin in Fig. 129, stability conditions can be obtained for certain frequencies of this fluctuation. Thus the pendulum will remain stable in the inverted position.

Vibrations with Damping.—As an example we take the case when damping is proportional to the velocity and the spring stiffness has a sinusoidal fluctuation of aperiod π/ω. The equation of motion in this case is

$$\ddot{x} + 2n\dot{x} + (p^2 - 2\alpha \sin 2\omega t)x = 0. \tag{o}$$

When α vanishes, this equation coincides with eq. (31), p. 70, for free vibrations with linear damping. From the discussion of the previous article we know that a steady vibration of a period twice as large as the period of the stiffness fluctuation can be expected in this case. We will now investigate under what conditions such a steady motion is possible. This motion will not be a simple harmonic vibration but we may represent it by a series of the period $2\pi/\omega$:

$$x = A_1 \sin \omega t + B_1 \cos \omega t + A_3 \sin 3\omega t + B_3 \cos 3\omega t + A_5 \sin 5\omega t + \cdots \tag{p}$$

and use a method of successive approximations.*

Substituting the series in eq. (o) and equating the coefficients of $\sin \omega t$, $\cos \omega t$, etc., to zero, we obtain:

$$\left. \begin{aligned} A_1(p^2 - \omega^2) - 2n\omega B_1 - \alpha B_1 + \alpha B_3 &= 0, \\ B_1(p^2 - \omega^2) + 2n\omega A_1 - \alpha A_1 - \alpha A_3 &= 0, \\ A_3(p^2 - 9\omega^2) - 6n\omega B_3 - \alpha B_1 + \alpha B_5 &= 0, \\ B_3(p^2 - 9\omega^2) + 6n\omega A_3 + \alpha A_1 - \alpha A_5 &= 0, \\ A_5(p^2 - 25\omega^2) - 10n\omega B_5 - \alpha B_3 + \alpha B_7 &= 0, \\ B_5(p^2 - 25\omega^2) + 10n\omega A_5 + \alpha A_3 - \alpha A_7 &= 0. \end{aligned} \right\} \tag{q}$$

These equations show that the coefficients A_3, B_3 are of the order α with respect to A_1, B_1; that A_5, B_5 are of order α with respect to A_3, B_3, and so on. Thus if α is small the series (p) is a rapidly converging series. The first approximation is obtained by keeping only the first two terms of the series. Omitting A_3 and B_3 in the first two of eqs. (q), we find that

$$\left. \begin{aligned} A_1(p^2 - \omega^2) - (2n\omega + \alpha)B_1 &= 0, \\ A_1(2n\omega - \alpha) + (p^2 - \omega^2)B_1 &= 0. \end{aligned} \right\} \tag{r}$$

Fig. 132

*Such a method of investigation was used by Lord Rayleigh, p. 82, *loc. cit.*

These equations will give solutions different from zero for A_1 and B_1 only if their determinant vanishes, whence

$$(p^2 - \omega^2)^2 = \alpha^2 - 4n^2\omega^2. \tag{s}$$

Thus, if the quantity α, defining the spring stiffness fluctuation, is known, the magnitude of the frequency ω, at which a steady motion is possible, can be found from eq. (s) which gives

$$\omega = \sqrt{p^2 - 2n^2 \pm \sqrt{(p^2 - 2n^2)^2 + \alpha^2 - p^4}}. \tag{t}$$

From eqs. (r) we also have

$$\frac{A_1}{B_1} = \frac{2n\omega + \alpha}{p^2 - \omega^2} = \frac{p^2 - \omega^2}{\alpha - 2n\omega}. \tag{u}$$

Then the first two terms of the series, representing the first approximation of the motion can be given in the following form:

$$x_1 = C \sin(\omega t + \beta),$$

where

$$C = \sqrt{A_1{}^2 + B_1{}^2} \quad \text{and} \quad \beta = \arctan(B_1/A_1). \tag{v}$$

The amplitude of the vibration remains indefinite while the phase-angle β can be calculated by using expression (v). If there is no damping, $2n = 0$ and we obtain

$$\omega = p\sqrt{1 \pm \frac{\alpha}{p^2}} \approx p\left(1 \pm \frac{\alpha}{2p^2}\right). \tag{w}$$

These two values of ω correspond to the two limits of the first region of instability, such as points aa in Fig. 129. Eq. (s) requires that α be not less than $2n\omega$. For $\alpha < 2n\omega$

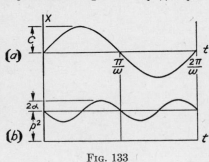

FIG. 133

sufficient energy cannot be supplied to maintain the motion. For $\alpha = 2n\omega$ we have $\omega = p$, i.e., the frequency of the stiffness fluctuation is exactly two times larger than the free vibration frequency of the system without damping and with the assumed constant spring stiffness defined by the quantity p. The phase-angle β, as may be seen from (u) and (v), is zero in this case and the relation between the motion and the spring fluctuation is such as is shown by curves (a) and (b) in Fig. 133. When $\alpha > 2n\omega$, two solutions for ω are obtained from (t) and the corresponding phase angles from (v). When α is much greater than $2n\omega$ the ratio A_1/B_1 in eq. (u) approaches unity and the phase angle is approximately equal to $\pm\pi/4$. For this case we therefore conclude that the curve (b) in Fig. 133 must be displaced along the horizontal axis so as to make its maximum or its minimum correspond to the zero points of the curve (a), i.e., the spring stiffness is a maximum or a minimum when the system passes through its position of equilibrium.

If a second approximation is desired we use the third and fourth of eqs. (q), from which, for small damping, we have approximately

$$A_3 = \frac{\alpha B_1}{p^2 - 9\omega^2}, \quad B_3 = -\frac{\alpha A_1}{p^2 - 9\omega^2}. \tag{x}$$

Thus the second approximation for the motion is

$$x = C \sin (\omega t + \beta) + \frac{\alpha C}{p^2 - 9\omega^2} \cos (3\omega t + \beta). \tag{y}$$

Substituting expressions (x) in the first two of eqs. (q), we find the following more accurate equation for determining the values of ω, at which a steady motion is possible:

$$\left(p^2 - \omega^2 - \frac{\alpha^2}{p^2 - 9\omega^2}\right)^2 = \alpha^2 - 4n^2 p^2, \tag{z}$$

and for the phase angle

$$\tan \beta = \left(p^2 - \omega^2 - \frac{\alpha^2}{p^2 - 9\omega^2}\right) \div (\alpha + 2n\omega).$$

Thus, by using the described method of successive approximations, we can establish the limits of the regions of instability, investigate how these limits depend on the amount of damping and determine the phase-angle β. All this information is of practical interest in investigating vibrations due to fluctuation of spring stiffness.

CHAPTER III

SYSTEMS WITH TWO DEGREES OF FREEDOM

30. Examples of Systems with Several Degrees of Freedom.—In all previous examples we have dealt only with systems that could be treated as a single mass attached to the foundation by weightless springs. In this way, only one coordinate was required to define the configuration of the system and we had *one degree of freedom*. Sometimes we encounter systems that consist of several masses connected between themselves and to the foundation by springs. It is then necessary to have several coordinates to specify the configuration of the system and we have *several degrees of freedom*. The number of degrees of freedom is always determined by the number of independent coordinates required to completely define the configuration of the system. The simplest cases are those with two degrees of freedom.

Several examples are shown in Fig. 134. In Fig. 134a two masses m_1 and m_2 are suspended vertically by springs k_1 and k_2. If these masses are

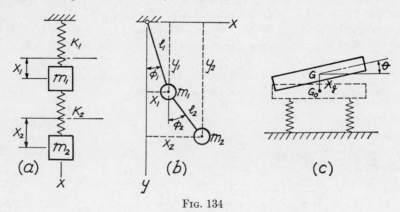

Fig. 134

constrained to move only vertically and we measure displacements x_1 and x_2 from the positions of static equilibrium as shown, we see that two coordinates completely specify the configuration of the system; thus it has two degrees of freedom.

186

The so-called double pendulum in Fig. 134b consists of two masses m_1 and m_2 interconnected by an inextensible bar l_2 and suspended from the ceiling by another inextensible bar l_1. If these masses are constrained to remain in the xy-plane, we see that their positions in this plane can be defined by the rectangular coordinates x_1, y_1 and x_2, y_2. However, these four coordinates are not independent; from the geometry of the figure, we see that

$$\left. \begin{array}{c} x_1{}^2 + y_1{}^2 = l_1{}^2, \\ (x_2 - x_1)^2 + (y_2 - y_1)^2 = l_2{}^2. \end{array} \right\} \tag{a}$$

Such equations as these which represent geometric relations between the coordinates of the system are called *equations of constraint*. Since there are four coordinates and two equations of constraint relating them, we conclude that only *two* are independent. For example, we can choose x_1 and x_2 arbitrarily and then find y_1 and y_2 from eqs. (a). Thus the system has only two degrees of freedom because there are only two independent coordinates required to specify its configuration completely. In general, if there are j coordinates and k equations of constraint, the number of degrees of freedom will be

$$n = j - k. \tag{b}$$

Instead of coordinates x_1, y_1, x_2, y_2, we can define the configuration of the double pendulum in Fig. 134b by the angles ϕ_1 and ϕ_2 that the two bars make with the vertical. These two independent coordinates completely define the configuration of the system. Choosing coordinates ϕ_1 and ϕ_2, we can easily express the rectangular coordinates in terms of them as follows:

$$\left. \begin{array}{c} x_1 = l_1 \sin \phi_1, \quad y_1 = l_1 \cos \phi_1, \\ x_2 = l_1 \sin \phi_1 + l_2 \sin \phi_2, \quad y_2 = l_1 \cos \phi_1 + l_2 \cos \phi_2. \end{array} \right\} \tag{c}$$

If the masses m_1 and m_2 in Fig. 134b are not constrained to remain in the xy-plane, we have a *double spherical pendulum*. In such case there are six rectangular coordinates, x_1, y_1, z_1, and x_2, y_2, z_2, and two equations of constraint,

$$\left. \begin{array}{c} x_1{}^2 + y_1{}^2 + z_1{}^2 = l_1{}^2, \\ (x_2 - x_1)^2 + (y_2 - y_1)^2 + (z_2 - z_1)^2 = l_2{}^2. \end{array} \right\} \tag{d}$$

Thus we conclude that the double spherical pendulum is a system with *four* degrees of freedom.

In Fig. 134c we have a rigid beam supported on springs k_1 and k_2 at its ends. Assuming that the system is constrained to remain in the vertical plane of the figure and that point G can move only vertically, we can define the position of the beam in this plane by the coordinates x_g and θ as shown. These two coordinates are independent and the system has two degrees of freedom.

In dealing with vibrations of systems with several degrees of freedom, we must write as many differential equations of motion as there are independent coordinates. The general problem of solution of such a system of simultaneous differential equations will then be our chief concern. In the following pages, we will consider various cases of this problem. We begin with the simplest case of free vibrations of a system with two degrees of freedom.

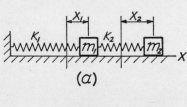

(a)

(b)

Fig. 135

31. Free Vibrations of Systems with Two Degrees of Freedom.—As an example of such a system let us consider the case shown in Fig. 135. Two masses m_1 and m_2 can slide without friction along the horizontal x-axis and the connecting springs have constants k_1 and k_2. We take, as coordinates, the displacements x_1 and x_2 of the masses from their positions of static equilibrium corresponding to no stresses in the springs. Then during motion, the forces exerted on the masses by the springs will be as shown in Fig. 135b, and the equations of motion for m_1 and m_2 become

$$\left.\begin{aligned} m_1\ddot{x}_1 &= -k_1x_1 + k_2(x_2 - x_1), \\ m_2\ddot{x}_2 &= -k_2(x_2 - x_1). \end{aligned}\right\} \quad (a)$$

To simplify these equations, we introduce the following notations:

$$\frac{k_1 + k_2}{m_1} = a, \quad \frac{k_2}{m_1} = b, \quad \frac{k_2}{m_2} = c. \quad (b)$$

Then eqs. (a) become

$$\left.\begin{aligned} \ddot{x}_1 + ax_1 - bx_2 &= 0, \\ \ddot{x}_2 - cx_1 + cx_2 &= 0. \end{aligned}\right\} \quad (c)$$

We see that these are simultaneous linear differential equations with constant coefficients. Assuming a particular solution of eqs. (c) in the form

$$\left.\begin{aligned} x_1 &= A \sin (pt + \alpha), \\ x_2 &= B \sin (pt + \alpha), \end{aligned}\right\} \quad (d)$$

and substituting back, we obtain

$$\left.\begin{array}{l} -Ap^2 \sin(pt + \alpha) + aA \sin(pt + \alpha) - bB \sin(pt + \alpha) = 0, \\ -Bp^2 \sin(pt + \alpha) - cA \sin(pt + \alpha) + cB \sin(pt + \alpha) = 0. \end{array}\right\} \quad (e)$$

We see that the assumed solutions (d) can satisfy the differential eqs. (c) for all values of time t only if the algebraic equations

$$\left.\begin{array}{l} A(a - p^2) - Bb = 0, \\ -Ac + B(c - p^2) = 0, \end{array}\right\} \quad (f)$$

are satisfied. One obvious solution of those equations is $A = B = 0$, which simply defines the equilibrium condition of the system and tells us nothing about vibrations. Eqs. (f) can yield, for A and B, solutions different from zero only if their determinant vanishes, which gives

$$(a - p^2)(c - p^2) - bc = 0, \quad (g)$$

or

$$p^4 - (a + c)p^2 + c(a - b) = 0. \quad (h)$$

This quadratic in p^2 is called the *frequency equation* for the system; its roots are

$$p_{1,2}{}^2 = \frac{a + c}{2} \mp \sqrt{\left(\frac{a + c}{2}\right)^2 - c(a - b)}, \quad (i)$$

which can also be written in the form

$$p_{1,2}{}^2 = \frac{a + c}{2} \mp \sqrt{\left(\frac{a - c}{2}\right)^2 + bc}. \quad (j)$$

Noting that the expression under the radical in eq. (j) is always positive, we conclude that both roots $p_1{}^2$ and $p_2{}^2$ are *real*. Furthermore, from notations (b) we see that $a - b$ is positive and hence the value of the radical in eq. (i) is always less than $\frac{1}{2}(a + c)$ and both roots are *positive*. Thus both roots are always real and positive and we obtain two angular frequencies p_1 and p_2 with plus or minus signs. For practical purposes, we need only consider the values with plus sign.

Returning now to eqs. (f), we see that we cannot obtain actual values for A and B but only their ratio,

$$\frac{A}{B} = \frac{b}{a - p^2} \quad \text{or} \quad \frac{A}{B} = \frac{c - p^2}{c}.$$

For $p^2 = p_1{}^2$ or $p_2{}^2$, both these ratios are equal by virtue of eq. (g). Substituting for p^2 the values (i), we obtain two different values of the amplitude ratio, namely:

$$\frac{A_1}{B_1} = \frac{b}{a - p_1{}^2} = \frac{c - p_1{}^2}{c} = \frac{1}{\lambda'}, \tag{k}$$

$$\frac{A_2}{B_2} = \frac{b}{a - p_2{}^2} = \frac{c - p_2{}^2}{c} = \frac{1}{\lambda''}. \tag{l}$$

Thus, although the magnitudes of A and B are indefinite, their ratio may have only two definite values (k) or (l). These ratios depend only on the physical constants a, b, c, as defined by notations (b).

Regarding the phase-angle α, we get no limitation, so that finally the particular solution (d) may have either of the following two forms:

$$x_1' = A_1 \sin (p_1 t + \alpha'), \quad x_2' = \lambda' A_1 \sin (p_1 t + \alpha'), \tag{m}$$

$$x_1'' = A_2 \sin (p_2 t + \alpha''), \quad x_2'' = \lambda'' A_2 \sin (p_2 t + \alpha''). \tag{n}$$

Using eq. (j), we see that

$$a - p_1{}^2 = \frac{a - c}{2} + \sqrt{\left(\frac{a - c}{2}\right)^2 + bc} > 0,$$

$$a - p_2{}^2 = \frac{a - c}{2} - \sqrt{\left(\frac{a - c}{2}\right)^2 + bc} < 0.$$

Hence we conclude that the amplitude ratio $\lambda' > 0$ while the amplitude ratio $\lambda'' < 0$. Thus when the system performs vibrations with the frequency p_1 as represented by the particular solution (m), the masses m_1 and m_2 move always in phase as represented schematically in Fig. 136a. When the system performs vibrations with the frequency p_2 as represented by the particular solution (n), the masses move always 180° out of phase as represented in Fig. 136b. These patterns of motion are called *principal modes* of vibration; that in Fig. 136a with the lower frequency p_1 is called the *first mode*, that in Fig. 136b with the higher frequency p_2 is called the *second mode*.

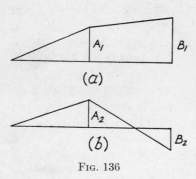

(a)

(b)

Fig. 136

From expressions (m) and (n) we see that the principal modes of vibration of the system are harmonic. After each interval of time equal to $2\pi/p_1$ for the first mode and $2\pi/p_2$ for the second mode, the system has the same configuration and the same velocities as before. The masses pass twice through their equilibrium positions during each cycle, both masses reach their extreme positions simultaneously and their displacements are always in a constant ratio.

The general solution of eqs. (c) can be obtained by superposition of the two particular solutions (m) and (n) representing principal modes. In this way we get

$$\left.\begin{aligned} x_1 &= A_1 \sin (p_1 t + \alpha') + A_2 \sin (p_2 t + \alpha''), \\ x_2 &= \lambda' A_1 \sin (p_1 t + \alpha') + \lambda'' A_2 \sin (p_2 t + \alpha''). \end{aligned}\right\} \quad (o)$$

This general solution contains four arbitrary constants A_1, A_2, α', and α'', which must be selected to satisfy the four initial conditions of motion, namely:

$$\left.\begin{aligned} (x_1)_{t=0} &= (x_1)_0, \quad (x_2)_{t=0} = (x_2)_0, \\ (\dot{x}_1)_{t=0} &= (\dot{x}_1)_0, \quad (\dot{x}_2)_{t=0} = (\dot{x}_2)_0. \end{aligned}\right\} \quad (p)$$

It will be noted that eqs. (o) represent a complicated motion which is not periodic unless the principal frequencies p_1 and p_2 happen to be commensurable. The system performs a pure harmonic motion only if carefully started in one of its principal modes.

Dealing with any two degree of freedom system as above, we will always obtain as our frequency equation a quadratic in p^2 which usually will have two distinct real positive roots. For each of these two roots, we will obtain a definite ratio of the amplitudes of the two coordinates. These amplitude ratios define two principal modes of free vibration of the system, such as illustrated in Fig. 136. By superposition of these principal modes in the proper proportion, the general case of free vibrations of the system can be represented.

If it happens that the two roots of the frequency equation are *equal*, we will find that the amplitude ratios λ' and λ'' will also be equal and the two principal modes are identical. In such case the general solution (o) can be put in the form

$$\left.\begin{aligned} x_1 &= C \sin (pt + \beta'), \\ x_2 &= D \sin (pt + \beta''), \end{aligned}\right\} \quad (q)$$

where C, D, β' and β'' are new arbitrary constants.

As an example of such a system, consider the mass m at the top of a slender vertical rod of uniform circular cross section, as shown in Fig. 137. For any small displacement δ of this mass defined by coordinates x and y, the restoring force exerted by the rod is $k\delta$ directed toward the equilibrium

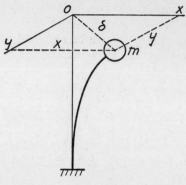

Fig. 137

position O. Resolving this force into x- and y- projection the equations of motion become

$$m\ddot{x} = -kx, \Big\}$$
$$m\ddot{y} = -ky. \Big\} \qquad (r)$$

Comparing these expressions with eqs. (a), we conclude that in this case

$$a = \frac{k}{m}, \quad b = 0, \quad c = \frac{k}{m},$$

and the frequency equation roots (i) become

$$p_{1,2}{}^2 = \frac{k}{m} \mp 0,$$

i.e., $p_1 = p_2 = \sqrt{k/m}$.

It may also happen in special cases that one of the roots of the frequency equation vanishes. Consider, for example, the shaft with two discs, as shown in Fig. 138. If we define the configuration of this system by angles of rotation ϕ_1 and ϕ_2 of the discs about the horizontal axis of the shaft, we see that the angle of twist in the

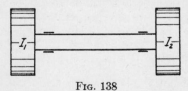

Fig. 138

shaft is $\phi_2 - \phi_1$. Then denoting by k_t the torsional spring constant of the shaft, the equations of motion of the discs become

$$\left.\begin{array}{l} I_1\ddot{\phi}_1 = k_t(\phi_2 - \phi_1), \\ I_2\ddot{\phi}_2 = -k_t(\phi_2 - \phi_1). \end{array}\right\} \tag{s}$$

Comparing again with eqs. (a), we see that in this case

$$a = \frac{k_t}{I_1}, \quad b = \frac{k_t}{I_1}, \quad c = \frac{k_t}{I_2},$$

and the roots of the frequency equation become

$$p_{1,2}{}^2 = \frac{I_1 + I_2}{2I_1I_2} k_t \mp \sqrt{\left(\frac{I_1 + I_2}{2I_1I_2}\right)^2 k_t{}^2}.$$

Thus $p_1{}^2 = 0$ and $p_2{}^2 = \dfrac{(I_1 + I_2)k_t}{I_1I_2}$. In this case the root $p_1 = 0$ simply indicates that one of the possible motions of the system is rigid body rotation about the axis of the shaft.

In discussing the example in Fig. 135, we selected as coordinates the displacements x_1 and x_2 of the two masses and obtained the two differential eqs. (a), each containing both unknowns x_1 and x_2. By a proper selection of the coordinates, it is always possible to bring the problem to two differential equations, each of which contains only one unknown quantity and can be solved independently of the other. Coordinates satisfying this condition are called *principal coordinates*. For illustration let us consider again the case in Fig. 135. Instead of defining the configuration of the system by the displacements x_1 and x_2, we can obtain any configuration by superposing the two principal modes of vibration, illustrated in Fig. 136 and given by eqs. (m) and (n). The displacements of the lower mode of vibration can be defined by the displacement ϕ_1 of the mass m_1. Then

$$(x_1)' = \phi_1, \quad (x_2)' = \frac{a - p_1{}^2}{b} \phi_1. \tag{t}$$

In the same way the displacements corresponding to the higher mode of vibration can be defined by the displacement ϕ_2 of the mass m_1, so that

$$(x_1)'' = \phi_2, \quad (x_2)'' = \frac{a - p_2{}^2}{b} \phi_2. \tag{u}$$

The quantities ϕ_1 and ϕ_2 can be taken as the new coordinates.

To obtain the differential equation for ϕ_1, we substitute for x_1 and x_2 expressions (t) into first of eqs. (c). Then we find

$$\ddot{\phi}_1 = -a\phi_1 + (a - p_1^2)\phi_1 = -p_1^2\phi_1. \tag{v}$$

We obtain the same equation by substituting (t) into the second of eqs. (c) and observing that

$$\frac{a - p_1^2}{b} = \frac{c}{c - p_1^2}.$$

By substituting (u) into eqs. (c), we obtain

$$\ddot{\phi}_2 = -p_2^2\phi_2. \tag{w}$$

Eqs. (v) and (w) are independent of each other so the new coordinates ϕ_1 and ϕ_2 are the principal coordinates of our system. We see that if we know the principal modes of vibrations we know also the principal coordinates.

32. Illustrative Examples of Free Vibration.—Following the general procedure of Art. 31, we shall now consider several examples of free vibrations of systems with two degrees of freedom.

(a) *Two Connected Simple Pendulums.*—Consider the two simple pendulums of equal mass m and length l connected by a spring of constant k at the distance h below the points of suspension A and B (Fig. 139). We assume that the bars of the pendulums

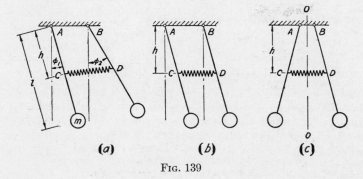

(a) (b) (c)

Fig. 139

are without mass and can move only in the vertical plane of the figure. For coordinates we choose the angles ϕ_1 and ϕ_2 as shown. Observing that the spring is without tension when the pendulums are vertical, we see that for any other configuration of the system the net extension of the spring is $h(\phi_2 - \phi_1)$. Limiting consideration to small angles of swing, the equations of motion are

$$\left.\begin{aligned} ml^2\ddot{\phi}_1 &= -mgl\phi_1 + kh^2(\phi_2 - \phi_1), \\ ml^2\ddot{\phi}_2 &= -mgl\phi_2 - kh^2(\phi_2 - \phi_1). \end{aligned}\right\} \tag{a}$$

Introducing the notations

$$a = \frac{g}{l} + \frac{kh^2}{ml^2}, \quad b = \frac{kh^2}{ml^2},$$ (b)

eqs. (a) may be expressed in the simplified form:

$$\ddot{\phi}_1 + a\phi_1 - b\phi_2 = 0, \left.\right\}$$
$$\ddot{\phi}_2 - b\phi_1 + a\phi_2 = 0. \left.\right\}$$ c)

Assuming, as a particular solution of those equations,

$$\phi_1 = A \sin (pt + \alpha),$$

$$\phi_2 = B \sin (pt + \alpha),$$

and substituting back, we obtain

$$(a - p^2)A - bB = 0, \left.\right\}$$
$$-bA + (a - p^2)B = 0. \left.\right\}$$ (d)

Equating to zero, the determinate of these equations, we find the frequency equation

$$p^4 - 2ap^2 + (a^2 - b^2) = 0,$$ (e)

the roots of which are $p_{1,2}{}^2 = a \mp b$, or using notations (b),

$$p_1{}^2 = \frac{g}{l}, \quad p_2{}^2 = \frac{g}{l} + \frac{2kh^2}{ml^2}.$$ (f)

From eqs. (d), we now find the amplitude ratios

$$\frac{A_1}{B_1} = \frac{b}{a - p_1{}^2} = +1, \quad \frac{A_2}{B_2} = \frac{b}{a - p_2{}^2} = -1.$$ (g)

These two modes of vibration are shown in Figs. 139b and 139c. In the first mode, the pendulums have the same amplitude and their vibrations are in phase. There evidently is no force in the spring, so that the frequency of vibration is the same as for a simple pendulum. In the second mode of vibration, Fig. 139c, there is a phase difference of 180 degrees in the oscillation of the two pendula and the spring comes into play which means that a higher frequency is obtained. This later frequency can be found in another way, if we observe that the configuration of the system is symmetrical with respect to the vertical axis oo. Considering the motion of one of the two pendula and noting that the force in the spring is $2k\varphi h$, the principle of moment of momentum with respect to the suspension point of the pendulum gives

$$\frac{d}{dt}(m\dot{\phi}l^2) = -(mgl\phi + 2k\phi h^2),$$

from which the frequency p_2, calculated above, results. Having found the principal modes of vibration, we may write the general solution by superposing these two vibrations, taking each mode of vibration with its proper amplitude and its proper phase angle. Thus we obtain the following general expressions for each coordinate:

$$\phi_1 = a_1 \sin (p_1 t + \alpha_1) + a_2 \sin (p_2 t + \alpha_2),$$

$$\phi_2 = a_1 \sin (p_1 t + \alpha_1) - a_2 \sin (p_2 t + \alpha_2),$$

in which the constants a_1, a_2, α_1 and α_2 are to be determined from the initial conditions.

Assume, for instance, that at the initial instant ($t = 0$) the pendulum to the left has the angle of inclination ϕ_0 while the pendulum to the right is vertical; moreover the initial velocities of both pendula are zero. Then

$$(\phi_1)_{t=0} = \phi_0, \quad (\phi_2)_{t=0} = 0, \quad (\dot\phi_1)_{t=0} = (\dot\phi_2)_{t=0} = 0.$$

These conditions are satisfied in the general solution by taking

$$a_1 = a_2 = \tfrac{1}{2}\phi_0 \quad \text{and} \quad \alpha_1 = \alpha_2 = \tfrac{1}{2}\pi.$$

Then

$$\phi_1 = \frac{\phi_0}{2} (\cos p_1 t + \cos p_2 t) = \phi_0 \cos \frac{p_1 - p_2}{2} t \cos \frac{p_1 + p_2}{2} t,$$

$$\phi_2 = \frac{\phi_0}{2} (\cos p_1 t - \cos p_2 t) = \phi_0 \sin \frac{p_2 - p_1}{2} t \cos \frac{p_1 + p_2}{2} t.$$

If the two frequencies p_1 and p_2 are close to one another, each coordinate contains a product of two trigonometric functions, one of low frequency $(p_1 - p_2)/2$ and the other of high frequency $(p_1 + p_2)/2$. Thus a phenomenon of beating (see p. 47) takes place. At the beginning we have vibrations of the pendulum to the left. Gradually its amplitude decreases, while the amplitude of the pendulum to the right increases and after an interval of time $\pi/(p_1 - p_2)$ only the second pendulum will be in motion. Immediately thereupon the vibration of the first pendulum begins to increase and so on.

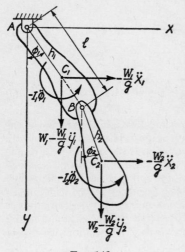

FIG. 140

(b) *Double Physical Pendulum.*—Consider the double pendulum shown in Fig. 140, which consists of two rigid bodies hinged together at B and suspended from point A. The centers of gravity of the bodies are denoted by C_1 and C_2 and dimensions are as shown in the figure. The system is constrained to remain in the vertical xy-plane and its configuration at any instant will be defined by the coordinates x_1, y_1 and x_2, y_2 of the points C_1 and C_2.

Using d'Alembert's principle, we apply to each body its inertia forces and inertia couples * as shown. This puts the system in dynamic equilibrium and allows us to write equations of motion as equilibrium equations. Friction in the pins at A and B is neglected.

* I_1 and I_2 are moments of inertia of the bodies with respect to their centroidal axes through C_1 and C_2 and perpendicular to the plane of motion.

Equating to zero the algebraic sums of moments with respect to A and B we obtain

$$\left.\begin{aligned}
-I_1\ddot{\phi}_1 - I_2\ddot{\phi}_2 - \frac{W_1}{g}\ddot{x}_1 y_1 - \left(W_1 - \frac{W_1}{g}\ddot{y}_1\right)x_1 - \frac{W_2}{g}\ddot{x}_2 y_2 - \left(W_2 - \frac{W_2}{g}\ddot{y}_2\right)x_2 = 0, \\
-I_2\ddot{\phi}_2 - \frac{W_2}{g}\ddot{x}_2 h_2 \cos\phi_2 - \left(W_2 - \frac{W_2}{g}\ddot{y}_2\right)h_2 \sin\phi_2 = 0.
\end{aligned}\right\} \quad (h)$$

In these equations, the rectangular coordinates x_1, y_1, x_2, y_2 are related to the coordinates ϕ_1 and ϕ_2 as follows:

$$\left.\begin{aligned}
x_1 &= h_1 \sin\phi_1, \quad y_1 = h_1 \cos\phi_1, \\
x_2 &= l\sin\phi_1 + h_2 \sin\phi_2, \quad y_2 = l\cos\phi_1 + h_2 \cos\phi_2.
\end{aligned}\right\} \quad (i)$$

We now introduce the limitation that the pendulum swings with small oscillations such that ϕ_1 and ϕ_2 are always small angles. In such case, $\sin\phi \approx \phi$ and $\cos\phi \approx 1$, so that eqs. (i) may be replaced by the approximate expressions

$$\left.\begin{aligned}
x_1 &\approx h_1\phi_1, \quad y_1 \approx h_1, \\
x_2 &\approx l\phi_1 + h_2\phi_2, \quad y_2 \approx l + h_2.
\end{aligned}\right\} \quad (j)$$

Substituting these relations into eqs. (h), we obtain

$$-I_1\ddot{\phi}_1 - I_2\ddot{\phi}_2 - \frac{W_1}{g}h_1{}^2\ddot{\phi}_1 - W_1 h_1\phi_1 - \frac{W_2}{g}(l\ddot{\phi}_1 + h_2\ddot{\phi}_2)(l + h_2) - W_2(l\phi_1 + h_2\phi_2) = 0,$$

$$-I_2\ddot{\phi}_2 - \frac{W_2}{g}(l\ddot{\phi}_1 + h_2\ddot{\phi}_2)h_2 - W_2 h_2\phi_2 = 0.$$

To obtain two still simpler equations in ϕ_1 and ϕ_2, we subtract the second from the first and write

$$-I_1\ddot{\phi}_1 - \frac{W_1}{g}h_1{}^2\ddot{\phi}_1 - W_1 h_1\phi_1 - \frac{W_2}{g}l^2\ddot{\phi}_1 - \frac{W_2}{g}lh_2\ddot{\phi}_2 - W_2 l\phi_1 = 0,$$

$$-I_2\ddot{\phi}_2 - \frac{W_2}{g}lh_2\phi_1 - \frac{W_2}{g}h_2{}^2\ddot{\phi}_2 - W_2 h_2\phi_2 = 0.$$

Finally, collecting terms, we have

$$\left.\begin{aligned}
\left(I_1 + \frac{W_1}{g}h_1{}^2 + \frac{W_2}{g}l^2\right)\ddot{\phi}_1 + \frac{W_2}{g}lh_2\ddot{\phi}_2 + (W_1 h_1 + W_2 l)\phi_1 = 0, \\
\frac{W_2}{g}lh_2\ddot{\phi}_1 + \left(I_2 + \frac{W_2}{g}h_2{}^2\right)\ddot{\phi}_2 + W_2 h_2\phi_2 = 0.
\end{aligned}\right\} \quad (k)$$

These are the two required simultaneous differential equations of motion for small free oscillations of the pendulum in its vertical plane. We note that they are equations with constant coefficients only because we have limited consideration to *small values* of ϕ_1 and ϕ_2 (see eqs. j).

Introducing now the notations

$$a_{11} = I_1 + \frac{W_1}{g} h_1{}^2 + \frac{W_2}{g} l^2, \quad c_{11} = W_1 h_1 + W_2 l,$$
$$a_{12} = \frac{W_2}{g} l h_2, \quad \cdots,$$
$$a_{22} = I_2 + \frac{W_2}{g} h_2{}^2, \quad c_{22} = W_2 h_2, \tag{l}$$

we may express eqs. (k) in the form

$$\begin{aligned} a_{11}\ddot{\phi}_1 + a_{12}\ddot{\phi}_2 + c_{11}\phi_1 &= 0, \\ a_{12}\ddot{\phi}_1 + a_{22}\ddot{\phi}_2 + c_{22}\phi_2 &= 0. \end{aligned} \tag{m}$$

Proceeding from here on as in previous examples, we will find the frequency equation

$$(a_{11}p^2 - c_{11})(a_{22}p^2 - c_{22}) - a_{12}{}^2 p^4 = 0, \tag{n}$$

or with notations (l),

$$\left[\left(I_1 + \frac{W_1}{g} h_1{}^2 + \frac{W_2}{g} l^2 \right) p^2 - (W_1 h_1 + W_2 l) \right] \left[\left(I_2 + \frac{W_2}{g} h_2{}^2 \right) p^2 - W_2 h_2 \right]$$
$$- h_2{}^2 l^2 \left(\frac{W_2}{g} \right)^2 p^4 = 0. \tag{n'}$$

To simplify the writing we introduce the further notations

$$\frac{c_{11}}{a_{11}} = \frac{W_1 h_1 + W_2 l}{I_1 + \dfrac{W_1}{g} h_1{}^2 + \dfrac{W_2}{g} l^2} = n_1{}^2, \quad \frac{c_{22}}{a_{22}} = \frac{W_2 h_2}{I_2 + \dfrac{W_2}{g} h_2{}^2} = n_2{}^2,$$

$$\frac{W_2{}^2 h_2{}^2 l^2}{g^2 \left(I_1 + \dfrac{W_1}{g} h_1{}^2 + \dfrac{W_2}{g} l^2 \right) \left(I_2 + \dfrac{W_2}{g} h_2{}^2 \right)} = n_3{}^2,$$

and the frequency equation will be

$$(1 - n_3{}^2)p^4 - (n_1{}^2 + n_2{}^2)p^2 + n_1{}^2 n_2{}^2 = 0. \tag{n''}$$

It should be noted that the quantities n_1 and n_2 have simple physical meanings, thus n_1 represents the frequency of oscillation of the upper body if the mass of the lower body is thought of as being concentrated at the hinge B. Likewise, n_2 is the frequency of oscillation of the lower body if the hinge B is at rest. The roots of eq. (n'') are

$$p_1{}^2 = \frac{1}{2(1 - n_3{}^2)} \left(n_1{}^2 + n_2{}^2 - \sqrt{(n_2{}^2 - n_1{}^2)^2 + 4 n_1{}^2 n_2{}^2 n_3{}^2} \right),$$

$$p_2{}^2 = \frac{1}{2(1 - n_3{}^2)} \left(n_1{}^2 + n_2{}^2 + \sqrt{(n_2{}^2 - n_1{}^2)^2 + 4 n_1{}^2 n_2{}^2 n_3{}^2} \right).$$

The ratios of the amplitudes of the corresponding modes of vibration are

$$\left(\frac{\phi_1}{\phi_2}\right)_1 = \frac{a_{12}p_1^2}{c_{11} - a_{11}p_1^2} = \frac{a_{12}}{a_{11}} \frac{p_1^2}{n_1^2 - p_1^2},$$ (o)

$$\left(\frac{\phi_1}{\phi_2}\right)_2 = \frac{a_{12}p_2^2}{c_{11} - a_{11}p_2^2} = \frac{a_{12}}{a_{11}} \frac{p_2^2}{n_1^2 - p_2^2}.$$ (p)

Assuming that $p_1 < p_2$ we find that for the mode with lower frequency the ratio of the amplitudes is positive and for the higher frequency it is negative. These two modes of vibration are shown diagrammatically in Fig. 141. Having found the principal modes of

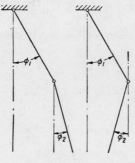

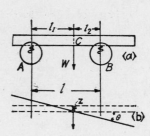

FIG. 141   FIG. 142

vibration, we obtain the general solution by superposing the two modes of vibration with proper amplitudes and with proper phase angles so as to satisfy the initial conditions. If the system is to vibrate in one of its principal modes the ratio between the angles φ_1 and φ_2, given by eq. (o) or eq. (p), must be established initially before the system is released without initial velocities.

(c) *Vibrations of Vehicles.*—The problem of the vibration of a four-wheel vehicle as a system with many degrees of freedom is a very complicated one. In the following pages this problem is simplified and only the pitching motion in one plane * (Fig. 142) will be considered. In such a case the system has only *two degrees of freedom* and its position during vibration can be specified by two coordinates: the vertical displacement z of the center of gravity C and the angle of rotation θ as shown in Fig. 142b. Both of these coordinates will be measured from the position of equilibrium.

Let W be the spring-borne weight of the vehicle;
  $I = (W/g)i^2$, the moment of inertia of the sprung mass about the axis through the center of gravity C;
  i, the radius of gyration;
  k_1, k_2, spring constants for the axes through A and B, respectively;
  l_1, l_2, distances of the center of gravity from the same axes.

* Rolling motion of the car is excluded from the following discussion.

With these notations, the equations of motion become

$$\frac{W}{g}\ddot{z} = -k_1(z - l_1\theta) - k_2(z + l_2\theta),$$

$$\frac{W}{g}i^2\ddot{\theta} = l_1k_1(z - l_1\theta) - l_2k_2(z + l_2\theta).$$

Letting

$$\frac{(k_1 + k_2)g}{W} = a, \quad \frac{(-k_1l_1 + k_2l_2)g}{W} = b, \quad \frac{(l_1{}^2k_1 + l_2{}^2k_2)g}{W} = c, \tag{q}$$

we have

$$\left.\begin{aligned} \ddot{z} + az + b\theta &= 0, \\ \ddot{\theta} + \frac{b}{i^2}z + \frac{c}{i^2}\theta &= 0. \end{aligned}\right\} \tag{r}$$

These two simultaneous differential equations show that in general the coordinates z and θ are not independent of each other and if, for instance, in order to produce vibrations, the frame of the car be displaced parallel to itself in the z direction and then suddenly released, not only a vertical displacement z but also a rotation θ will take place during the subsequent vibration. The coordinates z and θ become independent only in the case when $b = 0$. This occurs when $k_1l_1 = k_2l_2$, i.e., when the spring constants are inversely proportional to the spring distances from the center of gravity. In such cases a load applied at the center of gravity will produce only vertical displacement of the frame without rotation. Such conditions exist in the case of railway carriages where usually $l_1 = l_2$ and $k_1 = k_2$.

Returning now to the general case we take the solution of the eqs. (r) in the following form:

$$z = A \cos (pt + \alpha), \quad \theta = B \cos (pt + \alpha).$$

Substituting in eqs. (r) we obtain

$$\left.\begin{aligned} A(a - p^2) + bB &= 0, \\ \frac{b}{i^2}A + \left(\frac{c}{i^2} - p^2\right) B &= 0. \end{aligned}\right\} \tag{s}$$

Eliminating A and B from eqs. (s), the following frequency equation will be obtained,

$$(a - p^2)\left(\frac{c}{i^2} - p^2\right) - \frac{b^2}{i^2} = 0.$$

The two roots of eq. (t) considered as a quadratic in p^2 are

$$p^2 = \frac{1}{2}\left(\frac{c}{i^2} + a\right) \pm \sqrt{\frac{1}{4}\left(\frac{c}{i^2} + a\right)^2 - \frac{ac}{i^2} + \frac{b^2}{i^2}} = \frac{1}{2}\left(\frac{c}{i^2} + a\right) \pm \sqrt{\frac{1}{4}\left(\frac{c}{i^2} - a\right)^2 + \frac{b^2}{i^2}}. \tag{u}$$

Noting from notations (q) that

$$ac - b^2 = \frac{g^2}{W^2} k_1k_2(l_1 + l_2)^2,$$

it can be concluded that both roots of eq. (t) are real and positive.

Substituting (u) in the first of eqs. (s), the following values for the ratio A/B between the amplitudes will be obtained:

$$\frac{A}{B} = \frac{b}{p^2 - a} = \frac{b}{\frac{1}{2}\left(\frac{c}{i^2} - a\right) \pm \sqrt{\frac{1}{4}\left(\frac{c}{i^2} - a\right)^2 + \frac{b^2}{i^2}}}. \tag{v}$$

The $+$ sign corresponds to the mode of vibration having the higher frequency, while the $-$ sign corresponds to vibrations of lower frequency.

In further discussion it will be assumed that

$$b > 0 \quad \text{or} \quad k_2 l_2 > k_1 l_1.$$

This means that under the action of its own weight the displacement of the car is opposite to that shown in Fig. 142; the displacement in the downward direction is associated with a rotation in the direction of negative θ. Under this assumption the amplitudes A and B will have opposite signs if the negative sign be taken before the radical in the denominator of (v) and they will have the same signs when the positive sign be taken. The corresponding two types of vibration are shown in Fig. 143. The type (a)

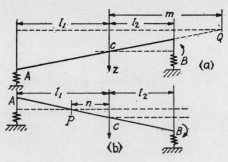

Fig. 143

has a lower frequency and can be considered as a rotation about a certain point Q to the right of the center of gravity C. The type (b) having a higher frequency, consists of a rotation about a certain point P to the left of C. The distances m and n of the points Q and P from the center of gravity are given by the absolute values of the right side of eq. (v) and we obtain a very simple relation,

$$mn = -\frac{b}{\frac{1}{2}\left(\frac{c}{i^2} - a\right) + \sqrt{\frac{1}{4}\left(\frac{c}{i^2} - a\right)^2 + \frac{b^2}{i^2}}} \cdot \frac{b}{\frac{1}{2}\left(\frac{c}{i^2} - a\right) - \sqrt{\frac{1}{4}\left(\frac{c}{i^2} - a\right)^2 + \frac{b}{i^2}}}^2 \tag{w}$$

which reduces to $mn = i^2$.

In the particular case, when $b = 0$, i.e., $k_1 l_1 = k_2 l_2$, the distance n becomes equal to zero and m becomes infinitely large. This means that in this case one of the principal modes of vibration consists of a rotation about the center of gravity and the other consists of a translatory movement without rotation. A vertical load applied at the center of gravity in this case will produce only a vertical displacement and both springs will get equal compressions.

If, in addition to $b = 0$, $(c/i^2) - a$ becomes equal to zero, both frequencies, as given by eq. (u), become equal and the two types of vibration will have the same period.

A numerical example of the above theory will now be considered.* Taking a case with the following data: $W = 966$ lb; $i^2 = 13$ ft^2; $l_1 = 4$ ft; $l_2 = 5$ ft; $k_1 = 1600$ lb per ft; $k_2 = 2400$ lb per ft, the corresponding static deflections are

$$\delta_a = \frac{Wl_2}{k_1 l} = 4.0 \text{ in.},$$

$$\delta_b = \frac{Wl_1}{k_2 l} = 2.15 \text{ in.},$$

and from eqs. (q)

$$a = 133.3, \quad b = 186.7, \quad c = 2853.$$

Substituting in (u) we obtain the following two roots: $p_1{}^2 = 109$, $p_2{}^2 = 244$. The corresponding frequencies are

$p_1 = 10.5$ radians per sec and $p_2 = 15.6$ radians per sec, respectively, or
$N_1 = 100$ and $N_2 = 150$ complete oscillations per min.

From eq. (v) we have

$$\frac{A}{B} = -7.71 \text{ ft} \quad \text{and} \quad \frac{A}{B} = 1.69 \text{ ft.}$$

This means that in the slower mode of vibration the sprung weight oscillates 7.71 ft per radian of pitching motion or 1.62 in. per degree.

In the higher mode of vibration the sprung weight oscillates 1.69 ft for every radian of pitching motion or 0.355 in. per degree.

Roughly speaking, in the slower mode of vibration the car is bouncing, the deflections of two springs being of the same sign and in the ratio

$$\frac{\delta_b{}'}{\delta_a{}'} = \frac{7.71 - 5}{7.71 + 4} = 0.23.$$

In the faster mode of vibration the car is mostly pitching.

It is interesting to note that a good approximation for the frequencies of the principal modes of vibration can be obtained by using the theory of a system with one degree of freedom. Assuming first that the spring at B is removed so that the car can bounce on the spring A about the axis B as a hinge, the equation of motion is

$$\left(I + \frac{W}{g} l_2{}^2 \right) \ddot{\theta} + k_1 l^2 \theta = 0,$$

* See H. S. Rowell. *Proc. Inst. Automobile Engrs.* (*London*), Vol. 17, Part II, p. 455, 1923.

so that the "constrained" frequency is

$$p_1' = l \sqrt{\frac{k_1}{I + \dfrac{W}{g} l_2^2}},$$

or substituting the numerical data above,

$$p_1' = 9 \sqrt{\frac{1600}{\dfrac{966}{32.2} (13 + 25)}} = 10.7.$$

This is in good agreement with the frequency 10.5 obtained above for the lower type of vibration of the car. In the same manner, considering the bouncing of the car on the spring B about the axis A as a hinge, we obtain $p_2' = 15.0$ as compared with $p_2 = 15.6$ given above for the higher mode of vibration.

On the basis of this a practical method for obtaining the frequencies of the principal modes of vibration by test is to lock the front springs and bounce the car; then lock the rear springs and again bounce the car. The frequencies obtained by these tests will represent a good approximation.

Returning now to the general solution of eqs. (r) and denoting by p_1 and p_2 the two roots obtained from (u), we have

$$\left. \begin{aligned} z &= A_1 \cos (p_1 t + \alpha_1) + A_2 \cos (p_2 t + \alpha_2), \\ \theta &= B_1 \cos (p_1 t + \alpha_1) + B_2 \cos (p_2 t + \alpha_2), \end{aligned} \right\} \qquad (x)$$

in which (see eq. v)

$$\frac{A_1}{B_1} = \frac{b}{p_1^2 - a}, \quad \frac{A_2}{B_2} = \frac{b}{p_2^2 - a}.$$

The general solution (x) contains four arbitrary constants A_1, A_2, α_1 and α_2, which must be determined for every particular case so as to satisfy the initial conditions. Assume, for instance, that in the initial moment a displacement λ exists in a downward direction without rotation and that the car is then suddenly released. In such a case the initial conditions are

$$(z)_{t=0} = \lambda, \quad (\dot{z})_{t=0} = 0, \quad (\theta)_{t=0} = 0, \quad (\dot{\theta})_{t=0} = 0.$$

These conditions will be satisfied by taking in eqs. (x)

$$\alpha_1 = \alpha_2 = 0,$$

$$A_1 = \lambda \frac{a - p_2^2}{p_1^2 - p_2^2}, \quad A_2 = \lambda \frac{p_1^2 - a}{p_1^2 - p_2^2},$$

$$B_1 = A_1 \frac{(p_1^2 - a)}{b}, \quad B_2 = A_2 \frac{(p_2^2 - a)}{b}. \qquad (y)$$

We see that under the assumed conditions both modes of vibration will be produced which at the beginning will be in the same phase but with elapse of time, due to the difference in frequencies, they will become displaced with respect to each other and a complicated combined motion will take place. If the difference of frequencies is a very small one the characteristic *beating phenomenon*, i.e., vibrations with periodically varying amplitude, will take place. In considering this particular case, assume in eq. (u) that

$$\frac{c}{i^2} - a = 0 \quad \text{and} \quad \frac{b}{i} = \delta,$$

where δ is a small quantity. Then

$$p_1{}^2 = a - \delta, \quad p_2{}^2 = a + \delta,$$

and from (y) we obtain

$$A_1 = \frac{\lambda}{2}, \quad A_2 = \frac{\lambda}{2}, \quad B_1 = -\frac{\lambda}{2i}, \quad B_2 = \frac{\lambda}{2i}.$$

Solution (x) becomes

$$\left.\begin{aligned}
z &= \frac{\lambda}{2}(\cos p_1 t + \cos p_2 t) = \lambda \cos \frac{p_1 + p_2}{2} t \cos \frac{p_1 - p_2}{2} t, \\
\theta &= \frac{\lambda}{2i}(-\cos p_1 t + \cos p_2 t) = \frac{\lambda}{i} \sin \frac{p_1 + p_2}{2} t \sin \frac{p_1 - p_2}{2} t.
\end{aligned}\right\} \tag{z}$$

Owing to the fact that $p_1 - p_2$ is a small quantity, the functions $\cos\{(p_1 + p_2)/2\}t$ and $\sin\{(p_1 + p_2)/2\}t$ will be quickly varying functions so that they will perform several cycles before the slowly varying function $\sin\{(p_1 - p_2)/2\}t$ or $\cos\{(p_1 - p_2)/2\}t$ can undergo considerable change. As a result, oscillations with periodically varying amplitudes will be obtained.

33. Forced Vibrations of Systems with Two Degrees of Freedom.—We now consider the general problem of steady-state forced vibrations of a two degree of freedom system under the influence of a harmonic disturbing force. As a specific example of such a system, we consider again the two masses m_1 and m_2 as shown in Fig. 135a and assume that in addition to the elastic spring forces there is an external force $Q \sin \omega t$ applied to the mass m_1. In such case the equations of motion (a) on p. 188 become

$$\left.\begin{aligned}
m_1 \ddot{x}_1 &= -k_1 x_1 + k_2(x_2 - x_1) + Q \sin \omega t, \\
m_2 \ddot{x}_2 &= -k_2(x_2 - x_1).
\end{aligned}\right\} \tag{a}$$

Introducing the notations

$$\frac{k_1 + k_2}{m_1} = a, \quad \frac{k_2}{m_1} = b, \quad \frac{k_2}{m_2} = c, \quad \frac{Q}{m_1} = q, \tag{b}$$

eqs. (a) may be expressed in the condensed form:

$$\left.\begin{aligned}
\ddot{x}_1 + a x_1 - b x_2 &= q \sin \omega t, \\
\ddot{x}_2 - c x_1 + c x_2 &= 0.
\end{aligned}\right\} \tag{c}$$

A particular solution of these equations can be taken in the form

$$x_1 = C \sin \omega t, \\ x_2 = D \sin \omega t. \tag{d}$$

To obtain the amplitudes C and D we substitute expressions (d) back into eqs. (c) and find

$$(a - \omega^2)C - bD = q, \\ -cC + (c - \omega^2)D = 0, \tag{e}$$

which give for C and D the following values:

$$C = \frac{q(c - \omega^2)}{(a - \omega^2)(c - \omega^2) - bc}, \\ D = \frac{qc}{(a - \omega^2)(c - \omega^2) - bc}. \tag{f}$$

With these values of C and D, expressions (d) satisfy the equations of motion (c) for all values of time. We see that expressions (d) represent simple harmonic motions of the two masses with the same angular frequency ω as the disturbing force that excites the motion. The amplitudes C and D however, depend on the intensity q of the disturbing force and on the value of the angular frequency ω.

For very small values of ω, i.e., for a very slowly varying disturbing force, we can neglect ω^2 in comparison with a or c in expressions (f) and take

$$C = D \approx \frac{q}{a - b} = \frac{Q}{k_1} = \lambda_{st}. \tag{g}$$

From this we see that a slowly varying disturbing force produces a purely statical effect in which the spring k_2 remains constant in length and both masses move together with displacements always equal to the static elongation of the spring k_1, under the action of the force $Q \sin \omega t$.

Comparing the denominator of expressions (f) with the frequency eq. (g) in Art. 31, we conclude that when $\omega = p_1$ or $\omega = p_2$, the amplitudes C and D become infinitely large. Thus for a two degree of freedom system there are two conditions of resonance, one corresponding to each of the two natural frequencies of free vibration.

The ratio of the amplitudes C and D of forced vibration, from expressions (f), is

$$\frac{C}{D} = \frac{c - \omega^2}{c}. \tag{h}$$

For either of the two resonance conditions, i.e., when $\omega = p_1$ or $\omega = p_2$, this ratio approaches the value A_1/B_1 or A_2/B_2 given by eqs. (k) and (l) of Art. 31. This means that in a condition of resonacne, the forced vibrations are in the corresponding principal mode (see Fig. 136).

To construct a complete response diagram like that in Fig. 36 for a system with two degrees of freedom, it is necessary to assume some definite relation between the spring constants k_1 and k_2 and the masses m_1 and m_2. As a particular case, we take $k_1 = k_2$ and $m_1 = 2m_2$. Then $a = c = 2p_0^2$ and $b = p_0^2$, where $p_0 = \sqrt{k_1/m_1}$ is the natural frequency of m_1 alone on the spring k_1 (see Fig. 135a). For this particular case, eq. (i) on p. 189 gives for the two principal frequencies

$$p_1^2 = 0.586p_0^2, \quad p_2^2 = 3.41p_0^2,$$

and eqs. (f), defining amplitudes, become, with notation (g),

$$C = \frac{\lambda_{st}(a - b)(1 - \omega^2/c)}{a(1 - \omega^2/a)(1 - \omega^2/c) - b} = \frac{\lambda_{st}(1 - \omega^2/2p_0^2)}{2(1 - \omega^2/2p_0^2)^2 - 1} = \alpha\lambda_{st}, \quad (i)$$

$$D = \frac{\lambda_{st}}{2(1 - \omega^2/2p_0^2)^2 - 1} = \beta\lambda_{st}, \quad (j)$$

where the factors α and β depend only on the ratio ω/p_0. These factors are represented graphically in Fig. 144. We see that when ω approaches zero, both factors approach unity and the amplitudes C and D approach the value λ_{st} as defined by expression (g). As ω increases, both amplitudes increase also and approach infinity as ω approaches the first natural frequency p_1. For this region both amplitudes are positive, which indicates that the two masses are vibrating *in phase* with the disturbing force. When ω becomes slightly greater than p_1, both amplitudes are large and have negative values. This indicates that the two masses are now moving out of phase with the disturbing force by 180°, but still in phase with each other. With further increase in ω, both amplitudes are diminishing until when $\omega = \sqrt{c} = \sqrt{2}\,p_0$, the amplitude C vanishes and the amplitude D becomes numerically equal to λ_{st} but 180° out of phase with the disturbing force. When ω becomes larger than $\sqrt{2}p_0$, the amplitude C becomes positive again while D remains negative. This means that the two masses are now 180° out of phase with each other, m_1 being again in phase with the disturbing force. Finally, as ω approaches the second natural frequency p_2, both amplitudes grow without limit and we have a second resonance condition. Beyond this, the masses continue to move out of phase but with less and less amplitude until when ω is very large, they will both tend to have no motion at all.

The fact that $C = 0$ when $\omega = \sqrt{c} = \sqrt{k_2/m_2}$ is of some practical importance. We see that to attain this condition, we need only to select k_2 and m_2 so that the natural frequency of this part of the system alone is tuned to the frequency of the disturbing force. Then the disturbing force acting on m_1 produces nevertheless only vibrations of the mass m_2.

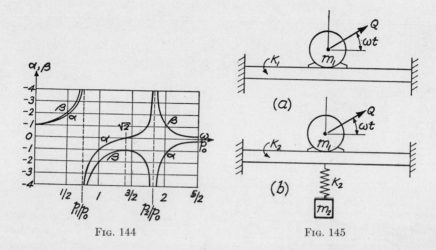

FIG. 144   FIG. 145

The amplitude D of these vibrations, as we see from the second of expressions (f) is simply

$$D = -\frac{q}{b} = -\frac{Q}{k_2}. \tag{k}$$

Consider, for example, the beam supporting a motor as shown in Fig. 145a. This may be considered as a one degree of freedom system and we know that the rotor unbalance Q may produce heavy forced vibrations if the impressed frequency ω happens to be near the natural frequency of the system as determined by $\sqrt{k_1/m_1}$. To prevent these forced vibrations, we attach the auxiliary system as shown in Fig. 145b and select k_2 and m_2 so that $\sqrt{k_2/m_2} = \omega$. In this way we make a two degree of freedom system to which the above general theory applies, and conclude that vibrations of the main mass m_1 vanish, while the auxiliary mass m_2 has the amplitude given by eq. (k). Such an auxiliary system attached to the main system is called a *dynamic damper*. To design the damper we select the spring k_2

so that eq. (k) gives a reasonable value for the amplitude D, and then select the mass m_2 so that $\sqrt{k_2/m_2} = \omega$.

In the preceding discussion we considered only a particular solution of eqs. (c). To get a general solution, the free vibrations represented by eqs. (o) on p. 191 must be superimposed on the forced vibrations. The arbitrary constants A_1, A_2, α', α'' must then be selected so as to satisfy the known initial conditions of motion.

The influence of damping was also neglected in all of the above discussion. This will be considered in the next article with particular reference to its effect on the dynamic damper, illustrated in Fig. 145b.

As another example of forced vibrations without damping, consider the system shown in Fig. 146. This consists of a slightly unbalanced rotor of mass m_1 mounted on a

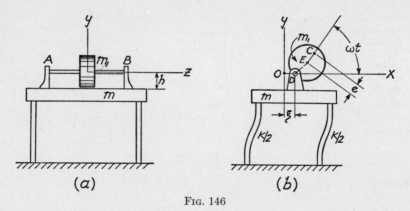

Fig. 146

shaft AB and rotating with constant angular velocity ω. The bearings A and B in turn are mounted on a heavy bed-plate of mass m supported by flexible vertical columns. We assume that the middle plane xy of the disc is a plane of symmetry of the structure and consider motion of the disc in this plane. Let the origin of coordinates (Fig. 146b) coincide with the unstrained position of the axis of the shaft, neglecting static deflection under dead weight. The displacement $\overline{OD} = \xi$ represents horizontal motion of the bed-plate, $\overline{DE} = f$, total lateral deflection of the shaft and $\overline{EC} = e$, the small eccentricity of the center of gravity C of the rotor. Thus the position of the disc is completely defined by the coordinates x, y, of point C and the angle of rotation ωt. The position of the bed-plate is completely defined by the horizontal displacement ξ.

To write the equations of motion for the system, we denote the spring constant for horizontal deflection of the columns by k and neglect their vertical deflections. For the lateral spring constant of the shaft we use the notation k_1. Then the force exerted on the disc by the bent shaft will be $k_1 f$, directed along $\overline{ED}$ and an equal and opposite force will be exerted on the bed-plate at the bearings A and B. We will neglect the effect of the moment arm h of this force in producing horizontal displacement ξ of the bed-plate. With these simplifications, equations of motion for the disc are

$$m_1\ddot{x}_1 = -k_1(x - \xi - e \cos \omega t) = 0,$$

$$m_1\ddot{y}_1 = -k_1(y - e \sin \omega t) = 0,$$

and for the bed-plate,

$$m\ddot{\xi} = -k\xi + k_1(x - \xi - e \cos \omega t).$$

Rearranging, we have

$$\left.\begin{array}{r} m\ddot{\xi} + (k + k_1)\xi - k_1 x = -ek_1 \cos \omega t, \\ m_1\ddot{x} + k_1 x - k_1\xi = ek_1 \cos \omega t, \\ m_1\ddot{y} + k_1 y = k_1 e \sin \omega t. \end{array}\right\} \qquad (l)$$

These are the equations of the forced vibrations of the system. It is seen that the third equation contains only the coordinate y. Thus the vertical vibrations of the shaft are not effected by the flexibility of the columns, and the corresponding critical speed is

$$\omega_1 = \sqrt{\frac{k_1}{m_1}}. \qquad (m)$$

In other words it is the same as for a shaft in rigid bearings. The first two of eqs. (l) give us the horizontal vibrations of the disc and of the bed-plate. We take the solutions of these equations in the form

$$x = \lambda_1 \cos \omega t, \quad \xi = \lambda_2 \cos \omega t.$$

Substituting in the equations, we obtain

$$\left.\begin{array}{r} (-m_1\omega^2 + k_1)\lambda_1 - k_1\lambda_2 = ek_1, \\ -k_1\lambda_1 + (-m\omega^2 + k + k_1)\lambda_2 = -ek_1, \end{array}\right\} \qquad (n)$$

from which the amplitudes λ_1 and λ_2 can be calculated. The corresponding critical speeds are obtained by equating the determinant of these equations to zero. Thus we find

$$(-m_1\omega^2 + k_1)(-m\omega^2 + k + k_1) - k_1{}^2 = 0,$$

or

$$(-m_1\omega^2 + k_1)(-m\omega^2 + k) - k_1 m_1 \omega^2 = 0. \qquad (o)$$

Taking ω^2 as abscissas and the magnitudes of the first term on the left side of eq. (o) as ordinates, a parabola is obtained (Fig. 147) intersecting the horizontal axis at $\omega^2 = k_1/m_1$ and $\omega^2 = k/m$. The critical speeds ω_2 and ω_3 are determined by the intersection points of this parabola with the inclined straight line $y = k_1 m_1 \omega^2$ as shown in the figure. It is seen that one of these speeds is less and the other is larger than the critical speed m for the vertical vibrations.

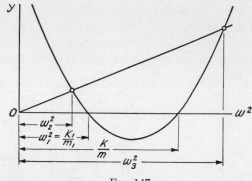

FIG. 147

If the angular velocity ω is different from the above-determined critical values, the determinant of eqs. (n), represented by the left side of (o), is different from zero. Denoting its value by Δ, we find from (n)

$$\lambda_1 = \frac{ek_1(-m\omega^2 + k + k_1) - ek_1^2}{\Delta}, \quad \lambda_2 = \frac{-ek_1(-m_1\omega^2 + k_1) + ek_1^2}{\Delta},$$

which determine the amplitudes of the horizontal forced vibrations.*

34. Vibrations with Viscous Damping.—In discussing the effect of viscous damping on vibrations of a system with two degrees of freedom, we return to the system shown in Fig. 135 and assume that, in addition to the spring forces and a disturbing force $Q \sin \omega t$ on the mass m_1, there is also a resisting force $-\mu\dot{x}$ acting on each mass. Under these conditions, the equations of motion become

$$\left.\begin{array}{l} m_1\ddot{x}_1 = -k_1x_1 + k_2(x_2 - x_1) - \mu\dot{x}_1 + Q \sin \omega t, \\ m_2\ddot{x}_2 = -k_2(x_2 - x_1) - \mu\dot{x}_2 = 0. \end{array}\right\} \quad (a)$$

Introducing the notations

$$\frac{k_1 + k_2}{m_1} = a, \quad \frac{k_2}{m_1} = b, \quad \frac{k_2}{m_2} = c, \quad \frac{\mu}{m_1} = d, \quad \frac{\mu}{m_2} = e, \quad \frac{Q}{m_1} = q, \quad (b)$$

eqs. (a) may be written as follows:

$$\left.\begin{array}{l} \ddot{x}_1 + ax_1 - bx_2 + d\dot{x}_1 = q \sin \omega t, \\ \ddot{x}_2 - cx_1 + cx_2 + e\dot{x}_2 = 0. \end{array}\right\} \quad (c)$$

* Vibration of rotors in flexible bearings has been discussed by V. Blaess. *Maschinenbau der Betrieb*, p. 281, 1923. See also D. M. Smith, *Proc. Roy. Soc. Ser. A (London)*, Vol. 142, p. 92, 1933.

The complete solution of these equations will consist of two parts: (1) free vibrations with damping, and (2) forced vibrations with damping. To find the solution for free vibrations, we ignore the right-hand side of the first equation and consider the corresponding homogeneous equations:

$$\left.\begin{aligned} \ddot{x}_1 + ax_1 - bx_2 + d\dot{x}_1 &= 0, \\ \ddot{x}_2 - cx_1 + cx_2 + e\dot{x}_2 &= 0. \end{aligned}\right\} \tag{d}$$

A solution of eqs. (d) can be taken in the form

$$\left.\begin{aligned} x_1 &= Ce^{st}, \\ x_2 &= De^{st}, \end{aligned}\right\} \tag{e}$$

where C, D and s are undetermined constants. Substituting back into eqs. (d), we find

$$\left.\begin{aligned} C(s^2 + ds + a) - Db &= 0, \\ -Cc + D(s^2 + es + c) &= 0. \end{aligned}\right\} \tag{f}$$

These equations can give values for C and D different from zero only if their determinant vanishes, i.e., if

$$(s^2 + ds + a)(s^2 + es + c) - bc = 0. \tag{g}$$

This is an equation of the fourth degree in s and we shall have four roots which give four particular solutions of eqs. (d) when substituted in (e). By combining these four solutions, the general solution of eqs. (d) is obtained.

If damping is small so that vibrations can occur, all four roots of eq. (g) are complex with negative real parts * and we shall have

$$\left.\begin{aligned} s_1 &= -n_1 + ip_1, \\ s_2 &= -n_1 - ip_1, \\ s_3 &= -n_2 + ip_2, \\ s_4 &= -n_2 - ip_2, \end{aligned}\right\} \tag{h}$$

where n_1 and n_2 are positive numbers. Substituting each of these roots in eqs. (f), the ratios C/D for each root will be obtained. Thus we find four particular solutions of the type (e) with four constants of integration which can be determined from four initial conditions, namely from the initial values of the coordinates x_1, x_2 and their derivatives $\dot{x}_1$, $\dot{x}_2$.

* The general proof of this statement was given by A. Hurwitz, *Math. Ann.*, Vol. 46, p. 273, 1895. The proof can be found in Riemann-Weber's *Differentialgleichungen der Physik*, Vol. 1, p. 125, 1925.

It is advantageous to proceed as in the case of systems with one degree of freedom (see Art. 12) and introduce trigonometric functions instead of exponential functions (e). Taking the first two roots (h) and observing that

$$e^{(-n_1 + ip_1)t} + e^{(-n_1 - ip_1)t} = 2e^{-n_1 t} \cos p_1 t,$$

$$e^{(-n_1 + ip_1)t} - e^{(-n_1 - ip_1)t} = 2ie^{-n_1 t} \sin p_1 t,$$

we can represent the combination of the first two particular solutions (e) in the following form:

$$x_1 = e^{-n_1 t}(C_1{}' \cos p_1 t + C_2{}' \sin p_1 t),$$

$$x_2 = e^{-n_1 t}(C_1{}'' \cos p_1 t + C_2{}'' \sin p_1 t).$$

Thus each coordinate represents a vibration with damping similar to what we had in the case of systems with one degree of freedom. The real part n_1 of the roots defines the rate at which the amplitudes of vibration are damped out and the imaginary part p_1 defines the frequency of vibrations.

In the same manner the last two roots (h) can be treated and finally we obtain the general solution of eqs. (d) in the following form:

$$x_1 = e^{-n_1 t}(C_1{}' \cos p_1 t + C_2{}' \sin p_1 t) + e^{-n_2 t}(D_1{}' \cos p_2 t + D_2{}' \sin p_2 t),$$
$$\tag{i}$$
$$x_2 = e^{-n_1 t}(C_1{}'' \cos p_1 t + C_2{}'' \sin p_1 t) + e^{-n_2 t}(D_1{}'' \cos p_2 t + D_2{}'' \sin p_2 t).$$

Owing to the fact that the ratio between the constants C, D is determined from eqs. (f) for each particular solution (e), there will be only four independent constants in expressions (i) to be determined from the initial conditions of the system.

In the case of small damping the numbers n_1 and n_2 in roots (h) are small and the effects of damping on the frequencies of vibrations are negligibly small quantities of the second order. Thus the frequencies p_1 and p_2 can be taken equal to the frequencies of vibrations without damping.

If we have a system with very large damping it is possible that two or all four roots (h) become real and negative. Assuming, for instance, that the last two roots are real, we shall find, as in the case of systems with one degree of freedom (p. 74), that the corresponding motion is aperiodic and that the complete expresion for the motion will consist of damped vibrations superposed on aperiodic motion.

From the general solution (i) we see that free vibrations are gradually damped out, so that we have, practically, only to deal with the steady-state forced vibrations sustained by the disturbing force $Q \sin \omega t$. These forced vibrations will be obtained as a particular solution of eqs. (c). Observing that owing to damping there must be a phase difference between the disturbing force and the motion that it induces, we take this particular solution in the form:

$$x_1 = C_1 \sin \omega t + C_2 \cos \omega t, \\ x_2 = C_3 \sin \omega t + C_4 \cos \omega t. \quad\quad (j)$$

Substituting these expressions back into eqs. (c) and equating to zero the coefficients before sin ωt and cos ωt, we obtain four linear algebraic equations for calculating the four constants $C_1 \cdots C_4$. Solving these equations and substituting the values of $C_1 \cdots C_4$ into eqs. (j), we obtain finally the desired forced vibrations of the system.

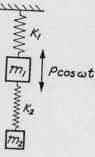

FIG. 148

As an example of application of the procedure just outlined above, let us consider the behavior of the dynamic damper shown in Fig. 145b and represented schematically in Fig. 148, when there is damping.* To make the damper most effective over an extended range of frequencies of the disturbing force, $P \cos \omega t$, it is most advantageous to introduce a damping device between the masses m_1 and m_2 such that damping is proportional to the relative velocity $\dot{x}_2 - \dot{x}_1$ between the two masses. Thus the equations of motion, similar to eqs. (a), become

$$m_1 \ddot{x}_1 = -k_1 x_1 + k_2(x_2 - x_1) + c(\dot{x}_2 - \dot{x}_1) + P \cos \omega t, \\ m_2 \ddot{x}_2 = -k_2(x_2 - x_1) - c(\dot{x}_2 - \dot{x}_1) = 0, \quad\quad (k)$$

in which the factor c denotes the magnitude of the damping force when the relative velocity between the two masses is equal to unity.

Considering only steady-state forced vibrations, we take a particular solution of eqs. (k) in the form:

$$x_1 = C_1 \cos \omega t + C_2 \sin \omega t, \\ x_2 = C_3 \cos \omega t + C_4 \sin \omega t. \quad\quad (l)$$

Substituting these expressions into eqs. (k), we obtain the four algebraic equations defining the constants $C_1 \cdots C_4$.

* J. Ormondroyd and J. P. Den Hartog, *Trans. A.S.M.E.*, Vol. 50, p. APM-241, 1928. See also papers by E. Hahnkamm, *Ann. Physik*, Ser. 5, Vol. 14, p. 683, 1932; *Z. angew. Math. u. Mech.*, Vol. 13, p. 183, 1933; *Ing.-Arch.*, Vol. 4, p. 192, 1933. The effect of internal friction on damping was discussed by O. Föppl, *Ing.-Arch.*, Vol. 1, p. 223, 1930. See also his book, *Aufschaukelung und Dämpfung von Schwingungen*, Berlin, 1936; and paper by G. Bock, *Z. angew. Math. u. Mech.*, Vol. 12, p. 261, 1932.

To simplify our further discussion and bring all expressions into dimensionless form, we introduce the following notations:

$\lambda_{st} = P/k_1$ is the static deflection of the main system produced by the force P,

$p_1 = \sqrt{k_2 g/W_2}$ is the natural frequency of the absorber,

$\beta = W_2/W_1$ is the ratio of the weights of the absorber and of the main system,

$\delta = p_1/p_0$ is the ratio of the natural frequencies of the absorber and of the main system,

$\gamma = \omega/p_0$ is the ratio of the frequency of the disturbing force to the natural frequency of the main system.

(m)

In further discussion, we will be interested in the amplitude of forced vibration of the mass W_1 which is equal to

$$(x_1)_{\max} = \lambda_1 = \sqrt{C_1^2 + C_2^2}.$$

Omitting all intervening calculations of the constants C_1 and C_2, and using notations (m), we obtain

$$\lambda_1^2/\lambda_{st}^2 = \frac{4\mu^2\gamma^2 + (\gamma^2 - \delta^2)^2}{4\mu^2\gamma^2(\gamma^2 - 1 + \beta\gamma^2)^2 + [\beta\delta^2\gamma^2 - (\gamma^2 - 1)(\gamma^2 - \delta^2)]^2}, \qquad (n)$$

in which the damping is defined by $\mu = cg/2W_2 p_0$.

From this expression the amplitude of the forced vibration of the weight W_1 can be calculated for any value of $\gamma = \omega/p_0$ if the quantities δ and β, defining the frequency and the weight of the absorber, and the quantity μ are known.

By taking $\mu = 0$, we obtain from (n)

$$\frac{\lambda_1}{\lambda_{st}} = \frac{\gamma^2 - \delta^2}{\beta\delta^2\gamma^2 - (\gamma^2 - 1)(\gamma^2 - \delta^2)}. \qquad (n')$$

The resonance curves ($\mu = 0$) giving the amplitude of vibration for $\beta = 1/20$, $\delta = 1$, and for various values of $\gamma = \omega/p$ are shown in Fig. 149 by dotted lines. It should be noted that the absolute values of expression (n') are plotted in the figure, whereas this expression is changing sign at $\gamma = 0.895$, $\gamma = 1$ and $\gamma = 1.12$.

Another extreme case is defined by taking $\mu = \infty$. If damping is infinitely large there will be no relative motion between W_1 and W_2. We obtain then a system with one degree of freedom of the weight $W_1 + W_2$

and with the spring constant k_1. For determining the amplitude of the forced vibration for this system we have, from (n),

$$\lambda_1^2/\lambda_{st}^2 = \frac{1}{(\gamma^2 - 1 + \beta\gamma^2)^2}. \qquad (n'')$$

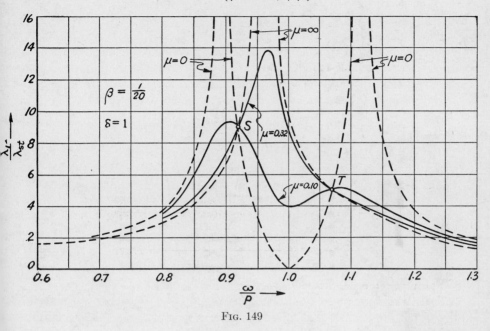

FIG. 149

The critical frequency for this system is obtained by equating the denominator of expression (n'') to zero. Thus

$$\gamma^2 - 1 + \beta\gamma^2 = 0 \qquad (o)$$

and

$$\gamma_{cr} = \sqrt{\frac{1}{1 + \beta}}. \qquad (p)$$

The resonance curves for $\mu = \infty$ are also shown in Fig. 149 by dotted lines. These curves are similar to those in Fig. 36 (p. 42) obtained before for systems with one degree of freedom. For any other value of μ the resonance curves can be plotted by using expression (n). In Fig. 149 the curves for $\mu = 0.10$ and for $\mu = 0.32$ are shown. It is interesting to note that all these curves are intersecting at points S and T. This means that for the two corresponding values of γ the amplitudes of the forced vibration of the weight W_1 are independent of the amount of damping. These values of γ can be found by equating the absolute values of λ_1/λ_{st} as obtained from eqs. (n') and (n''). Thus we have

$$\frac{\gamma^2 - \delta^2}{\beta\delta^2\gamma^2 - (\gamma^2 - 1)(\gamma^2 - \delta^2)} = \frac{1}{\gamma^2 - 1 + \beta\gamma^2}. \qquad (q)$$

The same equation can be deduced from expression (n). The points of intersection S and T define those values of γ for which the magnitude of the expression (n) does nor depend on damping, i.e., are independent of μ. The expression (n) has the form

$$\frac{M\mu^2 + N}{P\mu^2 + Q}$$

so that it will be independent of μ^2 only if we have $M/P = N/Q$; this brings us again to eq. (q). This equation can be put into the form

$$(\gamma^2 - \delta^2)(\gamma^2 - 1 + \beta\gamma^2) = \beta\delta^2\gamma^2 - (\gamma^2 - 1)(\gamma^2 - \delta^2)$$

or

$$\gamma^4 - 2\gamma^2 \frac{1 + \delta^2 + \beta\delta^2}{2 + \beta} + \frac{2\delta^2}{2 + \beta} = 0. \qquad (r)$$

From this equation two roots $\gamma_1{}^2$ and $\gamma_2{}^2$ can be found which determine the abscissas of the points S and T. The corresponding values of the amplitudes of the forced vibration are obtained by substituting $\gamma_1{}^2$ and $\gamma_2{}^2$ in eq. (n) or in eq. (n''). Using the latter as a simpler one, we obtain for the ordinates of points S and T the expressions *

$$-\frac{\lambda_{st}}{\gamma_1{}^2 - 1 + \beta\gamma_1{}^2} \quad \text{and} \quad \frac{\lambda_{st}}{\gamma_2{}^2 - 1 + \beta\gamma_2{}^2}, \qquad (s)$$

respectively. The magnitudes of these ordinates depend on the quantities β and δ defining the weight and the spring of the absorber. By a proper choice of these characteristics we can improve the efficiency of the absorber. Since all such curves as are shown in Fig. 149 must pass through the points S and T, the maximum ordinates of these curves giving the maximum amplitudes of the forced vibration will depend on the ordinates of points S and T, and it is reasonable to expect that the most favorable condition

---

* It is assumed that $\gamma_1{}^2$ is the smaller root of eq. (r) and the minus sign must be taken before the square root from (n'') to get a positive value for the amplitude.

will be obtained by making the ordinates of S and T equal.* This requires that

$$-\frac{\lambda_{st}}{\gamma_1^2 - 1 + \beta\gamma_1^2} = \frac{\lambda_{st}}{\gamma_2^2 - 1 + \beta\gamma_2^2}$$

or

$$\gamma_1^2 + \gamma_2^2 = \frac{2}{1 + \beta}. \tag{t}$$

Remembering that γ_1^2 and γ_2^2 are the two roots of the quadratic eq. (r) and that for such an equation the sum of the two roots is equal to the coefficient of the middle term with a negative sign, we obtain

$$\frac{2}{1 + \beta} = 2\frac{1 + \delta^2 + \beta\delta^2}{2 + \beta},$$

from which

$$\delta = \frac{1}{1 + \beta}. \tag{75}$$

This simple formula gives the proper way of "tuning" the absorber. If the weight W_2 of the absorber is chosen, the value of β is known and we determine, from eq. (75), the proper value of δ, which defines the frequency and the spring constant of the absorber.

To determine the amplitude of forced vibrations corresponding to points S and T we substitute in (s) the value of one of the roots of eq. (r). For a properly tuned absorber, eq. (75) holds, and this later equation becomes

$$\gamma^4 - \frac{2\gamma^2}{1 + \beta} + \frac{2}{(2 + \beta)(1 + \beta)^2} = 0, \tag{u}$$

from which

$$\gamma^2 = \frac{1}{1 + \beta}\left(1 \pm \sqrt{\frac{\beta}{2 + \beta}}\right).$$

Then, from (s)

$$\lambda_1/\lambda_{st} = \sqrt{\frac{2 + \beta}{\beta}}. \tag{76}$$

So far the quantity μ defining the amount of damping in the absorber did not enter into our discussion, since the position of the points S and T is independent of μ. But the maximum ordinates of the resonance curves

* This question is discussed with much detail in the above-mentioned paper by Hahnkamm, *loc. cit.*, p. 213.

passing through the points S and T depend, as we see from Fig. 149, on the magnitude of μ. We shall get the most favorable condition by selecting μ in such a way as to make the resonance curves have a horizontal tangent at S or at T. Two curves of this kind, one having a maximum at S and the other having a maximum at T are shown in Fig. 150. They are calculated for the case when $\beta = W_2/W_1 = \frac{1}{4}$. It is seen that the maximum ordinates of these curves differ only very little from the ordinate of the

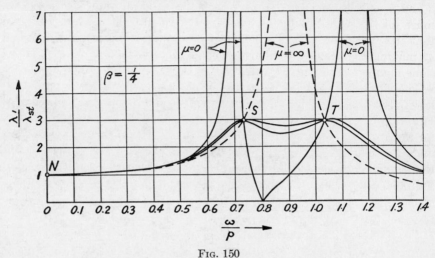

FIG. 150

points S and T so that we can state that eq. (76) gives the amplitude of the forced vibration of W_1 with a fair accuracy,* provided μ is chosen in the way explained above. It remains now to show how the damping must be selected to make the resonance curves a maximum at S or at T. We begin with expression (n) by putting it into the form

$$\lambda_1{}^2/\lambda_{st}{}^2 = \frac{M\mu^2 + N}{lP\mu^2 + Q},$$

where M, N, P and Q are functions of γ, δ and β. Solving for μ^2 we obtain

$$\mu^2 = \frac{N - Q(\lambda_1/\lambda_{st})^2}{P(\lambda_1/\lambda_{st})^2 - M}. \tag{v}$$

* From calculations by E. Hahnkamm (see *Versammlung der Schiffbautechnische Gesellschaft*, Berlin, Nov. 1935), it follows that the error increases with the increase in the weight of the absorber, i.e., with the increase of β. For $\beta = 0.06$ the error is 0.1%, for $\beta = 0.7$ the error is about 1%.

As soon as the weight W_2 of the absorber has been chosen β will be known, and we obtain δ from eq. (75), γ_1^2 and γ_2^2, corresponding to the points S and T, from eq. (u) and λ_1/λ_{st} from eq. (76). If all these quantities are substituted into (v) we obtain an indeterminate expression $0/0$ for μ^2, since the position of the points S and T are independent of μ. Let us take now a point very close to S on the resonance curve. If we have a maximum at S the value of λ_1/λ_{st} will not be changed by a slight shifting of the point, β and δ will also remain the same as before, and only instead of γ_1^2 we must take a slightly different quantity. With this change we shall find that the expression (v) has a definite value which is the required value of μ^2 making the tangent to the resonance curve horizontal at S. In the same manner we can get μ^2 which makes the tangent horizontal at T.

The successive steps in designing an absorber will therefore be as follows. For a given weight of the machine W_1 and its natural frequency of vibration p_0 we choose a certain absorber weight W_2. The spring constant for the absorber is now found by the use of eq. (75); then the value of the damping follows from eq. (v). Finally the amplitude of the forced vibration is given by eq. (76). To simplify these calculations the curves in Fig. 151 can be used. As abscissas the ratios $W_1/W_2 = 1/\beta$ are taken.

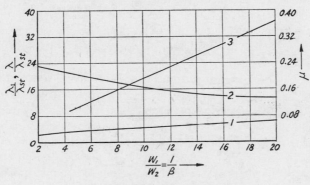

Fig. 151

The ordinates of curve 1 give the ratios λ_1/λ_{st} defining the amplitudes of vibration of the weight W_1. Curve 2 gives the amount of damping which must be used.

It remains now to design the spring of the absorber. The spring constant is determined from eq. (75). The maximum stress in the spring due to vibration may be found if we know the maximum relative displacement $\lambda = (x_2 - x_1)_{max}$. An exact calculation of this quantity requires a complicated investigation of the motion of W_2. A satisfactory approximation can be obtained by assuming that the vibration of the system is 90 degrees behind the pulsating load $P \cos \omega t$ acting on the weight W_1. In such a case the work done per cycle is (see p. 82)

$$\pi P \lambda_1.$$

The dissipation of energy per cycle due to damping forces proportional to the relative velocity is (see p. 82)

$$\pi \alpha \omega \lambda^2.$$

Equating the energy dissipated to the work produced per cycle we obtain

$$\pi P \lambda_1 = \pi \alpha \omega \lambda^2$$

from which

$$\lambda^2 = \frac{P \lambda_1}{\alpha \omega}$$

or, by introducing our previous notations

$$\mu = \alpha g / 2 W_2 p_0, \quad P/k_1 = \lambda_{st}, \quad W_2/W_1 = \beta,$$

we obtain

$$\left(\frac{\lambda}{\lambda_{st}}\right)^2 = \frac{\lambda_1}{\lambda_{st}} \frac{1}{2\mu\gamma\beta}. \tag{77}$$

Since μ and β are usually small quantities, the relative displacements λ, as obtained from this equation, will be several times larger than the displacement λ_1 of the weight W_1. The values of the ratio λ/λ_{st} are shown in Fig. 151 by curve 3. Large displacements produce large stresses in the absorber spring and since these stresses are changing sign during vibration, the question of sufficient safety against fatigue failure is of great practical importance. The theory of the vibration absorber which has been discussed can be applied also in the case of torsional vibrations. The principal field of application of absorbers is in internal-combustion engines. The application of an absorber with Coulomb friction in the case of torsional vibrations is discussed in Art. 42.

35. Stability of Steady-state Motions.—In previous examples, we have always discussed vibrations of a mechanical system about a configuration of *static equilibrium*. It is possible also to have vibrations about a steady state of motion, or what might be called a configuration of *dynamic equilibrium*. The steady rotation of a conical pendulum about a vertical axis, for example, represents a steady state of motion in which the inclination of the string of the pendulum to the vertical remains constant. If slightly disturbed, the conical pendulum will perform small vibrations about this steady state of motion much the same as a simple pendulum will oscillate about its equilibrium state if disturbed. Similarly, a spinning top performing regular precession under the influence of gravity represents a steady state of motion. If slightly disturbed, the axis of the top will begin to perform small high-frequency oscillations about its steady-state precession.

In all cases of this kind, it is important to know whether or not a given steady state of motion is *stable* or *unstable*. That is, if small vibrations about the steady state are produced, will they tend to die out with time so that the steady state is resumed, or will they grow with time so that the steady state is completely upset? The general method used in such cases is: (1) to assume that a small deviation or displacement from the steady form of motion is produced; (2) to investigate the resulting vibrations of the system with respect to the steady motion caused by the small deviation or displacement; (3) if these vibrations, as in the case of vibrations with viscous damping of the previous article, have the tendency to die out, we conclude that the steady motion is stable. Otherwise this motion is unstable. Thus the question of stability of motion requires an investigation of the small vibrations with respect to the steady motion of the system resulting from arbitrarily assumed deviations or displacements from the steady form of motion. Mathematically, such an investigation results in a system of linear differential equations similar to eqs. (*d*) of the previous article, and the question of stability or of instability of the steady motion depends on the roots of an algebraic equation similar to eq. (*g*) (p. 211). If all the roots have negative real parts, as was the case in the previous article, the vibration caused by the arbitrary deviation will be damped out, which means that the steady motion under consideration is stable. Otherwise the steady motion will be unstable.

Certain requirements regarding the coefficients of the algebraic equation, resulting from the differential equations similar to eqs. (*d*), have been established so that we can decide about the sign of real parts of the roots without solving the equations.* If we have, for instance, a cubic equation:

$$a_0 s^3 + a_1 s^2 + a_2 s + a_3 = 0,$$

all the roots will have a negative real part and, consequently, the motion will be stable if all the coefficients of the equation are positive and if

$$a_1 a_2 - a_0 a_3 > 0. \qquad (a)$$

---

* Such rules were established by E. J. Routh, *On the Stability of a Given Motion*, London, 1877. See also his *Rigid Dynamics*, London, Vol. 2, 1892; and paper by A. Hurwitz, *loc. cit.*, p. 211.

222 VIBRATION PROBLEMS IN ENGINEERING

In the case of an equation of the fourth degree

$$a_0 s^4 + a_1 s^3 + a_2 s^2 + a_3 s + a_4 = 0,$$

for stability of motion it is again necessary to have all the coefficients positive and also to have:

$$a_3(a_1 a_2 - a_0 a_3) - a_1^2 a_4 > 0. \tag{b}$$

Let us apply this general consideration of stability problems to particular cases. As a first example we will consider the stability of rotation of a pendulum with respect to its vertical axis oo, Fig. 152. The experiments show that if the angular velocity of rotation ω is below a certain limiting value, the rotation is stable and if by an arbitrary lateral impulse lateral oscillations of the pendulum about the horizontal pin A are produced, these oscillations gradually die out. If the angular velocity ω is above the limiting value, the vertical position of the pendulum is unstable and the slightest lateral force will produce a large deflection of the pendulum from its vertical position. In our discussion let us assume that the angular velocity of rotation about the vertical axis is constant and that the mass m of the pendulum can be assumed concentrated at the center C of the bob. If a lateral motion of the pendulum, defined by a small angle α, takes place, we will have inertia forces acting on the mass m as shown in Fig. 152. In accordance with d'Alembert's principle, the algebraic sum of moments about point A of these forces, together with the gravity force mg, must vanish. Treating α as a small angle so that $\sin \alpha \approx \alpha$ and $\cos \alpha \approx 1$, this condition gives

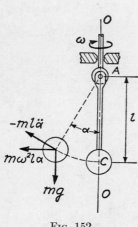

Fig. 152

$$ml^2 \ddot{\alpha} - m\omega^2 l^2 \alpha + mgl\alpha = 0$$

or

$$\ddot{\alpha} = \left(\frac{g}{l} - \omega^2\right)\alpha = 0. \tag{c}$$

If

$$\frac{g}{l} - \omega^2 > 0, \tag{d}$$

eq. (c) defines a simple harmonic oscillation, which, due to unavoidable friction, will gradually die out. Thus the steady rotation of the pendulum in this case is stable. If

$$\frac{g}{l} - \omega^2 < 0, \tag{e}$$

eq. (c) will have the same form as for an inverted pendulum so that, instead of oscillating, the angle α will grow continuously. Thus the rotation of the pendulum in this case is unstable. The limiting value of the angular velocity is

$$\omega = \sqrt{\frac{g}{l}}. \tag{f}$$

In other words, the limiting angular speed is that speed at which the number of revolutions per second of the pendulum about the vertical axis is equal to the frequency of its free lateral oscillations.

If we assume that there is viscous friction in the pendulum we shall have the following equation instead of eq. (c):

$$\ddot{\alpha} + 2n\dot{\alpha} + \left(\frac{g}{l} - \omega^2\right)\alpha = 0. \tag{g}$$

If condition (d) is fulfilled, we obtain damped vibrations. If condition (e) exists, we can put eq. (g) into the following form:

$$\ddot{\alpha} + 2n\dot{\alpha} - p^2\alpha = 0,$$

where $p^2 = \omega^2 - \dfrac{g}{l}.$

Taking the solution of this equation in the form $\alpha = e^{st}$, we find that

$$s^2 + 2ns - p^2 = 0,$$

from which

$$s = -n \pm \sqrt{n^2 + p^2}.$$

It is seen that one of the roots is positive. Thus the angle α has a tendency to grow and the rotation is unstable.

As a second example let us consider the stability of a steady rotation of a steam engine governor, shown in Fig. 153. Due to the centrifugal forces of the flyballs, a compression of the governor's spring is produced by the sleeve B which is in direct mechanical connection with the steam supply throttle valve. If, for some reason, the speed of the engine increases, the rotational speed of the governor, directly connected to the engine's shaft, increases also. The flyballs then rise higher and thereby lift the sleeve so that the opening of the steam valve C is reduced which means that the engine is throttled down. On the other hand, if the engine speed decreases below normal, the flyballs move downward and thereby increase the opening of the valve and the amount of steam admitted to the engine. To simplify our discussion, let us assume that the masses of the flyballs are each equal to $m_2/2$ and the mass of the sleeve is m_1, moreover that all masses are concentrated at the centers of gravity and that the masses of the inclined bars and of the spring can be neglected. As coordinates of the system we take

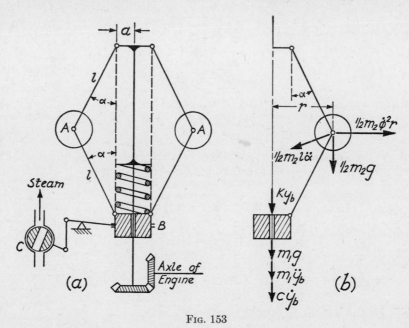

Fig. 153

the angle of rotation φ of the governor about its vertical axis and the angle of inclination α which the bars of the governor are making with the vertical axis.

To study possible small oscillations of the system about its steady state of motion, we assume a small variation in the angle α so that at any given instant there is an angular velocity $\dot\alpha$ and an angular acceleration $\ddot\alpha$, in addition to angular velocity $\dot\phi$ and angular acceleration $\ddot\phi$ about the vertical axis of the governor. Then correspondingly, we see from the geometry of the system that the sleeve B will have upward velocity and acceleration as follows:

$$\left.\begin{aligned}\dot y_b &= 2l\dot\alpha\sin\alpha, \\ \ddot y_b &= 2l\ddot\alpha\sin\alpha + 2l\dot\alpha^2\cos\alpha.\end{aligned}\right\} \tag{h'}$$

If now, in accordance with d'Alembert's principle, we apply to each flyball and to the sleeve B the inertia forces corresponding to the various accelerations associated with $\dot\alpha$, $\ddot\alpha$, and $\dot\phi$, $\ddot\phi$, we put the system in dynamic equilibrium and can write our equations of motion as equations of statics. In the case of a rather complex system like the governor this is done most easily by using the principle of virtual work. The various forces acting on the system, including inertia forces and also a viscous damping on the sleeve B, are shown in Fig. 153b.* Making a small virtual displacement $\delta\alpha$ and equating to zero the corresponding work of all forces, we write

$$m_2\dot\phi^2 r \cos\alpha \cdot l\delta\alpha - m_2 l\ddot\alpha \cdot l\delta\alpha - m_2 g \sin\alpha \cdot l\delta\alpha$$

$$- (k y_b + m_1 g + m_1 \ddot y_b + c\dot y_b) \cdot 2l\delta\alpha \sin\alpha = 0, \quad (i)$$

in which, besides the expressions (h') for $\dot y_b$ and $\ddot y_b$,

$$\left. \begin{aligned} r &= a + l \sin\alpha, \\ y_b &= 2l(1 - \cos\alpha). \end{aligned} \right\} \qquad (h'')$$

Making a small virtual displacement $\delta\phi$ and noting that each flyball has a translatory tangential acceleration $r\ddot\phi$ and Coriolis acceleration $2l\dot\alpha\dot\phi \cos\alpha$, our second equation of virtual work becomes

$$M \cdot \delta\phi - [I + m_2 r^2]\ddot\phi \cdot \delta\phi - 2m_2 l\dot\alpha\dot\phi \cos\alpha \cdot r\, \delta\phi = 0, \qquad (j)$$

where M denotes the reduced torque acting on the engine shaft and I is the reduced moment of inertia of the engine. Using notations (h') and (h'') and rearranging terms, eqs. (i) and (j) may be put in the form

$$\left. \begin{aligned} &\ddot\alpha l^2(m_2 + 4m_1 \sin^2\alpha) - m_2 l \cos\alpha(a + l\sin\alpha)\dot\phi^2 + 4m_1 l^2 \sin\alpha \cos\alpha\, \dot\alpha^2 \\ &\quad = -gl \sin\alpha(2m_1 + m_2) - 4kl^2 \sin\alpha(1 - \cos\alpha) - 4l^2 c\dot\alpha \sin^2\alpha, \\ &2m_2 l\dot\alpha\dot\phi(a + l\sin\alpha)\cos\alpha + [I + m_2(a + l\sin\alpha)^2]\ddot\phi = M. \end{aligned} \right\} \quad (k)$$

Let us consider first steady motion when $M = 0$. Then $\dot\phi = \omega_0$, $\ddot\phi = 0$, $\alpha = \alpha_0$, $\dot\alpha = 0$, $\ddot\alpha = 0$ and we obtain from the first equation

$$m_2 l \cos\alpha(a + l\sin\alpha)\omega^2 = gl \sin\alpha(2m_1 + m_2) + 4kl^2 \sin\alpha(1 - \cos\alpha). \qquad (l)$$

Let us now consider small vibrations about the steady motion discussed above. In such a case

$$\dot\phi = \omega_0 + \omega \quad \text{and} \quad \alpha = \alpha_0 + \eta, \qquad (m)$$

where ω denotes a small fluctuation in the angular velocity of rotation, and η a small fluctuation in the angle of inclination α. Substituting expressions (m) into eqs. (k) and keeping only small quantities of the first order, we can put

$$\dot\phi^2 = \omega_0{}^2 + 2\omega_0\omega, \quad \sin\alpha = \sin(\alpha_0 + \eta) = \sin\alpha_0 + \eta \cos\alpha_0,$$

$$\cos(\alpha_0 + \eta) = \cos\alpha_0 - \eta \sin\alpha_0.$$

* There are also horizontal inertia forces on each flyball corresponding to tangential acceleration $r\ddot\phi$ and to Coriolis acceleration which are not shown in Fig. 153b.

Then eqs. (k), with the use of eq. (l), become

$$m\ddot{\eta} + b\dot{\eta} + d\eta - e\omega = 0,$$

$$I_0\dot{\omega} = -f\eta, \tag{n}$$

where

$$m = l^2(m_2 + 4m_1 \sin^2 \alpha_0),$$

$$b = 4cl^2 \sin^2 \alpha_0,$$

$$d = m_2\omega_0^2[l \sin \alpha_0(a + l \sin \alpha_0) - l^2 \cos^2 \alpha_0]$$

$$+ gl \cos \alpha_0(2m_1 + m_2) + 4kl^2 [\cos \alpha_0 - \cos^2 \alpha_0 + \sin^2 \alpha_0],$$

$$e = 2\omega_0 l(a + l \sin \alpha_0)m_2,$$

$$I_0 = I + m_2(a + l \sin \alpha_0)^2 \text{ and}$$

f denotes the characteristic torque change factor of the engine, defined as $\dfrac{dM}{d\alpha}$ or as $\dfrac{\Delta M}{\eta}$.
or, in other words, as the factor which, multiplied by the angular change η, gives the change in torque acting on the shaft of the engine. Thus the vibration of the governor with respect to the steady motion is defined by the system of linear eqs. (n). Assuming solutions of these equations in the form

$$\eta = C_1e^{st}, \quad \omega = C_2e^{st},$$

and substituting these expressions in (n), we obtain

$$C_1(ms^2 + bs + d) - eC_2 = 0,$$

$$C_1f + I_0sC_2 = 0.$$

Equating the determinant of these equations to zero, we find

$$I_0s(ms^2 + bs + d) + ef = 0,$$

or

$$s^3 + \frac{b}{m}s^2 + \frac{d}{m}s + \frac{ef}{mI_0} = 0.$$

All constants entering into this equation are positive,* so that by using condition (a) (p. 221) we can state that the motion of the governor will be stable if

$$\frac{bd}{m^2} > \frac{ef}{mI_0}.$$

From this it follows that for a stable state of motion the quantity b, depending on viscous damping in the governor, must satisfy the condition

$$b > \frac{mef}{dI_0}.$$

---

* We assume that for any increase in angular velocity the corresponding angle α, as defined by eq. (l), increases also. In such a case expression (d), containing negative terms, is positive.

If this condition is not satisfied, vibrations of the governor produced by a sudden change in load of the engine will not be damped out gradually and the well-known phenomenon of *hunting* of a governor occurs.*

The method used above in discussing the stability of a governor has been applied successfully in several other problems of practical importance as, for instance, airplane-flutter,† automobile "shimmy,"‡ and axial oscillations of steam turbines.§

36. Whirling of a Rotating Shaft Caused by Hysteresis.—In our previous discussion of instability of motion of a rotating disc (see p. 35) it was assumed that the material of the shaft is perfectly elastic and any kind of damping has been neglected. On the basis of this assumption two forms of whirling of the shaft due to some eccentricity have been discussed, namely, (1) below the critical speed ω_{cr}, and (2) above the critical speed. It was found that in both cases the plane containing the bent axis of the shaft rotates with the same speed as the shaft itself. Both these forms of motion are theoretically stable ¶ so that if a small deviation from the circular path of the center of gravity of the disc is produced by impact, for example, the result is that small vibrations in a radial and in a tangential direction are superposed on the circular motion of the center of gravity. The existence of such motion can be demonstrated by the use of a suitable stroboscope.‖ In this way it can also be shown that due to unavoidable damping the vibrations gradually die out if the speed of the shaft is below ω_{cr}. However, if it is above ω_{cr} a peculiar phenomenon sometimes can be observed, namely, that the plane of the bent shaft rotates at the speed ω_{cr} while the shaft itself is rotating at a higher speed ω. Sometimes this motion has a steady character and the deflection of the shaft remains constant. At other times the deflection tends to grow with time up to the instant when the disc strikes the guard. To explain this phenomenon the imperfection in the elastic properties of the shaft must be considered.

Experiments with tension-compression show that all materials exhibit some *hysteresis* characteristic so that instead of a straight line AA, Fig. 154, representing Hooke's law, we usually obtain a loop of which the width depends on the limiting values of stresses applied in the experiment. If the loading and unloading is repeated several hundred times, the shape of the loop is finally stabilized ** and the area of the loop gives the amount of energy dissipated per cycle due to hysteresis. We will now investigate the

---

* In the case when the engine is rigidly coupled to an electric generator, an additional term proportional to φ will enter the second of eqs. (k) so that instead of eqs. (n) we obtain two equations of the second order. The stability discussion requires then an investigation of the roots of an equation of the 4th degree. Such an investigation was made by M. Stone, *Trans. A.I.E.E.*, p. 332, 1933.

† W. Birnbaum, *Z. angew. Math. u. Mech.*, Vol. 4, p. 277, 1924.

‡ G. Becker, H. Fromm and H. Maruhn, *Schwingungen in Automobillenkungen*, Berlin, 1931.

§ J. G. Baker, paper before A.S.M.E. meeting, New York, Dec. 1934.

¶ The first investigation of this stability problem was made by A. Föppl, *Civilingenieur*, Vol. 41, p. 333, 1895.

‖ Experiments of this kind were recently made by D. Robertson, *Engineer*, Vol. 156, p. 152, 1933; Vol. 158, p. 216, 1934. See also his papers in *Phil. Mag.*, Ser. 7, Vol. 20, p. 793, 1935; and before the Institute of Mechanical Engineers, Oct. 31, 1935 meeting. In the last two papers a bibliography on the subject is given.

** We assume that the limits of loading are below the endurance limit of the material.

effect of this hysteresis on bending of the shaft by first considering the case of static bending. We eliminate the effect of a gravity force by choosing a vertical shaft; moreover, we assume that it is deflected by a statically applied lateral force P in the plane of the figure (Fig. 155). The deflection δ may be taken proportional to the force

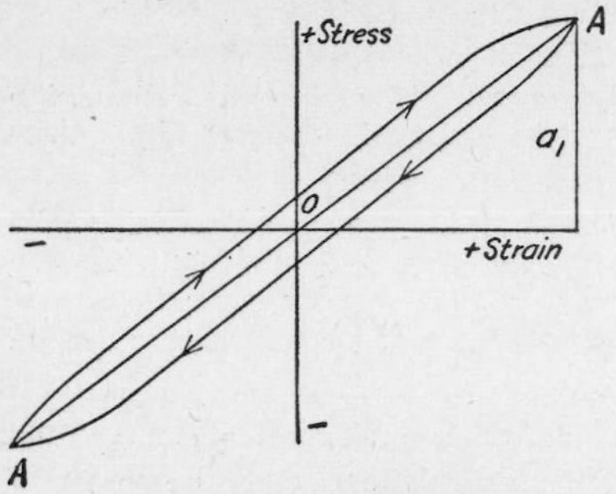

$$\delta = kP, \qquad (a)$$

k being the spring constant of the shaft. In our further discussion we assume that the middle plane of the disc is the plane of symmetry of the shaft so that during bending the disc is moving parallel to itself. In Fig. 155b, the cross section of the shaft is shown to a larger scale and the line nn perpendicular to the plane of bending indicates the neutral line, so that the fibers of the shaft to the right of this line are in tension and to the left, in compression.

FIG. 154

Let us now assume that a torque is applied in the plane of the disc so that the shaft is brought into rotation in a counter-clockwise direction, while the plane of bending of the shaft is stationary, i.e., the plane of the deflection curve of the axis of the shaft continues to remain in the xz-plane. In this way the longitudinal fibers of the shaft will undergo reversal of stresses. For instance, a fiber A_1 at the convex side of the bent shaft is in tension, but after half a revolution of the shaft the fiber will be in compression at

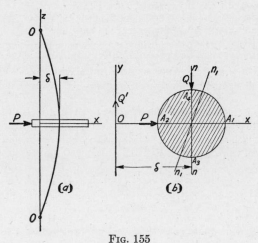

FIG. 155

A_2 on the concave side. In the case of an ideal material, following Hooke's law, the relation between stress and strain is given by the straight line AA in Fig. 154 and the distribution of bending stresses over the cross section of the shaft will not be affected by the rotation. But the condition is different if the material exhibits hysteresis characteristics. From the loop in Fig. 154 we see that for the same strain we have two different values of stress corresponding to the upper (loading) and the lower (unloading) branch of the loop, respectively. Returning to the consideration of the cross section of the rotating shaft in Fig. 155b, we see that during the motion of the fiber from position A_2 to position A_1 the stress is varying from compression to tension, consequently we must use the upper branch of the loop. In the same way we conclude that during the motion from A_1 to A_2 the lower branch of the loop must be used. From this it follows that we may take the hysteresis effect into account by superposing on the statical stresses, determined from Hooke's law, additional positive stresses on the fibers below the horizontal diameter A_1A_2, and additional negative stresses on the fibers above A_1A_2. This system of stresses corresponds to bending of the shaft in yz-plane. Physically these stresses represent bending stresses produced by a force Q which must be applied to the shaft if rotation of the plane of the deflection curve is to be prevented when the shaft is rotating.

From this discussion it follows that while the shaft is bent in the xz-plane the bending stresses do not produce a bending moment in the same plane but in a plane inclined to the xz-plane. In other words, the neutral axis with respect to stresses does not coincide with the neutral axis nn for strains, but assumes a position n_1n_1 slightly inclined to nn. The same conclusion can be drawn in another way. If we consider a fiber at A_2 moving toward position A_1 the stress will be changing from compression to tension so that the upper portion of the loop in Fig. 155 must be used; from this we see that for zero strain, corresponding to the position of the fiber at A_3, there is a tensile stress. In the same way considering the lower branch of the loop, we find that at A_4 there is a compressive stress, thus the vertical diameter A_3A_4, corresponding to points with zero strains, does not any longer represent the neutral axis with respect to stress and the latter must have an inclined position as, for instance, n_1n_1.

In order to get an idea of the magnitude of the force Q we observe that some energy is dissipated during the rotation of the shaft due to hysteresis. Hence a constant torque must act to maintain the constant speed of rotation of the disc. This torque is balanced by the couple represented by the force Q and the corresponding reactions Q' at the bearings, Fig. 155b. In this case the work done by the torque during one revolution of the shaft is

$$2\pi Q\delta. \tag{b}$$

This work must be equal to the energy dissipated per cycle due to hysteresis. Unfortunately there is not sufficient information in regard to the area of the hysteresis loop, but it is usually assumed that it does not depend on the frequency. It is also sometimes assumed that it is proportional to the square of the limiting strain,* i.e., in our case, that the dissipation per cycle can be taken in the form

$$E = 2\pi D\delta^2, \tag{c}$$

where D is a constant depending on the hysteresis characteristic of the material of the shaft.

Comparing (b) and (c) we find

$$Q = D\delta, \tag{d}$$

* See paper by A. L. Kimball and D. E. Lovell, *Trans. A.S.M.E.*, Vol. 48, p. 479, 1926.

i.e., the force required to prevent rotation of the deflection curve is proportional to the deflection δ, produced by a static load.

If the shaft is horizontal, it will deflect in a vertical plane due to the gravity force W of the disc, Fig. 156. By appling torque to the disc we can bring the shaft into rotation and we shall find that, owing to hysteresis, the plane of bending takes a slightly inclined position defined by the angle φ. The gravity force W together with the vertical reactions at the bearings form a couple with an arm c balancing the torque applied to the disc. This torque supplies the energy dissipated owing to hysteresis.[*]

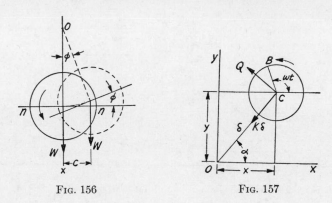

FIG. 156   FIG. 157

After this preliminary discussion let us derive the differential equations of motion of the center of gravity of the disc on the vertical rotating shaft, assuming: (1) that the speed ω of the rotating shaft is greater than ω_{cr}; (2) that the plane of the deflection curve of the shaft is free to rotate with respect to the axis z, Fig. 157; (3) that there is a torque acting on the disc so as to maintain the constant angular velocity ω of the shaft; and (4) that the disc is perfectly balanced and its center of gravity is on the axis of the shaft. Taking, as before, the xy-plane as the middle plane of the disc and letting the z-axis coincide with the unbent axis of the shaft, we assume (Fig. 157) that the center of the cross section of the bent shaft coinciding with the center of gravity of the disc is at C, so that $\overline{OC} = \delta$ represents the deflection of the shaft. The angle α between $\overline{OC}$ and the x-axis defines the instantaneous position of the rotating plane of the deflection curve of the shaft. We take also some fixed radius $\overline{CB}$ of the shaft and define its angular position during uniform rotation in counter-clockwise direction by the angle ωt measured from the x-axis. In writing the differential equations of motion [†] of the center C, we must consider the reaction $k\delta$ of the deflected shaft in the radial direction towards the axis O, and also the additional reaction Q in tangential direction due to hysteresis.

[*] The phenomenon of lateral deflection of a loaded rotating shaft due to hysteresis has been investigated and fully explained by W. Mason, *Engineering*, Vol. 115, p. 698, 1923.

[†] The discussion of this problem is given in J. G. Baker's paper, *loc. cit.*, p. 227. The consideration of the hysteresis effect in the problem of shaft-whirling was introduced first by A. L. Kimball, *Phys. Rev.*, June 1923; and *Phil. Mag.*, Ser. 6, Vol. 49, p. 724, 1925.

This later reaction is evidently equal and opposite to the force Q in Fig. 155b, which was required to prevent the plane of the shaft deflection from rotating. We assume here that $\omega > \dot{\alpha}$, so that the radius $\overline{BC}$ rotates with respect to $\overline{OC}$ in a counter-clockwise direction. Only on this assumption has the force Q the direction shown in Fig. 157 and tends to maintain the rotation of the $\overline{OC}$-plane in a counter-clockwise direction. Denoting by m the mass of the disc and resolving the forces along the x- and the y-axes, we obtain the following two equations:

$$m\ddot{x} = -k\delta \cos \alpha - Q \sin \alpha,$$
$$m\ddot{y} = -k\delta \sin \alpha + Q \cos \alpha. \tag{e}$$

Substituting for Q its expression (d), the equations can be written in the following form:

$$m\ddot{x} + kx + Dy = 0,$$
$$m\ddot{y} + ky - Dx = 0. \tag{f}$$

In solving these equations we assume that

$$x = Ce^{st}, \quad y = C'e^{st},$$

and we find in the usual way a biquadratic equation of which the roots are

$$s_{1,2,3,4} = \pm \sqrt{\frac{-k \pm Di}{m}}.$$

Introducing the notation

$$\sqrt{\frac{-k + Di}{m}} = n + p_1 i,$$

from which

$$n = +\sqrt{\frac{-k + \sqrt{k^2 + D^2}}{2m}},$$
$$p_1 = +\sqrt{\frac{k + \sqrt{k^2 + D^2}}{2m}}, \tag{g}$$

we can represent the general solution of eqs. (f) in the following form:

$$x = e^{nt}(-C_1 \sin p_1 t + C_2 \cos p_1 t) + e^{-nt}(C_3 \sin p_1 t - C_4 \cos p_1 t),$$
$$y = e^{nt}(C_1 \cos p_1 t + C_2 \sin p_1 t) + e^{-nt}(C_3 \cos p_1 t + C_4 \sin p_1 t). \tag{h}$$

In discussing this solution we must keep in mind that for a material such as steel the tangential force Q is very small in comparison with the radial force $k\delta$. Hence the quantity D is small in comparison with k and we find, from eqs. (g), that n is a small quantity approximately equal to $D/2\sqrt{km}$, while

$$p_1 \approx \sqrt{\frac{k}{m}} = \omega_{cr}.$$

Neglecting the second terms in expressions (h) which will be gradually damped out, and representing the trigonometric parts of the first terms by projections on the x- and the y-axes of vectors C_1 and C_2 rotating with the speed ω_{cr}, Fig. 158, we conclude that the shaft is whirling with constant speed ω_{cr} in a counter-clockwise direction, while its deflection, equal to $\delta = \sqrt{x^2 + y^2} = e^{nt} \sqrt{C_1^2 + C_2^2}$, is increasing indefinitely.

It should be noted, however, that in the derivation of eqs. (e) damping forces such as air resistance were entirely neglected. The effect of these forces may increase with the deflection of the shaft so that we may finally obtain a steady whirling of the shaft with the speed approximately equal to ω_{cr}.

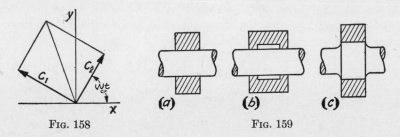

Fig. 158   Fig. 159

In the case of a built-up rotor any friction between the parts of the rotor during bending may have exactly the same effect on the whirling of the rotor as the hysteresis of the shaft material in our previous discussion. If a sleeve or a hub is fixed to a shaft, Fig. 159a, and subjected to reversal of bending, the surface fibers of the shaft must slip inside the hub as they elongate and shorten during bending so that some energy of dissipation due to friction is produced. Sometimes the amount of energy dissipated owing to such friction is much larger than that due to hysteresis of the material and may cause whirling of rotors running above their critical speeds.* To reduce the effect of friction the dimension of the hub in the axial direction of the shaft must be as short as possible; the construction, in Fig. 159b, with bearing surfaces at the ends only, should be avoided. An improvement is obtained by mounting the hub on a boss solid with the shaft, Fig. 159c, having large fillets in the corners.

* B. L. Newkirk, *Gen. Elec. Rev.*, Vol. 27, p. 169, 1924.

CHAPTER IV

SYSTEMS WITH SEVERAL DEGREES OF FREEDOM

37. Free Vibrations of Systems with Several Degrees of Freedom.—In the preceding chapter we have considered, for the most part, only systems with two degrees of freedom. Systems with more than two degrees of freedom may be handled in a similar manner although the difficulty increases rapidly with the number of equations that must be handled. As an example of a system with three degrees of freedom, let us consider the case shown in Fig. 160. Here we have a particle of mass m supported in space by three simple springs, the axes of which do not lie in one plane. We assume that the origin O is the position of equilibrium of the particle. Then if disturbed slightly from this position, the mass m will be-

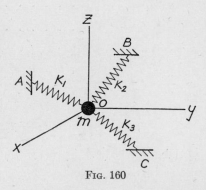

Fig. 160

gin to vibrate and we wish to find the nature of this motion. Since three coordinates x, y, z are required to specify the position of the particle, we have three degrees of freedom.

Let α_1, β_1, γ_1, α_2, β_2, γ_2 and α_3, β_3, γ_3 be the direction cosines of the axes DA, DB, and DC of the three springs and k_1, k_2, k_3, the spring constants. Then for any position of the particle m defined by coordinates x, y, z, the unbalanced tension in each spring will be *

$$S_i = -k_i(\alpha_i x + \beta_i y + \gamma_i z), \qquad (a)$$

provided x, y, z are small compared with the lengths of the springs. Thus the equations of motion become

$$\begin{aligned} m\ddot{x} &= S_1\alpha_1 + S_2\alpha_2 + S_3\alpha_3, \\ m\ddot{y} &= S_1\beta_1 + S_2\beta_2 + S_3\beta_3, \\ m\ddot{z} &= S_1\gamma_1 + S_2\gamma_2 + S_3\gamma_3. \end{aligned} \right\} \qquad (b)$$

* Initial tensions in the spring when $x = y = z = 0$ are ignored.

233

Substituting the values of S_1, S_2, S_3, from eq. (a) above and collecting terms, eqs. (b) can readily be reduced to the form

$$\left.\begin{array}{l} m\ddot{x} + c_{11}x + c_{12}y + c_{13}z = 0, \\ m\ddot{y} + c_{12}x + c_{22}y + c_{23}z = 0, \\ m\ddot{z} + c_{13}x + c_{23}y + c_{33}z = 0, \end{array}\right\} \qquad (c)$$

in which

$$c_{11} = k_1\alpha_1{}^2 + k_2\alpha_2{}^2 + k_3\alpha_3{}^2,$$

$$c_{12} = k_1\alpha_1\beta_1 + k_2\alpha_2\beta_2 + k_3\alpha_3\beta_3,$$

$$\cdot \; \cdot \; \cdot \; \cdot \; \cdot \; \cdot \; \cdot \; \cdot \; \cdot \; \cdot \; \cdot \; \cdot \; \cdot \; \cdot \; \cdot$$

$$\cdot \; \cdot \; \cdot \; \cdot \; \cdot \; \cdot \; \cdot \; \cdot \; \cdot \; \cdot \; \cdot \; \cdot \; \cdot \; \cdot \; \cdot$$

Proceding now as was done in Art. 31, we take the solution of eqs. (c) in the form

$$\left.\begin{array}{l} x = \lambda_1 \sin(pt + \delta), \\ y = \lambda_2 \sin(pt + \delta), \\ z = \lambda_3 \sin(pt + \delta). \end{array}\right\} \qquad (d)$$

Substituting back into eqs. (c), we obtain

$$\left.\begin{array}{l} (c_{11} - mp^2)\lambda_1 + c_{12}\lambda_2 + c_{13}\lambda_3 = 0, \\ c_{12}\lambda_1 + (c_{22} - mp^2)\lambda_2 + c_{23}\lambda_3 = 0, \\ c_{13}\lambda_1 + c_{23}\lambda_2 + (c_{33} - mp^2)\lambda_3 = 0. \end{array}\right\} \qquad (e)$$

This set of algebraic equations can give values of λ_1, λ_2, λ_3, different from zero only if their determinant vanishes. By setting this determinant equal to zero, we will obtain, as a *frequency equation*, a cubic in p^2 and it can be shown that it will have three real positive roots which we designate by $p_1{}^2$, $p_2{}^2$ and $p_3{}^2$. Substituting any one of those roots, say $p_1{}^2$, into eqs. (e), we will obtain the ratios λ_1'/λ_2' and λ_1'/λ_3' that define the mode of vibration having the frequency p_1. This mode will then be defined by the equations

$$\left.\begin{array}{l} x = \lambda_1' \sin(p_1 t + \delta_1), \\ y = \lambda_2' \sin(p_1 t + \delta_1), \\ z = \lambda_3' \sin(p_1 t + \delta_1). \end{array}\right\} \qquad (f)$$

It is seen that, during motion, the coordinates of the particle are always in the same ratio; from this, we conclude that the motion takes place along a straight line through the origin of coordinates. If α', β', γ' are the direction cosines of this line and A' is the amplitude, then we may write

$$\lambda_1' = \alpha'A', \quad \lambda_2' = \beta'A', \quad \lambda_3' = \gamma'A',$$

$$(A')^2 = (\lambda_1')^2 + (\lambda_2')^2 + (\lambda_3')^2.$$

As we have already seen, eqs. (e) define only the frequency of vibration and the corresponding amplitude ratios. The absolute values of amplitudes remain indefinite if no initial conditions of motion are taken into account. Thus, for simplicity, we can assume an amplitude $A' = 1$ so that

$$\lambda_1' = \alpha', \quad \lambda_2' = \beta', \quad \lambda_3' = \gamma'.$$

Then eqs. (f) become

$$x = \alpha' \sin (p_1 t + \delta_1),$$

$$y = \beta' \sin (p_1 t + \delta_1),$$

$$z = \gamma' \sin (p_1 t + \delta_1).$$

In the same way, for the frequency p_2, we can obtain

$$x = \alpha'' \sin (p_2 t + \delta_2),$$

$$y = \beta'' \sin + (p_2 t + \delta_2),$$

$$z = \gamma'' \sin (p_2 t + \delta_2).$$

If we substitute the amplitudes $(\alpha', \beta', \gamma')$ and $(\alpha'', \beta'', \gamma'')$ of these two normal modes of vibration into eqs. (e), we will obtain the following two sets of equations:

$$\left.\begin{aligned}
mp_1^2\alpha' &= c_{11}\alpha' + c_{12}\beta' + c_{13}\gamma', \\
mp_1^2\beta' &= c_{12}\alpha' + c_{22}\beta' + c_{23}\gamma', \\
mp_1^2\gamma' &= c_{13}\alpha' + c_{23}\beta' + c_{33}\gamma',
\end{aligned}\right\} \tag{g}$$

$$\left.\begin{aligned}
mp_2^2\alpha'' &= c_{11}\alpha'' + c_{12}\beta'' + c_{13}\gamma'', \\
mp_2^2\beta'' &= c_{12}\alpha'' + c_{22}\beta'' + c_{23}\gamma'', \\
mp_2^2\gamma'' &= c_{13}\alpha'' + c_{23}\beta'' + c_{33}\gamma''.
\end{aligned}\right\} \tag{h}$$

Multiplying the first of eqs. (g) by α'', the second by β'' and the third by γ'', and then adding them all together, we obtain the same thing on the right-hand side as we do by multiplying eqs. (h) respectively by α', β', γ' and adding them together. From this we conclude that

$$mp_1^2(\alpha'\alpha'' + \beta'\beta'' + \gamma'\gamma'') = mp_2^2(\alpha'\alpha'' + \beta'\beta'' + \gamma'\gamma'').$$

Then since $p_1{}^2$ and $p_2{}^2$ are two different roots of the frequency equation,* we conclude that

$$\alpha'\alpha'' + \beta'\beta'' + \gamma'\gamma'' = 0. \tag{i}$$

A similar conclusion can be reached by considering in pairs the modes defined by $p_1{}^2$ and $p_3{}^2$ and by $p_2{}^2$ and $p_3{}^2$. Thus we conclude, since expression (i) is a condition of orthogonality, that the three principal modes are vibrations along three mutually perpendicular straight lines. The direction cosines of these lines are determined from sets of equations such as (g) and (h). If by chance we had chosen the coordinate axes x, y, z to coincide with the three principal directions of vibration, each of eqs. (c) would contain only one coordinate and these would then be the principal coordinates of the system.

The conclusion that the three principal modes of vibration of the system in Fig. 160 are vibrations along three orthogonal straight lines can be arrived at in another way. Suppose that we give to the particle m in Fig. 160 an arbitrary initial displacement s away from the equilibrium position and then release it without initial velocity. In all probability, by so doing, we shall obtain a complicated motion of the particle in space which consists of some combination of the three principal modes discussed above. This results from the fact that for an arbitrary displacement s, the resultant action R of the three springs on the particle will probably not coincide in direction with the displacement s. Thus the particle begins to move in a direction which is not straight toward the origin O and we get a space motion.

On the other hand, the motion will be very simple if we carefully make the initial displacement s in such a direction that the resultant spring force on the particle is in the same direction but, of course, opposing the displacement. When this condition if fulfilled, the particle, upon release, begins to move along the line of initial displacement and we obtain a simple harmonic motion along this line.

The problem then is simply one of finding the proper directions (there are three possible ones) in which to make the initial displacement. To do this, we begin by assuming that such a displacement s has been made and that x, y, x are its components. Then from eqs. (c), we conclude that the corresponding components of the resultant force R on the particle are

$$\left.\begin{aligned}
X &= -c_{11}x - c_{12}y - c_{13}z, \\
Y &= -c_{12}x - c_{22}y - c_{23}z, \\
Z &= -c_{13}x - c_{23}y - c_{33}z.
\end{aligned}\right\} \tag{j}$$

* We neglect the special case where two roots of the frequency equation are equal.

Now since the line of action of R is to coincide with the displacement s, we must have also

$$X = -R\frac{x}{s}, \quad Y = -R\frac{y}{s}, \quad Z = -R\frac{z}{s}.$$

Substituting these values back into eqs. (j), we get

$$\left. \begin{aligned}
\left(c_{11} - \frac{R}{s}\right)x + c_{12}y + c_{13}z &= 0, \\
c_{12}x + \left(c_{22} - \frac{R}{s}\right)y + c_{23}z &= 0, \\
c_{13}x + c_{23}y + \left(c_{33} - \frac{R}{s}\right)z &= 0.
\end{aligned} \right\} \qquad (k)$$

Comparing these equations with eqs. (e), we conclude that to realize the desired end the components x, y, z of the displacement s must be in the same ratio as the amplitudes λ_1, λ_2, λ_3 of a principal mode of vibration. Hence the directions of displacements s for which the line of action of the resultant force R can coincide with the displacement are the same as the directions of principal coordinates found before.

As a second example of a system with three degrees of freedom, let us consider the case shown in Fig. 161a. A tightly stretched vertical string contains three equal and

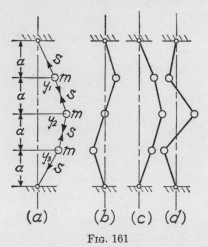

(a)   (b) (c) (d)

Fig. 161

equally spaced particles each of mass m, as shown. The tension S in the string is assumed to be large, so that for small lateral displacements of the particles it does not change appreciably. Then for any configuration of the system defined by displacements y_1, y_2, y_3, as shown in Fig. 161a, the equations of motion for the three particles become:

$$m\ddot{y}_1 = -\frac{S}{a}(2y_1 - y_2),$$
$$m\ddot{y}_2 = -\frac{S}{a}(2y_2 - y_1 - y_3), \qquad (l)$$
$$m\ddot{y}_3 = -\frac{S}{a}(2y_3 - y_2).$$

Assuming a solution in the form

$$y_1 = \lambda_1 \cos(pt - \alpha), \quad y_2 = \lambda_2 \cos(pt - \alpha), \quad y_3 = \lambda_3 \cos(pt - \alpha),$$

and substituting in eqs. (l), we find:

$$\lambda_1(p^2 - 2\beta) + \lambda_2\beta = 0,$$
$$\lambda_1\beta + \lambda_2(p^2 - 2\beta) + \lambda_3\beta = 0, \qquad (m)$$
$$\lambda_2\beta + \lambda_3(p^2 - 2\beta) = 0,$$

where

$$\beta = \frac{S}{ma}.$$

By calculating the determinant of eqs. (m) and equating it to zero, we obtain the frequency equation

$$(p^2 - 2\beta)(p^4 - 4p^2\beta + 2\beta^2) = 0. \qquad (n)$$

Substituting the root $p^2 = 2\beta$ of this equation in eqs. (m), we have

$$\lambda_2 = 0 \quad \text{and} \quad \lambda_1 = -\lambda_3;$$

the corresponding type of vibration is represented in Fig. 161b. The two other roots, $p^2 = (2 \pm \sqrt{2})\beta$, of the same eq. ($n$), substituted in eqs. ($m$) give us

$$\lambda_1 = \lambda_3 = \pm\frac{1}{\sqrt{2}}\lambda_2.$$

The corresponding types of vibration are shown in Figs. 161c and 161d. The configuration (c), where all the particles are moving simultaneously in the same direction, represents the lowest or *fundamental* type of vibration, its period being the largest. The type (d) is the highest type of vibration to which corresponds the highest frequency.

38. Free Torsional Vibrations of Shafts.

—In the previous discussion of torsional vibrations (see Art. 2) a simple problem of a shaft with two rotating masses at the ends was considered. In the following, the general case of vibration of a shaft with several rotating masses will be discussed,

Fig. 162. Many problems on torsional vibrations in electric machinery, Diesel engines and propeller shafts can be reduced to such a system.*

Let I_1, I_2, I_3, $\cdots$ be moments of inertia of the rotating masses about the axis of the shaft, φ_1, φ_2, φ_3, $\cdots$ angles of rotation of these masses during vibration, and k_1, k_2, k_3, $\cdots$ spring constants of the shaft for the length ab, bc and cd, respectively. Then $k_1(\varphi_1 - \varphi_2)$, $k_2(\varphi_2 - \varphi_3)$, $\cdots$ represent torsional moments for the above lengths. If we proceed as in Art. 2 and observe that on the first disc a torque

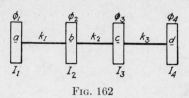

FIG. 162

$- k_1(\varphi_1 - \varphi_2)$ acts during vibration, while on the second disc the torque is $k_1(\varphi_1 - \varphi_2) - k_2(\varphi_2 - \varphi_3)$ and so on, the differential equations of motion for consecutive discs become

$$
\left.
\begin{aligned}
I_1\ddot{\varphi}_1 + k_1(\varphi_1 - \varphi_2) &= 0, \\
I_2\ddot{\varphi}_2 - k_1(\varphi_1 - \varphi_2) + k_2(\varphi_2 - \varphi_3) &= 0, \\
I_3\ddot{\varphi}_3 - k_2(\varphi_2 - \varphi_3) + k_3(\varphi_3 - \varphi_4) &= 0, \\
\cdots \cdots \cdots \cdots \cdots \cdots \cdots \cdots \cdots \cdots \\
\cdots \cdots \cdots \cdots \cdots \cdots \cdots \cdots \cdots \cdots \\
I_{n-1}\ddot{\varphi}_{n-1} - k_{n-2}(\varphi_{n-2} - \varphi_{n-1}) + k_{n-1}(\varphi_{n-1} - \varphi_n) &= 0, \\
I_n\ddot{\varphi}_n - k_{n-1}(\varphi_{n-1} - \varphi_n) &= 0.
\end{aligned}
\right\} \quad (a)
$$

Adding these equations together, we get

$$I_1\ddot{\varphi}_1 + I_2\ddot{\varphi}_2 + \cdots + I_n\ddot{\varphi}_n = 0, \tag{b}$$

which means that the moment of momentum of the system about the axis of the shaft remains constant during free vibration. In the following this moment of momentum will be taken equal to zero. In this manner any rotation of the shaft as a rigid body will be excluded and only vibratory motion due to twist of the shaft will be considered. To find the frequencies of the natural vibrations of this system we proceed as before and take the solutions of eqs. (a) in the form

$$\varphi_1 = \lambda_1 \cos pt, \quad \varphi_2 = \lambda_2 \cos pt, \quad \varphi_3 = \lambda_3 \cos pt, \cdots.$$

* The bibliography of this subject can be found in the very complete investigation of torsional vibration in the Diesel engine made by F. M. Lewis, *Trans. Soc. Nav. Architects Marine Engrs.*, Vol. 33, p. 109, 1925. A number of practical examples are calculated in the books: W. K. Wilson, *Practical Solution of Torsional Vibration Problems*, New York, 1935; W. A. Tuplin, *Torsional Vibration*, New York, 1934.

Substituting in eqs. (*a*), we obtain

$$
\left.\begin{array}{c}
I_1\lambda_1 p^2 - k_1(\lambda_1 - \lambda_2) = 0, \\
I_2\lambda_2 p^2 + k_1(\lambda_1 - \lambda_2) - k_2(\lambda_2 - \lambda_3) = 0, \\
\cdot\ \cdot\ \cdot\ \cdot\ \cdot\ \cdot\ \cdot\ \cdot\ \cdot\ \cdot\ \cdot\ \cdot\ \cdot\ \cdot\ \cdot \\
\cdot\ \cdot\ \cdot\ \cdot\ \cdot\ \cdot\ \cdot\ \cdot\ \cdot\ \cdot\ \cdot\ \cdot\ \cdot\ \cdot\ \cdot \\
I_n\lambda_n p^2 + k_{n-1}(\lambda_{n-1} - \lambda_n) = 0.
\end{array}\right\}
\quad (c)
$$

Eliminating λ_1, λ_2, $\cdots$ from these equations, we obtain an equation of the nth degree in p^2 called the *frequency equation*. The n roots of this equation give us the n frequencies corresponding to the n principal modes of vibration of the system.

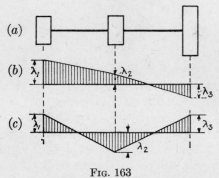

Fig. 163

Let us apply the above general discussion to the problem of three discs, Fig. 163. The system of eqs. (*c*) in this case becomes:

$$
\left.\begin{array}{c}
I_1\lambda_1 p^2 - k_1(\lambda_1 - \lambda_2) = 0, \\
I_2\lambda_2 p^2 + k_1(\lambda_1 - \lambda_2) - k_2(\lambda_2 - \lambda_3) = 0, \\
I_3\lambda_3 p^2 + k_2(\lambda_2 - \lambda_3) = 0.
\end{array}\right\}
\quad (d)
$$

From the first and the third of these equations we find that

$$
\lambda_1 = -\frac{k_1\lambda_2}{I_1 p^2 - k_1}, \quad \lambda_3 = -\frac{k_2\lambda_2}{I_3 p^2 - k_2}. \quad (e)
$$

Substituting these expressions into the equation

$$
(I_1\lambda_1 + I_2\lambda_2 + I_3\lambda_3)p^2 = 0,
$$

which is obtained by adding together eqs. (d), we find

$$p^2\{I_1I_2I_3p^4 - [(I_1I_2 + I_1I_3)k_2 + (I_2I_3 + I_1I_3)k_1]p^2$$
$$+ k_1k_2(I_1 + I_2 + I_3)\} = 0.$$

This is a cubic equation in p^2 of which one of the roots is $p^2 = 0$. This root corresponds to the possibility of having the shaft rotate as a rigid body without any torsion. The two other roots can be readily found from the quadratic equation

$$I_1I_2I_3p^4 - [k_2(I_1I_2 + I_1I_3) + k_1(I_2I_3 + I_1I_3)]p^2$$
$$+ k_1k_2(I_1 + I_2 + I_3) = 0. \quad (78)$$

Let $p_1{}^2$ and $p_2{}^2$ be these two roots. Substituting $p_1{}^2$ instead of p^2 in eqs. (e) we find that

$$\frac{\lambda_1}{\lambda_2} = -\frac{k_1}{I_1p_1{}^2 - k_1}, \quad \frac{\lambda_3}{\lambda_2} = -\frac{k_2}{I_3p_1{}^2 - k_2}.$$

If $p_1{}^2$ is the smaller root, we shall find that one of these two ratios is positive while the other is negative; this means that during vibrations two adjacent discs will rotate in one direction while the third disc rotates in an opposite direction giving the mode of vibration shown in Fig. 163b.* For the larger root $p_2{}^2$ both ratios become negative and the mode of vibration, corresponding to the higher frequency, is shown in Fig. 163c. During this vibration the middle disc rotates in the direction opposite to the rotation of the two other discs.

In the case of four discs we shall have four equations in the system (c), and proceeding as in the previous case, we get a frequency equation of fourth degree in p^2. One of the roots is again zero so that for calculating the remaining three roots we obtain a cubic equation. To simplify the writing of this equation, let us introduce the notations

$$\frac{k_1}{I_1} = \alpha_1, \quad \frac{k_1}{I_2} = \alpha_2, \quad \frac{k_2}{I_2} = \alpha_3, \quad \frac{k_2}{I_3} = \alpha_4, \quad \frac{k_3}{I_3} = \alpha_5, \quad \frac{k_3}{I_4} = \alpha_6,$$

$$\alpha_1 + \alpha_2 = a_1, \quad \alpha_3 + \alpha_4 = a_2, \quad \alpha_5 + \alpha_6 = a_3.$$

Then the frequency equation is

$$p^6 - p^4(a_1 + a_2 + a_3) + p^2(a_1a_2 + a_1a_3 + a_2a_3 - \alpha_2\alpha_3 - \alpha_4\alpha_5)$$
$$- (a_1a_2a_3 - a_3\alpha_2\alpha_3 - a_1\alpha_4\alpha_5) = 0. \quad (79)$$

* It is assumed that $I_3/k_2 > I_1/k_1$.

In solving this equation one of the approximate methods for calculating the roots of algebraic equations of higher degree must be used.*

When the number of discs is larger than four, the derivation of the frequency equation and its solution become too complicated and the calculation of frequencies is usually made by one of the approximate methods, which will be discussed in the next article.

Geared Systems.—Sometimes we have to deal with geared systems as shown in Fig. 164a, instead of with a single shaft. The general equations

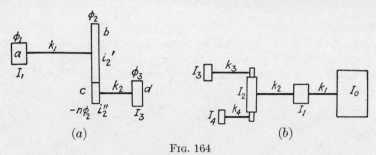

(a)   (b)

FIG. 164

of vibration of such systems can be readily derived. Considering the system in Fig. 164a, let

I_1, I_3 be moments of inertia of rotating masses;
φ_1, φ_3, the corresponding angles of rotation;
i_2', i_2'', moments of inertia of gears;
n, gear ratio;
φ_2, $-n\varphi_2$, angles of rotation of gears;
k_1, k_2, spring constants of shafts.

For the discs I_1 and I_3 we write equations of motion as before and obtain

$$I_1\ddot{\varphi}_1 + k_1(\varphi_1 - \varphi_2) = 0,$$
$$I_3\ddot{\varphi}_3 - k_2(-n\varphi_2 - \ddot{\varphi}_3) = 0. \qquad (f)$$

To obtain the third equation, we consider the motion of the gears. Applying d'Alembert's principle, we conclude that the rotational moment applied to the gear i_2' is

$$k_1(\varphi_1 - \varphi_2) - i_2'\ddot{\varphi}_2,$$

while that applied to the gear i_2'' is

$$k_2(n\varphi_2 + \varphi_3) + i_2''n\ddot{\varphi}_2.$$

* Such methods are discussed in von Sanden's book, *loc. cit.*, p. 100.

The condition of equilibrium gives then the required equation of motion:

$$k_1(\varphi_1 - \varphi_2) - i_2'\ddot{\varphi}_2 = n[k_2(n\varphi_2 + \varphi_3) + i_2''n\ddot{\varphi}_2]$$

or

$$(i_2' + n^2 i_2'')\ddot{\varphi}_2 - k_1(\varphi_1 - \varphi_2) + nk_2(n\varphi_2 + \varphi_3) = 0. \qquad (g)$$

Introducing the notations

$$i_2' + n^2 i_2'' = I_2, \quad n^2 I_3 = I_3',$$

$$\varphi_3 = -n\varphi_3', \quad k_2 n^2 = k_2',$$

we will bring eqs. (f) and (g) to the same form as eqs. (a); then proceeding as before, the required frequency equation will be obtained.

In the case of the arrangement shown in Fig. 164b, and considering I_0 as very large $(\varphi_0 = 0)$ and the moments of inertia of the gears connected with the disc I_2 as very small, we obtain the following system of equations of motion:

$$I_1\ddot{\varphi}_1 + k_1\varphi_1 - k_2(\varphi_2 - \varphi_1) = 0,$$

$$I_2\ddot{\varphi}_2 + k_2(\varphi_2 - \varphi_1) + nk_3(\varphi_3 + n\varphi_2) + nk_4(\varphi_4 + n\varphi_2) = 0,$$

$$I_3\ddot{\varphi}_3 + k_3(\varphi_3 + n\varphi_2) = 0,$$

$$I_4\ddot{\varphi}_4 + k_4(\varphi_4 + n\varphi_2) = 0,$$

from which the frequency equation can be obtained in the same manner as before and the frequencies will then be represented by the roots of this equation.

EXAMPLE

1. Determine the natural frequencies of a steel shaft with three discs, Fig. 163a, if the weights of the discs are 3000 lb, 2000 lb and 1000 lb, the diameters of the discs are 40 in., the distances between the discs are $l_1 = l_2 = 30$ in., the diameter of the shaft is 5 in. and the modulus of elasticity in shear is $G = 11.5 \cdot 10^6$ lb per sq in. Determine the ratios between the angular deflections $\lambda_1 : \lambda_2$, $\lambda_2 : \lambda_3$ for the two principal modes of vibration.

Solution. Making our calculations in inches and in pounds, we find that

$$I_1 = 1553, \quad I_2 = 1035, \quad I_3 = 517.7, \quad k_1 = k_2 = 23.5 \cdot 10^6.$$

Eq. (78) becomes

$$p^4 - 106{,}000 p^2 + 2060 \cdot 10^6 = 0,$$

from which

$$p_1{}^2 = 25{,}600, \quad p_2{}^2 = 80{,}400.$$

The corresponding frequencies are

$$f_1 = \frac{p_1}{2\pi} = 25.5 \text{ per sec.,} \quad f_2 = \frac{p_2}{2\pi} = 45.2 \text{ per sec.}$$

The ratios of amplitudes for the fundamental mode of vibration are

$$\lambda_1/\lambda_2 = -1.44, \quad \lambda_3/\lambda_2 = 2.29.$$

For the higher mode of vibration,

$$\lambda_1/\lambda_2 = -0.232, \quad \lambda_3/\lambda_2 = -1.30.$$

39. Approximate Methods of Calculating Frequencies of Natural Vibrations.*—In practical applications it is usually the lowest frequency or the two lowest frequencies of vibration of a shaft with several discs that are important, and in many cases these can be approximately calculated by using the results obtained in the case of two and three discs. Take, as a first example, a shaft with four discs of which the moments of inertia are $I_1 = 302$ lb in. sec^2, $I_2 = 87,500$ lb in. sec^2, $I_3 = 1200$ lb in. sec^2, $I_4 = 0.373$ lb in. sec.^{2} The spring constants of the three portions of the shaft are $k_1 = 316 \cdot 10^6$ lb in. per radian, $k_2 = 114.5 \cdot 10^6$ lb in. per radian, $k_3 = 1.09 \cdot 10^6$ lb in. per radian. Since I_1 and I_4 are very small, we can neglect them entirely in calculating the lowest frequency and consider only the two discs I_2 and I_3. Applying equation (13) for this system, we obtain

$$f_1 = \frac{1}{2\pi} \sqrt{\frac{(I_2 + I_3)k_2}{I_2 I_3}} = 49.6 \text{ per sec.}$$

In dealing with the vibration of the disc I_1 we can consider the disc I_2 as being infinitely large and assume that it does not vibrate, then the frequency of the disc I_1, from eq. (10), is

$$f_2 = \frac{1}{2\pi} \sqrt{\frac{k_1}{I_1}} = 163 \text{ per sec.}$$

Noting again that the disc I_4 is very small in comparison with I_3 and neglecting the motion of the latter disc, we find

$$f_3 = \frac{1}{2\pi} \sqrt{\frac{k_3}{I_4}} = 272 \text{ per sec.}$$

A more elaborate calculation for this case by using the cubic eq. (78) gives

---

* A comparison of various approximate methods was recently made by K. Klotter. *Ing.-Arch.*, Vol. 17, pp. 1–61, 1949.

$f_1 = 49.5, f_2 = 163, f_3 = 272$, so that for the given proportions of the discs it is not necessary to go into a refined calculation.

As a second example let us consider the system shown in Fig. 165, where the moments of inertia of the generator, flywheel, 6 cylinders and 2 air pumps, as well as the distances between these masses are given.* The shaft is replaced by an *equivalent shaft* of uniform section (see p. 262) with a torsional rigidity $C = 10^{10}$ kg $\times$ cm.^{2} Due to the fact that the masses of the generator and of the flywheel are much larger than the remaining masses, a good approximation for the frequency of the lowest type of vibration can be obtained by replacing all the small masses by one mass

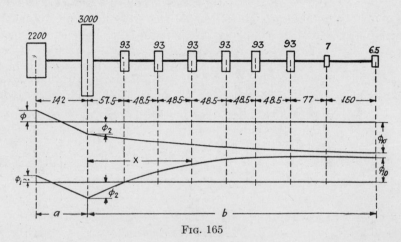

FIG. 165

having a moment of inertia $I_3 = 93 \times 6 + 7 + 6.5 \approx 572$ and located at the distance $57.5 + 2.5 \times 48.5 \approx 179$ centimeters from the flywheel. Reducing in this manner the given system to three masses only, the frequencies can be easily calculated from eq. (78) and we obtain $p_1{}^2 = 49,000$ and $p_2{}^2 = 123,000$. The exact solution for the same problem gives $p_1{}^2 = 49,840$ and $p_2{}^2 = 141,000$.

As soon as we have an approximate value of a frequency, we can improve the accuracy of the solution by the method of successive approximations. For this purpose eqs. (c) (p. 240) must be written in the form:

$$\lambda_2 = \lambda_1 - \frac{I_1 p^2}{k_1} \lambda_1, \tag{a}$$

---

* This example is discussed in the book by Holzer, *loc. cit.*, p. 246. Kilogram and centimeter are taken as units.

$$\lambda_3 = \lambda_2 - \frac{p^2}{k_2} (I_1\lambda_1 + I_2\lambda_2), \qquad\qquad (b)$$

$$\lambda_4 = \lambda_3 - \frac{p^2}{k_3} (I_1\lambda_1 + I_2\lambda_2 + I_3\lambda_3), \qquad\qquad (c)$$

. . . .

. . . .

Making now a rough estimate of the value p^2 and taking an arbitrary value for λ_1, the angular deflection of the first disc, the corresponding value of λ_2 will be found from eq. (a). Then, from eq. (b), λ_3 will be found; λ_4 from eq. (c) and so on. If the magnitude of p^2 had been chosen correctly, the equation

$$I_1\lambda_1 p^2 + I_2\lambda_2 p^2 + \cdots I_n\lambda_n p^2 = 0,$$

representing the sum of the eqs. (c) (p. 240), would be satisfied. Otherwise the angles λ_2, λ_3, $\cdots$ would have to be calculated again with a new

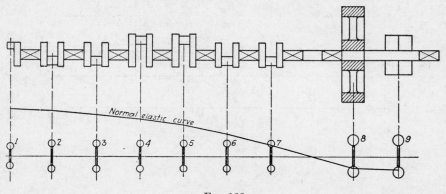

Normal elastic curve

Fig. 166

estimate for p^2.* It is convenient to put the results of these calculations in tabular form. As an example, the calculations for a Diesel installation, shown in Fig. 166, are given in the tables on p. 247.† Column 1 of the tables gives the moments of inertia of the masses, inch, pound and second being taken as units. Column 3 begins with an arbitrary value of the angle of rotation of the first mass. This angle is taken equal to 1. Column 4

---

* Several examples of this calculation may be found in H. Holzer, *Die Berechnung der Drehschwingungen*, Berlin, 1921. See also F. M. Lewis, *loc. cit.*, p. 239, and Max Tolle, *Regelung der Kraftmaschinen*, 3d Ed., 1921.

† These calculations were taken from Lewis paper mentioned above.

gives the moments of the inertia forces of the consecutive masses and column 5, the total torque of the inertia forces of all masses to the left of the cross section considered. Dividing the torque by the spring constants given in column 6, we obtain the angles of twist for consecutive portions of the shaft. These are given in column 7. The last number in column 5 represents the sum of the moments of the inertia forces of all the masses. This sum must be equal to zero in the case of free vibration. By taking $p = 96.2$ in the first table, the last value in column 5 becomes positive.

TABLE FOR $p = 96.2$; $p^2 = 9250$

Mass No.	1 I	2 Ip^2	3 λ	4 $Ip^2\lambda$	5 $\Sigma Ip^2\lambda$	6 k	7 $\frac{1}{k}\Sigma Ip^2\lambda$
1	708	6.55×10^6	1.0000	6.55×10^6	6.55×10^6	2070×10^6	0.0031
2	3920	36.25×10^6	0.9969	36.1×10^6	42.65×10^6	730×10^6	0.0585
3	3920	36.25×10^6	0.9383	34.0×10^6	76.65×10^6	730×10^6	0.1050
4	3920	36.25×10^6	0.8333	30.2×10^6	106.85×10^6	730×10^6	0.1462
5	3920	36.25×10^6	0.6871	24.9×10^6	131.75×10^6	730×10^6	0.1803
6	3920	36.25×10^6	0.5068	18.38×10^6	150.1×10^6	730×10^6	0.2060
7	3920	36.25×10^6	0.3008	10.90×10^6	161.0×10^6	402×10^6	0.4010
8	139800	1293×10^6	−0.1002	$−130.0 \times 10^6$	31.0×10^6	1334×10^6	0.0233
9	26400	244×10^6	−0.1235	$−30.2 \times 10^6$	$+800000$		

TABLE FOR $p = 96.8$; $p^2 = 9380$

Mass No.	1 I	2 Ip^2	3 λ	4 $Ip^2\lambda$	5 $\Sigma Ip^2\lambda$	6 k	7 $\frac{1}{k}\Sigma Ip^2\lambda$
1	708	6.65×10^6	1.0000	6.65×10^6	6.65×10^6	2070×10^6	0.0032
2	3920	36.8×10^6	0.9968	36.7×10^6	43.35×10^6	730×10^6	0.0594
3	3920	36.8×10^6	0.9374	34.5×10^6	77.85×10^6	730×10^6	0.1069
4	3920	36.8×10^6	0.8305	30.6×10^6	108.45×10^6	730×10^6	0.1487
5	3920	36.8×10^6	0.6818	25.1×10^6	133.55×10^6	730×10^6	0.1830
6	3920	36.8×10^6	0.4988	18.36×10^6	151.91×10^6	730×10^6	0.2080
7	3920	36.8×10^6	0.2908	10.70×10^6	162.61×10^6	402×10^6	0.4040
8	139800	1312×10^6	−0.1132	$−148.5 \times 10^6$	14.11×10^6	1334×10^6	0.0106
9	26400	248×10^6	−0.1238	$−30.70 \times 10^6$	$−16.59 \times 10^6$		

For $p = 96.8$, taken in the second table, the corresponding value is negative. This shows that the exact value of p lies between the above two values and the correct values in columns 3 and 5 will be obtained by interpolation. By using the values in column 3, the elastic curve representing the *mode of vibration* can be constructed as shown in Fig. 166. Column 5 gives the corresponding torque for each portion of the shaft when the amplitude of the first mass is 1 radian. If this amplitude has any other value λ_1, the amplitudes and the torque of the other masses may be obtained by multiplying the values in columns 3 and 5 by λ_1. The described method can be applied also to calculate frequencies of higher modes of vibration. Each time we have to begin with some assumed value of p^2 and then, by trial and error, find the value which will make the summation in column 5 of the table vanish.

Instead of working with amplitudes $\lambda_1 \cdots, \lambda_2, \cdots$, we can consider as unknowns the twisting moments in the consecutive portions of the shaft.* Introducing for these moments the notation

$$m_i = (\lambda_i - \lambda_{i+1})k_i, \tag{d}$$

we can rewrite eqs. (c) on p. 240 in the following form:

$$\left.\begin{aligned}
I_1\lambda_1 p^2 - m_1 &= 0, \\
I_2\lambda_2 p^2 + m_1 - m_2 &= 0, \\
\cdots \cdots \cdots \cdots \cdots \cdots \\
I_i\lambda_i p^2 + m_{i-1} - m_i &= 0, \\
\cdots \cdots \cdots \cdots \cdots \cdots \\
I_n\lambda_n p^2 + m_{n-1} &= 0.
\end{aligned}\right\} \tag{e}$$

From these equations follows

$$\lambda_i = \frac{m_i - m_{i-1}}{I_i p^2}, \quad \lambda_{i-1} = \frac{m_{i-1} - m_{i-2}}{I_{i-1} p^2}.$$

Substituting into eqs. (e), we obtain the following relation between the three consecutive twisting moments:

$$\frac{m_i k_{i-1}}{I_i} = m_{i-1}\left(\frac{k_{i-1}}{I_{i-1}} + \frac{k_{i-1}}{I_i} - p^2\right) - \frac{m_{i-2}k_{i-1}}{I_{i-1}}. \tag{f}$$

With notation (d), the twisting moment in the first portion of the shaft will be m_1 and from the first of eqs. (e) we obtain

$$m_1 = I_1\lambda_1 p^2. \tag{g}$$

* See W. A. Tuplin, *loc. cit.*, p. 239.

The consecutive values of the twisting moment, by using eq. (f), will be

$$
\left.
\begin{aligned}
\frac{m_2 k_1}{I_2} &= m_1\left(\frac{k_1}{I_1} + \frac{k_1}{I_2} - p^2\right), \\
\frac{m_3 k_2}{I_3} &= m_2\left(\frac{k_2}{I_2} + \frac{k_2}{I_3} - p^2\right) - \frac{m_1 k_2}{I_2}, \\
\frac{m_4 k_3}{I_4} &= m_3\left(\frac{k_3}{I_3} + \frac{k_3}{I_4} - p^2\right) - \frac{m_2 k_3}{I_3}, \\
&\cdots\cdots\cdots\cdots\cdots\cdots\cdots\cdots\cdots \\
\frac{m_{n-1}k_{n-2}}{I_{n-1}} &= m_{n-2}\left(\frac{k_{n-2}}{I_{n-2}} + \frac{k_{n-2}}{I_{n-1}} - p^2\right) - m_{n-3}\frac{k_{n-2}}{I_{n-2}}, \\
m_n = 0 &= m_{n-1}\left(\frac{k_{n-1}}{I_{n-1}} + \frac{k_{n-1}}{I_n} - p^2\right) - m_{n-2}\frac{k_{n-1}}{I_{n-1}}.
\end{aligned}
\right\} \quad (h)
$$

We assumed that the number of discs is equal to n, so that the last twisting moment is m_{n-1} and the last of the eqs. (h) is obtained from eq. (f) on the assumption that the twisting moment m_n to the right from the last disc vanishes.

In practical application of eqs. (h), we will divide all these equations by an arbitrarily taken quantity k/I having the dimension $\sec^{-2}$ and introduce the notations

$$
\frac{k_i}{I_i} : \frac{k}{I} = c_i, \qquad \frac{k_i}{I_{i+1}} : \frac{k}{I} = c_i{}', \qquad p^2 : \frac{k}{I} = x, \tag{i}
$$

in which the quantities c_i, $c_i{}'$, x are pure numbers which can be readily calculated for a given system and for an assumed value of p^2. With these notations eqs. (h) become

$$
\left.
\begin{aligned}
m_2 c_1{}' &= m_1(c_1 + c_1{}' - x), \\
m_3 c_2{}' &= m_2(c_2 + c_2{}' - x) - m_1 c_2, \\
m_4 c_3{}' &= m_3(c_3 + c_3{}' - x) - m_2 c_3, \\
&\cdots\cdots\cdots\cdots\cdots\cdots\cdots\cdots\cdots \\
m_{n-1} c_{n-2}{}' &= m_{n-2}(c_{n-2} + c_{n-2}{}' - x) - m_{n-3} c_{n-2}, \\
m_n = 0 &= m_{n-1}(c_{n-1} + c_{n-1}{}' - x) - m_{n-2} c_{n-1}.
\end{aligned}
\right\} \quad (j)
$$

In calculating natural frequencies of vibration, we can use eqs. (j) in the same manner as we previously used eqs. (a), (b), (c). We take m_1 arbitrarily, say $m_1 = 1$, assume some value for

$$
x = \frac{p^2 I}{k}
$$

and, using eqs. (j), calculate the moments m_2, m_3, $\cdots$. Since x was taken arbitrarily, the last of eqs. (j) will usually not be satisfied and it will be necessary to repeat the calculations several times before the value of x will be determined with sufficient accuracy. The right-hand side of the last eq. (j) is a function of x and, repeating the above-described calculations for a sufficient number of times, we can represent this function graphically by a curve. The points of intersection of this curve with the x-axis will then define the required frequencies of natural vibrations of the system.

The system of eqs. (h) becomes especially simple in the case of a uniform shaft and a series of equal and equidistant discs (homogeneous engine). Then $I_1 = I_2 = \cdots = I_n$. $k_1 = k_2 = \cdots = k_{n-1}$. Taking, in eqs. ($i$), $k/I = k_1/I_1 = k_2/I_2 = \cdots$, we obtain

$$c_i = c_i' = 1,$$

and eqs. (j) become

$$\left.\begin{aligned}
m_2 &= m_1(2 - x), \\
m_3 &= m_2(2 - x) - m_1, \\
m_4 &= m_3(2 - x) - m_2, \\
&\cdots \cdots \cdots \cdots \cdots \cdots \cdots \\
m_{n-1} &= m_{n-2}(2 - x) - m_{n-3}, \\
m_n &= m_{n-1}(2 - x) - m_{n-2} = 0.
\end{aligned}\right\} \qquad (k)$$

Starting with the value $m_1 = 1$, we can calculate consecutively the twisting moments $m_2, m_3, \cdots$. We see that any moment m_i will be a polynomial of the power $i - 1$ in x. The numerical values of the coefficients of these polynomials are given in the table below.* The sign of the highest term in x will be $(-1)^{i-1}$ and the signs of other terms

COEFFICIENTS IN THE POLYNOMIAL m_i

i	x^0	x^1	x^2	x^3	x^4	x^5	x^6	x^6	x^8	x^9	x^{10}
1	1										
2	2	1									
3	3	4	1								
4	4	10	6	1							
5	5	20	21	8	1						
6	6	35	56	36	10	1					
7	7	56	126	120	55	12	1				
8	8	84	252	330	220	78	14	1			
9	9	120	462	792	715	364	105	16	1		
10	10	165	792	1716	2002	1365	560	136	18	1	
11	11	220	1278	3432	5005	4368	2380	816	171	20	1

* The use of this function in solving torsional vibration problems was introduced by R. Grammel, see his papers in *Ing.-Arch.*, Vol. 2, p. 228, 1931; Vol. 3, pp. 76 and 277, 1932; Vol. 5, p. 23, 1934. See also C. B. Biezeno and R. Grammel, *Technische Dynamik*, Berlin, p. 985, 1939.

are alternating, so that by using the table, we obtain, for example,

$$m_3 = x^2 - 4x + 3,$$
$$m_4 = -x^3 + 6x^2 - 10x + 4,$$
$$m_5 = x^4 - 8x^3 + 21x^2 - 20x + 5.$$

The values of the roots x_i of the equations $m_i = 0$ are tabulated below. Using these roots, the critical frequencies f_i for systems with identical and equidistant discs can be readily calculated by using notations (i), which give

$$p_i = \sqrt{\frac{x_i k}{I}} \quad \text{and} \quad f_i = \frac{p_i}{2\pi} = \frac{1}{2\pi}\sqrt{\frac{x_i k}{I}}. \tag{l}$$

ROOTS x_i OF THE EQUATIONS $m_i = 0$

m_2	m_3	m_4	m_5	m_6	m_7	m_8	m_9	m_{10}	m_{11}	m_{12}
2	1	0.586	0.382	0.268	0.198	0.152	0.121	0.098	0.081	0.068
	3	2.000	1.382	1.000	0.753	0.586	0.468	0.382	0.317	0.268
		3.414	2.618	2.000	1.555	1.235	1.000	0.824	0.690	0.586
			3.618	3.000	2.445	2.000	1.653	1.382	1.169	1.000
				3.732	3.247	2.765	2.347	2.000	1.715	1.482
					3.802	3.414	3.000	2.618	2.285	2.000
						3.848	3.532	3.176	2.831	2.518
							3.879	3.618	3.310	3.000
								3.902	3.683	3.414
									3.919	3.732
										3.932

With the number of discs increasing, the frequencies of the first modes of vibrations will approach those calculated for a shaft with continuously distributed masses. For such a shaft, as we will see later, the consecutive frequencies are defined by the equation

$$p_i = i\pi \sqrt{\frac{k_0}{I_0}}, \tag{m}$$

in which k_0 is the spring constant calculated for the entire length of the shaft and I_0 is the moment of inertia of the shaft with respect to its axis. If the continuously distributed mass of the shaft is replaced by n concentrated discs as shown in Fig. 167, the moment of inertia of each individual disc will be $I = I_0/n$ and the spring constant of a portion of the shaft between two consecutive discs will be $k = k_0 n$. With these notations for I and k, the formula (m) becomes

$$p_i = \frac{i\pi}{n}\sqrt{\frac{k}{I}}.$$

Comparing this result with that of eq. (l), we conclude that the continuous shaft theory gives us the values $i^2\pi^2/n^2$, instead of quantities x_i, given in the table above. Taking, for example, $n = 12$, we get for $i = 1, 2, 3, 4$, the values

$$\frac{i^2\pi^2}{n^2} = 0.0685, 0.274, 0.617, 1.096.$$

Comparing this with the numbers of the last column of the table, we conclude that the continuous shaft theory gives the first two frequencies with good accuracy. The error in the third frequency $(i = 3)$ is about 1.5% and for the fourth frequency the error is larger than 4%.

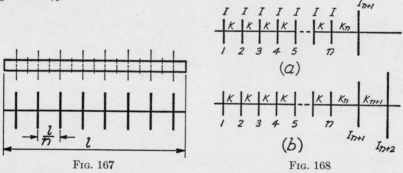

FIG. 167   FIG. 168

Using the table of roots x_i or eq. (m), the frequencies of natural vibrations of systems with equal and equidistant discs can be readily calculated. In practical applications we usually have more complicated cases in which a system of equal and equidistant discs is combined with one or more discs of different magnitude, as shown in Fig. 168. For solving such problems, R. Grammel calculated * numerical tables for polynomials m_i. By using these tables the calculations of natural frequencies is greatly simplified. Let us begin with the case shown in Fig. 168a. For the first n discs we use eqs. (k). The last equation, expressing the fact that the moment m_{n+1} to the right of the disc $n + 1$ vanishes, will have the same form as the last equation of the system (i) and we obtain

$$m_{n+1}c_n' = 0 = m_n(c_n + c_n' - x) - m_{n-1}c_n, \tag{n}$$

where

$$c_n = \frac{k_n}{I} : \frac{k}{I}, \quad c_n' = \frac{k_n}{I_{n+1}} : \frac{k}{I}. \tag{o}$$

* See reference on p. 250.   Grammel tabulated functions $\phi_i = m_{i+1}(-1)^i$.

The required frequencies of vibrations are defined by the roots of eq. (n). Representing this equation in the form

$$m_n(c_n + c_n' - x) = m_{n-1}c_n \qquad (p)$$

and using Grammel's tables,* we can readily calculate numerical values of both sides of eq. (p) for any assumed value of x. Using now graphical representations of both sides,

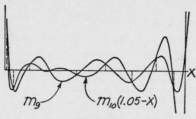

$$m_{10}(1.05 - x) = m_9$$

FIG. 169

as functions of x, we obtain the roots from the intersection points of the curves. In Fig. 169 † is shown such a graphical determination of roots for the case when $n = 10$, $k_n = k$ and $I_{n+1} = 20I$, $\dfrac{k}{I} = 4 \cdot 10^6$ sec^{-2}, representing a ten-cylinder Diesel engine with a flywheel. Eq. (p) then becomes

$$m_{10}(1.05 - x) = m_9.$$

The ten roots of this equation and the corresponding frequencies are:

$x_i =$	0.0311	0.207	0.542	1.008	1.558	2.153	2.735	3.253	3.655	3.910	
$f_i =$	56.5	145	234	320	397	467	527	574	609	629	sec^{-1}.

In the case represented in Fig. 168b the two last equations, corresponding to the two last equations of the system (i), will be

$$m_{n+1}c_n' = m_n(c_n + c_n' - x) - m_{n-1}c_n,$$
$$m_{n+2}c_{n+1}' = 0 = m_{n+1}(c_{n+1} + c_{n+1}' - x) - m_nc_{n+1}.$$

Eliminating m_{n+1}, we obtain

$$m_n[(c_n + c_n' - x)(c_{n+1} + c_{n+1}' - x) - c_{n+1}c_n'] = m_{n-1}c_n(c_{n+1} + c_{n+1}' - x). \qquad (q)$$

Again using tables, the numerical values of both sides of this equation can be readily calculated for any assumed value of x and the roots of the equation, defining the natural frequencies of the system, will be determined by the points of intersection of the two curves graphically representing the two sides of eq. (q).

* In Grammel's tables there are given values of functions ϕ_i, which are related to our functions m_i by the equation $\phi_i = (-1)^i m_{i+1}$.

† This figure is taken from C. B. Biezeno and R. Grammel, p. 988, loc. cit.

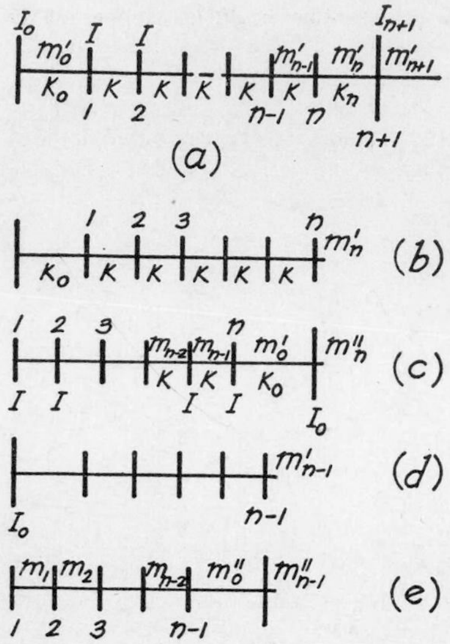

(a)

(b)

(c)

(d)

(e)

FIG. 170

In the case of n equidistant discs with moment of inertia I and two additional discs I_0 and I_{n+1}, as shown in Fig. 170, we observe that the moment m_{n+1}' to the right of the disc I_{n+1} vanishes and eq. (n) becomes

$$0 = m_n'(c_n + c_n' - x) - m_{n-1}'c_n, \qquad (n')$$

where

$$c_n = \frac{k_n}{I} : \frac{k}{I}, \quad c_n' = \frac{k_n}{I_{n+1}} : \frac{k}{I}.$$

We use here notations m_n' and m_{n-1}' to indicate that these moments are different from the tabulated moments, since we have the disc I_0 on the left end of the shaft. To express m_n' and m_{n-1}' by the tabulated moments we use the following consideration. Comparing the two systems of Figs. 170b and 170c, we can see that they are identical and must have the same frequency equation. If we start with the twisting moment equal to unity in the first portion of each shaft, we will get the identical expressions for the twisting moments to the right from the last disc, i.e., $m_n' = m_n''$. For calculation of m_n'' we can use with the proper change of notations eq. (n) and write

$$m_n''c_0' = m_0'(c_0 + c_0' - x) - m_{n-1}c_0, \quad m_0' = m_{n-1}(2 - x) - m_{n-2} = m_n,$$

where

$$c_0 = \frac{k_0}{I} : \frac{k}{I}, \quad c_0' = \frac{k_0}{I_0} : \frac{k}{I}$$

and m_n, m_{n-1} are tabulated moments,

Similarly, comparing systems (d) and (e), Fig. 170, we find

$$m_{n-1}' = m_{n-1}'', \quad m_{n-1}''c_0' = m_0''(c_0 + c_0' - x) - m_{n-2}c_0,$$

$$m_0'' = m_{n-2}(2 - x) - m_{n-3} = m_{n-1}.$$

From this calculation we have

$$m_n' = m_n'' = m_n(c_0 + c_0' - x) - m_{n-1}c_0,$$

$$m_{n-1}' = m_{n-1}'' = m_{n-1}(c_0 + c_0' - x) - m_{n-2}c_0.$$

Substituting into eq. (n) and observing that, from the last of eqs. (k),

$$m_{n-2} = m_{n-1}(2 - x) - m_n,$$

we obtain

$$m_n[(c_0 + c_0' - x)(c_n + c_n' - x) - c_0c_n] = m_{n-1}[x(c_0c_n - c_0 - c_n) + c_0c_n' + c_nc_0'].$$

Again, by using the tabulated values of m_n and m_{n-1}, both sides of the equation can be readily calculated for any assumed value of x, and the required frequencies will be defined by the points of intersection of the two curves, as we had before.

From these examples it may be seen that in the case of systems containing groups of equal and equidistant discs, as in Diesel engines, the calculation of natural frequencies is greatly simplified by using Grammel's tables.

PROBLEMS

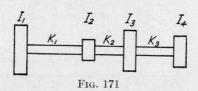

FIG. 171

1. Find critical frequencies for the system shown in Fig. 171 if

$$\frac{k_1}{I_1} = \frac{25}{9} \cdot 10^{-1} \sec^{-2}, \qquad \frac{k_1}{I_2} = \frac{2}{3} \cdot 10^5 \sec^{-2},$$

$$\frac{k_2}{I_2} = \frac{2}{9} \cdot 10^6 \sec^{-2}, \qquad \frac{k_2}{I_3} = \frac{1}{63} \cdot 10^7 \sec^{-2},$$

$$\frac{k_3}{I_3} = \frac{1}{147} \cdot 10^7 \sec^{-2}, \qquad \frac{k_3}{I_4} = \frac{1}{63} \cdot 10^7 \sec^{-2}$$

Answer. $f_1 = 32.5 \sec^{-1}, f_2 = 70.2 \sec^{-1}, f_3 = 108.8 \sec^{-1}$

2. Find critical frequencies for the system shown in Fig. 172 if $\dfrac{k}{I} = 4 \cdot 10^6 \sec^{-2}$

FIG. 172

Answer. $f_1 = 31.9, f_2 = 141, f_3 = 308.8, f_4 = 475.6, f_5 = 593.3.$

40. Forced Torsional Vibration of a Shaft with Several Discs.—If a torque $M_t \sin \omega t$ is applied to one of the discs of Fig. 173, forced vibrations of the period $\tau = 2\pi/\omega$ will be produced; moreover the vibration of each disc will be of the form $\lambda \sin \omega t$. The procedure of calculating the amplitudes of forced vibration will now be illustrated by an example.

Let us take a shaft (Fig. 173) with four discs of which the moments of inertia are $I_1 = 777, I_2 = 518, I_3 = I_4 = 130$, and the spring constants are $k_1 = 24.6 \cdot 10^6$, $k_2 = k_3 = 36.8 \cdot 10^6$, inches, pounds and seconds being taken as units. Assume that a pulsating torque $M_t \sin \omega t$ is acting on the first disc and that it is required to find the amplitudes of the forced vibra-

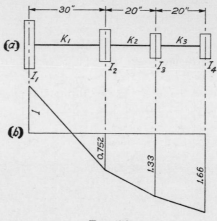

Fig. 173

tion of all the discs for the given frequency $\omega = \sqrt{31,150}$. The equations of motion in this case are

$$\left.\begin{aligned} I_1\ddot{\varphi}_1 + k_1(\varphi_1 - \varphi_2) &= M_t \sin \omega t, \\ I_2\ddot{\varphi}_2 - k_1(\varphi_1 - \varphi_2) + k_2(\varphi_2 - \varphi_3) &= 0, \\ I_3\ddot{\varphi}_3 - k_2(\varphi_2 - \varphi_3) + k_3(\varphi_3 - \varphi_4) &= 0, \\ I_4\ddot{\varphi}_4 - k_3(\varphi_3 - \varphi_4) &= 0. \end{aligned}\right\} \quad (a)$$

Substituting in these equations

$$\varphi_1 = \lambda_1 \sin \omega t, \quad \varphi_2 = \lambda_2 \sin \omega t, \quad \cdots,$$

we obtain

$$\left.\begin{aligned} I_1\lambda_1\omega^2 - k_1(\lambda_1 - \lambda_2) &= -M_t, \\ I_2\lambda_2\omega^2 + k_1(\lambda_1 - \lambda_2) - k_2(\lambda_2 - \lambda_3) &= 0, \\ I_3\lambda_3\omega^2 + k_2(\lambda_2 - \lambda_3) - k_3(\lambda_3 - \lambda_4) &= 0, \\ I_4\lambda_4\omega^2 + k_3(\lambda_3 - \lambda_4) &= 0. \end{aligned}\right\} \quad (b)$$

By adding these equations we find that

$$\omega^2(I_1\lambda_1 + I_2\lambda_2 + I_3\lambda_3 + I_4\lambda_4) = -M_t. \quad (c)$$

If λ_1 is the amplitude of the first disc, the amplitude of the second disc is found from the first of eqs. (b),

$$\lambda_2 = \lambda_1 - \frac{I_1\lambda_1}{k_1}\omega^2 - \frac{M_t}{k_1}. \qquad (d)$$

Substituting this expression into the second of eqs. (b), we find λ_3 and from the third of eqs. (b) we find λ_4. Thus all the amplitudes will be expressed by λ_1. Substituting them in eq. (c), we obtain a linear equation in λ_1.

It is advantageous to make all the calculations in tabular form as shown in the following table:

1	2	3	4	5
I	λ	$I\omega^2\lambda$	$\Sigma I\omega^2\lambda$	$\frac{1}{k}\Sigma I\omega^2\lambda$
777	λ_1	$24.2\cdot10^6\lambda_1$	$24.2\cdot10^6\lambda_1$	$0.984\lambda_1$
518	$0.016\lambda_1 - 4.07\cdot10^{-8}M_t$	$0.256\cdot10^6\lambda_1 - 0.655M_t$	$24.5\cdot10^6\lambda_1 - 0.655M_t$	$0.666\lambda_1 - 1.78\cdot10^{-8}M_t$
130	$-0.650\lambda_1 - 5.01\cdot10^{-8}M_t$	$-2.63\cdot10^6\lambda_1 - 0.203M_t$	$21.9\cdot10^6\lambda_1 - 0.858M_t$	$0.595\lambda_1 - 2.33\cdot10^{-8}M_t$
130	$-1.24\lambda_1 \ - 5.41\cdot10^{-8}M_t$	$-5.02\cdot10^6\lambda_1 - 0.219M_t$	$16.9\cdot10^6\lambda_1 - 1.077M_t$	

We begin with the first row of the table. By using the given numerical values of I_1, ω^2 and k_1, we calculate $I_1\omega^2$ and $I_1\omega^2/k_1$. Starting with the second row we calculate λ_2 by using eq. (d) and the figures from the first row. In this way the expression in the second column and the second row is obtained. Multiplying it with $\omega^2 I_2$, the expression in the third column and the second row is obtained. Adding it to the expression in the fourth column of the first row and dividing afterwards by k_2 the last two terms of the second row are obtained. Having these quantities, we start with the third row by using the second of eqs. (b) for calculating λ_3 and then continue our calculations as before. Finally we obtain the expression in the fourth row and the fourth column which represents the left side of eq. (c). Substituting this expression into eq. (c), we find the equation for calculating λ_1

$$16.9\cdot10^6\lambda_1 - 1.077M_t = -M_t.$$

This gives

$$\lambda_1 = \frac{0.077\,M_t}{16.9\cdot10^6}.$$

If this value λ_1 be substituted into the expressions of the second column, the amplitudes of the forced vibration of all the discs may be caculated. Having these amplitudes, we may calculate the angles of twist of the shaft between the consecutive discs since they are equal to $\lambda_1 - \lambda_2$, $\lambda_2 - \lambda_3$ and $\lambda_3 - \lambda_4$. With these values of the angles of twist and with the known dimensions of the shaft, the shearing stresses produced by the forced vibration may be found by applying the known formula of strength of material.

Effect of Damping on Torsional Vibrations at Resonance.—If the period of the external harmonic torque coincides with the period of one of the natural modes of vibration of the system, a condition of resonance takes place. This mode of vibration becomes very pronounced and the damping forces must be taken into consideration in order to obtain the actual value of the amplitude of vibration.* Assuming that the damping force is proportional to the velocity and neglecting the effect of this force on the *mode of vibration,* i.e., assuming that the ratios between the amplitudes of the steady forced vibration of the rotating masses are the same as for the corresponding type of free vibration, the approximate values of the amplitudes of forced vibration may be calculated as follows: Let $\varphi_m = \lambda_m \sin pt$ be the angle of rotation of the mth disc during vibration with damping. Then, the resisting moment of the damping forces will be

$$-c\frac{d\varphi_m}{dt} = -c\lambda_m p \cos pt,$$

where c is a constant depending upon the damping condition. The phase difference between the torque which produces the forced vibration and the displacement must be 90 degrees for resonance. Hence we take this moment in the form $M_t \cos pt$. Assuming $\varphi_n = \lambda_n \sin pt$ for the angle of rotation of the nth mass on which the torque is acting, the amplitude of the forced vibration will be found from the condition that in the steady state of forced vibration the work done by the harmonic torque during one oscillation must be equal to the energy absorbed at the damping point.

---

* The approximate method of calculating forced vibration with damping has been developed by H. Wydler in, *Drehschwingungen in Kolbenmaschinenanlagen*, Berlin, 1922. See also F. M. Lewis, *loc. cit.*, p. 109; John F. Fox, "Some Experiences with Torsional Vibration Problems in Diesel Engine Installations," *J. Am. Soc. Nav. Engrs.*, 1926; G. G. Eichelberg, "Torsionsschwingungauschlag," *Festschrift Prof. Dr. A. Stodola zum 70. Geburtstag*, Zürich, p. 122, 1929; Albert Stieglitz, "Neure Ergebnisse auf dem Gebiet der Kurbelwellen Schwingungen," *Jahrb. deut. Versuchsanstalt f. Luftfahrt*, p. 281, 1930; and *Luftfahrt—Forschung*, Vol. 4, p. 133, 1929.

In this manner we obtain

$$\int_0^{\frac{2\pi}{p}} c \, \frac{d\varphi_m}{dt} \frac{d\varphi_m}{dt} \, dt = \int_0^{\frac{2\pi}{p}} M_t \cos pt \, \frac{d\varphi_n}{dt} \, dt,$$

or substituting

$$\varphi_m = \lambda_m \sin pt, \quad \varphi_n = \lambda_n \sin pt,$$

we obtain

$$\lambda_m = \frac{M_t}{cp} \frac{\lambda_n}{\lambda_m}, \tag{e}$$

and the amplitude of vibration for the first mass will be

$$\lambda_1 = \frac{M_t}{cp} \frac{\lambda_n}{\lambda_m} \frac{\lambda_1}{\lambda_m}. \tag{f}$$

Knowing the damping constant c and taking the ratios λ_n/λ_m and λ_1/λ_m from the *normal elastic curve* (see Fig. 166), the amplitudes of forced vibration may be calculated for the case of a simple harmonic torque with damping applied at a certain section of the shaft.

Consider again the example of the four discs shown in Fig. 173. By using the method of successive approximation we shall find with sufficient accuracy that the angular frequency of the lowest mode of vibration is approximately $p = 235$ radians per second, and that the ratios of the amplitudes for this mode of vibration are $\lambda_2/\lambda_1 = -0.752$, $\lambda_3/\lambda_1 = -1.33$, $\lambda_4/\lambda_1 = -1.66$. The corresponding normal elastic curve is shown in Fig. 173b. Assume now that the periodic torque $M \cos pt$ is applied at the first disc and that the damping is applied at the fourth disc.* Then from eq. (f)

$$\lambda_1 = \frac{M \lambda_1}{cp} \frac{\lambda_1}{\lambda_4} \frac{\lambda_1}{\lambda_4}.$$

Substituting the value from the normal elastic curve for the ratio λ_1/λ_4, we find

$$\lambda_1 = 0.36 \frac{M_t}{cp}.$$

From this equation the amplitude λ_1 can be calculated for any given torque M_t and any given value of damping factor c.

* The same reasoning holds if damping is applied to any other disc.

If several simple harmonic torques are acting on the shaft, the resultant amplitude λ_1, of the first mass, may be obtained from eq. (f) above by the principle of superposition. It will be equal to

$$\lambda_1 = \frac{1}{cp}\frac{\lambda_1}{\lambda_m^2}\Sigma M_t \lambda_n, \qquad (g)$$

where the summation sign indicates the vector sum, each torque being taken with the corresponding phase.

In actual cases the external torque is usually of a more complicated nature. In the case of a Diesel engine, for instance, the *turning effort* produced by a single cylinder depends on the position of the crank, on the gas pressure and on inertia forces. The *turning effort curve* of each cylinder may be constructed from the corresponding gas pressure diagram, taking into account the inertia forces of the reciprocating masses. In analyzing forced vibrations this curve must be represented by a trigonometric series *

$$f(\varphi) = a_0 + a_1 \cos \varphi + a_2 \cos 2\varphi + \cdots + b_1 \sin \varphi + b_2 \sin 2\varphi + \cdots, \quad (h)$$

in which $\varphi = 2\pi$ represents the period of the curve. This period is equal to one revolution of the crankshaft in a two-cycle engine and to two revolutions in a four-cycle engine. The condition of resonance occurs and a critical speed will be obtained each time when the frequency of one of the terms of the series (h) coincides with the frequency of one of the natural modes of vibration of the shaft. For a single cylinder in a two-cycle engine there will be obtained in this manner critical speeds of the order $1, 2, 3, \cdots$, where the index indicates the number of vibration cycles per revolution of the crankshaft. In the case of a four-cycle engine, we may have critical speeds of the order $\frac{1}{2}, 1, 1\frac{1}{2}, \cdots$; i.e., of every integral order and half order. There will be a succession of such critical speeds for each mode of natural vibration. The amplitude of a forced vibration of a given type produced by a single cylinder may be calculated as has been explained before. In order to obtain the summarized effect of all cylinders, it will be necessary to use the principle of superposition, taking the turning effort of each cylinder at the corresponding phase. In particular cases, when the number of vibrations per revolution is equal to, or a multiple of the number of firing impulses (a major critical speed), the phase difference is zero and

---

* Examples of such an analysis may be found in the papers of H. Wydler, *loc. cit.*, p. 258 ; and F. M. Lewis, *loc. cit.*, p. 109. See also paper by F. P. Porter, *Trans. A.S.M.E.*, Vol. 50, p. APM-25, 1928.

the vibrations produced by the separate cylinders will be simply added together. Several examples of the calculation of amplitudes of forced vibration are to be found in papers by H. Wydler and F. M. Lewis.* They contain also data on the amount of damping in such parts as the marine propeller, the generator and the cylinders, as well as data on the losses due to internal friction.† The application in particular cases of the described approximate method gives satisfactory accuracy in computing the amplitude of forced vibration and the corresponding maximum stress.

41. Torsional Vibration of Diesel Engine Crankshafts.—We have been dealing so far with a uniform shaft having rigid discs mounted on it. There

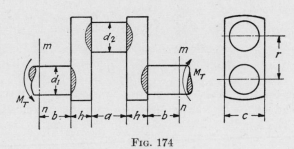

Fig. 174

are, however, cases in which the problem of torsional vibration is more complicated. An example of such a problem we have in the torsional vibrations of Diesel engine crankshafts. Instead of a cylindrical shaft we have here a crankshaft of a complicated form and instead of rotating circular discs we have rotating cranks connected to reciprocating masses of the engine. If the crankshaft be replaced by an equivalent cylindrical shaft the torsional rigidity of one crank (Fig. 174) must be considered first. This rigidity depends on the conditions of constraint at the bearings. Assuming that the clearances in the bearings are such that free displacements of the cross sections mn and mn during twist are possible, the angle of twist produced by a torque M_t can be easily obtained. This angle consists of three parts: (a) twist of the journals, (b) twist of the crankpin and (c) bending of the web.

---

* See preceding footnote.

† Bibliography on this subject and some new data on internal friction may be found in the E. Lehr dissertation, *Die Abkürzungsverfahren zur Ermittelung der Schwingungs-festigkeit,* Stuttgart, 1925. See also E. Jaquet, *Festschrift Prof. Dr. A. Stodola zum 70. Geburtstag, Zürich,* p. 308, 1929; S. F. Dorey, *Proc. Inst. Mech. Engrs. (London),* Vol. 123, p. 479, 1932; advance paper, O. Föppl, Iron and Steel Institute, Oct. 1936.

Let $C_1 = \dfrac{\pi d_1{}^4 G}{32}$ be the torsional rigidity of the journal;

$C_2 = \dfrac{\pi d_2{}^4 G}{32}$, the torsional rigidity of the crankpin;

$B = \dfrac{hc^3}{12} E$, the flexural rigidity of the web.

In order to take into account local deformations of the web in the regions shaded in the figure, due to twist, the lengths of the journal and of the pin are taken equal to $2b_1 = 2b + 0.9h$ and $a_1 = a + 0.9h$, respectively.* The angle of twist θ of the crank produced by a torque M_t will then be

$$\theta = \frac{2b_1 M_t}{C_1} + \frac{a_1 M_t}{C_2} + \frac{2r M_t}{B}.$$

In calculating the torsional vibrations of a crankshaft every crank must be replaced by an equivalent shaft of uniform cross section of a torsional rigidity C. The length l of the equivalent shaft will be found from the equation

$$\frac{M_t l}{C} = \theta,$$

in which θ is the angle of twist calculated above.

Then the length l of equivalent shaft will be,

$$l = C \left(\frac{2b_1}{C_1} + \frac{a_1}{C_2} + \frac{2r}{B} \right). \tag{80}$$

Another extreme case will be obtained on the assumption that the constraint at the bearings is complete, corresponding to no clearances. In this case the length l of the *equivalent shaft* will be found from the equation,†

---

* Such an assumption is in good agreement with experiments made; see a paper by Dr. Seelmann, *Z. Ver. deut. Ing.*, Vol. 69, p. 601, 1925; and F. Sass, *Maschinenbau*, Vol. 4, p. 1223, 1925. See also F. M. Lewis, *loc. cit.*, p. 109.

† A detailed consideration of the twist of a crankshaft is given by the writer in *Trans. A.S.M.E.*, Vol. 44, p. 653, 1922; see also Timoshenko and J. M. Lessells, *Applied Elasticity*, p. 188, 1924. Further discussion of this subject and bibliography can be found in paper by R. Grammel, *Ing.-Arch.*, Vol. 4, p. 287, 1933; in the doctoral thesis by A Kimmel, Stuttgart, 1935; and in the paper by W. A. Tuplin, "The Torsional Rigidity of Crankshafts," *Engineering*, Vol. 144, p. 275, 1937. There are also empirical formulas for the calculation of the equivalent length, see B. C. Carter, *Engineering*, Vol. 126, p. 36, 1928; and C. A. Norman and K. W. Stinson, *S.A.E. Journal*, Vol. 23, p. 83, 1928.

$$l = C \left\{ \frac{2b_1}{C_1} + \frac{a_1}{C_2}\left(1 - \frac{r}{k}\right) + \frac{2r}{B}\left(1 - \frac{r}{2k}\right) \right\}, \tag{81}$$

in which

$$k = \frac{\dfrac{r(a+h)^2}{4C_3} + \dfrac{ar^2}{2C_2} + \dfrac{a^3}{24B_1} + \dfrac{r^3}{3B} + \dfrac{1.2}{G}\left(\dfrac{a}{2F} + \dfrac{r}{F_1}\right)}{\dfrac{ar}{2C_2} + \dfrac{r^2}{2B}}, \tag{82}$$

$C_3 = \dfrac{c^3 h^3 G}{3.6(c^2 + h^2)}$ is the torsional rigidity of the web as a bar of rectangular cross section with sides h and c,

$B_1 = \dfrac{\pi d_2{}^4 E}{64}$ is the flexural rigidity of the crankpin and

F, F_1 are the cross-sectional areas of the pin and of the web, respectively.

By taking $a_1 = 2b_1$ and $C_1 = C_2$ the complete constraint as it is seen from eqs. (80) and (81) reduces the equivalent length of shaft in the ratio $1 : \{1 - (r/2k)\}$. In actual conditions the length of the equivalent shaft will have an intermediate value between the two extreme cases considered above.

Another question to be decided in considering torsional vibration of crankshafts is the calculation of the inertia of the moving masses. Let us assume that the mass m of the connecting rod is replaced in the usual way * by two masses $m_1 = (I/l^2)$ at the crankpin and $m_2 = m - (I/l^2)$ at the crosshead, where I denotes the moment of inertia of the connecting rod about the center of crosshead. All other moving masses also can be replaced by masses concentrated in the same two points so that finally only two masses M and M_1 must be taken into consideration (Fig. 175). Let ω be a constant angular velocity; ωt, the angle of the crank measured from the dead position as shown in Fig. 175. Then the velocity of the

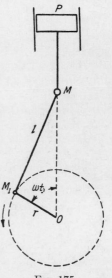

FIG. 175

* For a more complete discussion of this problem, see Timoshenko and D. H. Young, *Advanced Dynamics*, pp. 136 and 174, *loc. cit.*

mass M_1 is equal to ωr and the velocity of the mass M, as shown in Art. 17 (see p. 98), is equal to

$$\omega r \sin \omega t + \frac{r^2 \omega}{2l} \sin 2\omega t.$$

The kinetic energy of the moving masses of one crank will be

$$T = \frac{1}{2} M_1 \omega^2 r^2 + \frac{1}{2} M \omega^2 r^2 \left(\sin \omega t + \frac{r}{2l} \sin 2\omega t \right)^2.$$

The average value of T during one revolution is

$$T_0 = \frac{1}{2\pi} \int_0^{2\pi} T d(\omega t) = \frac{1}{2} \left\{ M_1 + \frac{1}{2} M \left(1 + \frac{r^2}{4l^2} \right) \right\} \omega^2 r^2.$$

By using this average value, the inertia of the moving parts connected with one crank can be replaced by the inertia of an equivalent disc having a moment of inertia

$$I = \left\{ M_1 + \frac{1}{2} M \left(1 + \frac{r^2}{4l^2} \right) \right\} r^2.$$

By replacing all cranks by *equivalent lengths* of shaft and all moving masses by *equivalent discs* the problem of the vibration of crankshafts will be reduced to that of the torsional vibration of a cylindrical shaft and the critical speeds can be calculated as has been shown before. It should be noted that such a method of investigating the vibration must be considered only as a rough approximation. The actual problem is much more complicated and in the simplest case of only one crank with a flywheel it reduces to a problem in torsional vibrations of a shaft with two discs, one of which has a variable moment of inertia. More detailed investigations show * that in such a system *forced vibrations* do not arise only from the pressure of the expanding gases on the piston. They are also produced by the incomplete balance of the reciprocating parts. Practically all the phenomena associated with dangerous critical speeds would appear if the fuel were cut off and the engine made to run without resistance at the requisite speed.

The positions of the critical speeds in such systems are approximately those found by the usual method, i.e., by replacing the moving masses by *equivalent discs.*† Stresses produced in crankshafts during vibrations have

* See paper by G. R. Goldsbrough, "Torsional Vibration in Reciprocating Engine Shafts," *Proc. Roy. Soc. (London)*, Vol. 109, p. 99, 1925; and Vol. 113, p. 259, 1927.

† The bibliography on torsional vibration of discs of variable moment of inertia is given on p. 239.

been investigated experimentally in recent times by S. Olberg and C. Lipson.[*]

42. Damper with Solid Friction.—In order to reduce the amplitudes of torsional vibrations of crankshafts a damper with solid friction,[†] commonly known as the Lanchester damper, is very often used in gas and Diesel engines. The damper, Fig. 176, consists of two flywheels a free to rotate on bushings b, and driven by the crankshaft through friction rings c. The flywheels are pressed against these rings by means of loading springs and adjustable nuts d. If, due to resonance, large vibrations of the shaft end e and of the damper hub occur, the inertia of the flywheel prevents it from following the motion; the resultant relative motion between the hub and the flywheel gives rise to rubbing on the friction surfaces and a certain amount of energy will be dissipated.

It was shown in the discussion of Art. 40 (see p. 259) that the amplitude of torsional vibration at resonance can be readily calculated if the amount of energy dissipated in the damper per cycle is known. To calculate this energy in the case of the Lanchester damper, the motion of the damper flywheels must be considered. Under steady conditions the flywheels are rotating with an average angular velocity equal to the average angular velocity of the crankshaft. On this motion a motion relative to the oscillating hub will be superimposed. It will be periodic motion and its frequency will

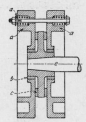

Fig. 176

be the same as that of the oscillating shaft. The three possible types of the superimposed motion are illustrated by the velocity diagrams in Fig. 177. The sinusoidal curves represent the angular velocity ω_h of the oscillating hub. During slipping, the flywheel is acted upon by a constant friction torque M_f, therefore its angular velocity is a linear function of time, which is represented in the diagrams by straight lines. If the flywheel is slipping continuously we have the condition shown in Fig. 177a. The velocity ω_f [‡] of the flywheel is represented by the broken line which shows that the flywheel has a periodically symmetrical motion. The velocity of this motion increases when the hub velocity ω_h is greater and decreases when the hub velocity is less than the flywheel velocity ω_f. The slopes of the straight lines are equal to the angular accelerations of the flywheel, i.e., equal to M_f/I where I is the total moment of inertia of the damper flywheels. As the damper loading springs are tightened up, the friction torque increases and the straight lines of the flywheel velocity diagram become steeper. Finally we arrive at the limiting condition shown in Fig. 177b when the straight line becomes tangent to the sine curve. This represents the limit of the friction torque below which slipping of the flywheel is continuous. If the friction is increased further, the flywheel clings to the hub until the acceleration of the hub is large enough to overcome the friction and we obtain the condition shown in Fig. 177c.

---

[*] See *Exptl. Stress Analysis*, Vol. 2, Part 2, p. 118; also in same volume, papers by A. Goloff and M. L. Frey.

[†] The theory of this damper has been developed by J. P. Den Hartog and J. Ormondroyd, *Trans. A.S.M.E.*, Vol. 52, p. APM-133, 1930. See also K. Klotter, "Theorie der Reibungsschwingungsdämpfer," *Ing.-Arch.*, Vol. 9, p. 137, 1938.

[‡] ω_f and ω_h denote the velocities of the flywheel and of the hub superimposed on the uniform average velocity of rotation of the crankshaft.

In our further discussion we assume that the damper flywheel is always sliding and we use the diagram in Fig. 177a. Noting that the relative angular velocity of the flywheel with respect to the hub is $\omega_f - \omega_h$, we see that the energy dissipated during an interval of time dt will be $M_f(\omega_h - \omega_f)\,dt$ so that the energy dissipated per cycle may be obtained by an integration,

$$E = \int_0^\tau M_f(\omega_h - \omega_f)\,dt \qquad (a)$$

where $\tau = 2\pi/\omega$ is the period of the torsional vibration of the shaft. In Fig. 177a this integral is represented to certain scale by the shaded area. In order to simplify the

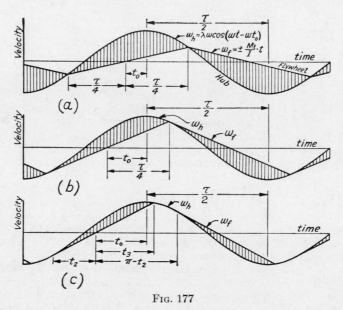

Fig. 177

calculation of this area we take the time as being zero at the instant the superimposed velocity ω_f of the flywheel is zero and about to become positive, and we denote by t_0 the time corresponding to the maximum of the superimposed velocity ω_h of the hub. In this case the oscillatory motion of the hub is

$$\lambda \sin \omega(t - t_0),$$

and by differentiation we obtain

$$\omega_h = \lambda\omega \cos \omega(t - t_0). \qquad (b)$$

The velocity of the flywheel for the interval of time $-\tau/4 < t < \tau/4$ will be

$$\omega_f = M_f t/I. \qquad (c)$$

The time t_0 may be found from the condition that when $t = \pm\tau/4$ (see Fig. 177a), $\omega_f = \omega_h$. Then by using (b) and (c) we obtain

$$\frac{M_f}{I} \cdot \frac{\pi}{2\omega} = \lambda\omega \cos\left(\frac{\pi}{2} - \omega t_0\right) = \lambda\omega \sin \omega t_0,$$

and

$$\sin \omega t_0 = \frac{M_f}{I} \cdot \frac{\pi}{2\lambda\omega^2}. \qquad (d)$$

In calculating the amount of energy dissipated per cycle we note that the two shaded areas in Fig. 177a are equal. Hence

$$E = \int_0^\tau M_f(\omega_h - \omega_f)\, dt = 2\int_{-\tau/4}^{+\tau/4} M_f(\omega_h - \omega_f)\, dt,$$

or, substituting from (b) and (c),

$$E = 2M_f \int_{-\pi/2\omega}^{+\pi/2\omega} \left[\lambda\omega \cos \omega(t - t_0) - \frac{M_f t}{I} \right] dt.$$

Performing the integration we obtain

$$E = 4M_f\lambda \cos \omega t_0,$$

or by using (d) we find the final expression for the amount of energy dissipated per cycle:

$$E = 4M_f\lambda \sqrt{1 - \left(\frac{M_f}{I}\frac{\pi}{2\lambda\omega^2}\right)^2}. \qquad (e)$$

By a change in the adjustable nuts d the friction torque M_f can be properly chosen. If the force exerted by the loading springs is very small the friction force is also small and its damping effect on the torsional vibrations of the crankshaft will be negligible. By tightening up the nuts we can get another extreme case when the friction torque is so large that the flywheel does not slide at all and no dissipation of energy takes place. The most effective damping action is obtained when the friction torque has the magnitude at which expression (e) becomes a maximum. Taking the derivative of this expression with respect to M_f and equating it to zero we find the most favorable value for the torque

$$M_f = \frac{\sqrt{2}}{\pi} \lambda\omega^2 I. \qquad (f)$$

With this value substituted in (e) the energy dissipated per cycle becomes

$$E_{\max} = \frac{4}{\pi} \lambda^2\omega^2 I. \qquad (g)$$

Having this expression we may calculate the amplitude of the forced vibration at resonance in the same manner as in the case of a viscous damping acting on one of the vibrating discs (see p. 259). If a pulsating torque $M \cos \omega(t - t_0)$ is acting on a disc of which the amplitude of torsional vibration is λ_m, the work done by this torque per cycle is (see p. 82) $M\lambda_m\pi$. Equating this work to the energy dissipated (g) we find

$$\lambda = \frac{\pi^2 M}{4\omega^2 I} \cdot \frac{\lambda_m}{\lambda}. \tag{h}$$

The ratio λ_m/λ can be taken from the normal elastic curve of the vibrating shaft so that if M and I are given, the amplitude λ can be calculated from eq. (h). Usually eq. (h) may be applied for determining the necessary moment of inertia I of the damper. In such a case the amplitude λ should be taken of such a magnitude as to have the maximum torsional stress in the shaft below the allowable stress for the material of the shaft. Then the corresponding value of I may be calculated from eq. (h).

43. Lateral Vibrations of Shafts on Many Supports.—*Analytical Method.* —In our previous discussion (Art. 5) the simplest case of a shaft on two supports was considered and it was then shown that the critical speed of rotation of a shaft is that speed at which the number of revolutions per second is equal to the frequency of its natural lateral vibrations. In practice, however, cases of shafts on *many* supports are encountered and consideration will now be given to the various methods which may be employed for calculating the frequencies of the natural modes of lateral vibration of such shafts.*

This analytical method can be applied without much difficulty in the case of a shaft of uniform cross section carrying several discs.

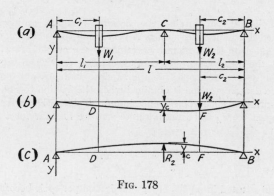

Fig. 178

Let us consider first the simple example of a shaft on three supports carrying two discs (Fig. 178) the weights of which are W_1 and W_2. The

* This subject is discussed in detail by A. Stodola, *Dampf-und Gasturbinen*, 6th Ed., Berlin, 1924. See also, C. B. Biezeno and R. Grammel, *Technische Dynamik*, Berlin, pp. 807–842, 1939.

statical deflections of the shaft under these loads can be represented by the equations

$$\delta_1 = a_{11}W_1 + a_{12}W_2, \tag{a}$$

$$\delta_2 = a_{21}W_1 + a_{22}W_2, \tag{b}$$

the constants a_{11}, a_{12}, a_{21} and a_{22} of which can be calculated in the following manner. Remove the intermediate support C and consider the deflections produced by load W_2 alone (Fig. 178b); then the equation of the deflection curve for the left part of the shaft will be

$$y = \frac{W_2c_2}{6lEI}(-x^3 + l^2x - c_2{}^2x), \tag{c}$$

and the deflection at the point C becomes

$$y_c = \frac{W_2c_2}{6lEI}(-l_1{}^3 + l^2l_1 - c_2{}^2l_1).$$

Now determine the reaction R_2 in such a manner as to reduce this deflection to zero (Fig. 178c). Applying eq. (c) for calculating the deflection under R_2 and putting this deflection equal to y_c, obtained above, we have,

$$\frac{W_2c_2}{6lEI}(-l_1{}^3 + l^2l_1 - c_2{}^2l_1) = \frac{R_2l_2}{6lEI}(-l_1{}^3 + l^2l_1 - l_2{}^2l_1),$$

from which

$$R_2 = \frac{W_2c_2(l^2 - l_1{}^2 - c_2{}^2)}{2l_1l_2{}^2}.$$

In the same manner the reaction R_1 produced by the load W_1 can be calculated and the complete reaction $R = R_1 + R_2$ at the middle support will be obtained. Now, by using eq. (c) the deflection δ_1 produced by the loads W_1, W_2 and the reaction R can be represented in the form (a) in which

$$a_{11} = \frac{1}{12ll_1{}^2EI}\{4l_1{}^2(l-c_1)^2c_1{}^2 - c_1(-c_1{}^3 + l^2c_1 - l_2{}^2c_1)(l^2 - l_2{}^2 - c_1{}^2)\},$$

$$\tag{d}$$

$$a_{12} = \frac{1}{12ll_1l_2EI}\{2l_1l_2c_1c_2(l^2 - c_1{}^2 - c_2{}^2) - c_2c_1(l^2 - l_2{}^2 - c_1{}^2)(l^2 - l_1{}^2 - c_2{}^2)\}.$$

Interchanging l_2 and l_1 and c_2 and c_1 in the above equations, the constants a_{21} and a_{22} of eq. (b) will be obtained and it will be seen that

$a_{12} = a_{21}$, i.e., that a load put at the location D produces at F the same deflection as a load of the same magnitude at F produces at D. Such a result should be expected on the basis of the *reciprocal theorem*.

Consider now the vibration of the loads W_1 and W_2 about their position of equilibrium, found above, and in the plane of the figure. Let y_1 and y_2 now denote the variable displacements of W_1 and W_2 from their positions of equilibrium during vibration. Letting, for simplicity, $a_{11} = a$, $a_{12} = a_{21} = b$, $a_{22} = c$,* we obtain from the above eqs. (a) and (b) the following forces necessary to produce the deflections y_1 and y_2:

$$P_1 = \frac{cy_1 - by_2}{ac - b^2}, \quad P_2 = \frac{ay_2 - by_1}{ac - b^2},$$

and the equations of motion of the weights W_1 and W_2 become

$$\left. \begin{aligned}
\frac{W_1}{g} \ddot{y}_1 + P_1 &= \frac{W_1}{g} \ddot{y}_1 + \frac{c}{ac - b^2} y_1 - \frac{b}{ac - b^2} y_2 = 0, \\
\frac{W_2}{g} \ddot{y}_2 + P_2 &= \frac{W_2}{g} \ddot{y}_2 - \frac{b}{ac - b^2} y_1 + \frac{a}{ac - b^2} y_2 = 0.
\end{aligned} \right\} \quad (e)$$

Assuming that the shaft performs one of the natural modes of vibration and substituting in eqs. (e)

$$y_1 = \lambda_1 \cos pt, \quad y_2 = \lambda_2 \cos pt,$$

we obtain

$$\left. \begin{aligned}
\lambda_1 \left(\frac{c}{ac - b^2} - \frac{W_1}{g} p^2 \right) - \frac{b}{ac - b^2} \lambda_2 &= 0, \\
- \frac{b}{ac - b^2} \lambda_1 + \lambda_2 \left(\frac{a}{ac - b^2} - \frac{W_2}{g} p^2 \right) &= 0.
\end{aligned} \right\} \quad (f)$$

By putting the determinant of these equations equal to zero, the following *frequency equation* will be obtained:

$$\left(\frac{c}{ac - b^2} - \frac{W_1}{g} p^2 \right) \left(\frac{a}{ac - b^2} - \frac{W_2}{g} p^2 \right) - \frac{b^2}{(ac - b^2)^2} = 0, \quad (g)$$

from which

$$p^2 = \frac{g}{2(ac - b^2)} \left\{ \frac{c}{W_1} + \frac{a}{W_2} \pm \sqrt{\left(\frac{c}{W_1} + \frac{a}{W_2} \right)^2 - \frac{4(ac - b^2)}{W_1 W_2}} \right\}. \quad (83)$$

* The constants a, b and c can be calculated for any particular case by using eqs. (d).

In this manner two positive roots for p^2, corresponding to the two principal modes of vibration of the shaft, are obtained. Substituting these two roots in one of the eqs. (f) two different values for the ratio λ_1/λ_2 will be obtained. For the larger value of p^2 the ratio λ_1/λ_2 becomes positive, i.e., both discs during the vibration move simultaneously in the same direction and the mode of vibration is as shown in Fig. 179a. If the smaller root of p^2 be

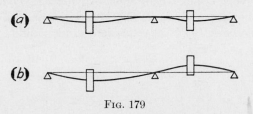

FIG. 179

substituted in eqs. (f) the ratio λ_1/λ_2 becomes negative and the corresponding mode of vibration will be as shown in Fig. 179b. Take, for instance, the particular case when (see Fig. 178) $W_1 = W_2$, $l_1 = l_2 = (l/2)$ and $c_1 = c_2 = (l/4)$. Substituting in eqs. (d) and using the conditions of symmetry, we obtain

$$a = c = \frac{23}{48 \times 256} \frac{l^3}{EI} \quad \text{and} \quad b = -\frac{9}{48 \times 256} \frac{l^3}{EI}.$$

Substituting in eq. (83), we have

$$p_1{}^2 = \frac{g}{(a - b)W} = \frac{48EIg}{W(l/2)^3}, \quad p_2{}^2 = \frac{768EIg}{7W(l/2)^3}.$$

These two frequencies can also be easily derived by substituting in eq. 4 (see p. 3) the statical deflections

$$\delta_{st}{}' = \frac{W(l/2)^3}{48EI} \quad \text{and} \quad \delta_{st}{}'' = \frac{7W(l/2)^3}{768EI}$$

for the cases shown in Fig. 180.

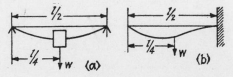

FIG. 180

Another method of solution of the problem on the lateral vibrations of shafts consists in the application of d'Alembert's principle. In using this principle the equations of vibration will be written in the same manner as equations of statics. It is only necessary to add to the loads acting on the shaft the inertia forces. Denoting, as before, by y_1 and y_2 the deflections of the shaft from the position of equilibrium under the loads W_1 and W_2, respectively, the inertia forces will be $-(W_1/g)\ddot{y}_1$ and $-(W_2/g)\ddot{y}_2$. These inertia forces must be in equilibrium with the elastic forces due to the additional deflection and two equations equivalent to (a) and (b) can be written down as follows:

$$\left.\begin{array}{l} y_1 = -a\dfrac{W_1}{g}\ddot{y}_1 - b\dfrac{W_2}{g}\ddot{y}_2, \\[2mm] y_2 = -b\dfrac{W_1}{g}\ddot{y}_1 - c\dfrac{W_2}{g}\ddot{y}_2. \end{array}\right\} \qquad (h)$$

Assuming, as before,

$$y_1 = \lambda_1 \cos pt, \quad y_2 = \lambda_2 \cos pt,$$

and substituting in eqs. (h), we obtain,

$$\left.\begin{array}{l} \lambda_1\left(1 - \dfrac{aW_1}{g}p^2\right) - \lambda_2 b\dfrac{W_2}{g}p^2 = 0, \\[3mm] -\lambda_1 b\dfrac{W_1}{g}p^2 + \lambda_2\left(1 - \dfrac{cW_2}{g}p^2\right) = 0. \end{array}\right\} \qquad (i)$$

Putting the determinant of these two equations equal to zero, an equation similar to the frequency eq. (g), which we had before, will be obtained.

The methods developed above for calculating frequencies of lateral vibrations can be used also in cases where the number of discs or the number of spans is greater than two. Take, for instance, the case shown in Fig. 181. By using a method analogous to the one employed in the previous example, the statical deflections of the shaft under the discs can be represented in the following form:

$$\left.\begin{array}{l} \delta_1 = a_{11}W_1 + a_{12}W_2 + a_{13}W_3, \\ \delta_2 = a_{21}W_1 + a_{22}W_2 + a_{23}W_3, \\ \delta_3 = a_{31}W_1 + a_{32}W_2 + a_{33}W_3, \end{array}\right\}$$

in which a_{11}, a_{12}, $\cdots$ are constants depending on the distances between the supports, the distances of the discs from the supports and on the flexural rigidity of the shaft. From the *reciprocal theorem* it can be concluded at once that $a_{12} = a_{21}$, $a_{13} = a_{31}$ and $a_{23} = a_{32}$. Applying now d'Alembert's principle and denoting by y_1, y_2 and y_3 the displacements

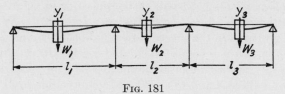

FIG. 181

of the discs during vibration from the position of equilibrium, the following equations of vibration will be derived from the statical eqs. (j):

$$
\left.
\begin{aligned}
y_1 &= -a_{11} \frac{W_1}{g} \ddot{y}_1 - a_{12} \frac{W_2}{g} \ddot{y}_2 - a_{13} \frac{W_3}{g} \ddot{y}_3, \\[1em]
y_2 &= -a_{21} \frac{W_1}{g} \ddot{y}_1 - a_{22} \frac{W_2}{g} \ddot{y}_2 - a_{23} \frac{W_3}{g} \ddot{y}_3, \\[1em]
y_3 &= -a_{31} \frac{W_1}{g} \ddot{y}_1 - a_{32} \frac{W_2}{g} \ddot{y}_2 - a_{33} \frac{W_3}{g} \ddot{y}_3,
\end{aligned}
\right\}
\qquad (k)
$$

from which the *frequency equation*, a cubic in p^2, can be obtained in the usual manner. The three roots of this equation will give the frequencies of the three principal modes of vibration of the system under consideration.*

It should be noted that the frequency equations for the lateral vibrations of shafts can be used also for calculating *critical speeds* of rotation. A critical speed of rotation is a speed at which the centrifugal forces of the rotating masses are sufficiently large to keep the shaft in a bent condition (see Art. 5). Take again the case of two discs (Fig. 178a) and assume that y_1 and y_2 are the deflections, produced by the centrifugal forces †$(W_1/g)\omega^2 y_1$ and $(W_2/g)\omega^2 y_2$ of the rotating discs. Such deflections can exist only if the centrifugal forces satisfy the following conditions of equilibrium (see eqs. *a* and *b*):

$$
\left.
\begin{aligned}
y_1 &= a_{11} \frac{W_1}{g} \omega^2 y_1 + a_{12} \frac{W_2}{g} \omega^2 y_2, \\[1em]
y_2 &= a_{21} \frac{W_1}{g} \omega^2 y_1 + a_{22} \frac{W_2}{g} \omega^2 y_2.
\end{aligned}
\right\}
\qquad (l)
$$

* A graphical method of solution of frequency equations has been developed by C. R. Soderberg, *Phil. Mag.*, Vol. 5, p. 47, 1928.

† The effect of the weight of the shaft on the critical speeds will be considered later.

These equations can give for y_1 and y_2 solutions different from zero only in the case when their determinant vanishes. Observing that eqs. (l) are identical with eqs. (i) above, and equating their determinant to zero, an equation identical with eq. (g) will be obtained for calculating the critical speeds of rotation.

Graphical Method.—In the preceding discussion, it was assumed that the constants a_{11}, a_{12}, a_{22}, $\cdots$ are calculated analytically. In the case of shafts of variable cross section, it is advantageous to use a graphical method for determining these constants. To explain the method, let us again consider the case of a shaft on three supports and having one disc in each span, as shown in Fig. 178. In the solution of this problem, we may proceed exactly in the same manner as before in the analytical solution and establish first the equations

$$\delta_1 = a_{11}W_1 + a_{12}W_2, \tag{a'}$$

$$\delta_2 = a_{21}W_1 + a_{22}W_2, \tag{b'}$$

between the acting forces and the resultant deflections.

In order to obtain the values of the constants a_{11}, a_{12}, $\cdots$ graphically we assume first that the load W_1 is acting alone and thatt he middle sup-

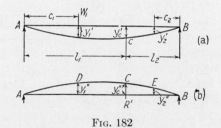

Fig. 182

port is removed (Fig. 182a); then the deflections y_1', y_2' and y_c' can be obtained by using the graphical method, described before (see p. 37). Now, by using the same method, the deflection curve produced by a vertical force R' applied at C and acting in an upward direction should be constructed and the deflections y_1'', y_c'' and y_2'' measured. Taking into consideration that the deflection at the support C should be equal to zero, the reaction R of this support will now be found from the equation

$$R = R'\frac{y_c'}{y_c''}, ^* \tag{m}$$

* Absolute values of the deflections are taken in this equation.

and the actual deflections at D and E, produced by the load W_1, will be

$$
\left.
\begin{aligned}
y_{11} &= y_1' - y_1'' \frac{y_c'}{y_c''}, \\[2ex]
y_{21} &= y_2' - y_2'' \frac{y_c'}{y_c''}.
\end{aligned}
\right\} \tag{n}
$$

Comparing these equations with the eqs. (a') and (b') for $W_2 = 0$, we obtain

$$
\left.
\begin{aligned}
a_{11}W_1 &= y_1' - y_1'' \frac{y_c'}{y_c''}, \\[2ex]
a_{21}W_1 &= y_2' - y_2'' \frac{y_c'}{y_c''},
\end{aligned}
\right\} \tag{o}
$$

from which the constants a_{11} and a_{21} can be calculated. In the same manner, considering the load $W_1 = 0$, the constants a_{12} and a_{22} can be found. All constants of eqs. (a') and (b') being determined, the two critical speeds of the shaft can be calculated by using formula (83), in which $a = a_{11}; b = a_{12} = a_{21}; c = a_{22}$.

In the previous calculations, the reaction R at the middle support has been taken as the statically indeterminate quantity. If there are many supports, it is simpler to take as statically indeterminate quantities the bending moments at the intermediate supports. To illustrate this method of calculation, let us consider a motor generator set consisting of an induction motor and a D.C. generator supported on three bearings.* The dimensions of the shaft of variable cross section are given in Fig. 183a. We assume that the masses of the induction-motor armature W_3, D.C. armature W_2 and also D.C. commutator W_1 are concentrated at their centers of gravity (Fig. 183a). In order to take into account the mass of the shaft, one-half of the mass of the left span of the shaft has been added to the mass of the induction motor and one-half of the mass of the right span of the shaft has been equally distributed between the D.C. armature and D.C. commutator. In this manner the problem is reduced to one of three degrees of freedom and the deflections y_1, y_2, y_3 of the masses W_1, W_2 and W_3 during vibration will be taken as coordinates. The statical deflections under the action of loads W_1, W_2, W_3 can be represented by eqs. (j) and the constants a_{11}, a_{12}, $\cdots$ of these equations will now be determined by

* These numerical data represent an actual case calculated by J. P. Den Hartog, Research Engineer, Westinghouse Electric Corporation, East Pittsburgh, Pa.

taking the bending moment at the intermediate support as the statically in-determinate quantity. In order to obtain a_{11}, let us assume that the shaft is cut into two parts at the intermediate support and that the right-hand span is loaded by a 1-lb load at the cross section where W_1 is applied (Fig. 183b). By using the graphical method, explained in Art. 5, we obtain the

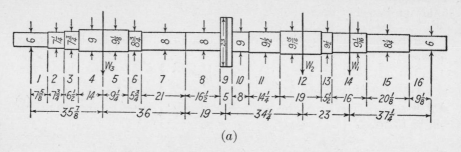

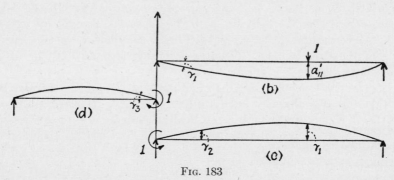

Fig. 183

deflection under the load $a_{11}' = 2.45 \times 10^{-6}$ inch and the slope at the left support $\gamma_1 = 5.95 \times 10^{-8}$ radian. By applying now a bending moment of 1 inch-pound at the intermediate support and using the same graphical method, we obtain the slopes $\gamma_2 = 4.23 \times 10^{-9}$ (Fig. 183c) and $\gamma_3 = 3.5 \times 10^{-9}$ (Fig. 183d). From the *reciprocity theorem* it follows that the deflection at the point W_1 for this case is numerically equal to the slope γ_1, in the case shown in Fig. 183b. The bending moment M at the intermediate support produced by a load of 1 lb at the point W_1 is now found from the condition that at the middle support the two spans must have a common tangent. Hence $\gamma_1 - M\gamma_2 = M\gamma_3$ which gives

$$M = \frac{\gamma_1}{\gamma_2 + \gamma_3} \text{ lbs} \times \text{inch.}$$

Then the deflection under the load W_1 is

$$a_{11} = a_{11}' - \frac{\gamma_1^2}{\gamma_2 + \gamma_3} = 19.9 \times 10^{-7}.$$

Proceeding in the same manner with the other constants of eqs. (j), the following numerical values have been obtained:

$$a_{22} = 19.6 \times 10^{-7}, \quad a_{33} = 7.6 \times 10^{-7}, \quad a_{12} = a_{21} = 18.1 \times 10^{-7}.$$

$$a_{13} = a_{31} = -3.5 \times 10^{-7}, \quad a_{23} = a_{32} = -4.6 \times 10^{-7}.$$

Now substituting in eqs. (j) the centrifugal forces $W_1\omega^2 y_1/g$, $W_2\omega^2 y_2/g$ and $W_3\omega^2 y_3/g$ instead of the loads W_1, W_2, W_3, the following equations will be found:

$$\left.\begin{aligned}
\left(1 - a_{11}\frac{W_1\omega^2}{g}\right)y_1 - a_{12}\frac{W_2\omega^2}{g}y_2 - a_{13}\frac{W_3\omega^2}{g}y_3 &= 0, \\
-a_{21}\frac{W_1\omega^2}{g}y_1 + \left(1 - a_{22}\frac{W_2\omega^2}{g}\right)y_2 - a_{23}\frac{W_3\omega^2}{g}y_3 &= 0, \\
-a_{31}\frac{W_1\omega^2}{g}y_1 - a_{32}\frac{W_2\omega^2}{g}y_2 + \left(1 - a_{33}\frac{W_3\omega^2}{g}\right)y_3 &= 0.
\end{aligned}\right\} \quad (p)$$

If the determinant of this system of equations be equated to zero and the quantities calculated above be used for the constants a_{11}, a_{12}, $\cdots$, the following frequency equation for calculating the critical speeds will be found:

$$(\omega^2 10^{-7})^3 - 3.76(\omega^2 10^{-7})^2 + 1.93(\omega^2 10^{-7}) - 0.175 = 0,$$

from which the three critical speeds in r.p.m. are:

$$n_1 = \frac{\omega_1 60}{2\pi} = 1070, \quad n_2 = \frac{\omega_2 60}{2\pi} = 2240, \quad n_3 = \frac{\omega_3 60}{2\pi} = 5620.$$

Critical speeds for a rotating shaft can be found also in a purely graphical way. This graphical method we will explain first for the case of a shaft with simply supported ends, Fig. 33 (p. 36).

Assume some *initial deflection* of the rotating shaft satisfying the end conditions where y_1, y_2, $\cdots$ are the deflections at the discs W_1, W_2, $\cdots$. Assume also some angular velocity ω; then the corresponding centrifugal forces will be $(W_1/g)\omega^2 y_1$, $(W_2/g)\omega^2 y_2$, $\cdots$. Considering these forces as statically applied to the shaft, the corresponding deflection curve can be obtained graphically as was explained in Art. 5. If our assumption about the shape of the *initial* deflection curve was correct, the deflections y_1', y_2', $\cdots$, as obtained *graphically*, should be proportional to the deflections y_1, y_2, $\cdots$ initially assumed, and the critical speed will be found from the equation

$$\omega_{cr} = \omega \sqrt{\frac{y_1}{y_1'}}, \quad \text{or} \quad \omega_{cr} = \omega \sqrt{\frac{y_2}{y_2'}}. \tag{84}$$

This can be explained in the following manner.

By taking ω_{cr} as given by (84) instead of ω, in calculating the centrifugal forces as above, all these forces will increase in the ratio y_1/y_1'; the deflections graphically derived will now also increase in the same proportion and the deflection curve, as obtained graphically, will now coincide with the *initially assumed* deflection curve. This means that at a speed given by eq. (84), the centrifugal forces are sufficient to keep the rotating shaft in a deflected form. Such a speed is called a *critical speed* (see p. 34).

It was assumed in the previous discussion that the deflection curve, as obtained graphically, had deflections proportional to those of the curve initially taken. If there is a considerable difference in the shape of these two curves and a closer approximation for ω_{cr} is desired, the construction described above should be repeated by taking the deflection curve, obtained graphically, as the initial deflection curve.*

The method can be applied also in more complicated cases. Considering, for example, the case of a shaft with two spans, as shown in Fig. 179, we first assume an initial deflection curve satisfying the conditions at the supports (Figs. 179a and 179b) and a certain angular velocity ω. The centrifugal forces acting on the shaft will then be

$$\frac{W_1}{g} \omega^2 y_1 \quad \text{and} \quad \frac{W_2}{g} \omega^2 y_2.$$

By using the graphical method the deflection curve produced by these two forces can be constructed and if the initial curve was chosen correctly the constructed deflection curve will have deflections y_1', y_2' proportional to the initial deflections y_1, y_2 and the critical speed will be obtained from an equation analogous to eq. (84). If there is a considerable difference in

---

* It was pointed out in considering Rayleigh's method (see Art. 4), that a considerable error in the shape of the assumed deflection curve produces only a small effect on the magnitude of ω_{cr} provided the conditions at the ends are satisfied.

the shape of these two curves the construction should be repeated by considering the obtained deflection curve as the initial curve.*

The method can be applied also to the case of many discs and to cases where the mass of the shaft should be taken into consideration. We begin again by taking an initial deflection curve (Fig. 184) and by assuming a certain angular velocity ω. Then the centrifugal forces $P_1, P_2, \cdots$ acting

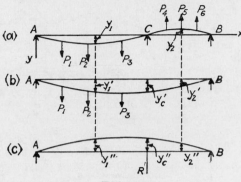

Fig. 184

on the discs and on portions of the shaft can easily be calculated, and the corresponding deflection curve can be constructed as follows. Consider first the forces acting on the left span of the shaft and, removing the middle support C, construct the deflection curve shown in Fig. 184b. In the same manner the deflection curve produced by the vertical load R' applied at C and acting in an upward direction can be obtained (Fig. 184c) and the reaction R at the middle support produced by loading of the left span of the shaft can be calculated by using eq. (m) above. The deflection produced at any point by loading of the left side of the shaft can then be found by using equations similar to eqs. (n).

Taking, for instance, the cross sections in which the initial curve has the largest deflections y_1 and y_2 (Fig. 184a), the deflections produced at these cross sections by the loading acting on the left side of the shaft will be

$$
\left.
\begin{aligned}
y_{1a} &= y_1{}' - y_1{}'' \frac{y_c{}'}{y_c{}''}, \\[2mm]
y_{2a} &= y_2{}' - y_2{}'' \frac{y_c{}'}{y_c{}''}.
\end{aligned}
\right\}
\qquad (q)
$$

* It can be shown that this process is convergent, when calculating the slowest critical speed, and by repeating the construction described above we approach the true critical speed. See A. Stodola, *loc. cit.*, p. 268.

In the same manner the deflections y_{1b} and y_{2b} produced in these cross sections by the loading of the right side of the shaft can be obtained and the complete deflections $y_{1a} + y_{1b}$ and $y_{2a} + y_{2b}$ can be calculated.* If the assumed initial deflection curve was chosen correctly, the following equation should be fulfilled:

$$\frac{y_{1a} + y_{1b}}{y_{2a} + y_{2b}} = \frac{y_1}{y_2}, \qquad (r)$$

and the critical speed will be calculated from the equation

$$\omega_{cr} = \omega \sqrt{\frac{y_1}{y_{1a} + y_{1b}}}. \qquad (85)$$

If there is a considerable deviation from the condition (r), the calculation of a second approximation becomes necessary for which purpose the following procedure can be adopted.† It is easy to see that the deflections y_{1a} and y_{2a}, found above, should be proportional to ω^2 and to the initial deflection y_1, so that we can write the equations

$$y_{1a} = a_1 y_1 \omega^2,$$
$$y_{2a} = a_2 y_1 \omega^2,$$

from which the constants a_1 and a_2 can be calculated. In the same manner from the equations

$$y_{1b} = b_1 y_2 \omega^2,$$
$$y_{2b} = b_2 y_2 \omega^2,$$

the constants b_1 and b_2 can be found.

Now, if the initial deflection curve had been chosen correctly and if $\omega = \omega_{cr}$, the following equations should be satisfied:

$$y_1 = y_{1a} + y_{1b} = a_1 y_1 \omega^2 + b_1 y_2 \omega^2,$$
$$y_2 = y_{2a} + y_{2b} = a_2 y_1 \omega^2 + b_2 y_2 \omega^2,$$

which can be written as follows:

$$(1 - a_1\omega^2)y_1 - b_1\omega^2 y_2 = 0,$$
$$-a_2 y_1 \omega^2 + (1 - b_2\omega^2)y_2 = 0. \qquad (s)$$

* Deflections in a downward direction are taken as positive.

† This method was developed by Mr. Borowicz in his thesis "Beiträge zur Berechnung krit. Geschwindigkeiten zwei und mehrfach gelagerter Wellen," München, 1915. See also E. Rausch, *Ing.-Arch.*, Vol. 1, p. 203, 1930; and K. Karas, *Die kritischen Drehzahlen wichtiger Rotorformen*, Vienna. 1935.

The equation for calculating the critical speed will now be obtained by equating to zero the determinant of these equations, and we obtain,

$$(a_1b_2 - a_2b_1)\omega^4 - (a_1 + b_2)\omega^2 + 1 = 0.$$

The root of this equation which makes the ratio y_1/y_2 of eqs. (s) negative, corresponds to the assumed shape of the curve (Fig. 184a) and gives the lowest critical speed. For obtaining a closer approximation the ratio y_1/y_2, as obtained from eqs. (s), should be used in tracing the new shape of the initial curve and with this new curve the graphical solution should be repeated. In actual cases this further approximation is often unnecessary.

The described graphical method gives satisfactory results in the calculation of the lowest critical speed. If higher critical speeds are required, recourse should be made to the previously described analytical method. In the case of a large number of rotating discs the derivation and solution of the frequency equation represents a complicated problem and the calculation can be simplified by using the iteration method described in the preceding chapter.*

44. Gyroscopic Effects on the Critical Speeds of Rotating Shafts.—
General.—In our previous discussion on the critical speeds of rotating shafts only the centrifugal forces of the rotating masses were taken into consideration. Under certain conditions not only these forces, but also the moments of the inertia forces due to angular movements of the axes of the rotating masses are of importance and should be taken into account in calculating the critical speeds. In the following, the simplest case of a single circular disc on a shaft will be considered (Fig. 185).

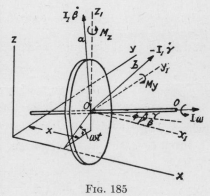

Assuming that the deflections y and z of the shaft during vibration are

FIG. 185

very small and that the center of gravity O of the disc coincides with the axis of the shaft, the position of the disc will be completely determined by the coordinates y and z of its center and by the angles β and γ which the axis OO perpendicular to the plane of the disc and tangent to the

* A numerical example of the application of this method is given by C. B. Biezeno and R. Grammel, *Technische Dynamik*, Berlin, p. 829, 1939. See also paper by N. A. Boukidis and R. J. Ruggiero, *J. Aeronaut. Sci.*, Vol. 11, p. 319, 1944.

deflection curve of the shaft makes with the fixed planes xz and xy, perpendicular to each other and drawn through the x axis joining the centers of the bearings. Letting W equal the weight of the disc and taking into consideration the elastic reactions of the shaft * only, the equations of motion of the center of gravity of the disc will be

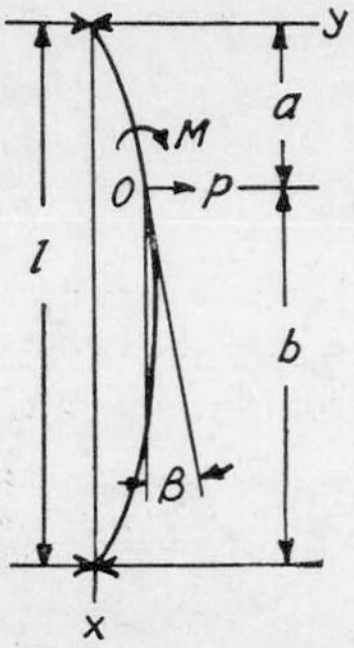

$$\frac{W}{g}\ddot{y} = Y, \quad \frac{W}{g}\ddot{z} = Z, \tag{a}$$

in which Y and Z are the components of the reaction of the shaft in the y and z directions. These reactions are linear functions of the coordinates y, z and of the angles β, γ which can be determined from the consideration of the bending shaft.

Fig. 186

Take, for instance, the bending of a shaft with simply supported ends, in the xy-plane (Fig. 186) under the action of a force P and of a couple M. Considering in the usual way the deflection curve of the shaft, we obtain the deflection at O equal to †

$$y = \frac{Pa^2b^2}{3lB} + \frac{Mab(a-b)}{3lB}, \tag{b}$$

and the slope at the same point equal to

$$\beta = \frac{Pab(b-a)}{3lB} - \frac{M(a^2 - ab + b^2)}{3lB}, \tag{c}$$

where B is the flexural rigidity of the shaft.

From eqs. (b) and (c) we obtain

$$P = 3lB\left(\frac{a^2 - ab + b^2}{a^3b^3}y + \frac{a-b}{a^2b^2}\beta\right), \tag{d}$$

$$M = 3lB\left(\frac{b-a}{a^2b^2}y - \frac{1}{ab}\beta\right). \tag{e}$$

---

* The conditions assumed here correspond to the case of a vertical shaft when the weight of the disc does not affect the deflections of the shaft. The effect of this weight will be considered later (see p. 290).

† See author's *Strength of Materials*, 2d Ed., Vol. 1, p. 160, 1940.

By using eq. (d), the eqs. (a) of motion of the center of gravity of the disc become

$$\frac{W}{g}\ddot{y} + my + n\beta = 0, \quad \frac{W}{g}\ddot{z} + mz + n\gamma = 0, \tag{86}$$

in which

$$m = 3lB\frac{a^2 - ab + b^2}{a^3b^3}, \quad n = 3lB\frac{a - b}{a^2b^2}. \tag{f}$$

In considering the relative motion of the disc about its center of gravity it will be assumed that the moment of the external forces acting on the disc with respect to the axis OO is always equal to zero, then the angular velocity ω with respect to this axis remains constant. The moments M_y and M_z, taken about the y_1- and z_1-axes parallel to the y- and z-axes (see Fig. 185) and representing the action of the elastic forces of the shaft on the disc, can be written in the following form:

$$M_y = -m'z + n'\gamma,$$

$$M_z = m'y - n'\beta, \tag{g}$$

in which m' and n' are constants which can be obtained from the deflection curve of the shaft.* The positive directions for the angles β and γ and for the moments M_y and M_z are indicated in the figure.

In the case considered above (see eq. e), we have

$$m' = 3lB\frac{b - a}{a^2b^2}, \quad n' = \frac{3lB}{ab}. \tag{h}$$

The equations of relative motion of the disc with respect to its center of gravity will now be obtained by using the principle of *angular momentum* which states that the *rate of increase* of the total moment of momentum of any moving system about any *fixed* axis is equal to the total moment of the external forces about this axis. In calculating the *rate of change* of the angular momentum about a fixed axis drawn through the instantaneous position of the center of gravity O we may take into consideration only the relative motion.†

In calculating the components of the angular momentum the principal axes of inertia of the disc will be taken. The axis of rotation OO is one of these axes. The two other axes will be two perpendicular diameters of the

---

* It is assumed that the flexibility of the shaft including the flexibility of its supports is the same for both directions.

† See *Advanced Dynamics*, p. 123, *loc. cit.*

disc. One of these diameters Oa we take in the plane OOz_1 (see Fig. 185). It will make a small angle γ with the axis Oz_1. Another diameter Ob will make the angle β with the axis Oy_1.

Let I = moment of inertia of the disc about the axis OO and $I_1 = I/2$ = moment of inertia of the disc about a diameter.

Then, the component of angular momentum about the axis OO will be $I\omega$, and the components about the diameters Oa and Ob will be $I_1\dot{\beta}$ and $-I_1\dot{\gamma}$, respectively.* Positive directions of these components of the angular momentum are shown in Fig. 185. Projecting these components on the fixed axes Oy_1 and Oz_1 through the instantaneous position of the center of gravity O, we obtain $I\omega\beta - I_1\dot{\gamma}$ and $I\omega\gamma + I_1\dot{\beta}$, respectively. Then from the principle of angular momentum we have

$$\frac{d}{dt}(I\omega\beta - I_1\dot{\gamma}) = M_y \quad \text{and} \quad \frac{d}{dt}(I\omega\gamma + I_1\beta) = M_z,$$

or, by using eqs. (g),

$$\left.\begin{array}{l} I\omega\dot{\beta} - I_1\ddot{\gamma} = -m'z + n'\gamma, \\ I\omega\dot{\gamma} + I_1\ddot{\beta} = m'y - n'\beta. \end{array}\right\} \tag{87}$$

Four eqs. (86) and (87) describing the motion of the disc will be satisfied by substituting

$$y = A \sin pt, \quad z = B \cos pt, \quad \beta = C \sin pt, \quad \gamma = D \cos pt. \tag{i}$$

In this manner four linear homogeneous equations in A, B, C, D will be obtained. Putting the determinant of these equations equal to zero, the equation for calculating the frequencies p of the natural vibrations will be determined.† Several particular cases will now be considered.

As a first example consider the case in which the principal axis OO perpendicular to the plane of the disc remains always in a plane containing the x-axis and rotating with the constant angular velocity ω, with which the disc rotates. Putting r equal to the deflection of the shaft and φ equal to the angle between OO- and x-axes (see Fig. 185), we obtain for this particular case,

$$y = r \cos \omega t, \quad z = r \sin \omega t, \quad \beta = \varphi \cos \omega t, \quad \gamma = \varphi \sin \omega t. \tag{j}$$

---

* It is assumed, as before, that β and γ are small. Then β and $-\dot{\gamma}$ will be approximate values of the angular velocities about the diameters Oa and Ob.

† See A. Stodola, *Z. ges. Turbinenwesen*, p. 253, 1918; p. 1, 1920.

Considering r and φ as constants and considering the instantaneous position when the plane of the deflected line of the shaft coincides with the xy-plane (Fig. 187), we obtain from eqs. (j),

$$
\begin{aligned}
\beta &= \varphi, & \dot\beta &= 0, & \ddot\beta &= -\varphi\omega^2, \\
\gamma &= 0, & \dot\gamma &= \varphi\omega, & \ddot\gamma &= 0, \\
y &= r, & \dot y &= 0, & \ddot y &= -r\omega^2, \\
z &= 0, & \dot z &= r\omega, & \ddot z &= 0.
\end{aligned}
$$

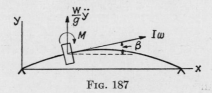

FIG. 187

Substituting in eqs. (86) and (87), we obtain

$$
\frac{W}{g}\ddot y + my + n\beta = 0,
$$

$$
(I - I_1)\beta\omega^2 = m'y - n'\beta. \tag{k}
$$

It is seen that the shaft is bent not only by centrifugal force but also by the moment $M = (I - I_1)\beta\omega^2$ which represents the *gyroscopic effect* of the rotating disc in this case and makes the shaft stiffer. Substituting

$$
y = r\cos\omega t, \quad \beta = \varphi\cos\omega t,
$$

in eqs. (k), we obtain

$$
\left(m - \omega^2\frac{W}{g}\right)r + n\varphi = 0,
$$

$$
-m'r + \{n' + (I - I_1)\omega^2\}\varphi = 0. \tag{l}
$$

The deflection of the shaft, assumed above, becomes possible if eqs. (l) may have for r and φ roots other than zero, i.e., when the angular velocity ω is such that the determinant of these equations becomes equal to zero. In this manner the following equation for calculating the critical speeds will be found:

$$
\left(m - \frac{\omega^2 W}{g}\right)\{n' + (I - I_1)\omega^2\} + nm' = 0, \tag{m}
$$

or letting

$$
\frac{mg}{W} = p^2, \quad \frac{n'}{I - I_1} = q^2,
$$

and noting that, from eqs. (f) and (h), that

$$nm' = -cmn', \quad \text{where } c = \frac{(a - b)^2}{a^2 - ab + b^2},$$

we obtain

$$(p^2 - \omega^2)(q^2 + \omega^2) - cp^2q^2 = 0$$

or

$$\omega^4 - (p^2 - q^2)\omega^2 - p^2q^2(1 - c) = 0. \tag{n}$$

It is easy to see that (for $c < 1$) eq. (n) has only one positive root for ω^2, namely,

$$\omega^2 = \tfrac{1}{2}(p^2 - q^2) + \sqrt{\tfrac{1}{4}(p^2 - q^2)^2 + (1 - c)p^2q^2}. \tag{o}$$

When the gyroscopic effect can be neglected, $I - I_1 = 0$ should be substituted in (m) and we obtain,

$$\frac{\omega^2 W}{g} = \frac{mn' + nm'}{n'} = \frac{3lB}{a^2b^2},$$

from which

$$\omega_{cr} = \sqrt{\frac{3glB}{a^2b^2W}} \quad \text{or} \quad \omega_{cr} = \sqrt{\frac{g}{\delta}},$$

where

$$\delta = \frac{a^2b^2W}{3lB}$$

represents the statical deflection of the shaft under the load W. This result coincides completely with that found before (see Art. 5), considering the disc on the shaft as a system with one degree of freedom.

In the above discussion it was assumed that the angular velocity of the plane of the deflected shaft is the same as that of the rotating disc. It is possible also that these two velocities are different. Assuming, for instance, that the angular velocity of the plane of the deflected shaft is ω_1 and substituting

$$y = r \cos \omega_1 t, \quad z = r \sin \omega_1 t, \quad \beta = \varphi \cos \omega_1 t, \quad \gamma = \varphi \sin \omega_1 t$$

in eqs. (86) and (87), we obtain

$$\frac{W}{g} \ddot{y} + my + n\beta = 0,$$

$$(I\omega\omega_1 - I_1\omega_1{}^2)\beta = m'y - n'\beta, \tag{k'}$$

instead of eqs. (k).

By putting $\omega_1 = \omega$ the previous result will be obtained. If $\omega_1 = -\omega$ we obtain from the second of eqs. (k')

$$-(I + I_1)\omega^2\beta = m'y - n'\beta. \tag{p}$$

This shows that when the plane of the bent shaft rotates with the velocity ω in the direction opposite to that of the rotation of the disc, the gyroscopic effect will be represented by the moment

$$M = -(I + I_1)\omega^2\beta.$$

The minus sign indicates that under such conditions the gyroscopic moment is acting in the direction of increasing the deflection of the shaft and hence lowers the critical speed of the shaft. If the shaft with the disc is brought up to the speed ω from the condition of rest, the condition $\omega_1 = \omega$ usually takes place. But if there are disturbing forces of the same frequency as the critical speed for the condition $\omega_1 = -\omega$, then rotation of the bent shaft in a direction opposite to that of the rotating disc may take place.*

Vibration of a Rigid Rotor with Flexible Bearings.—Eqs. (86) and (87) can be used also in the study of vibrations of a rigid rotor, having bearings in flexible pedestals (Fig. 188). Let y_1, z_1 and y_2, z_2 be small displacements of the bearings during vibration. Taking these displacements as coordinates of the oscillating rotor, the displacements of the center of gravity and the angular displacements of the axis of the rotor will be (see Fig. 188)

$$y_0 = y_1\frac{l_2}{l} + y_2\frac{l_1}{l},$$

$$z_0 = z_1\frac{l_2}{l} + z_2\frac{l_1}{l},$$

$$\beta = \frac{y_2 - y_1}{l},$$

$$\gamma = \frac{z_2 - z_1}{l}.$$

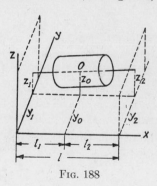

Fig. 188

Let c_1, c_2, d_1 and d_2 be constants depending on the flexibility of the pedestals in the horizontal and vertical directions, such that $-c_1y_1$, $-c_2y_2$ are horizontal and $-d_1z_1, -d_2z_2$ are the vertical reactions of the bearings due to

---

* See A. Stodola, *Dampf-und Gasturbinen*, p. 367, *loc. cit.* For a further study of gyroscopic effect, see R. B. Green, *J. Appl. Mech.*, Vol. 15, p. 369, 1948; also K. Karas, *loc. cit.*, p. 280.

the small displacements y_1, y_2, z_1 and z_2 in the y and z directions. Then the equations of motion of the center of gravity (86) become

$$\left.\begin{array}{l} \dfrac{W}{gl}\,(l_2\ddot{y}_1 + l_1\ddot{y}_2) + c_1y_1 + c_2y_2 = 0, \\[2mm] \dfrac{W}{gl}\,(l_2\ddot{z}_1 + l_1\ddot{z}_2) + d_1z_1 + d_2z_2 = 0. \end{array}\right\} \qquad (q)$$

The eqs. (87) representing the rotations of the rotor about the y- and z-axes will be in this case

$$\left.\begin{array}{l} I\omega\,\dfrac{\dot{y}_2 - \dot{y}_1}{l} - I_1\,\dfrac{\ddot{z}_2 - \ddot{z}_1}{l} = z_2d_2l_2 - z_1d_1l_1, \\[3mm] I\omega\,\dfrac{\dot{z}_2 - \dot{z}_1}{l} + I_1\,\dfrac{\ddot{y}_2 - \ddot{y}_1}{l} = -y_2c_2l_2 + y_1c_1l_1. \end{array}\right\} \qquad (r)$$

The four eqs. (q) and (r) completely describe the free vibrations of a rigid rotor on flexible pedestals. Substituting in these equations

$$y_1 = A \sin pt, \quad y_2 = B \sin pt, \quad z_1 = C \cos pt, \quad z_2 = D \cos pt,$$

four homogeneous linear equations in A, B, C and D will be obtained. Equating the determinant of these equations to zero, we get the frequency equation from which the frequencies of the four natural modes of vibration of the rotor can be calculated.

Consider now a forced vibration of the rotor produced by some eccentrically attached mass. The effect of such an unbalance will be equivalent to the action of a disturbing force with the components

$$Y = A \cos \omega t, \quad Z = B \sin \omega t,$$

applied to the center of gravity, and to a couple with the components

$$M_y = C \sin \omega t, \quad M_z = D \cos \omega t.$$

Instead of the eqs. (q) and (r) we obtain

$$\left.\begin{array}{l} \dfrac{W}{gl}\,(l_2\ddot{y}_1 + l_1\ddot{y}_2) + c_1y_1 + c_2y_2 = A \cos \omega t, \\[3mm] \dfrac{W}{gl}\,(l_2\ddot{z}_1 + l_1\ddot{z}_2) + d_1z_1 + d_2z_2 = B \sin \omega t, \\[3mm] I\omega\,\dfrac{\dot{y}_2 - \dot{y}_1}{l} - I_1\,\dfrac{\ddot{z}_2 - \ddot{z}_1}{l} = z_2d_2l_2 - z_1d_1l_1 + C \sin \omega t, \\[3mm] I\omega\,\dfrac{\dot{z}_2 - \dot{z}_1}{l} + I_1\,\dfrac{\ddot{y}_2 - \ddot{y}_1}{l} = -y_2c_2l_2 + y_1c_1l_1 + D \cos \omega t. \end{array}\right\} \qquad (s)$$

The particular solution of these equations representing the forced vibration of the rotor will be of the form

$$y_1 = A' \cos \omega t, \quad y_2 = B' \cos \omega t, \quad z_1 = C' \sin \omega t, \quad z_2 = D' \sin \omega t.$$

Substituting in eqs. (s), the amplitude of the forced vibration will be found. During this vibration the axis of the rotor describes a surface given by the equations

$$y = (a + bx) \cos \omega t,$$

$$z = (c + dx) \sin \omega t,$$

in which a, b, c and d are constants. We see that every point of the axis describes an ellipse given by the equation

$$\frac{y^2}{(a + bx)^2} + \frac{z^2}{(c + dx)^2} = 1.$$

For two points of the axis, namely, for

$$x_1 = -\frac{a}{b} \quad \text{and} \quad x_2 = -\frac{c}{d},$$

the ellipses reduce to straight lines and the general shape of the surface described by the axis of the rotor will be as shown in Fig. 189. It is seen

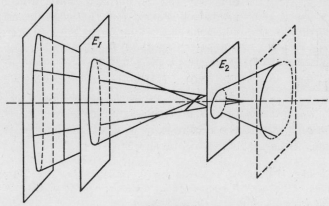

FIG. 189

that the displacements of a point on the axis of the rotor depend not only upon the magnitude of the disturbing force (amount of unbalance) but also upon the position of the point along the axis and on the direction in which the displacement is measured.

In the general case the unbalance can be represented by two eccentrically attached masses (see Art. 10) and the forced vibrations of the rotor can be obtained by superimposing two vibrations of such kind as considered above and having a certain difference in phase.* From the linearity of the eqs. (s) it can also be concluded that by putting correction weights in two planes the unbalance always can be removed; it is only necessary to determine the correction weights in such a manner that the corresponding centrifugal forces will be in equilibium with the disturbing forces due to unbalance.†

45. Effect of Weight of Shaft and Discs on the Critical Speed.—In our previous discussion the effect of the weight of the rotating discs was excluded by assuming that the axis of the shaft is vertical. In the case of horizontal shafts the weights of the discs must be considered as disturbing forces which at a certain speed produce considerable vibration in the shaft. This speed is usually called *critical speed of the second order*.‡ For determining this speed a more detailed study of the motion of discs is necessary. In the following, the simplest case of a single disc will be considered and it will be assumed that the disc is attached to the shaft at the cross section in which the tangent to the deflection curve of the shaft remains parallel to the center line of the bearings. In this manner the *gyroscopic effect* discussed in the previous article will be excluded and only the motion of the disc in its own plane needs to be considered. Let us begin with the case when the shaft is vertical. Then xy represents the horizontal plane of the disc and O the center of the vertical shaft in its undeflected position (see Fig. 190). During the vibration let S be the instantaneous position of the center of the shaft and C, the instantaneous position of the center of gravity of the disc so that $CS = e$ represents the eccentricity with which the disc is attached to the shaft. Other notations will be as follows:

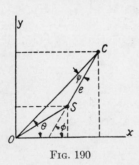

Fig. 190

* This question is discussed in detail by V. Blaess, "Über den Massenausgleich raschumlaufender Körper," *Z. angew. Math. u. Mech.*, Vol. 6, p. 429, 1926; see also D. M. Smith, *loc. cit.*, p. 210.

† The effect of flexibility of the shaft will be considered later (see Art. 46).

‡ A. Stodola was the first to discuss this problem. The literature on the subject can be found in his book, p. 929, *loc. cit.* See also T. Pöschl, *Z. angew. Math. u. Mech.*, Vol. 3, p. 297, 1923; and C. R. Soderberg, *Trans. A.S.M.E.*, Vol. 54, p. APM-45, 1932

m = the mass of the disc,

mi^2 = moment of inertia of the disc about the axis through C and perpendicular to the disc,

k = spring constant of the shaft equal to the force in the xy-plane necessary to produce unit deflection in this plane,

ω_{cr} = $\sqrt{k/m}$ = the critical speed of the first order (see Art. 5),

x, y = coordinates of the center of gravity C of the disc during motion,

φ = the angle of rotation of the disc equal to the angle between the radius SC and x-axis,

θ = the angle of rotation of the vertical plane OC,

ψ = the angle of rotation of the disc with respect to the plane OC.

Then $\varphi = \psi + \theta$. The coordinates x and y of the center of gravity C and the angle of rotation φ will be taken as coordinates determining the position of the disc in the plane xy.

The differential equations of motion of the center of gravity C can easily be written in the usual way if we note that only one force, the elastic reaction of the shaft, is acting on the disc in the xy-plane. This force is proportional to the deflection OS of the shaft and its components in the x and y directions, proportional to the coordinates of the point S, will be $-k(x - e \cos \varphi)$ and $-k(y - e \sin \varphi)$, respectively. Then the differential equations of motion of the center C will be

$$m\ddot{x} = -k(x - e \cos \varphi), \quad m\ddot{y} = -k(y - e \sin \varphi),$$

or

$$m\ddot{x} + kx = ke \cos \varphi,$$

$$m\ddot{y} + ky = ke \sin \varphi. \tag{a}$$

The third equation will be obtained by using the principle of angular momentum. The angular momentum of the disc about the O-axis consists of (1) the angular momentum $mi^2\dot{\varphi}$ of the disc rotating with the angular velocity $\dot{\varphi}$ about its center of gravity, and (2) the angular momentum $m(x\dot{y} - y\dot{x})$ of the mass m of the disc concentrated at its center of gravity. Then the principle of angular momentum gives the equation

$$\frac{d}{dt}\{mi^2\dot{\varphi} + m(x\dot{y} - y\dot{x})\} = M,$$

or

$$mi^2\ddot{\varphi} + m(x\ddot{y} - y\ddot{x}) = M, \tag{b}$$

in which M is the torque transmitted to the disc by the shaft.

The eqs. (a) and (b) completely describe the motion of the disc. When $M = 0$ a particular solution of the eqs. (a) and (b) will be obtained by assuming that the center of gravity C of the disc remains in the plane OS of the deflection curve of the shaft and describes, while rotating at constant angular velocity $\dot{\varphi} = \omega$, a circle of radius r. Then substituting in eqs. (a), $x = r \cos \omega t$, $y = r \sin \omega t$ and taking $\varphi = \omega t$ for the case represented in Fig. 191a, and $\varphi = \omega t + \pi$ for the case represented in Fig. 191b, we obtain

$$r_0 = \frac{ke}{k - m\omega^2} = \frac{e\omega_{cr}^2}{\omega_{cr}^2 - \omega^2} \quad \text{for} \quad \omega < \omega_{cr},$$

$$r_0 = -\frac{ke}{k - m\omega^2} = \frac{e\omega_{cr}^2}{\omega^2 - \omega_{cr}^2} \quad \text{for} \quad \omega > \omega_{cr}.$$

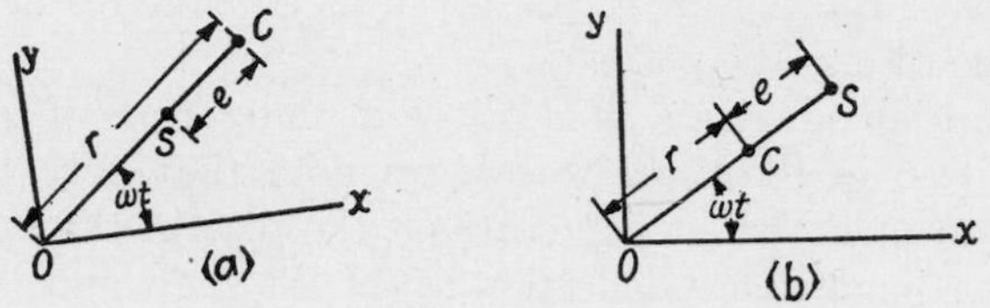

FIG. 191

These results coincide with those obtained before from elementary considerations (see Art. 5).

Let us now consider the case when the torque M is different from zero and such that *

$$M = m(x\ddot{y} - y\ddot{x}). \tag{c}$$

Then from eq. (b) we conclude that

$$\dot{\varphi} = \omega = \text{const.},$$

and by integrating we obtain

$$\varphi = \omega t + \varphi_0, \tag{d}$$

in which φ_0 is an arbitrary constant determining the initial magnitude of the angle φ.

Substituting (d) in eqs. (a) and using the notation $\omega_{cr}^2 = k/m$, we obtain

$$\left. \begin{aligned} \ddot{x} + \omega_{cr}^2 x &= \omega_{cr}^2 e \cos (\omega t + \varphi_0), \\ \ddot{y} + \omega_{cr}^2 y &= \omega_{cr}^2 e \sin (\omega t + \varphi_0). \end{aligned} \right\} \tag{e}$$

* This case is discussed in detail in P. Schröder's dissertation, "Die kritischen Zustände zweiter Art rasch umlaufender Wellen," Stuttgart, 1924.

It is easy to show by substitution that

$$x = -\frac{M_1}{ek} \cos(\omega_{cr}t + \gamma_1 + \varphi_0) + \frac{e\omega_{cr}^2}{\omega_{cr}^2 - \omega^2} \cos(\omega t + \varphi_0),$$
$$y = -\frac{M_1}{ek} \sin(\omega_{cr}t + \gamma_1 + \varphi_0) + \frac{e\omega_{cr}^2}{\omega_{cr}^2 - \omega^2} \sin(\omega t + \varphi_0),$$

(f)

represent a solution of the eqs. (e).

Substituting (f) in eq. (c) we obtain

$$M = M_1 \sin\{(\omega_{cr} - \omega)t + \gamma_1\}. \tag{g}$$

It can be concluded that under the action of the *pulsating moment* (g) the disc is rotating with a constant angular velocity and at the same time its center of gravity performs a combined oscillatory motion represented by the eqs. (f).

In the same manner it can be shown that under the action of a pulsating torque
$$M = M_2 \sin\{(\omega_{cr} + \omega)t + \gamma_2\},$$

the disc also rotates with a constant speed ω and its center performs oscillatory motions given by the equations

$$x = \frac{M_2}{ek} \cos(\omega_{cr}t + \gamma_2 - \varphi_0) + \frac{e\omega_{cr}^2}{\omega_{cr}^2 - \omega^2} \cos(\omega t + \varphi_0),$$
$$y = -\frac{M_2}{ek} \sin(\omega_{cr}t + \gamma_2 - \varphi_0) + \frac{e\omega_{cr}^2}{\omega_{cr}^2 - \omega^2} \sin(\omega t + \varphi_0).$$

(h)

Combining the solutions (f) and (h) the complete solution of the eqs. (e), containing four arbitrary constants M_1, M_2, γ_1 and γ_2, will be obtained. This result can now be used for explaining the vibrations produced by the weight of the disc itself.

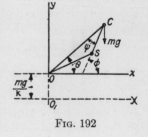

Fig. 192

Assume that the shaft is in a horizontal position and the y-axis is upwards; then by adding the weight of the disc we will obtain Fig. 192, instead of Fig. 190. The eqs. (a) and (b) will be replaced in this case by the following system of equations:

$$m\ddot{x} + kx = ke\cos\varphi,$$
$$m\ddot{y} + ky = ke\sin\varphi - mg,$$
$$mi^2\ddot{\varphi} + m(x\ddot{y} - y\ddot{x}) = M - mgx.$$

(i)

Let us displace the origin of coordinates from O to O_1 as shown in the figure; then by letting

$$y_1 = y + \frac{mg}{k},$$

eqs. (i) can be represented in the following form:

$$\left.\begin{array}{r}
m\ddot{x} + kx = ke\cos\varphi, \\
m\ddot{y}_1 + ky_1 = ke\sin\varphi, \\
mi^2\ddot{\varphi} + m(x\ddot{y}_1 - y_1\ddot{x}) = M - mge\cos\varphi.
\end{array}\right\} \qquad (j)$$

This system of equations coincides with the system of eqs. (a) and (b) and the effect of the disc's weight is represented by the pulsating torque $-mge\cos\varphi$. Imagine now that $M = 0$ and that the shaft is rotating with a constant angular velocity $\omega = \frac{1}{2}\omega_{cr}$. Then the effect of the weight of the disc can be represented in the following form:

$$-mge\cos\varphi = -mge\cos(\omega t) = mge\sin(\omega t - \pi/2)$$

$$= mge\sin\{(\omega_{cr} - \omega)t - \pi/2\}. \qquad (k)$$

This disturbing moment has exactly the same form as the pulsating moment given by eq. (g) and it can be concluded that at the speed $\omega = \frac{1}{2}\omega_{cr}$, the pulsating moment due to the weight of the disc will produce vibrations of the shaft given by the eqs. (f). This is the so-called *critical speed of the second order*, which in many actual cases has been observed.* It should be noted, however, that vibrations of the same frequency can be produced also by variable flexibility of the shaft (see p. 172) and it is quite possible that in some cases where a critical speed of the second order has been observed the vibrations were produced by this latter cause.

46. Effect of Flexibility of Shafts on the Balancing of Rotors.—In our previous discussion of the balancing of machines (see Art. 10) it was assumed that the rotor was an absolutely rigid body. In such a case complete balancing may be accomplished by putting correction weights in two arbitrarily chosen planes. The assumption neglecting the flexibility of the shaft is accurate enough at low speeds but for high-speed machines and especially in the cases of machines working above the critical speed the deflection of the shaft may have a considerable effect and as a result of this, the rotor can be balanced only for one definite speed or at certain conditions cannot be balanced at all and will always give vibration troubles.

The effect of the flexibility of the shaft will now be explained by a simple example of a shaft supported at the ends and carrying two discs (see Fig. 193). The deflection of

* See O. Föppl, *Z. Ver. duet. Ing.*, Vol. 63, p. 867, 1919.

the shaft y_1 under a load W_1 will depend not only on the magnitude of this load, but also on the magnitude of the load W_2. The same conclusion holds also for the deflection y_2 under the load W_2. By using the equations of the deflection curve of a shaft on two supports, the following expressions for the deflections can be obtained:

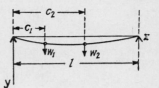

$$y_1 = a_{11}W_1 + a_{12}W_2,$$
$$y_2 = a_{21}W_1 + a_{22}W_2,$$ $\quad (a)$

in which a_{11}, a_{12}, a_{21}, and a_{22} remain constant for a given shaft and a given position of loads. These equations can be used now in calculating the deflections produced in the shaft by the centrifugal forces due to eccentricities of the discs.

Fig. 193

Let m_1, m_2 = masses of discs I and II,
ω = angular velocity,
y_1, y_2 = deflections at the discs I and II, respectively,
c_1, c_2 = distances from the left support to the discs I and II,
Y_1, Y_2 = centrifugal forces acting on the shaft.

Assuming that only disc I has a certain eccentricity e_1 and taking the deflection in the plane of this eccentricity, the centrifugal forces acting on the shaft will be

$$Y_1 = (e_1 + y_1)m_1\omega^2, \quad Y_2 = y_2 m_2\omega^2,$$

or, by using for y_1 and y_2 equations similar to eqs. (a), we obtain

$$Y_1 = e_1 m_1\omega^2 + m_1\omega^2(a_{11}Y_1 + a_{12}Y_2),$$

$$Y_2 = m_2\omega^2(a_{21}Y_1 + a_{22}Y_2),$$

from which

$$Y_1 = \frac{e_1 m_1\omega^2(1 - a_{22}m_2\omega^2)}{(1 - a_{11}m_1\omega^2)(1 - a_{22}m_2\omega^2) - m_1 m_2 a_{12}a_{21}\omega^4},$$
$$Y_2 = \frac{e_1 a_{21} m_1 m_2\omega^4}{(1 - a_{11}m_1\omega^2)(1 - a_{22}m_2\omega^2) - m_1 m_2 a_{12}a_{21}\omega^4}.$$ $\quad (b)$

It is seen that instead of a centrifugal force $e_1 m_1\omega^2$, which we have in the case of a rigid shaft, two forces Y_1 and Y_2 are acting on the flexible shaft. The unbalance will be the same as in the case of a rigid shaft on which a force $R_1 = Y_1 + Y_2$ is acting at the distance from the left support equal to

$$l_1 = \frac{Y_1 c_1 + Y_2 c_2}{Y_1 + Y_2}.$$ $\quad (c)$

It may be seen from eqs. (b) that l_1 does not depend on the amount of eccentricity e_1, but only on the elastic properties of the shaft, the position and magnitude of the masses m_1 and m_2 and on the speed ω of the machine.

In the same manner as above, the effect of eccentricity in disc II can be discussed and the result of eccentricities in both discs can be obtained by the principle of superposition. From this it can be concluded that at a given speed the unbalance in two discs on a flexible shaft is dynamically equivalent to unbalances in two definite planes of a rigid shaft. The position of these planes can be determined by using eq. (c) for one of the planes and an analogous equation for the second plane.

Similar conclusions can be made for a flexible shaft with any number n of discs * and it can be shown that the unbalance in these discs is equivalent to the unbalance in n definite planes of a rigid shaft. These planes remaining fixed at a given speed of the shaft, the balancing can be accomplished by putting correction weights in two planes arbitrarily chosen. At any other speed the planes of unbalance in the equivalent rigid shaft change their position and the rotor goes out of balance. This explains why a rotor perfectly balanced in a balancing machine at a comparatively low speed

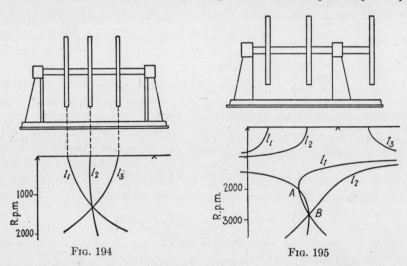

FIG. 194   FIG. 195

may become out of balance at service speed. Thus balancing in the field under actual conditions becomes necessary. The displacements of the planes of unbalance with variation in speed is shown below for two particular cases. In Fig. 194 a shaft carrying three discs is represented. The changes with the speed in the distances l_1, l_2, l_3 of the planes of unbalance in the equivalent rigid shaft are shown in the figure by the curves l_1, l_2, l_3. It is seen that with an increase in speed these curves first approach each other, then go through a common point of intersection at the critical speed and above it diverge again. Excluding the region near the critical speed, the rotor can be balanced at any other speed by putting correction weights in any two of the three discs. More difficult conditions are shown in Fig. 195. It is seen that at a speed equal to about 2150 r.p.m. the curves l_1 and l_3 go through the same point A. The two planes of the equivalent rigid shaft coincide and it becomes impossible to balance the machine by putting correction weights in the discs I and III. Practically in a considerable region near the point A the conditions will be such that it will be difficult to obtain satisfactory balancing and heavy vibration troubles can be expected.

* A general investigation of the effect of flexibility of the shaft on balancing can be found in the paper by V. Blaess, *loc. cit.*, p. 290. From this paper Figs. 194 and 195 have been taken. See also D. M. Smith, *loc. cit.* p. 210.

CHAPTER V

VIBRATIONS OF ELASTIC BODIES

In considering vibrations of elastic bodies it will be assumed that the material of the body is homogeneous, isotropic and that it follows Hooke's law. The differential equations of motion established in the previous chapter for a system of particles will also be used here.

In the case of elastic bodies, however, instead of several concentrated masses, we have a system consisting of an infinitely large number of particles between which elastic forces are acting. This system requires an infinitely large number of coordinates for specifying its position and it therefore has an infinite number of degrees of freedom becuase any small displacement satisfying the condition of continuity, i.e., a displacement which will not produce cracks in the body, can be taken as a possible or virtual displacement. On this basis it is seen that any elastic body can have an infinite number of natural modes of vibration.

In the case of thin bars and plates the problem of vibration can be considerably simplified. These problems, which are of great importance in many engineering applications, will be discussed in more detail * in this chapter.

47. Free Longitudinal Vibrations of Prismatical Bars.—*Differential Equation of Longitudinal Vibrations.*—The following consideration is based on the assumption that during longitudinal vibration of a prismatical bar the cross sections of the bar remain plane and the particles in these cross sections perform only motion in an axial direction of the bar. The longitudinal extensions and compressions which take place during such a vibration of the bar will certainly be accompanied by some lateral deformation, but in the following only those cases will be considered where the length of the longitudinal waves is large in comparison with the cross-sec-

---

* A more complete discussion of the vibration problems of elastic systems can be found in the famous book by Lord Rayleigh, *Theory of Sound*, 2d Ed., 1894–1896. See also H. Lamb, *The Dynamical Theory of Sound*, London, 1925; A. E. H. Love, *Mathematical Theory of Elasticity*, Cambridge, 4th Ed., 1927; *Handbuch der Physik*, Vol. 6, 1928; Barré de Saint-Venant, *Théorie de l'élasticité des corps solides*, Paris, 1883; and C. B. Biezeno and R. Grammel, *loc. cit.*, p. 177.

tional dimensions of the bar. In these cases the lateral displacements during longitudinal vibration can be neglected without substantial errors.*
Under these conditions the differential equation of motion of an element of the bar between two adjacent cross sections mn and m_1n_1 (see Fig. 196) may be written in the same manner as for a particle.

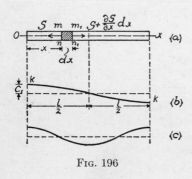

FIG. 196

Let u denote the longitudinal displacement of any cross section mn of the bar during vibration;

ϵ, the unit elongation;

E, the modulus of elasticity;

A, the cross-sectional area;

$S = AE\epsilon$, the longitudinal tensile force;

γ, the weight of the material of the bar per unit volume;

l, the length of the bar.

Then, the unit elongation and the tensile force at any cross section mn of the bar will be

$$\epsilon = \frac{\partial u}{\partial x}, \quad S = AE \frac{\partial u}{\partial x}.$$

For an adjacent cross section the tensile force will be

$$S + dS = AE \left(\frac{\partial u}{\partial x} + \frac{\partial^2 u}{\partial x^2} dx \right).$$

Taking into consideration that the inertia force of the element mnm_1n_1 of the bar is

$$- \frac{A\gamma \, dx}{g} \frac{\partial^2 u}{\partial t^2},$$

and using d'Alembert's principle, the following differential equation of motion of the element mnm_1n_1 will be obtained:

* A complete solution of the problem on longitudinal vibrations of a cyclindrical bar of circular cross section, in which the lateral displacements are also taken into consideration, was given by L. Pochhammer, *J. Math. (Crelle)*, Vol. 81, p. 324, 1876. See. also E. Giebe and E. Blechschmidt, *Ann. Physik*, Ser. 5, Vol. 18, p. 457, 1933.

$$-\frac{A\gamma}{g}\frac{\partial^2 u}{\partial t^2} + AE\frac{\partial^2 u}{\partial x^2} = 0,$$

or

$$\frac{\partial^2 u}{\partial t^2} = a^2 \frac{\partial^2 u}{\partial x^2}, \tag{88}$$

in which *

$$a^2 = \frac{Eg}{\gamma}. \tag{89}$$

Solution by Trigonometric Series.—The displacement u, depending on the coordinate x and on the time t, should be such a function of x and t as to satisfy the partial differential eq. (88). Particular solutions of this equation can easily be found by taking into consideration (1) that in the general case any vibration of a system can be resolved into the natural modes of vibration and (2) when a system performs one of its natural modes of vibration all points of the system execute a simple harmonic vibration and keep step with one another so that they pass simultaneously through their equilibrium positions. Assume now that the bar performs a natural mode of vibration, the frequency of which is $p/2\pi$, then the solution of eq. (88) should be taken in the following form:

$$u = X(A \cos pt + B \sin pt), \tag{a}$$

in which A and B are two constants and X is a certain function of x alone, determining the shape of the normal mode of vibration under consideration, and called a *normal function*. This function should be determined in every particular case so as to satisfy the conditions at the ends of the bar. As an example consider now the longitudinal vibrations of a bar with free ends. In this case the tensile force at the ends during vibration should be equal to zero and we obtain the following end conditions (see Fig. 196):

$$\left(\frac{\partial u}{\partial x}\right)_{x=0} = 0, \quad \left(\frac{\partial u}{\partial x}\right)_{x=l} = 0. \tag{b}$$

Substituting expression (a) in eq. (88) we obtain

$$-p^2 X = a^2 \frac{d^2 X}{dx^2},$$

from which

$$X = C \cos \frac{px}{a} + D \sin \frac{px}{a}. \tag{c}$$

---

* It can be shown that a is the velocity of propagation of waves along the bar, see p. 419.

In order to satisfy the first of the conditions (b) it is necessary to put $D = 0$. The second of the conditions (b) will be satisfied if

$$\sin \frac{pl}{a} = 0. \tag{90}$$

This is the *frequency equation* for the case under consideration, from which the frequencies of the natural modes of the longitudinal vibrations of a bar with free ends can be calculated. This equation will be satisfied by putting

$$\frac{pl}{a} = i\pi, \tag{d}$$

where i is an integer. Taking $i = 1, 2, 3, \cdots$, the frequencies of the various modes of vibration will be obtained. The frequency of the fundamental type of vibration will be found by putting $i = 1$ in eq. (d), which gives

$$p_1 = \frac{a\pi}{l} = \frac{\pi}{l} \sqrt{\frac{Eg}{\gamma}}. \tag{91}$$

The corresponding period of vibration will be

$$\tau_1 = \frac{2\pi}{p_1} = 2l \sqrt{\frac{\gamma}{Eg}}. \tag{92}$$

The shape of this mode of vibration, obtained from eq. (c), is represented in Fig. 196b, by the curve kk, the ordinates of which are equal to

$$X_1 = C_1 \cos \frac{p_1 x}{a} = C_1 \cos \frac{\pi x}{l}.$$

In Fig. 196c, the second mode of vibration is represented in which

$$\frac{p_2 l}{a} = 2\pi \quad \text{and} \quad X_2 = C_2 \cos \frac{2\pi x}{l}.$$

The general form of a particular solution (a) of eq. (88) will be

$$u = \cos \frac{i\pi x}{l} \left(A_i \cos \frac{i\pi a t}{l} + B_i \sin \frac{i\pi a t}{l} \right). \tag{e}$$

Superimposing such particular solutions, any longitudinal vibration of the bar * can be represented in the following form:

$$u = \sum_{i=1,2,3,\cdots}^{i=\infty} \cos\frac{i\pi x}{l}\left(A_i \cos\frac{i\pi at}{l} + B_i \sin\frac{i\pi at}{l}\right).\tag{93}$$

The constants A_i, B_i can always be chosen in such a manner as to satisfy any initial conditions.

Assume, for instance, that at the initial moment $t = 0$, the displacements u are given by the equation $(u)_{t=0} = f(x)$ and the initial velocities, by the equation $(\dot{u})_{t=0} = f_1(x)$. Substituting $t = 0$ in eq. (93), we obtain

$$f(x) = \sum_{i=1}^{i=\infty} A_i \cos\frac{i\pi x}{l}.\tag{f}$$

By substituting $t = 0$ in the derivative with respect to t of eq. (93), we obtain

$$f_1(x) = \sum_{i=1}^{i=\infty} \frac{i\pi a}{l} B_i \cos\frac{i\pi x}{l}.\tag{g}$$

The coefficients A_i and B_i in eqs. (f) and (g) can now be calculated, as explained before (see Art. 17) by using the formulas

$$A_i = \frac{2}{l}\int_0^l f(x)\cos\frac{i\pi x}{l}\,dx,\tag{h}$$

$$B_i = \frac{2}{i\pi a}\int_0^l f_1(x)\cos\frac{i\pi x}{l}\,dx.\tag{i}$$

As an example, consider now the case when a prismatical bar compressed by forces applied at the ends is suddenly released of this compression at the initial moment $t = 0$. By taking †

$$(u)_{t=0} = f(x) = \frac{\epsilon l}{2} - \epsilon x,\quad f_1(x) = 0,$$

where ϵ denotes the unit compression at the moment $t = 0$, we obtain

---

* Displacement of the bar as a rigid body is not considered here.
† It is assumed that the middle of the bar is stationary.

from eqs. (h) and (i)

$$A_i = \frac{4\epsilon l}{\pi^2 i^2} \quad \text{for} \quad i = \text{odd}, \qquad A_i = 0 \quad \text{for} \quad i = \text{even}, \qquad B_i = \mathbf{0},$$

and the general solution (93) becomes

$$u = \frac{4\epsilon l}{\pi^2} \sum_{i=1,3,5,\cdots}^{i=\infty} \frac{\cos\dfrac{i\pi x}{l}\cos\dfrac{i\pi a t}{l}}{i^2}.$$

Only odd integers $i = 1, 3, 5, \cdots$ enter in this solution and the vibration is symmetrical about the middle cross section of the bar.

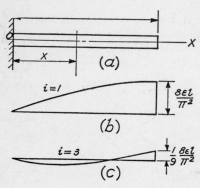

(a)

$i = 1$

$\dfrac{8\epsilon l}{\pi^2}$

(b)

$i = 3$

$\dfrac{1}{9}\dfrac{8\epsilon l}{\pi^2}$

(c)

FIG. 197

On the general solution (93) representing the vibration of the bar any longitudinal displacement of the bar as a rigid body can be superimposed.

As a second example let us consider free longitudinal vibrations of a bar, one end of which is fixed and the other free, Fig. 197. The end conditions in this case are

$$(u)_{x=0} = 0, \quad \left(\frac{du}{dx}\right)_{x=l} = 0. \quad (j)$$

To satisfy the first of these conditions, we take $C = 0$ in the general expression (c) for normal functions. The second condition gives us then the frequency equation

$$\cos\frac{pl}{a} = 0,$$

from which the frequencies and the periods of various modes of vibration ar

$$p_i = \frac{i\pi a}{2l}, \quad \tau_i = \frac{2\pi}{p_i} = \frac{4l}{ia}, \quad i = 1, 3, 5, \cdots \tag{k}$$

Then the general expression (a) of various modes of vibrations becomes:

$$u_i = \sin\frac{i\pi x}{2l}\left(A_i\cos\frac{i\pi a t}{2l} + B_i\sin\frac{i\pi a t}{2l}\right). \tag{l}$$

A general expression for longitudinal vibration is then obtained by super-position, which gives

$$u = \sum_{i=1,3,5,\cdots} \sin\frac{i\pi x}{2l}\left(A_i \cos\frac{i\pi at}{2l} + B_i \sin\frac{i\pi at}{2l}\right). \qquad (m)$$

The constants A_i, B_i are to be determined in each particular case from the conditions at the time $t = 0$.

Assume, for example, that the bar was stretched by an axial force P, applied at the free end, and at the time $t = 0$ was suddenly released. Using the notation ϵ for the initial unit elongation P/AE, the initial conditions are

$$(u)_{t=0} = \epsilon x, \quad (\dot{u})_{t=0} = 0.$$

The second of these conditions will be satisfied by making the constants B_i vanish in expression (m). For determining the constants A_i, we have then the equation

$$\sum_{i=1,3,5,\cdots} A_i \sin\frac{i\pi x}{2l} = \epsilon x.$$

Using equations similar to eq. (h), we then find

$$A_i = \frac{2\epsilon}{l}\int_0^l x \sin\frac{i\pi x}{2l}\,dx = \frac{8\epsilon l}{i^2\pi^2}(-1)^{\frac{i-1}{2}},$$

and expression (m) gives

$$u = \frac{8\epsilon l}{\pi^2}\sum_{i=1,3,5,\cdots}\frac{(-1)^{\frac{-1}{2}}}{i^2}\sin\frac{i\pi x}{2l}\cos\frac{i\pi at}{2l}. \qquad (n)$$

In Figs. 197b and 197c the first two modes of vibration are represented graphically. It may be appreciated that the amplitudes of various modes of vibration are rapidly decreasing as i increases. The displacements of the free end of the bar are obtained by substituting $x = l$ into expression (n). For $t = 0$, this gives

$$(u)_{\substack{x=l\\t=0}} = \frac{8\epsilon l}{\pi^2}\left(1 + \frac{1}{9} + \frac{1}{25} + \cdots\right) = \frac{8\epsilon l}{\pi^2}\cdot\frac{\pi^2}{8} = \epsilon l,$$

as it should be.

EXAMPLES

1. Find the normal functions for longitudinal vibration of a bar of length l if both ends are fixed.

Solution. The end conditions in this case are

$$(u)_{x=0} = (u)_{x=l} = 0.$$

To satisfy these conditions, we put $C = 0$ in the general expression (c) and obtain the frequency equation

$$\sin \frac{p_i l}{a} = 0,$$

from which

$$p_i = \frac{i\pi a}{l}.$$

Hence the normal functions will be

$$X_i = A_i \sin \frac{i\pi x}{l}, \quad \text{where } i = 1, 2, 3, \cdots.$$

2. A bar with built-in ends is acted upon by a constant axial force P, applied at the middle, Fig. 198. What vibrations will be produced if the force P is suddenly removed?

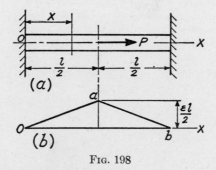

Fig. 198

Solution. The unit elongation in the left-hand part of the bar, equal to the unit compression in the right-hand part, is

$$\epsilon = \frac{P}{2AE}.$$

The initial displacements, $(u)_{t=0}$, are

$$f(x) = \epsilon x \quad \text{for} \quad 0 < x < l/2,$$

$$f(x) = \epsilon(l - x) \quad \text{for} \quad l/2 < x < l,$$

as represented by the triangle Oab in Fig. 198b. From the preceding example, the normal functions in this case are

$$X_i = A_i \sin \frac{p_i x}{a} = A_i \sin \frac{i\pi x}{l}$$

and the general expression for vibration, satisfying the initial condition $(\dot{u})_{t=0} = 0$, is

$$u = \sum_{i=1,2,3,\cdots} A_i \sin \frac{i\pi x}{l} \cos \frac{i\pi a t}{l}.$$

The constants A_i are found from the second initial condition, which requires:

$$f(x) = \Sigma A_i \sin \frac{i\pi x}{l}.$$

Then

$$A_i = \frac{2}{l} \left[\int_0^{l/2} \epsilon x \sin \frac{i\pi x}{l}\, dx + \int_{l/2} \epsilon(l - x) \sin \frac{\pi x}{l}\, dx \right]$$

$$= \frac{4\epsilon l}{\pi^2} \cdot \frac{(-1)^{\frac{i-1}{2}}}{i^2} \quad \text{for} \quad i = 1, 3, 5, \cdots, \qquad A_i = 0 \quad \text{for} \quad = 2, 4, \cdots,$$

and

$$u = \frac{4\epsilon l}{\pi^2} \sum_{i=1,3,\cdots} (-1)^{\frac{i-1}{2}} \cdot \frac{1}{i^2} \sin \frac{i\pi x}{l} \cos p_i t.$$

3. A bar moving along the x-axis with constant velocity v is suddenly stopped at the end $x = 0$, Fig. 197a, so that the initial conditions are $(u)_{t=0} = 0$; $(\dot{u})_{t=0} = v$. Find the ensuing vibrations.

Solution. The general expression for displacements is given by expression (m). Since the initial displacements vanish, we put $A_i = 0$ in that expression. The constants B_i are obtained from the equation

$$(\dot{u})_{t=0} = \sum_{i=1,3,\cdots} B_i \frac{i\pi a}{2l} \sin \frac{\pi x}{2l} = v,$$

which gives

$$B_i = \frac{8vl}{\pi^2 i^2 a}.$$

Hence

$$u = \frac{8vl}{\pi^2 a} \sum_{i=1,3,\cdots} \frac{1}{i^2} \sin \frac{i\pi x}{2l} \sin p_i t.$$

By using this formula, the displacement of any cross section of the bar at any given time can be calculated. Taking, for example, the free end of the bar ($x = l$) and assuming $t = l/a$, which is the time required for sound to travel the distance l, we obtain

$$(u)_{\substack{x=l \\ t=l/a}} = \frac{8vl}{\pi^2 a} \left(1 + \frac{1}{9} + \frac{1}{25} + \cdots \right) = \frac{vl}{a}.$$

Unit elongation of the bar during vibration is

$$\frac{du}{dx} = \frac{8vl}{\pi^2 a} \sum_{i=1,3,5,\cdots} \frac{1}{i^2} \frac{i\pi}{2l} \cos \frac{i\pi x}{2l} \sin p_i t.$$

At the fixed end ($x = 0$) we obtain

$$\left(\frac{du}{dx} \right)_{x=0} = \frac{4v}{\pi a} \sum_{i=1,3,5,\cdots} \frac{1}{i} \sin \frac{i\pi a t}{2l} = \frac{v}{a}, \quad \text{for} \quad 0 < \frac{\pi a t}{2l} < \frac{\pi}{2}.$$

We see that the tension wave which was originated at the left end of the bar at the instant of stopping ($t = 0$) is moving along the bar with speed a and at the instant $t = l/a$ it reaches the free end of the bar. At this instant, the velocities of all particles of the bar vanish and at the same time it is uniformly extended and the unit extension is $\epsilon = v/a$.

48. Forced Longitudinal Vibrations of Prismatical Bars.—Let us begin with a prismatical bar the upper end of which is fixed, Fig. 199, and to the lower end of which a disturbing force P is applied. Free vibrations of such a bar were already investigated and we found that normal functions in this case are (see eq. m of the preceding article):

$$X_i = A_i \sin \frac{i\pi x}{2l}, \quad \text{where} \quad i = 1, 3, 5, \cdots. \tag{a}$$

Any displacement $u = f(x)$ can be obtained by superposition of displacements corresponding to normal modes of vibration (a) and vibrations produced by the disturbing force P can be represented by the series

$$u = \phi_1 \sin \frac{\pi x}{2l} + \phi_3 \sin \frac{3\pi x}{2l} + \phi_5 \sin \frac{5\pi x}{2l} + \cdots, \tag{b}$$

in which ϕ_1, ϕ_3, $\cdots$ are some unknown functions of time. In the case of free vibration these functions are represented by the expressions in parenthesis of eq. (m) of the preceding article. To find these functions for the case of forced vibrations, we will apply d'Alembert's principle together with the principle of virtual work. We have to consider here three kinds of forces: the inertia forces applied to each element of the vibrating bar, the elastic forces due to deformation of the bar and the disturbing force. As a virtual displacement, we can take any longitudinal displacement δu satisfying the condition of continuity and the condition at the fixed end ($\delta u_{x=0} = 0$). For our further analysis it is advantageous to assume that various types of virtual displacements are given by normal functions (a). Thus

$$\delta u_i = A_i \sin \frac{i\pi x}{2l}. \tag{c}$$

Fig. 199

Observing that the mass of an element between two adjacent cross sections of the bar is $\dfrac{A\gamma}{g} dx$, we find that the work done by inertia forces on the assumed virtual displacement is

$$-\int_0^l \frac{A\gamma}{g} \ddot{u} A_i \sin \frac{i\pi x}{2l} \, dx.$$

Substituting for u the series (b) and observing that

$$\int_0^l \sin \frac{i\pi x}{2l} \cdot \sin \frac{j\pi x}{2l} \, dx = 0, \quad \int_0^l \sin^2 \frac{i\pi x}{2l} \, dx = \frac{l}{2},$$

we obtain

$$-\frac{A\gamma}{g} \cdot \frac{l}{2} \cdot A_i \ddot{\varphi}_i. \tag{d}$$

For the calculation of the virtual work produced by elastic forces it is advantageous to use the expression for the strain energy of the vibrating bar. This energy is

$$V = \frac{1}{2} \int_0^l AE \left(\frac{\partial u}{\partial x}\right)^2 dx.$$

Substituting for u the series (b) and observing that

$$\int_0^l \cos \frac{i\pi x}{2l} \cdot \cos \frac{j\pi x}{2l} \, dx = 0, \quad \int_0^l \cos^2 \frac{i\pi x}{2l} \, dx = \frac{l}{2},$$

we find the strain energy to be

$$V = \frac{i^2 \pi^2 AE}{16l} \sum_{i=1,3,5,\cdots} \phi_i^2. \tag{e}$$

We see that the amount of strain energy in the bar at any instant depends on the quantities ϕ_i defining the displacement (b) of the bar. If we give to one of these quantities, say ϕ_i, an increment $\delta\phi_i$, the corresponding displacement is

$$\delta\phi_i \sin \frac{i\pi x}{2l} \tag{f}$$

and the corresponding increment of the strain energy is

$$\delta V = \frac{\partial V}{\partial \phi_i} \delta\phi_i = \frac{i^2 \pi^2 AE}{8l} \cdot \phi_i \cdot \delta\phi_i. \tag{g}$$

The same quantity taken with negative sign will represent the work of elastic forces on the displacement (f). To get the work of elastic forces on the virtual displacement (c), we have only to replace $\delta\phi_i$ by A_i. In this way we obtain for that work the expression

$$-\frac{i^2\pi^2 AE}{8l}\,\phi_i A_i. \tag{h}$$

To get the virtual work of the disturbing force, applied at the end, we observe that the virtual displacement of this end is obtained by substituting l for x into expression (c) and the corresponding virtual work then is

$$PA_i \sin\frac{i\pi}{2} = PA_i(-1)^{\frac{i-1}{2}}. \tag{i}$$

The summation of expressions (d), (h) and (i) gives us the total virtual work. Equating it to zero we obtain

$$\frac{A\gamma l}{2g}\,\ddot{\phi}_i + \frac{i^2\pi^2 AE}{8l}\,\phi_i = P(-1)^{\frac{i-1}{2}},$$

or

$$\ddot{\phi}_i + \frac{i^2\pi^2 a^2}{4l^2}\,\phi_i = \frac{2g}{A\gamma l}\cdot P(-1)^{\frac{i-1}{2}}, \tag{j}$$

where $a^2 = Eg/\gamma$ and $i = 1, 3, 5, \cdots$.

We see that each quantity ϕ_i in the series (b) can be readily obtained from eq. (j) if P is known as a function of time. If the initial velocities and displacements vanish and we have to consider only vibration produced by the disturbing force P, we take the solution of eq. (j) in the form given on p. 106. Then

$$\phi_i = \frac{4g(-1)^{\frac{i-1}{2}}}{a\pi i\gamma A}\int_0^t P \sin\left[\frac{i\pi a}{2l}(t - t_1)\right] dt_1.$$

Substituting into expression (b), we obtain vibrations produced by the disturbing force P in the following form:

$$u = \frac{4g}{a\pi\gamma A}\sum_{i=1,3,5,\cdots}\frac{(-1)^{\frac{i-1}{2}}}{i}\sin\frac{i\pi x}{2l}\int_0^t P\sin\left[\frac{i\pi a}{2l}(t - t_1)\right]dt_1. \tag{k}$$

Let us take, as a particular example, the case of vibrations produced in the bar by a constant force P suddenly applied at the time $t = 0$. In such a case the integrals in the series (k) can be readily evaluated and we obtain

$$u = \frac{8glP}{a^2\pi^2\gamma A}\sum_{i=1,3,5,\cdots}\frac{(-1)^{\frac{i-1}{2}}}{i^2}\sin\frac{i\pi x}{2l}\left(1 - \cos\frac{i\pi at}{2l}\right).$$

Substituting $x = l$ in this series, we obtain the displacement of the end of the bar

$$(u)_{x=l} = \frac{8glP}{a^2\pi^2\gamma A} \sum_{i=1,3,5,\cdots} \frac{1}{i^2}\left(1 - \cos\frac{i\pi at}{2l}\right).$$

It is seen that by a sudden application of the force P all modes of vibration of the bar will be produced. The maximum deflection occurs when $t = 2l/a$. At that instant

$$1 - \cos\frac{i\pi at}{2l} = 2$$

and we obtain

$$(u)_{x=l} = \frac{16glP}{a^2\pi^2\gamma A} \sum_{i=1,3,5,\cdots} \frac{1}{i^2}.$$

Observing that

$$\sum_{i=1,3,5,\cdots} \frac{1}{i^2} = \frac{\pi^2}{8} \quad \text{and} \quad a^2 = \frac{Eg}{\gamma},$$

we obtain

$$(u)_{x=l} = \frac{2lP}{AE}.$$

Thus we arrive at the conclusion that a suddenly applied force produces twice as great a deflection as one gradually applied.

As a second example, let us consider the longitudinal vibration of a bar with free ends (Fig. 196) produced by a longitudinal force P suddenly applied at the end $x = l$.* Proceeding as in the preceding example and using normal functions for a bar with free ends (see eq. 93, p. 301), we can represent longitudinal displacements of the vibrating bar by the series

$$u = \phi_0 + \phi_1 \cos\frac{\pi x}{l} + \phi_2 \cos\frac{2\pi x}{l} + \phi_3 \cos\frac{3\pi x}{l} + \cdots, \qquad (l)$$

in which the first term represents the motion of the bar as a rigid body. On this motion various modes of longitudinal vibrations of the bar are superimposed. For determining the function ϕ_0, we have the equation

$$\frac{\gamma lA}{g} \ddot{\phi}_0 = P. \qquad (m)$$

---

* A similar problem is encountered in investigation of the vibrations produced during the lifting of a long drill stem as used in deep oil wells. The problem was discussed by B. F. Langer and E. H. Lamberger, *J. Appl. Mech.*, Vol. 10, p. 1, 1943.

The functions ϕ_1, ϕ_2, ϕ_3, $\cdots$ will be found by using as before the principle of virtual displacements together with d'Alembert's principle. Taking a virtual displacement

$$\delta u = A_i \cos \frac{i\pi x}{l}, \tag{n}$$

we find that the work of inertia forces on this displacement is

$$-\int_0^l \frac{\gamma A}{g} \ddot{u} A_i \cos \frac{i\pi x}{l} \, dx = \frac{\gamma A}{g} \cdot \frac{l}{2} A_i \ddot{\phi}_i. \tag{o}$$

The strain energy of the vibrating bar at any instant is

$$V = \frac{1}{2} \int_0^l AE \left(\frac{\partial u}{\partial x}\right)^2 dx = \frac{\pi^2 AE}{4l} \sum_{i=1,2,3,\cdots} i^2 \phi_i^2$$

and the work of the elastic forces on the displacement (n) will be

$$-\frac{i^2 \pi^2 AE}{2l} \phi_i A_i. \tag{p}$$

Finally the work of the force P on the displacement (n) is

$$PA_i \cos i\pi = A_i P(-1)^i. \tag{q}$$

Equating to zero the sum of expressions (o), (p) and (q), we obtain the equation

$$\ddot{\phi}_i + \frac{i^2 \pi^2 a^2}{l^2} \phi_i = \frac{2g}{\gamma l A} P(-1)^i. \tag{r}$$

From this equation and eq. (m), we obtain

$$\phi_0 = \frac{gt^2 P}{2\gamma l A},$$

$$\phi_i = (-1)^i \frac{2g}{ia\pi\gamma A} \int_0^t P \sin\left[\frac{i\pi a}{l}(t - t_1)\right] dt_1,$$

$$= \frac{(-1)^i 2glP}{i^2 \pi^2 a^2 \gamma A}\left(1 - \cos\frac{i\pi at}{l}\right).$$

Substituting into expression (l), we find

$$u = \frac{gt^2 P}{2\gamma l A} + \frac{2glP}{\pi^2 a^2 \gamma A} \sum_{i=1,2,3,\cdots} \frac{(-1)^i}{i^2} \cos\frac{i\pi x}{l}\left(1 - \cos\frac{i\pi at}{l}\right). \tag{s}$$

To obtain the displacement of the end of the bar to which the force P is applied, we substitute $x = l$ into solution (s) which gives

$$(u)_{x=l} = \frac{gt^2 P}{2\gamma lA} + \frac{2glP}{\pi^2 a^2 \gamma A} \sum_{i=1,3,\cdots} \frac{1}{i^2}\left(1 - \cos\frac{i\pi at}{l}\right). \qquad (t)$$

For $t = l/a$, we obtain

$$(u)_{x=l} = \frac{Pl}{2AE} + \frac{4Pl}{\pi^2 AE}\left(1 + \frac{1}{9} + \frac{1}{25} + \cdots\right) = \frac{Pl}{AE}. \qquad (u)$$

The displacement, as we see, is at this instant equal to the extension of the bar under the action of the uniform tensile force P.

An application of the theory of forced longitudinal vibration of a bar with free ends was made by O. R. Wikander in investigating coupling forces in long freight trains.*

EXAMPLES

1. Find the forced vibrations of a bar with one end fixed and the other free, Fig. 199, produced by a pulsating axial force $P = P_0 \sin \omega t$ acting at the free end of the bar.

Solution. Eq. (j) in this case becomes

$$\ddot{\phi}_i + \frac{i^2 \pi^2 a^2}{4l^2}\phi_i = \frac{2g(-1)^{\frac{i-1}{2}}}{A\gamma l}P_0 \sin \omega t,$$

and the corresponding forced vibration is

$$\phi_i = \frac{P_0}{\gamma lA} \cdot \frac{2g(-1)^{\frac{i-1}{2}}}{(p_i^2 - \omega^2)} \sin \omega t.$$

Substituting this into expression (b), the required forced vibrations of the bar are obtained. It is seen that if ω is approaching the value of one of the natural frequencies of the bar, the amplitude of the corresponding type of vibration becomes large.

2. A drill stem is a steel tube 4000 ft long. Considering it as a bar with free ends, find the period τ of the fundamental mode of vibration. Find the displacement δ of the end $(x = l)$ at $t = \tau/2$ produced by a tensile stress $\sigma = P/A = 3000$ lb per sq in. suddenly applied to this end. Take $E = 30 \cdot 10^6$ lb per sq in.; $\gamma = 0.278$ lb per cu in.

Solution. The velocity of sound in this bar is

$$a = \sqrt{\frac{Eg}{\gamma}} = 204 \cdot 10^3 \text{ in. per sec.}$$

The period of the fundamental mode of vibration is

$$\tau = \frac{2l}{a} = 0.470 \text{ sec.}$$

* See *Trans. A.S.M.E.*, Vol. 57, p. 317, 1935.

The required displacement, from eq. (u), is

$$\delta = \frac{3000 \cdot 4000}{30 \cdot 10^6} = 0.4 \text{ ft.}$$

3. Find vibrations produced in a bar with one end built in and another free, Fig. 199, by suddenly applied axial forces q uniformly distributed along the length of the bar.

Hint. The virtual work produced by forces q is

$$\int_0^l q A_i \sin \frac{i\pi x}{2l} dx = \frac{2ql}{i\pi} A_i$$

and to obtain the required vibrations we have to substitute $2ql/i\pi$, instead of $P(-1)^{\frac{i-1}{2}}$, in the calculations made on p. 308.

FIG. 200

49. Vibration of a Bar with a Load at the End.—*Free Vibrations.*— The problem of vibration of a bar with a load at the end (Fig. 200) may have a practical application not only in the case of prismatical bars but also when the load is supported by a helical spring as in the case of an indicator spring (see p. 52). If the mass of the bar or of the spring be small in comparison with the mass of the load at the end it can be neglected and the problem will be reduced to that of a system with one degree of freedom (see Fig. 1). In the following, the effect of the mass of the bar will be considered in detail.* Denoting the longitudinal displacements from the position of equilibrium by u and using the differential eq. (88) of the longitudinal vibrations developed in Art. 47, we obtain

$$\frac{\partial^2 u}{\partial t^2} = a^2 \frac{\partial^2 u}{\partial x^2}, \tag{88'}$$

where

$$a^2 = \frac{Eg}{\gamma}$$

for a prismatical bar, and

$$a^2 = \frac{klg}{w}$$

for a helical spring. In this latter case k is the spring constant, this being the load necessary to produce a total elongation of the spring equal to unity, l is the length of the spring and w is the weight of the spring per unit length. The end conditions will be as follows.

At the built-in end the displacement should be zero during vibration and we obtain

$$(u)_{x=0} = 0. \tag{a}$$

At the lower end, at which the load is attached, the tensile force in the bar must be

* See author's papers: *Bull. Polytech. Inst.* (*Kiev*), 1910; and *Z. Math. u. Phys.*, Vol. 59, p. 163, 1911. See also A. N. Krylov *Differential Equations in Mathematics and Physics* (Russian), St. Petersburg, p. 308, 1913.

equal to the inertia force of the oscillating load W and we have *

$$AE\left(\frac{\partial u}{\partial x}\right)_{x=l} = -\frac{W}{g}\left(\frac{\partial^2 u}{\partial t^2}\right)_{x=l}. \qquad (b)$$

Assuming that the system performs one of the principal modes of vibration, we obtain

$$u = X(A\cos pt + B\sin pt), \qquad (c)$$

in which X is a *normal function* of x alone, defining the shape of the mode of vibration. Substituting (c) in eq. $(88')$ we obtain

$$a^2\frac{d^2X}{dx^2} + p^2X = 0,$$

from which

$$X = C\cos\frac{px}{a} + D\sin\frac{px}{a}, \qquad (d)$$

where C and D are constants of integration.

In order to satisfy condition (a) we have to take $C = 0$ in solution (d). From condition (b) we obtain

$$AE\frac{p}{a}\cos\frac{pl}{a} = \frac{W}{g}p^2\sin\frac{pl}{a}. \qquad (b')$$

Let $\alpha = A\gamma l/W$ be the ratio of the weight of the bar to the weight of the load W and $\beta = pl/a$. Then eq. (b') becomes

$$\alpha = \beta\tan\beta. \qquad (94)$$

This is the *frequency equation* for the case under consideration, the roots of which can be easily obtained graphically, provided the ratio α be known. The fundamental type of vibration is usually the most important in practical applications and the values β_1 of the smallest root of eq. (94) for various values of α are given in the table below.

$\alpha =$	.01	.10	.30	.50	.70	.90	1.00	1.50	2.00	3.00	4.00	5.00	10.0	20.0	100.0	∞
$\beta_1 =$	.10	.32	.52	.65	.75	.82	.86	.98	1.08	1.20	1.27	1.32	1.42	1.52	1.568	$\pi/2$

If the weight of the bar is small in comparison with the load W, the quantity α and the root β_1 will be small and eq. (94) can be simplified by putting $\tan\beta = \beta$, then

$$\beta^2 = \alpha = \frac{A\gamma l}{W},$$

and we obtain

$$\beta = \frac{pl}{a} = \sqrt{\frac{A\gamma l}{W}} \qquad (e)$$

$$\text{and } p = \frac{a}{l}\sqrt{\frac{A\gamma l}{W}} = \sqrt{\frac{g}{\delta_{st}}}, \qquad (f)$$

where $\delta_{st} = Wl/AE$ represents the statical elongation of the bar under the action of the load W.

* The constant load W, being in equilibrium with the uniform tension of the bar in its position of equilibrium, will not affect the end condition.

This result coincides with the one obtained before for a system with one degree of freedom (see eq. 4, p. 3). A better approximation will be obtained by substituting $\tan \beta = \beta + \beta^3/3$ in eq. (94). Then

$$\beta(\beta + \beta^3/3) = \alpha,$$

or

$$\beta = \sqrt{\frac{\alpha}{1 + \beta^2/3}}. \tag{g}$$

Substituting the first approximation (e) for β in the right side of this equation, we obtain

$$\beta = \sqrt{\frac{\alpha}{1 + \alpha/3}} \quad \text{and} \quad p = \sqrt{\frac{g}{\delta_{st}(1 + \alpha/3)}}. \tag{h}$$

Comparing (h) with (f) it can be concluded that the better approximation is obtained by adding one third of the weight of the bar to the weight W of the load. This is the well-known approximate solution obtained before by using Rayleigh's method (see p. 26).

Comparing the approximate solution (h) with the data of the table on p. 313, it can be concluded that for $\alpha = 1$ the error arising from the use of the approximate formula is less than 1% and in all cases when the weight of the bar is less than the weight of the load the approximate formula (h) is satisfactory for practical applications.

Assuming that for a given α the consecutive roots $\beta_1, \beta_2, \beta_3, \cdots$ of the frequency eq. (94) are calculated, and substituting $\beta_i a/l$ for p in solution (c) we obtain,

$$u_i = \sin \frac{\beta_i x}{l} \left(A_i \cos \frac{\beta_i a t}{l} + B_i \sin \frac{\beta_i a t}{l} \right).$$

This solution represents a principal mode of vibration of the order i of our system. By superimposing such vibrations any vibration of the bar with a load at the end can be obtained in the form of a series,

$$u = \sum_{i=1}^{i=\infty} \sin \frac{\beta_i x}{l} \left(A_i \cos \frac{\beta_i a t}{l} + B_i \sin \frac{\beta_i a t}{l} \right), \tag{i}$$

the constants A_i and B_i of which should be determined from the initial conditions.

Assume, for example, that the bar is at rest under the action of a tensile force P applied at the lower end and that at the time $t = 0$ this force is suddenly removed. For this case all the coefficients B_i in eq. (i) should be taken equal to zero because the initial velocities are zero. The coefficients A_i should be determined in such a manner as to represent the initial configuration of the system. From the uniform extension of the bar at the time $t = 0$ we obtain

$$(u)_{t=0} = \frac{Px}{AE}.$$

Eq. (i), for $t = 0$, yields

$$(u)_{t=0} = \sum_{i=1}^{i=\infty} A_i \sin \frac{\beta_i x}{l}.$$

The coefficients A_i should be determined in such a manner as to satisfy the equation

$$\sum_{i=1}^{i=\infty} A_i \sin \frac{\beta_i x}{l} = \frac{Px}{AE}. \tag{j}$$

In determining these coefficients we proceed exactly as was explained in Art. 17. In order to obtain any coefficient A_i both sides of the above equation should be multiplied with $\sin(\beta_i x/l)\, dx$ and integrated from $x = 0$ to $x = l$. By integration we obtain

$$\int_0^l \sin^2 \frac{\beta_i x}{l}\, dx = \frac{l}{2}\left(1 - \frac{\sin 2\beta_i}{2\beta_i}\right),$$

$$\frac{P}{AE}\int_0^l x \sin \frac{\beta_i x}{l}\, dx = \frac{Pl^2}{AE}\left(-\frac{\cos \beta_i}{\beta_i} + \frac{\sin \beta_i}{\beta_i^2}\right),$$

and also, by taking into consideration eq. (94) for every integer $m \neq i$

$$\int_0^l \sin \frac{\beta_i x}{l} \sin \frac{\beta_m x}{l}\, dx = -\frac{W}{A\gamma}\sin \beta_i \sin \beta_m = -\frac{l}{\alpha}\sin \beta_i \sin \beta_m.$$

Then multiplying eq. (j) by $\sin\left(\dfrac{\beta_i x}{l}\right) dx$ and integrating, we obtain

$$\int_0^l \sin \frac{\beta_i x}{l} \sum_{i=1}^{i=\infty} A_i \sin \frac{\beta_i x}{l}\, dx = \frac{P}{AE}\int_0^l x \sin \frac{\beta_i x}{l}\, dx,$$

or

$$A_i\frac{l}{2}\left(1 - \frac{\sin 2\beta_i}{2\beta_i}\right) - \frac{l}{\alpha}\sin \beta_i \left\{\sum_{m=1,2,3,\cdots,i-1,i+1,\cdots}^{m=\infty} A_m \sin \beta_m\right\}$$

$$= \frac{Pl^2}{AE}\left(-\frac{\cos \beta_i}{\beta_i} + \frac{\sin \beta_i}{\beta_i^2}\right).$$

Remembering that, from eq. (i),

$$\sum_{i=1,2,3,\cdots,i-1,i+1,\cdots}^{i=\infty} A_m \sin \beta_m = (u)_{\substack{x=l \\ t=0}} - A_i \sin \beta_i = \frac{Pl}{AE} - A_i \sin \beta_i,$$

we obtain

$$A_i\frac{l}{2}\left(1 - \frac{\sin 2\beta_i}{2\beta_i}\right) - \frac{l}{\alpha}\sin \beta_i \left(\frac{Pl}{AE} - A_i \sin \beta_i\right) = \frac{Pl^2}{AE}\left(-\frac{\cos \beta_i}{\beta_i} + \frac{\sin \beta_i}{\beta_i^2}\right),$$

from which, by taking into consideration that (from eq. 94)

$$\frac{l}{\alpha}\sin \beta_i = \frac{l \cos \beta_i}{\beta_i},$$

we obtain

$$A_i = \frac{4Pl \sin \beta_i}{AE\beta_i(2\beta_i + \sin 2\beta_i)},$$

the initial displacement will be

$$(u)_{t=0} = \frac{Px}{AE} = \frac{4Pl}{AE}\sum_{i=1}^{i=\infty} \frac{\sin \beta_i \sin \dfrac{\beta_i x}{l}}{\beta_i(2\beta_i + \sin 2\beta_i)}, \tag{95}$$

and the vibration of the bar will be represented in this case by the following series:

$$u = \frac{4Pl}{AE} \sum_{i=1}^{t=\infty} \frac{\sin \beta_i \sin \dfrac{\beta_i x}{l} \cos \dfrac{\beta_i at}{l}}{\beta_i(2\beta_i + \sin 2\beta_i)}. \tag{96}$$

Forced Vibrations.—In analyzing forced vibrations, we proceed as in the preceding article and assume displacements in the form of the series

$$u = \phi_1 \sin \frac{\beta_1 x}{l} + \phi_2 \sin \frac{\beta_2 x}{l} + \cdots, \tag{k}$$

in which $\sin \dfrac{\beta_i x}{l}$ are normal functions for our case and $\phi_1, \phi_2, \cdots$ are unknown functions of time. For determining these functions we use, as before, d'Alembert's principle together with the principle of virtual work. Assuming that a disturbing force P is applied at the lower end of the bar, we will find that the work of this force at a virtual displacement,

$$\delta u = A_i \sin \frac{\beta_i x}{l},$$

is $PA_i \sin \beta_i$ and the differential equation for determining the functions ϕ_i becomes

$$\frac{\gamma l}{2g} \left(1 + \frac{\sin 2\beta_i}{2\beta_i} \right) \ddot{\phi}_i + \frac{E}{2l} \beta_i{}^2 \left(1 + \frac{\sin 2\beta_i}{2\beta_i} \right) \phi_i = \frac{P \sin \beta_i}{A}. \tag{l}$$

Considering only vibrations produced by a disturbing force and neglecting the free vibrations due to initial displacements and initial impulses, the solution of eq. (l) will be *

$$\phi_i = \frac{2g}{A\gamma l} \cdot \frac{l}{a\beta_i} \frac{2\beta_i}{2\beta_i + \sin 2\beta_i} \int_0^t P \sin \beta_i \sin \frac{a\beta_i}{l} (t - t_1) \, dt_1,$$

where, as before,

$$a = \sqrt{\frac{Eg}{\gamma}}.$$

Substituting this into (k), the following general solution of the problem will be obtained:

$$u = \frac{4g}{A a \gamma} \sum_{i=1}^{i=\infty} \frac{\sin \dfrac{\beta_i x}{l}}{2\beta_i + \sin 2\beta_i} \int_0^t P \sin \beta_i \sin \frac{a\beta_i}{l} (t - t_1) \, dt_1. \tag{97}$$

In any particular case the corresponding expression for the disturbing force should be substituted in this solution. By putting $x = l$ the displacements of the load W during vibration will be obtained.

Suddenly Applied Force.—Consider, as an example, the vibration produced by a constant force P suddenly applied at the lower end of the bar. Substituting $x = l$ in eq. (97) and considering P as constant, we obtain for the displacements of the load W the following expression:

$$(u)_{x=l} = \frac{4gPl}{Aa^2\gamma} \sum_{i=1}^{i=\infty} \frac{\sin^2 \beta_i}{\beta_i(2\beta_i + \sin 2\beta_i)} \left(1 - \cos \frac{a\beta_i t}{l} \right). \tag{98}$$

* See eq. (46) p. 106.

Consider now the particular case when the load W at the end of the bar diminishes to zero and the conditions approach those considered in the previous article. In such a case α in eq. (94) becomes infinitely large and the roots of that transcendental equation will be

$$\beta_i = \frac{(2i - 1)\pi}{2}.$$

Substituting in eq. (98), the same result as in the previous article will be obtained.

A second extreme case is when the load W is very large in comparison with the weight of the rod and α in eq. (94) approaches zero. The roots of this equation then approach the values

$$\beta_i = (i - 1)\pi.$$

All terms in the series (98), except the first term, tend towards zero and the system approaches the case of one degree of freedom. The displacement of the lower end of the rod will be given in this case by the first term of (98) and will be

$$(u)_{x=l} = \frac{4gPl}{Aa^2\gamma} \frac{\sin^2 \beta_1}{\beta_1(2\beta_1 + \sin 2\beta_1)} \left(1 - \cos \frac{a\beta_1 t}{l} \right),$$

or by putting $\sin \beta_1 = \beta_1$ and $\sin 2\beta_1 = 2\beta_1$ we obtain

$$(u)_{x=l} = \frac{gPl}{Aa^2\gamma} \left(1 - \cos \frac{a\beta_1 t}{l} \right).$$

This becomes a maximum when

$$\cos \frac{a\beta_1 t}{l} = -1,$$

then

$$(u)_{max} = \frac{2gPl}{Aa^2\gamma} = \frac{2Pl}{AE}.$$

This shows that the maximum displacement produced by a suddenly applied force is twice as great as the static elongation produced by the same force.

This conclusion also holds for the case when $W = 0$ (see p. 309) but it will not be true in the general case given by eq. (98). To prove this, it is necessary to observe that in the two particular cases mentioned above the system at the end of a half period of the fundamental mode of vibration will be in a condition of instantaneous rest. At this moment the kinetic energy becomes equal to zero and the work done by the suddenly applied constant force is completely transformed into potential energy of deformation and it can be concluded from a statical consideration that the displacement of the point of application of the force should be twice as great as in the equilibrium configuration.

In the general case represented by eq. (98) the roots of eq. (94) are incommensurable and the system never passes into a configuration in which the energy is purely potential. Part of the energy always remains in the form of kinetic energy and the displacement of the point of application of the force will be less than twice that in the equilibrium configuration.

If, instead of a constant force P, a pulsating force $P \sin \omega t$ is applied, we substitute $P \sin \omega t$ for P in the series (97). Then performing the integration, we obtain

$$(u)_{x=l} = \frac{2gP}{A\gamma l} \sum_{i=1}^{i=\infty} \frac{\sin^2 \beta_i \left(\sin \omega t - \dfrac{\omega l}{a\beta_i} \sin \dfrac{a\beta_i t}{l} \right)}{\left(1 + \dfrac{\sin 2\beta_i}{2\beta_i} \right) \left(\dfrac{a^2 \beta_i^2}{l^2} - \omega^2 \right)}. \qquad (m)$$

It is seen that the vibration consists of two parts: (1) forced vibrations proportional to $\sin \omega t$ having the same period as the disturbing force, and (2) free vibrations proportional to $\sin (a\beta_i t/l)$. When the frequency of the disturbing force approaches one of the natural frequencies of vibration ω approaches the value $a\beta_i/l$ for this mode of vibration and a condition of resonance takes place. The amplitude of vibration of the corresponding term in the series (m) will then increase indefinitely, as was explained before (see pp. 42 and 206). In order to approach the static condition the quantity ω should be considered as small in comparison with $a\beta_i/l$ in the series (m). Neglecting then the terms having $\omega l/a\beta_i$ as a factor, we obtain, for a very slow variation of the pulsating load,

$$(u)_{x=l} = \frac{4lP \sin \omega t}{AE} \sum_{i=1}^{i=\infty} \frac{\sin^2 \beta_i}{\beta_i(2\beta_i + \sin 2\beta_i)}, \qquad (n)$$

which represents the static elongation of the bar (see eq. 95). By comparing the series (n) and (m) the difference between static and dynamic deflections can be established. It is seen that a satisfactory record of steam or gas pressure can be obtained only if the frequency of the fundamental mode of vibration of the indicator is high in comparison with the frequency of the pulsating force.

50. Torsional Vibration of Circular Shafts.—*Free Vibration.*—In our previous discussions of torsional vibrations (see pp. 9 and 238), the mass of the shaft was either neglected or considered small in comparison with the rotating masses attached to the shaft. In the following, a more complete theory of the torsional vibrations of a circular shaft with two discs at the ends is given * on the basis of which the accuracy of our previous solution can be shown. It is assumed in the following discussion that the circular cross sections of the shaft during torsional vibration remain plane and the radii of these cross sections remain straight.† Let

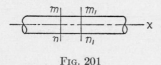

FIG. 201

$GI_p = C$ be torsional rigidity of shaft;

γ, weight per unit volume of shaft;

θ, angle of twist at any cross section mn (see Fig. 201) during torsional vibration;

* See writer's papers: *Bull. Polytech. Inst.* (*St. Petersburg*), 1905; and "Erzwungene Schwingungen Prismatischer Stäbe," *Z. Math. u. Phys.*, Vol. 59, p. 163, 1911.

† A more complete theory can be found in L. Pochhammer's paper, *loc. cit.*, p. 298.

I_1, I_2, moments of inertia of the discs at the ends of the shaft about the shaft axis.

Considering an element of the shaft between two adjacent cross sections mn and m_1n_1, the twisting moments at these cross sections will be

$$GI_p \frac{\partial\theta}{\partial x} \quad \text{and} \quad GI_p \left(\frac{\partial\theta}{\partial x} + \frac{\partial^2\theta}{\partial x^2} dx \right).$$

The differential equation of rotatory motion of the elemental disc mnm_1n_1 (see Fig. 201) during torsional vibration will be

$$\frac{\gamma I_p}{g} \frac{\partial^2\theta}{\partial t^2} = GI_p \frac{\partial^2\theta}{\partial x^2},$$

or by using the notation

$$\frac{Gg}{\gamma} = a^2, \tag{99}$$

we obtain

$$\frac{\partial^2\theta}{\partial t^2} = a^2 \frac{\partial^2\theta}{\partial x^2}. \tag{100}$$

This equation is identical with the eq. (88) obtained before for the longitudinal vibration and the previous results can be used in various particular cases. For instance, in the case of a shaft with free ends the frequency equation will be identical with eq. (90) and the general solution will be (see eq. 93):

$$\theta = \sum_{i=1}^{i=\infty} \cos \frac{i\pi x}{l} \left(A_i \cos \frac{i\pi at}{l} + B_i \sin \frac{i\pi at}{l} \right). \tag{101}$$

In the case of a shaft with discs at the ends (Fig. 202) the problem becomes more complicated. From the condition that the twisting of the shaft at the ends is produced by the inertia forces of the discs we obtain (see Fig. 202):

$$I_1 \left(\frac{\partial^2\theta}{\partial t^2} \right)_{x=0} = GI_p \left(\frac{\partial\theta}{\partial x} \right)_{x=0}, \qquad (a)$$

$$I_2 \left(\frac{\partial^2\theta}{\partial t^2} \right)_{x=l} = -GI_p \left(\frac{\partial\theta}{\partial x} \right)_{x=l} \qquad (b)$$

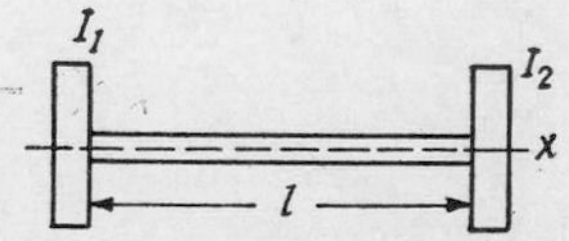

Fig. 202

Assume that the shaft performs one of the normal modes of vibration, so that

$$\theta = X(A \cos pt + B \sin pt),\qquad(c)$$

where X is a function of x alone, defining the shape of the mode of vibration under consideration.

Substituting (c) in eq. (100) we obtain

$$a^2 \frac{d^2X}{dx^2} + p^2X = 0,$$

from which

$$X = C \cos \frac{px}{a} + D \sin \frac{px}{a}.\qquad(d)$$

The constants C and D should be determined in such a manner as to satisfy the end conditions. Substituting (d) in eqs. (a) and (b) we obtain

$$\left.\begin{array}{c} -Cp^2I_1 = D\,\dfrac{p}{a}\,GI_p, \\[2ex] p^2\left(C \cos \dfrac{pl}{a} + D \sin \dfrac{pl}{a}\right) I_2 = \dfrac{p}{a}\,GI_p\left(-C \sin \dfrac{pl}{a} + D \cos \dfrac{pl}{a}\right). \end{array}\right\}\quad(e)$$

Eliminating the constants C and D, the following *frequency equation* will be obtained:

$$p^2\left(\cos \frac{pl}{a} - \frac{paI_1}{GI_p} \sin \frac{pl}{a}\right) I_2 = -\frac{p}{a}\,GI_p\left(\sin \frac{pl}{a} + \frac{paI_1}{GI_p} \cos \frac{pl}{a}\right).\quad(f)$$

Letting

$$\frac{pl}{a} = \beta,\qquad \frac{I_1 g}{\gamma l I_p} = \frac{I_1}{I_0} = m,\qquad \frac{I_2}{I_0} = n,\qquad(g)$$

where $I_0 = (\gamma l I_p/g)$ is the moment of inertia of the shaft about its axis, we obtain, from eq. (f) the frequency equation in the following form:

$$\beta n(1 - m\beta \tan \beta) = -(\tan \beta + m\beta),$$

or

$$\tan \beta = \frac{(m+n)\beta}{mn\beta^2 - 1}.\qquad(102)$$

Let

$$\beta_1, \beta_2, \beta_3, \cdots$$

be the consecutive roots of this transcendental equation, then the corresponding normal functions from (d) and (e) will be

$$X_i = C_i \left(\cos \frac{\beta_i x}{l} - m\beta_i \sin \frac{\beta_i x}{l} \right),$$

and we obtain for the general solution in this case

$$\theta = \sum_{i=1}^{i=\infty} \left(\cos \frac{\beta_i x}{l} - m\beta_i \sin \frac{\beta \cdot x}{l} \right) \left(A_i \cos \frac{\beta_i at}{l} + B_i \sin \frac{\beta_i at}{l} \right). \quad (103)$$

If the moments of inertia I_1 and I_2 of the discs are small in comparison with the moment of inertia I_0 of the shaft, the quantities m and n in eq. (102) become small, the consecutive roots of this equation will approach the values $\pi, 2\pi, \cdots$ and the general solution (103) approaches the solution (101) given above for a shaft with free ends.

Consider now another extreme case, more interesting from a practical standpoint, when I_1 and I_2 are large in comparison with I_0; the quantities m and n will then be large numbers. In this case unity can be neglected in comparison with $mn\beta^2$ in the denominator on the right side of eq. (102) and, instead of eq. (102), we obtain

$$\beta \tan \beta = (1/m + 1/n). \quad (104)$$

This equation is of the same form as eq. (94) (see p. 313) for longitudinal vibrations. The right side of this equation is a small quantity and an approximate solution for the first root will be obtained by substituting $\tan \beta_1 = \beta_1$. Then

$$\beta_1 = \sqrt{1/m + 1/n}. \quad (h)$$

The period of the corresponding mode of vibration, from eq. (103), will be

$$\tau_1 = 2\pi : \frac{\beta_1 a}{l} = \frac{2\pi l}{\beta_1 a},$$

or, by using eqs. (99), (g) and (h), we obtain

$$\tau_1 = 2\pi \sqrt{\frac{l I_1 I_2}{G I_p (I_1 + I_2)}}. \quad (105)$$

This result coincides with eq. (12) (see p. 13) obtained by considering the system as having one degree of freedom and neglecting the mass of the shaft.

The approximate values of the consecutive roots of eq. (104) will be,

$$\beta_2 = \pi + 1/\pi(1/m + 1/n), \quad \beta_3 = 2\pi + 1/2\pi(1/m + 1/n), \cdots.$$

It is seen that all these roots are large in comparison with β_1, and the frequencies of the corresponding modes of vibration will be very high in comparison with the frequency of fundamental type of vibration.

In order to get a closer approximation for the first root of eq. (102), we substitute $\tan \beta_1 = \beta_1 + \beta_1{}^3/3$, then

$$\beta_1 + \frac{1}{3}\beta_1{}^3 = \frac{\beta_1(m + n)}{mn\beta_1{}^2 - 1}$$

or

$$\beta_1{}^2 = \frac{m + n}{\left(mn - \dfrac{1}{\beta_1{}^2}\right)\left(1 + \dfrac{1}{3}\beta_1{}^2\right)}.$$

Substituting in the right-hand side of this equation the value of β_1 from eq. (h) and neglecting small quantities of higher order, we obtain

$$\beta_1 = \sqrt{\frac{1}{m} + \frac{1}{n} - \frac{1}{3}\left(\frac{1}{n^2} + \frac{1}{m^2} - \frac{1}{mn}\right)},$$

and the corresponding frequency of the fundamental vibration will be

$$f_1 = \frac{\beta_1 a}{2\pi l} = \frac{a}{2\pi l}\sqrt{\frac{1}{m} + \frac{1}{n} - \frac{1}{3}\left(\frac{1}{n^2} + \frac{1}{m^2} - \frac{1}{mn}\right)}. \tag{106}$$

The same result will be obtained if in the first approximation for the frequency

$$f = \frac{1}{2\pi}\sqrt{\frac{GI_p(I_1 + I_2)}{lI_1I_2}},$$

as obtained from eq. (105), we substitute

$$I_1 + \frac{1}{3}I_0\frac{I_2}{I_1 + I_2} \quad \text{and} \quad I_2 + \frac{1}{3}I_0\frac{I_1}{I_1 + I_2} \quad \text{for } I_1 \text{ and } I_2.$$

This means that the second approximation (106) coincides with the result which would have been obtained by the Rayleigh method (see Art. 4,

p. 24). According to this method one third of the moment of inertia of the part of the shaft between the disc and the nodal cross section should be added to the moment of inertia of each disc. This approximation is always sufficient in practical applications for calculating the frequency of the fundamental mode of vibration.*

Forced Vibration.—In investigating the forced vibrations of a shaft with two discs, we proceed in the same way as we did in investigating longitudinal vibrations (Art. 48). The general expression for the angle of twist θ we take in the form

$$\theta = \sum_{i=1,2,3,\cdots} \phi_i \left(\cos \frac{\beta_i x}{l} - m\beta_i \sin \frac{\beta_i x}{l} \right), \tag{107}$$

in which the expressions in the parenthesis are the normal functions for our case and $\phi_1, \phi_2, \cdots$ are functions of time. To obtain the differential equation for a function ϕ_i, we use d'Alembert's principle together with the principle of virtual work. Taking a virtual displacement in the form

$$\delta\theta = A_i \left(\cos \frac{\beta_i x}{l} - m\beta_i \sin \frac{\beta_i x}{l} \right),$$

and assuming that a disturbing torque M is acting at the end $x = l$, we find that the virtual work of this torque is

$$MA_i(\cos \beta_i - m\beta_i \sin \beta_i),$$

and we obtain for ϕ_i the equation

$$\ddot{\phi}_i + \frac{a^2 \beta_i^2}{l^2} \phi_i = \frac{4\beta_i}{I_0 N_i} M(\cos \beta_i - m\beta_i \sin \beta_i), \tag{108}$$

in which

$$N_i = 2\beta_i(1 + m^2\beta_i^2) - \sin 2\beta_i + m^2\beta_i^2 \sin 2\beta_i + 2\beta_i m(1 - \cos 2\beta_i). \tag{109}$$

Considering only the vibration produced by the disturbing torque M, we obtain, from eq. (108)

$$\phi_i = \frac{4l}{aI_0 N_i} \int_0^t M(\cos \beta_i - m\beta_i \sin \beta_i) \sin \left[\frac{a\beta_i}{l} (t - t_1) \right] dt_1. \tag{110}$$

Substituting this expression into the series (107), the general expression for the vibrations produced by the disturbing torque M is obtained. It remains only in each particular case to substitute for M the corresponding function of time and to calculate the integrals shown in eq. (110).

---

* A graphical method for determining the natural frequencies of torsional vibration of shafts with discs has been developed by F. M. Lewis, see papers: "Torsional Vibrations of Irregular Shafts," *J. Am. Soc. Nav. Engrs.*, p. 857, Nov. 1919; and "Critical Speeds of Torsional Vibration," *J. Soc. Automotive Engrs.*, p. 413, Nov. 1920.

51. Free Lateral Vibration of Prismatical Bars.—*Differential Equation of Lateral Vibration.*—Assuming that the bar has a plane of symmetry and that vibrations occur in that plane, the known differential equation of the deflection curve (Fig. 203)

$$EI \frac{d^2y}{dx^2} = -M \tag{111}$$

will now be used, in which

EI is flexural rigidity and

M is bending moment at any cross section. The direction of the axes and the positive directions of bending moments and shearing forces Q are as shown in Fig. 203.

Differentiating eq. (111) twice we obtain

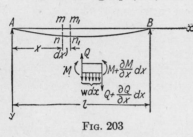

$$\left.\begin{aligned}\frac{d}{dx}\left(EI \frac{d^2y}{dx^2}\right) &= -\frac{dM}{dx} = -Q, \\ \frac{d^2}{dx^2}\left(EI \frac{d^2y}{dx^2}\right) &= -\frac{dQ}{dx} = w.\end{aligned}\right\} \tag{a}$$

Fig. 203

This last equation representing the differential equation of a bar subjected to a continuous load of intensity w can be used also for obtaining the equation of lateral vibration. It is only necessary to apply d'Alembert's principle and to imagine that the vibrating bar is loaded by inertia forces, the intensity of which varies along the length of the bar and is given by

$$-\frac{\gamma A}{g} \frac{\partial^2 y}{\partial t^2}, \tag{b}$$

where γ is the weight of material of the bar per unit volume and A is the cross-sectional area.

Substituting (b) for w in eq. (a) the general equation for the lateral vibration of the bar becomes *

$$\frac{\partial^2}{\partial x^2}\left(EI \frac{\partial^2 y}{\partial x^2}\right) = -\frac{\gamma A}{g} \frac{\partial^2 y}{\partial t^2}. \tag{112}$$

---

* The differential equation in which damping is taken into consideration has been discussed by H. Holzer, *Z. angew. Math. u. Mech.*, Vol. 8, p. 272, 1928. See also K. Sezawa, *ibid.*, Vol. 12, p. 275, 1932.

In the particular case of a prismatical bar the flexural rigidity EI remains constant along the length of the bar and we obtain from eq. (112)

$$EI \frac{\partial^4 y}{\partial x^4} = -\frac{\gamma A}{g} \frac{\partial^2 y}{\partial t^2}$$

or

$$\frac{\partial^2 y}{\partial t^2} + a^2 \frac{\partial^4 y}{\partial x^4} = 0, \tag{113}$$

in which

$$a^2 = \frac{EIg}{A\gamma}. \tag{114}$$

We begin with studying the *normal modes* of vibration. When a bar performs a normal mode of vibration the deflection at any location varies harmonically with the time and can be represented as follows:

$$y = X(A \cos pt + B \sin pt), \tag{c}$$

where X is a function of the coordinate x defining the shape of the normal mode of vibration under consideration, i.e., *normal function*. Substituting (c) in eq. (113), we obtain

$$\frac{d^4 X}{dx^4} = \frac{p^2}{a^2} X, \tag{115}$$

from which the normal functions for any particular case can be obtained.

By using the notation

$$\frac{p^2}{a^2} = \frac{p^2 A\gamma}{EIg} = k^4, \tag{116}$$

it can be easily verified that $\sin kx$, $\cos kx$, $\sinh kx$ and $\cosh kx$ will be particular solutions of eq. (115) and the general solution of this equation will be obtained in the form,

$$X = C_1 \sin kx + C_2 \cos kx + C_3 \sinh kx + C_4 \cosh kx, \tag{117}$$

in which $C_1, \cdots C_4$ are constants which should be determined in each particular case from the conditions at the ends of the bar. At an end which is simply supported, i.e., where the deflection and bending moment are equal to zero, we have,

$$X = 0, \quad \frac{d^2 X}{dx^2} = 0. \tag{d}$$

At a built-in end, i.e., where the deflection and slope of the deflection curve are equal to zero, we have

$$X = 0, \quad \frac{dX}{dx} = 0. \qquad (e)$$

At a free end the bending moment and the shearing force both vanish and we obtain

$$\frac{d^2X}{dx^2} = 0, \quad \frac{d^3X}{dx^3} = 0. \qquad (f)$$

For the two ends of a vibrating bar we always will have four end conditions from which the ratios between the constants of the general solution (117) and the *frequency equation* can be obtained. In this manner the modes of natural vibration and their frequencies will be established. By superimposing all possible normal vibrations (c), the general expression for the free lateral vibrations becomes:

$$y = \sum_{i=1}^{i=\infty} X_i(A_i \cos p_i t + B_i \sin p_i t) \cdots. \qquad (118)$$

Applications of this general theory to particular cases will be considered later.

For our further study of the lateral vibration of prismatical bars, it will be advantageous at this point to consider some general properties of normal functions.

Let X_m and X_n be two normal functions corresponding to normal modes of vibration of the order m and n, having frequencies $p_m/2\pi$ and $p_n/2\pi$. Substituting in eq. (115), we obtain

$$\left.\begin{aligned} \frac{d^4X_m}{dx^4} &= \frac{p_m{}^2}{a^2} X_m, \\[2mm] \frac{d^4X_n}{dx^4} &= \frac{p_n{}^2}{a^2} X_n. \end{aligned}\right\} \qquad (119)$$

Multiplying the first of these equations with X_n and the second with X_m, subtracting one from another and integrating, we have

$$\frac{p_n{}^2 - p_m{}^2}{a^2} \int_0^l X_m X_n \, dx = \int_0^l \left(X_m \frac{d^4X_n}{dx^4} - X_n \frac{d^4X_m}{dx^4} \right) dx, \qquad (120)$$

from which, integrating by parts, follows

$$\frac{p_n{}^2 - p_m{}^2}{a^2} \int_0^l X_m X_n \, dx$$

$$= \left| X_m \frac{d^3 X_n}{dx^3} - X_n \frac{d^3 X_m}{dx^3} + \frac{dX_n}{dx} \frac{d^2 X_m}{dx^2} - \frac{dX_m}{dx} \frac{d^2 X_n}{dx^2} \right|_0^l \cdots . \quad (121)$$

From the end conditions (d), (e) and (f) it can be concluded that in all cases the right side of the above equation is equal to zero, hence,

$$\int_0^l X_m X_n \, dx = 0 \quad \text{when} \quad m \neq n. \quad (122)$$

This is the *condition of orthogonality* of the normal functions. We encountered already this condition in the case of systems with several degrees of freedom (see p. 236) and also in the case of longitudinal vibration of bars (see p. 297). Due to this property, free vibrations, produced by any initial conditions, can be readily resolved into a series of natural vibrations and the analysis of forced vibrations is reduced to the solution of the same differential equation which we have in discussing vibration of systems with one degree of freedom.

Eq. (121) can be used also for the calculation of integrals such as

$$\int_0^l X_m{}^2 \, dx \quad \text{and} \quad \int_0^l \left(\frac{d^2 X_m}{dx^2} \right)^2 dx, \quad (g)$$

which we will need in our further study of lateral vibrations.

It is easy to see that by directly substituting $m = n$ into this equation, the necessary results cannot be obtained because both sides of the equation become equal to zero. Therefore the following procedure should be adopted for calculating the integrals (g). Substitute for X_n in eq. (121) a function which is very near to the function X_m and which will be obtained from eqs. (115) and (116) by giving to the quantity k an infinitely small increment δk, so that X_n approaches X_m when δk approaches zero. Then

$$\frac{p_n{}^2}{a^2} = (k + \delta k)^4 = k^4 + 4k^3 \, \delta k,$$

$$\frac{p_n{}^2 - p_m{}^2}{a^2} = 4k^3 \, \delta k,$$

$$X_n = X_m + \frac{dX_m}{dk} \, \delta k.$$

Substituting in eq. (121) and neglecting small quantities of higher order, we obtain

$$4k^3 \int_0^l X_m{}^2 \, dx =$$

$$\left| X_m \frac{d}{dk} \frac{d^3 X_m}{dx^3} - \frac{dX_m}{dk} \frac{d^3 X_m}{dx^3} + \frac{d}{dk}\left(\frac{dX_m}{dx}\right)\frac{d^2 X_m}{dx^2} - \frac{dX_m}{dx}\frac{d}{dk}\left(\frac{d^2 X_m}{dx^2}\right) \right|_0^l. \quad (h)$$

In the following we denote by X', X'', $\cdots$ consecutive derivatives of X with respect to kx, then

$$\frac{dX_m}{dx} = kX_m', \quad \frac{dX_m}{dk} = xX_m'.$$

With these notations eq. (115) becomes

$$X'''' = X,$$

and eq. (h) will have the following form:

$$4k^3 \int_0^l X_m{}^2 \, dx = |\, 3X_m k^2 X_m''' + k^3 x X_m{}^2 - k^3 x X_m' X_m{}'{}^,{}'$$
$$+ k^2 X_m''(X_m' + kx X_m'') - k X_m'(2k X_m'' + k^2 x X_m''') \,|_0^l$$

or

$$4k \int_0^l X_m{}^2 \, dx =$$

$$|\, 3X_m X_m''' + kx X_m{}^2 - 2kx X_m' X_m''' - X_m' X_m'' + kx(X_m'')^2 \,|_0^l. \quad (i)$$

From the end conditions (d), (e) and (f) it can be seen that the terms in eq. (i) containing the products $X_m X_m'''$ and $X_m' X_m''$ are equal to zero for any manner of fastening the ends, hence

$$\int_0^l X_m{}^2 \, dx = \tfrac{1}{4} |\, x\{X_m{}^2 - 2X_m' X_m''' + (X_m'')^2\} \,|_0^l$$

$$= \frac{l}{4} \{X_m{}^2 - 2X_m' X_m''' + (X_m'')^2\}_{x=l}. \quad (123)$$

From this equation the first of the integrals (g) can easily be calculated for any kind of fastening of the ends of the bar. If the right end ($x = l$) of the bar is free,

$$(X_m'')_{x=l} = 0, \quad (X_m''')_{x=l} = 0,$$

and we obtain, from (123),

$$\int_0^l X_m{}^2 \, dx = \frac{l}{4} (X_m{}^2)_{x=l}. \tag{124}$$

If the same end is built in, we obtain

$$\int_0^l X_m{}^2 \, dx = \frac{l}{4} (X_m{}'')^2_{x=l}. \tag{125}$$

For the hinged end we obtain

$$\int_0^l X_m{}^2 \, dx = -\frac{l}{2} (X_m{}'X_m{}''')_{x=l}. \tag{126}$$

In calculating the second of the integrals (g), eq. (115) should be used. Multiplying this equation by X and integrating along the length of the bar,

$$\frac{p^2}{a^2} \int_0^l X^2 \, dx = \int_0^l \frac{d^4X}{dx^4} X \, dx.$$

Integrating the right side of this equation by parts, we obtain

$$\int_0^l \left(\frac{d^2X}{dx^2}\right)^2 dx = \frac{p^2}{a^2} \int_0^l X^2 \, dx. \tag{127}$$

This result together with eq. (123) gives us the second of the integrals (g). Eqs. (123) and (127) are very useful in investigating forced vibrations of bars with other end conditions than hinged ones.

Effect of Shearing Force and Rotatory Inertia.—In the previous discussion the cross-sectional dimensions of the bar were considered to be small in comparison with the length and the simple eq. (111) was used for the deflection curve. Corrections will now be given, taking into account the effect of the cross-sectional dimensions on the frequency. These corrections may be of considerable importance in studying the modes of vibration of higher frequencies when a vibrating bar is subdivided by *nodal cross sections* into comparatively short portions.

*Rotatory Inertia.**—It is easy to see that during vibration the elements of the bar such as mnm_1n_1 (see Fig. 203) perform not only a translatory motion but also rotate. The variable angle of rotation which is equal to the slope of the deflection curve will be expressed by $\partial y/\partial x$ and the corresponding angular velocity and angular acceleration will be given by

$$\frac{\partial^2 y}{\partial x \partial t} \quad \text{and} \quad \frac{d^3y}{\partial x \partial t^2}.$$

* See Lord Rayleigh, paragraph 186, *loc. cit.*

Therefore the moment of the inertia forces of the element mnm_1n_1 about the axis through its center of gravity and perpendicular to the xy-plane will be *

$$- \frac{I\gamma}{g} \frac{\partial^3 y}{\partial x \partial t^2} dx.$$

This moment should be taken into account in considering the variation in bending moment along the axis of the bar. Then, instead of the first of the eqs. (a), p. 324, we will have

$$\frac{dM}{dx} = Q - \frac{I\gamma}{g} \frac{\partial^3 y}{\partial x \partial t^2}. \tag{j}$$

Substituting this value of dM/dx in the equation for the deflection curve

$$EI \frac{d^4 y}{dx^4} = - \frac{d^2 M}{dx^2},$$

and using eq. (b), p. 324, we obtain

$$EI \frac{\partial^4 y}{\partial x^4} = - \frac{\gamma A}{g} \frac{\partial^2 y}{\partial t^2} + \frac{I\gamma}{g} \frac{\partial^4 y}{\partial x^2 \partial t^2}. \tag{128}$$

This is the differential equation for the lateral vibration of prismatical bars in which the second term on the right side represents the effect of rotatory inertia.

A still more accurate differential equation is obtained if not only the rotatory inertia, but also the deflection due to shear, will be taken into account.† The slope of the deflection curve depends not only on the rotation of cross sections of the bar but also on the shear. Let ψ denote the slope of the deflection curve when the shearing force is neglected and β the angle of shear at the neutral axis in the same cross section, then we find for the total slope

$$\frac{dy}{dx} = \psi + \beta.$$

From the elementary theory of bending we have for bending moment and shearing force the following equations:

$$M = -EI \frac{d\psi}{dx}, \quad Q = k'\beta AG = k' \left(\frac{dy}{dx} - \psi \right) AG, \tag{k}$$

in which k' is a numerical factor depending on the shape of the cross section, A is the cross-sectional area and G is modulus of elasticity in shear. The differential equation of rotation of an element mnm_1n_1 (Fig. 203) will be

$$- \frac{\partial M}{\partial x} dx + Q \, dx = \frac{I\gamma}{g} \frac{\partial^2 \psi}{\partial t^2} dx.$$

---

* The moment is taken positive when it is a clockwise direction.

† See writer's paper, *Phil. Mag.* Ser. 6, Vol. 41, p. 744, and Vol. 43, p. 125, 1921; and his book, *Theory of Elasticity* (Russian), Vol. 2, p. 206, 1916. An experimental verification of shear effect was made by E. Goens, *Ann. Physik*, Ser. 5, Vol. 11, p. 649, 1931; see also, R. M. Davies, *Phil. Mag.*, Ser. 7, Vol. 23, p. 1129, 1937. The need to consider shear deformation in the case of impact action on a beam was discussed by W. Flügge, *Z. angew. Math. u. Mech.*, Vol. 22, p. 312, 1942.

Substituting (k), we obtain

$$EI \frac{\partial^2 \psi}{\partial x^2} + k' \left(\frac{\partial y}{\partial x} - \psi \right) AG - \frac{I\gamma}{g} \frac{\partial^2 \psi}{\partial t^2} = 0. \tag{l}$$

The differential equation for the translatory motion of the same element in a vertical direction will be

$$\frac{\partial Q}{\partial x} dx = \frac{\gamma A}{g} \frac{\partial^2 y}{\partial t^2} dx,$$

or

$$\frac{\gamma A}{g} \frac{\partial^2 y}{\partial t^2} - k' \left(\frac{\partial^2 y}{\partial x^2} - \frac{\partial \psi}{\partial x} \right) AG = 0. \tag{m}$$

Eliminating ψ from eqs. (l) and (m), the following more complete differential equation for the lateral vibration of prismatical bars will be obtained:

$$EI \frac{\partial^4 y}{\partial x^4} + \frac{\gamma A}{g} \frac{\partial^2 y}{\partial t^2} - \left(\frac{\gamma I}{g} + \frac{EI\gamma}{gk'G} \right) \frac{\partial^4 y}{\partial x^2 \partial t^2} + \frac{\gamma I}{g} \frac{\gamma}{gk'G} \frac{\partial^4 y}{\partial t^4} = 0. \tag{129}$$

The application of this equation in calculating the frequencies will be shown in the following article.

52. Free Vibration of a Bar with Hinged Ends.—*General Solution.*—
In considering particular cases of vibration of bars it is useful to present the general solution (117) in the following form:

$$X = C_1(\cos kx + \cosh kx) + C_2(\cos kx - \cosh kx)$$

$$+ C_3(\sin kx + \sinh kx) + C_4(\sin kx - \sinh kx) \cdots. \tag{130}$$

In the case of hinged ends the end conditions are

$$\left.\begin{array}{ll} (1) \quad (X)_{x=0} = 0, & (2) \quad \left(\dfrac{d^2 X}{dx^2} \right)_{x=0} = 0, \\[3mm] (3) \quad (X)_{x=l} = 0, & (4) \quad \left(\dfrac{d^2 X}{dx^2} \right)_{x=l} = 0. \end{array}\right\} \tag{a}$$

From the first two conditions (a) it can be concluded that the constants C_1 and C_2 in solution (130) should be taken equal to zero. From conditions (3) and (4) we obtain $C_3 = C_4$ and

$$\sin kl = 0, \tag{131}$$

which is the *frequency equation* for the case under consideration. The consecutive roots of this equation are

$$kl = \pi, 2\pi, 3\pi \cdots. \tag{132}$$

The angular frequencies of the consecutive modes of vibration will be obtained from eq. (116):

$$p_1 = ak_1{}^2 = \frac{a\pi^2}{l^2}, \quad p_2 = \frac{4a\pi^2}{l^2}, \quad p_3 = \frac{9a\pi^2}{l^2}, \cdots, \tag{133}$$

and the frequency f_n of any mode of vibration will be found from the equation

$$f_n = \frac{p_n}{2\pi} = \frac{n^2 a\pi}{2l^2} = \frac{\pi n^2}{2l^2} \sqrt{\frac{EIg}{A\gamma}}. \tag{134}$$

The corresponding period of vibration will be

$$\tau_n = \frac{1}{f_n} = \frac{2l^2}{\pi n^2} \sqrt{\frac{A\gamma}{EIg}}. \tag{135}$$

It is seen that the period of vibration is proportional to the square of the length and inversely proportional to the radius of gyration of the cross section. For geometrically similar bars the periods of vibration increase in the same proportion as the linear dimensions.

In the case of rotating circular shafts of uniform cross section the frequencies calculated by eq. (134) represent the critical numbers of revolutions per second. When the speed of rotation of the shaft approaches one of the frequencies (134) a considerable lateral vibration of the shaft should be expected.

The shape of the deflection curve for the various modes of vibration is determined by the normal function (130). It was shown that in the case we are considering, $C_1 = C_2 = 0$ and $C_3 = C_4$, hence the normal function has a form

$$X = D \sin kx, \tag{b}$$

where D is a constant. Substituting for k its values, from eq. (132), we obtain

$$X_1 = D_1 \sin \frac{\pi x}{l}, \quad X_2 = D_2 \sin \frac{2\pi x}{l}, \quad X_3 = D_3 \sin \frac{3\pi x}{l}, \cdots.$$

It is seen that the deflection curve during vibration is a sine curve, the number of half waves in the consecutive modes of vibration being equal to 1, 2, 3 $\cdots$. By superimposing such sinusoidal vibrations any kind of free vibration due to any initial conditions can be represented. Substituting (b) in the general solution (118) we obtain

$$y = \sum_{i=1}^{i=\infty} \sin \frac{i\pi x}{l} (C_i \cos p_i t + D_i \sin p_i t). \tag{136}$$

The constants C_i, D_i, of this solution should be determined in every particular case so as to satisfy the initial conditions. Assume, for instance, that the initial deflections and initial velocities along the bar are given by the equations

$$(y)_{t=0} = f(x) \quad \text{and} \quad (\dot{y})_{t=0} = f_1(x).$$

Substituting $t = 0$ in expression (136) and in the derivative of this expression with respect to t, we obtain,

$$(y)_{t=0} = f(x) = \sum_{i=1}^{i=\infty} C_i \sin \frac{i\pi x}{l}, \tag{c}$$

$$(\dot{y})_{t=0} = f_1(x) = \sum_{i=1}^{i=\infty} p_i D_i \sin \frac{i\pi x}{l}. \tag{d}$$

Now the constants C_i and D_i can be calculated in the usual way by multiplying (c) and (d) by $\sin (i\pi x/l) \, dx$ and by integrating both sides of these equations from $x = 0$ to $x = l$. In this manner we obtain

$$C_i = \frac{2}{l} \int_0^l f(x) \sin \frac{i\pi x}{l} \, dx, \tag{e}$$

$$D_i = \frac{2}{l p_i} \int_0^l f_1(x) \sin \frac{i\pi x}{l} \, dx. \tag{f}$$

Assume, for example, that in the initial moment $t = 0$ the axis of the bar is straight and that due to impact an initial velocity v is given to a short portion δ of the bar at the distance c from the left support. Then, $f(x) = 0$ and $f_1(x)$ also is equal to zero at all points except the point $x = c$ for which $f_1(c) = v$. Substituting this into eqs. (e) and (f) we obtain,

$$C_i = 0, \quad D_i = \frac{2}{l p_i} v \delta \sin \frac{i\pi c}{l}.$$

Substituting in eq. (136)

$$y = \frac{2v\delta}{l} \sum_{i=1}^{i=\infty} \frac{1}{p_i} \sin \frac{i\pi c}{l} \sin \frac{i\pi x}{l} \sin p_i t. \tag{137}$$

If $c = (l/2)$, i.e., the impact is produced at the middle of the span, we obtain

$$y = \frac{2v\delta}{l}\left(\frac{1}{p_1}\sin\frac{\pi x}{l}\sin p_1 t - \frac{1}{p_3}\sin\frac{3\pi x}{l}\sin p_3 t + \frac{1}{p_5}\sin\frac{5\pi x}{l}\sin p_5 t - \cdots\right)$$

$$= \frac{2v\delta l}{a\pi^2}\left(\frac{1}{1}\sin\frac{\pi x}{l}\sin p_1 t - \frac{1}{9}\sin\frac{3\pi x}{l}\sin p_3 t + \frac{1}{25}\sin\frac{5\pi x}{l}\sin p_5 t - \cdots\right) \tag{g}$$

It is seen that in this case only modes of vibration symmetrical about the middle of the span will be produced and the amplitudes of consecutive modes of vibration entering in eq. (g) decrease as $1/i^2$.

Effect of Rotatory Inertia and of Shear.—In order to find the values of the frequencies more accurately eq. (129) instead of eq. (113) should be taken. Dividing eq. (129) by $A\gamma/g$ and using the notation

$$r^2 = \frac{I}{A}, \tag{h}$$

we obtain

$$a^2\frac{\partial^4 y}{\partial x^4} + \frac{\partial^2 y}{\partial t^2} - r^2\left(1 + \frac{E}{k'G}\right)\frac{\partial^4 y}{\partial x^2 \partial t^2} + r^2\frac{\gamma}{gk'G}\frac{\partial^4 y}{\partial t^4} = 0. \tag{138}$$

This equation and the end conditions will be satisfied by taking

$$y = C\sin\frac{m\pi x}{l}\cos p_m t. \tag{i}$$

Substituting in eq. (138) we obtain the following equation for calculating the frequencies:

$$a^2\frac{m^4\pi^4}{l^4} - p_m^2 - p_m^2\frac{m^2\pi^2 r^2}{l^2} - p_m^2\frac{m^2\pi^2 r^2}{l^2}\frac{E}{k'G} + \frac{r^2\gamma}{gk'G}p_m^4 = 0. \tag{139}$$

Considering only the first two terms in this equation, we have

$$p_m = a\frac{m^2\pi^2}{l^2} = \frac{a\pi^2}{\lambda^2}, \tag{j}$$

in which $\lambda = (l/m)$ is the length of the half waves in which the bar is subdivided during vibration.

This coincides with the result (133) obtained before. By taking the three first terms in eq. (139) and considering $\pi^2 r^2/\lambda^2$ as a small quantity, we obtain

$$p_m = \frac{a\pi^2}{\lambda^2}\left(1 - \frac{\pi^2 r^2}{2\lambda^2}\right). \tag{k}$$

In this manner the *effect of rotatory inertia* is taken into account and we see that this correction becomes more and more important with a decrease of λ, i.e., with an increase in the frequency of vibration.

In order to obtain the *effect of shear* all terms of eq. (139) should be taken into consideration. Substituting the first approximation (j) for p_m in the last term of this equation, it can be shown that this term is a small quantity of the second order as compared with the small quantity $\pi^2 r^2/\lambda^2$. Neglecting this term, we obtain

$$p_m = \frac{a\pi^2}{\lambda^2}\left\{1 - \frac{1}{2}\frac{\pi^2 r^2}{\lambda^2}\left(1 + \frac{E}{k'G}\right)\right\}. \tag{140}$$

Assuming $E = 8G/3$ and taking a bar of rectangular cross section for which $k' = 0.833,$* we have

$$\frac{E}{k'G} = 3.2.$$

The correction due to shear is 3.2 times larger than the correction due to rotatory inertia.†

Assuming that the wave length λ is ten times larger than the depth of the beam, we obtain

$$\frac{1}{2}\cdot\frac{\pi^2 r^2}{\lambda^2} = \frac{1}{2}\cdot\frac{\pi^2}{12}\cdot\frac{1}{100} = 0.004,$$

and the correction for rotatory inertia and shear together will be about 2%.

PROBLEMS

1. Find the frequencies of vibration of an I-beam with simply supported ends, vibrating in the plane of its maximum rigidity, if $l = 30$ ft, $E = 30\cdot10^6$ lb per sq in., $I = 3021$ in.^{4} and the weight per foot is 100 lb.

Answer. $f_i = 24.8i^2$ osc. per sec.

2. A simply supported beam is deflected by a force P applied at the middle. What vibrations of the beam will ensue if the load P is suddenly removed?

Answer. $y = \dfrac{2Pl^3}{\pi^4 EI}\displaystyle\sum_{i=1,3,5,\cdots}\frac{(-1)^{\frac{i-1}{2}}}{i^4}\cos p_i t \sin\frac{i\pi x}{l}.$

3. Solve the preceding problem, assuming that the force P is applied at the distance c from the end $(x = 0)$.

Answer. $y = \dfrac{2Pl^3}{\pi^4 EI}\displaystyle\sum_{i=1,2,3,\cdots}\frac{1}{i^4}\sin\frac{\pi c}{l}\cos p_i t \sin\frac{i\pi x}{l}.$

4. A simply supported beam carries a uniform load of intensity w. Find the vibrations which ensue when the load is suddenly removed.

Answer. $y = \dfrac{4wl^4}{\pi^5 EI}\displaystyle\sum_{i=1,3,5,\cdots}\frac{1}{i^5}\cos p_i t \sin\frac{i\pi x}{l}.$

* A somewhat different value for k' was suggested by R. G. Olsson, see *Z. angew. Math. u. Mech.*, Vol. 15, p. 245, 1935.

† Regarding the solution of eq. (138), see the paper by Roger A. Anderson, presented at the A.S.M.E. Semi-Annual Meeting, Los Angeles, Calif., June 29, 1953, and Julius Miklowitz, Navord Report 2049, September 1953, Underwater Ordnance Department.

5. Find vibrations of a simply supported beam to which a lateral velocity v is communicated, at $t = 0$, in all points except the ends.

Answer. $y = \dfrac{4v}{\pi} \displaystyle\sum_{i=1,3,5,\ldots} \dfrac{1}{ip_i} \sin p_i t \sin \dfrac{i\pi x}{l}.$

53. Free Vibration of Bars with Other End Conditions.—*Bar with Free Ends.*—In this case we have the following end conditions:

$$
\left.
\begin{array}{llll}
(1) & \left(\dfrac{d^2X}{dx^2}\right)_{x=0} = 0, & (2) & \left(\dfrac{d^3X}{dx^3}\right)_{x=0} = 0, \\[4mm]
(3) & \left(\dfrac{d^2X}{dx^2}\right)_{x=l} = 0, & (4) & \left(\dfrac{d^3X}{dx^3}\right)_{x=l} = 0.
\end{array}
\right\} \quad (a)
$$

In order to satisfy the conditions (1) and (2) we have to take in the general solution (130)

$$ C_2 = C_4 = 0, $$

so that

$$ X = C_1(\cos kx + \cosh kx) + C_3(\sin kx + \sinh kx). \qquad (b) $$

From the conditions (3) and (4) we then obtain

$$
\left.
\begin{array}{l}
C_1(-\cos kl + \cosh kl) + C_3(-\sin kl + \sinh kl) = 0, \\
C_1(\sin kl + \sinh kl) + C_3(-\cos kl + \cosh kl) = 0.
\end{array}
\right\} \quad (c)
$$

A solution for the constants C_1 and C_3, different from zero, can be obtained only in the case when the determinant of eqs. (c) is equal to zero. In this manner the following *frequency equation* is obtained:

$$ (-\cos kl + \cosh kl)^2 - (\sinh^2 kl - \sin^2 kl) = 0 $$

or, remembering that

$$ \cosh^2 kl - \sinh^2 kl = 1, $$

$$ \cos^2 kl + \sin^2 kl = 1, $$

we obtain

$$ \cos kl \cosh kl = 1. \qquad (141) $$

The first six consecutive roots of this equation are as follows:

k_1l	k_2l	k_3l	k_4l	k_5l	k_6l
0	4.730	7.853	10.996	14.137	17.279

Now the frequencies can be calculated by using eq. (116), which gives

$$f_1 = 0, \quad f_2 = \frac{p_2}{2\pi} = \frac{k_2{}^2 a}{2\pi}, \quad f_3 = \frac{p_3}{2\pi} = \frac{k_3{}^2 a}{2\pi}, \quad \cdots .$$

Substituting the consecutive roots of eq. (141) into eqs. (c), the ratios C_1/C_3 for the corresponding modes of vibration can be calculated and the shape of the deflection curve during vibration will then be obtained from eq. (b). In Fig. 204 the first three modes of vibration, corresponding to the frequencies f_2, f_3 and f_4 are shown. On these vibrations a displacement of the bar as a rigid body can be superimposed. This displacement corresponds to the root $k_1 l = 0$, for which $p = 0$, and the right-hand side of eq. (115) vanishes. Integrating eq. (115) and taking into consideration the end conditions (a), we obtain

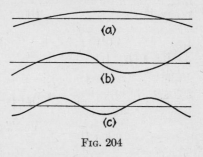

FIG. 204

$$X = a + bx,$$

which represents a translatory displacement together with rotation which can be superimposed on the free vibrations.

Bar with Built-in Ends.—The end conditions in this case are:

$$(1) \quad (X)_{x=0} = 0, \qquad (2) \quad \left(\frac{dX}{dx}\right)_{x=0} = 0,$$

$$(3) \quad (X)_{x=l} = 0, \qquad (4) \quad \left(\frac{dX}{dx}\right)_{x=l} = 0. \qquad\qquad (d)$$

The first two conditions will be satisfied if in the general solution (130) we take

$$C_1 = C_3 = 0.$$

From the two other conditions the following equations will be obtained:

$$C_2(\cos kl - \cosh kl) + C_4(\sin kl - \sinh kl) = 0,$$

$$C_2(\sin kl + \sinh kl) + C_4(-\cos kl + \cosh kl) = 0,$$

from which the same frequency eq. (141), as in the preceding case, can be

deduced. This means that the consecutive frequencies of vibration of a bar with built-in ends are the same as for the same bar with free ends.*
↳ *Bar with One End Built in, Other End Free.*—Assuming that the left end $(x = 0)$ is built in, the following end conditions will be obtained:

$$(1) \qquad (X)_{x=0} = 0, \qquad (2) \quad \left(\frac{dX}{dx}\right)_{x=0} = 0,$$

$$(3) \quad \left(\frac{d^2X}{dx^2}\right)_{x=l} = 0, \qquad (4) \quad \left(\frac{d^3X}{dx^3}\right)_{x=l} = 0.$$

From the first two conditions we conclude that $C_1 = C_3 = 0$ in the general solution (130). The remaining two conditions give us the following frequency equation:

$$\cos kl \cosh kl = -1.$$

The consecutive roots of this equation are as follows:

k_1l	k_2l	k_3l	k_4l	k_5l	k_6l
1.875	4.694	7.855	10.996	14.137	17.279

It is seen that with increasing frequency these roots approach the roots obtained above for a bar with free ends. The frequency of vibration of any mode will be

$$f_i = \frac{p_i}{2\pi} = \frac{ak_i^2}{2\pi}.$$

Taking, for instance, the fundamental mode of vibration, we obtain

$$f_1 = \frac{a}{2\pi}\left(\frac{1.875}{l}\right)^2.$$

The corresponding period of vibration will be:

$$\tau_1 = \frac{1}{f_1} = \frac{2\pi}{a}\frac{l^2}{1.875^2} = \frac{2\pi}{3.515}\sqrt{\frac{A\gamma l^4}{EIg}}.$$

This differs by less than 1.5% from the approximate solution obtained by using Rayleigh's method (see p. 28).

---

* From the end conditions and from eq. (115), it can be concluded that in this case there will be no motion corresponding to $k_1l = 0$.

Bar with One End Built in, Other End Supported.—In this case the frequency equation will be

$$\tan kl = \tanh kl.$$

The consecutive roots of this equation are:

k_1l	k_2l	k_3l	k_4l	k_5l
3.927	7.069	10.210	13.352	16.493

These roots are given with satisfactory accuracy by the formula

$$k_il = (i + \tfrac{1}{4})\pi.$$

For all end conditions which we have considered, the normal functions and their consecutive derivatives have been tabulated.* By using these tables, the solution of vibration problems of bars can be greatly simplified. We will use them later in discussing forced vibrations of beams.

Here we will show the application of the same tables in the analysis of statical deflections of beams.

Since, by superposition of normal modes of vibration, any shape of a vibrating beam can be obtained, we can use the normal functions also for representation of statical deflection curves of beams and take these curves in the form of the series †

$$y = a_1X_1 + a_2X_2 + a_3X_3 + \cdots, \tag{e}$$

in which X_1, X_2, $\cdots$ are the normal functions, corresponding to the given end conditions, and the constants a_1, a_2, $\cdots$ are to be determined from the consideration of the strain energy of bending, V. Observing (see p. 327) that

$$\int_0^l X_mX_n \, dx = 0 \quad \text{and} \quad \int_0^l \left(\frac{d^2X}{dx^2}\right)^2 dx = \frac{p^2}{a^2}\int_0^l X^2 \, dx,$$

we find

$$V = \frac{EI}{2}\int_0^l \left(\frac{d^2y}{dx^2}\right)^2 dx = \frac{EI}{2}\sum_{i=1,2,3,\cdots} a_i^2 \int_0^l \left(\frac{d^2X_i}{dx^2}\right)^2 dx$$

$$= \frac{EI}{2}\sum_{i=1,2,3,\cdots} k_i^4 a_i^2 \int_0^l X_i^2 \, dx. \tag{f}$$

* The tables were prepared by Dana Young and R. P. Felgar, *Univ. Texas Publ.*, No. 4913, 1949.

† For the development of the method see the writer's paper in Bulletin Kiev Polytechnical Institute. 1909.

The constants a_1, a_2, $\cdots$ can now be determined by using the principle of virtual work, which states that for any virtual displacement, $\delta a_i X_i$, the work done by the external forces must be equal to the increment of the strain energy. Take as a simple example the case of a beam with built-in ends bent by a load P applied at the middle. The normal functions in this case, from eqs. (b) and (c), are

$$X_i = \cosh k_i x - \cos k_i x - \alpha_i (\sinh k_i x - \sin k_i x), \qquad (g)$$

where $\alpha_1 = 0.9825$, $\alpha_2 = 1.0008$, $\alpha_3 \approx 1$, $\alpha_4 \approx 1$, $\cdots$. The equation of virtual work for a load P, applied at the middle, is

$$P\delta a_i (X_i)_{x=l/2} = \frac{\partial V}{\partial a_i} \delta a_i = EI k_i^4 a_i \delta a_i \int_0^l (X_i)^2 \, dx, \qquad (h)$$

and we obtain

$$a_i = \frac{P(X_i)_{x=l/2}}{EI k_i^4 \displaystyle\int_0^l (X_i)^2 \, dx}. \qquad (i)$$

It is seen from this equation that the deflection given by the series (e), will not change if we multiply the functions X_i by some factors. In the above-mentioned tables, the factors are selected so that

$$\int_0^l (X_i)^2 \, dx = l.$$

Then,

$$a_i = \frac{Pl^3 (X_i)_{x=l/2}}{EI (k_i l)^4}.$$

Substituting into the series (e) we obtain

$$y = \frac{Pl^3}{EI} \sum_{i=1,2,3,\cdots} \frac{(X_i)_{x=l/2}}{(k_i l)^4} \cdot X_i.$$

For the deflection at the center, we obtain then

$$(y)_{x=l/2} = \frac{Pl^3}{EI} \sum_{i=1,2,3,\cdots} \frac{(X_i^2)_{x=l/2}}{(k_i l)^4}.$$

Using now for the values of the normal functions the above-mentioned table and for $k_i l$ the table on p. 336, we obtain

$$(y)_{x=l/2} = \frac{Pl^3}{EI} \left(\frac{(1.588)^2}{(4.730)^4} + \frac{(1.406)^2}{(10.996)^4} + \frac{(1.415)^2}{(17.279)^4} + \cdots \right)$$

$$= \frac{Pl^3}{EI} (5037 \cdot 10^{-6} + 135 \cdot 10^{-6} + 23 \cdot 10^{-6} + \cdots)$$

$$= 5195 \cdot 10^{-6} \frac{Pl^3}{EI}. \tag{j}$$

Comparing this result with the exact solution

$$Pl^3/192EI = 5208 \cdot 10^{-6} Pl^3/EI,$$

we conclude that the first term of the series (j) gives us the deflection with an error of about 3.6% and the first two terms give already an accuracy higher than 1%, so that it is not necessary to calculate many terms in the series (e) to obtain deflections with an accuracy satisfactory for practical applications.

PROBLEMS

1. Find the normal functions for a bar with one end built in and the other hinged and make the deflection curves for the first and the second mode of vibration.
Answer. The expression for the normal functions (from eqs. (b) and (c), p. 336) is

$$X_i = \cosh k_i x - \cos k_i x - \alpha_i (\sinh k_i x - \sin k_i x).$$

Using the roots of the frequency equation on p. 339, we find

$$k_1 l = 4.730, \quad k_2 l = 7.853, \quad \alpha_1 = 1.00078, \quad \alpha_2 = 1.00000.$$

With these numerical values the required curves can be constructed.

2. Solve the preceding problem assuming that the end $x = 0$ of the bar is built in and the end $x = l$ is free.
Answer. The normal function in this case is

$$X_i = \cosh k_i x - \cos k_i x - \alpha_i (\sinh \beta_i x - \sin \beta_i x).$$

Using the table on p. 338, we obtain

$$k_1 l = 1.875, \quad k_2 l = 4.694, \quad \alpha_1 = 0.734, \quad \alpha_2 = 1.018.$$

3. Find the expression for free vibrations of a bar with built-in ends if initially the bar is bent by a concentrated force P applied at a distance c from the end $x = 0$ and at the instant $t = 0$ this force is suddenly removed.

Answer. The coefficients a_i in the series (e) are given now by the formula

$$a_i = \frac{Pl^3(X_i)_{x=c}}{EI(k_il)^4},$$

and the expression for vibrations is

$$y = \frac{Pl^3}{EI} \sum_{i=1,2,3,\cdots} \frac{(X_i)_{x=c}}{(k_il)^4} X_i \cos p_it.$$

4. Solve the preceding problem for a beam one end of which is built in and the other free. Initial deflection is produced by a load P applied at the free end.

54. Free Vibration of a Beam on Many Supports.*—Consider the case of a continuous beam with n spans simply supported at the ends and at $(n - 1)$ intermediate supports. Let $l_1, l_2, \cdots, l_n$ be the lengths of consecutive spans, the flexural rigidity of the beam being the same for all spans. Taking the origin of coordinates at the left end of each span, solution (117) p. 325 will be used for the shape of the deflection curve of each span during vibration. Considering span r and observing that the deflection at the left end ($x = 0$) is equal to zero, the normal function for the span r will be

$$X_r = a_r(\cos kx - \cosh kx) + c_r \sin kx + d_r \sinh kx, \qquad (a)$$

in which a_r, c_r and d_r are constants to be determined from the conditions at the ends of the span. The consecutive derivatives of (a) will be

$$X_r' = -a_rk(\sin kx + \sinh kx) + c_rk \cos kx + d_rk \cosh kx, \qquad (b)$$

$$X_r'' = -a_rk^2(\cos kx + \cosh kx) - c_rk^2 \sin kx + d_rk^2 \sinh kx. \qquad (c)$$

Substituting $x = 0$ in eqs. (b) and (c) we obtain

$$(X_r')_{x=0} = k(c_r + d_r), \quad (X_r'')_{x=0} = -2k^2a_r.$$

It is seen that $c_r + d_r$ is proportional to the slope of the deflection curve, and a_r is proportional to the bending moment at the support r. From the conditions at the simply supported ends of the beam it can now be concluded that $a_1 = a_{n+1} = 0$.

---

* See E. R. Darnley, *Phil. Mag.*, Vol. 41, p. 81, 1921. See also D. M. Smith, *Engineering*, Vol. 120, p. 808, 1925; K. Hohenemser and W. Prager, *Dynamik der Stabwerke*, Berlin, p. 127, 1933; K. Federhofer, *Bautechnik*, Vol. 11, p. 647, 1933; F. Stüssi, *Schweiz. Bauzeitung*, Vol. 104, p. 189, 1934; and W Mudrak, *Ing.-Arch.*, Vol. 7, p. 51, 1936.

Considering the conditions at the right end of the span r we have,

$$(X_r)_{x=l_r} = 0, \quad (X_r')_{x=l_r} = (X'_{r+1})_{x=0}, \quad (X_r'')_{x=l_r} = (X''_{r+1})_{x=0},$$

or by using eqs. (a), (b) and (c),

$$a_r(\cos kl_r - \cosh kl_r) + c_r \sin kl_r + d_r \sinh kl_r = 0, \qquad (d)$$

$$-a_r(\sin kl_r + \sinh kl_r) + c_r \cos kl_r + d_r \cosh kl_r = c_{r+1} + d_{r+1}, \quad (e)$$

$$a_r(\cos kl_r + \cosh kl_r) + c_r \sin kl_r - d_r \sinh kl_r = 2a_{r+1}. \qquad (f)$$

Adding and subtracting (d) and (f) we obtain

$$a_r \cos kl_r + c_r \sin kl_r = a_r; \quad \cosh kl_r - d_r \sinh kl_r = a_{r+1},$$

from which, provided $\sin kl_r$ is not zero,

$$c_r = \frac{a_{r+1} - a_r \cos kl_r}{\sin kl_r}, \quad d_r = \frac{-a_{r+1} + a_r \cosh kl_r}{\sinh kl_r} \qquad (g)$$

and

$$c_r + d_r = a_r (\coth kl_r - \cot kl_r) - a_{r+1}(\operatorname{cosech} kl_r - \operatorname{cosec} kl_r). \quad (h)$$

Using the notations:

$$\left. \begin{aligned} \coth kl_r - \cot kl_r &= \varphi_r, \\ \operatorname{cosech} kl_r - \operatorname{cosec} kl_r &= \psi_r, \end{aligned} \right\} \qquad (i)$$

we obtain

$$c_r + d_r = a_r \varphi_r - a_{r+1}\psi_r.$$

In the same manner for the span $r + 1$,

$$c_{r+1} + d_{r+1} = a_{r+1}\varphi_{r+1} - a_{r+2}\,\psi_{r+1}. \qquad (j)$$

Substituting (g) and (j) in eq. (e), we obtain

$$a_r\psi_r - a_{r+1}(\varphi_r + \varphi_{r+1}) + a_{r+2}\,\psi_{r+1} = 0. \qquad (k)$$

Writing an analogous equation for each intermediate support, the following system of $(n - 1)$ equations will be obtained:

$$\left. \begin{aligned} -a_2(\varphi_1 + \varphi_2) + a_3\psi_2 &= 0, \\ a_2\psi_2 - a_3(\varphi_2 + \varphi_3) + a_4\psi_3 &= 0, \\ \cdots \cdots \cdots \cdots \cdots \cdots & \\ \cdots \cdots \cdots \cdots \cdots \cdots & \\ a_{n-1}\psi_{n-1} - a_n(\varphi_{n-1} + \varphi_n) &= 0. \end{aligned} \right\} \qquad (l)$$

Proceeding as before and putting equal to zero the determinant of these equations, the frequency equation for the vibration of continuous beams will be obtained.

Take, for example, a bar on three supports, then only one equation of the system (l) remains and the *frequency equation* will be

$$\varphi_1 + \varphi_2 = 0$$

or

$$\varphi_1 = -\varphi_2. \qquad (m)$$

The frequencies of the consecutive modes of vibration will be obtained from the condition,

$$\varphi(kl_1) = -\varphi(kl_2).$$

In the solution of this transcendental equation it is convenient to draw a graph of the functions φ and $-\varphi$. In Fig. 205 φ and $-\varphi$ are given as functions of the argument kl expressed in degrees. The problem then re-

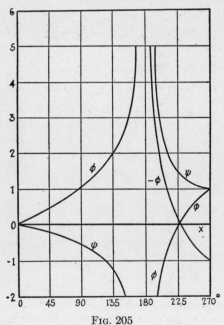

FIG. 205

duces to finding by trial and error a line parallel to the x-axis which cuts the graphs of φ and $-\varphi$ in points whose abscissas are in the ratio of the lengths of the spans.

Taking, for example, $l_1 : l_2 = 6 : 4.5$, we obtain for the smallest root

$$kl_1 = 3.416,$$

from which the frequency of the fundamental mode of vibration becomes

$$f_1 = \frac{k_1{}^2 a}{2\pi} = \frac{3.416^2}{2\pi l_1{}^2} \sqrt{\frac{EIg}{A\gamma}}.$$

For the next higher frequency we obtain

$$kl_1 = 4.787.$$

The third frequency is given approximately by $kl_1 = 6.690$ so that the consecutive frequencies are in the ratio $1 : 1.96 : 3.82$.

If the lengths of the spans tend to become equal it is seen from Fig. 205 that the smallest root tends to $kl_1 = kl_2 = \pi$. In the case of the fundamental type of vibration each span will be in the condition of a bar with hinged ends. Another type of vibration will be obtained by assuming the tangent at the intermediate support to be horzontal, then each span will be in the condition of a bar with one end built in and another simply supported.

In the case of three spans we obtain, from eqs. (*l*),

$$-a_2(\varphi_1 + \varphi_2) + a_3\psi_2 = 0,$$

$$a_2\psi_2 - a_3(\varphi_2 + \varphi_3) = 0,$$

and the frequency equation becomes

$$(\varphi_1 + \varphi_2)(\varphi_2 + \varphi_3) - \psi_2{}^2 = 0. \qquad (n)$$

Having tables of the functions φ and ψ,* the frequency of the fundamental mode can be found, from eq. (*n*), by a process of trial and error.

The method developed here for calculating frequencies of vibration of continuous beams can be applied in investigating vibration of frames. If lateral motion of the frame is eliminated by some constraint (Fig. 206), the vibration of the system will be the same as that of a three-span continuous beam and the above discussed theory can be applied. If the frame can move laterally the continuous beam theory cannot be directly applied and additional considerations are required.† The fundamental mode of vibration can be approximately investigated by using Rayleigh's method.‡

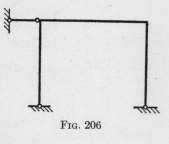

Fig. 206

55. Forced Vibration of a Beam with Supported Ends.—*General.*—In discussing forced lateral vibration of bars, we will use the same method as was applied in the case of longitudinal vibration. We assume that lateral

---

* Such tables are given by E. R. Darnley, *loc. cit.*, p. 342. Another method by using nomographic solution is given in a paper by D. M. Smith, *loc. cit.*, p. 342, in which the application of this problem to the vibration of condenser tubes is shown. The use of the *admittance method* in finding frequencies of vibration of continuous beams was developed by W. J. Duncan, *Phil. Mag.*, ser. 7, Vol. 34, p. 49, 1943. The frequencies of vibration of continuous beams with spans of equal length are discussed by R. S. Ayre and L. S. Jacobsen, *J. Appl. Mech.*, Vol. 17, p. 391, 1950.

† See W. Prager and S. Gradstein, *Ing.-Arch.*, Vol. 2, p. 622, 1932.

‡ See T. Pöschl, *ibid.*, Vol. 1, p. 469, 1930.

vibrations produced by external disturbing forces are represented by a series

$$y = \phi_1 X_1 + \phi_2 X_2 + \phi_3 X_3 + \cdots, \qquad (a)$$

in which $X_1, X_2, \cdots$ are the normal functions, corresponding to the end conditions of the vibrating bar, and $\phi_1, \phi_2, \cdots$ are certain functions of time. The equations for determining these functions can be readily obtained by using d'Alembert's principle together with the principle of virtual work.

In the case of a bar with simply supported ends, the normal modes of vibration are represented by sine curves: $\sin\dfrac{\pi x}{l}$, $\sin\dfrac{2\pi x}{l}$, $\cdots$ and the series (a) becomes

$$y = \sum_{j=1,2,3,\cdots} \phi_j \sin\frac{j\pi x}{l}. \qquad (b)$$

The intensity of inertia forces distributed along the length of the vibrating bar is

$$-\frac{\gamma A}{g}\ddot{y} = -\frac{\gamma A}{g}\sum_{j=1,2,3,\cdots}\ddot{\phi}_j \sin\frac{j\pi x}{l}.$$

Assuming a virtual displacement

$$\delta y = \delta\phi_i \sin\frac{i\pi x}{l},$$

we find for the virtual work of inertia forces:

$$-\frac{\gamma A}{g}\int_0^l \ddot{y}\,\delta y\,dx = -\frac{\gamma A}{g}\sum_{j=1,2,3,\cdots}\ddot{\phi}_i\,\delta\phi_i\int_0^l \sin\frac{i\pi x}{l}\sin\frac{j\pi x}{l}\,dx$$

$$= -\frac{\gamma A}{g}\cdot\frac{l}{2}\ddot{\phi}_i. \qquad (c)$$

The strain energy of bending of the bar at any instance is

$$V = \frac{EI}{2}\int_0^l \left(\frac{d^2y}{dx^2}\right)^2 dx = \frac{EI}{2}\cdot\frac{\pi^4}{l^4}\int_0^l \left(\sum_{j=1,2,3,\cdots}\phi_j j^2 \sin\frac{j\pi x}{l}\right)^2 dx$$

$$= \frac{\pi^4 EI}{4l^3}\sum_{j=1,2,3,\cdots} j^4\phi_j^2, \qquad (142)$$

and for the virtual work of elasticity forces, we obtain

$$-\frac{\partial V}{\partial\phi_i}\delta\phi_i = -\frac{\pi^4 EI}{2l^3}i^4\phi_i\,\delta\phi_i. \qquad (d)$$

If vibration is produced by some disturbing force P applied at the distance c from the end of the bar (Fig. 207), the virtual work of this force is

$$P(\delta y)_{x=c} = P \,\delta\phi_i \sin\frac{i\pi c}{l}. \tag{e}$$

Summing up expressions (c), (d) and (e), we obtain the equation

$$\frac{\gamma A}{g}\cdot\frac{l}{2}\ddot{\phi}_i + \frac{\pi^4 E I i^4}{2l^3}\phi_i = P\sin\frac{i\pi c}{l}, \tag{f}$$

or by using our previous notation (114),

$$\ddot{\phi}_i + \frac{i^4\pi^4 a^2}{l^4}\phi_i = \frac{2Pg}{A\gamma l}\sin\frac{i\pi c}{l}. \tag{143}$$

The general solution of eq. (143) is

$$\phi_i = A_i\cos\frac{i^2\pi^2 at}{l^2} + B_i\sin\frac{i^2\pi^2 at}{l^2}$$

$$+ \frac{l^2}{i^2\pi^2 a}\frac{2g}{A\gamma l}\int_0^t P\sin\frac{i\pi c}{l}\sin\frac{i^2\pi^2 a(t-t_1)}{l^2}\,dt_1. \tag{g}$$

The first two terms in this solution represent the free vibration determined by the initial conditions, while the third term represents the vibration produced by the disturbing force.

As an example let us consider now the case of a pulsating force $P = P_0\sin\omega t_1$ applied at a distance c from the left support (see Fig. 207).

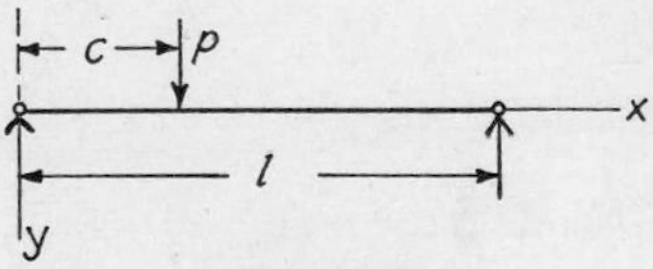

FIG. 207

Substituting in eq. (g) and considering only that part of the vibrations produced by the pulsating force, we obtain, after integration,

$$\phi_i = \frac{2g}{A\gamma}P_0\sin\frac{i\pi c}{l}\left(\frac{l^3}{i^4\pi^4 a^2 - \omega^2 l^4}\sin\omega t\right.$$

$$\left. - \frac{\omega l^5}{i^2\pi^2 a(i^4\pi^4 a^2 - \omega^2 l^4)}\sin\frac{i^2\pi^2 at}{l^2}\right). \tag{h}$$

Substituting in eq. (b), we have

$$y = \frac{2gP_0l^3}{A\gamma} \sum_{i=1}^{i=\infty} \frac{\sin\dfrac{i\pi c}{l} \sin\dfrac{i\pi x}{l}}{i^4\pi^4a^2 - \omega^2l^4} \sin\omega t$$

$$- \frac{2g\omega P_0l^5}{A\gamma\pi^2a} \sum_{i=1}^{i=\infty} \frac{\sin\dfrac{i\pi c}{l} \sin\dfrac{i\pi x}{l}}{i^2(i^4\pi^4a^2 - \omega^2l^4)} \sin\frac{i^2\pi^2at}{l^2}. \quad (144)$$

It is seen that the first series in this solution is proportional to $\sin\omega t$. It has the same period as the disturbing force and represents *forced vibrations* of the beam. The second series represents *free vibrations* of the beam produced by application of the force. These latter vibrations due to various kinds of resistance will be gradually damped out and only the forced vibrations, given by the equation

$$y = \frac{2gP_0l^3}{A\gamma} \sum_{i=1}^{i=\infty} \frac{\sin\dfrac{i\pi c}{l} \sin\dfrac{i\pi x}{l}}{i^4\pi^4a^2 - \omega^2l^4} \sin\omega t, \quad (i)$$

are of practical importance.

If the pulsating force P is varying very slowly, ω is a very small quantity and ω^2l^4 can be neglected in the denominator of the series (i), then

$$y = \frac{2gPl^3}{A\gamma\pi^4a^2} \sum_{i=1}^{i=\infty} \frac{1}{i^4} \sin\frac{i\pi c}{l} \sin\frac{i\pi x}{l}, \quad (j)$$

or, by using eq. (114),

$$y = \frac{2Pl^3}{EI\pi^4} \sum_{i=1}^{i=\infty} \frac{1}{i^4} \sin\frac{i\pi c}{l} \sin\frac{i\pi x}{l}. \quad (k)$$

This expression represents the statical deflection of the beam produced by the load P.* In the particular case, when the force P is applied at the middle, $c = l/2$ and we obtain

$$y = \frac{2Pl^3}{EI\pi^4}\left(\sin\frac{\pi x}{l} - \frac{1}{3^4}\sin\frac{3\pi x}{l} + \frac{1}{5^4}\sin\frac{5\pi x}{l} - \cdots\right). \quad (l)$$

---

* See Timoshenko and Lessells, *Applied Elasticity*, p. 131, *op. cit.*; and Timoshenko, *Strength of Materials*, 2d Ed., Vol. 2, p. 417, 1941.

The series converges rapidly and a satisfactory approximation for the deflections will be obtained by taking the first term only. In this manner we find for the deflection at the middle:

$$(y)_{x=l/2} = \frac{2Pl^3}{EI\pi^4} = \frac{Pl^3}{48.7EI}.$$

The error of this approximation is about 1.5%.

Denoting by α the ratio of the frequency of the disturbing force to the frequency of the fundamental type of free vibration, we obtain

$$\alpha = \frac{\omega l^2}{a\pi^2},$$

and the series (i), representing forced vibrations, becomes

$$y = \frac{2P_0l^3 \sin \omega t}{EI\pi^4} \sum_{i=1}^{i=\infty} \frac{\sin \dfrac{i\pi c}{l} \sin \dfrac{i\pi x}{l}}{i^4 - \alpha^2}. \qquad (m)$$

If the pulsating force is applied at the middle, we obtain

$$y = \frac{2P_0l^3 \sin \omega t}{EI\pi^4} \left(\frac{\sin \dfrac{\pi x}{l}}{1 - \alpha^2} - \frac{\sin \dfrac{3\pi x}{l}}{3^4 - \alpha^2} + \frac{\sin \dfrac{5\pi x}{l}}{5^4 - \alpha^2} \cdots \right). \qquad (n)$$

For small α the first term of this series represents the deflection with good accuracy and comparing (n) with (l) it can be concluded that the ratio of the dynamical deflection to the statical deflection is approximately equal to

$$\frac{y_d}{y_s} = \frac{1}{1 - \alpha^2}. \qquad (o)$$

If, for example, the frequency of the disturbing force is four times as small as the frequency of the fundamental mode of vibration, the dynamical deflection will be about 6% greater than the statical deflection.

From the series (i), we can obtain also forced vibration produced by a pulsating couple applied at the end $(x = 0)$. This condition we approach more and more closely as the distance c of the pulsating force from the end diminishes. Taking it as very small and considering only the first few terms of the series (i), we can assume

$$\sin \frac{i\pi c}{l} \approx \frac{i\pi c}{l}.$$

Substituting into the series and using the notation $M = P_0 c$, we then obtain

$$y = \frac{2\pi M l^2}{A\gamma} \sum_{i=1,2,3,\cdots} \frac{i}{i^4 \pi^4 a^2 - \omega^2 l^4} \sin \frac{i\pi x}{l} \sin \omega t, \qquad (p)$$

which represents forced vibrations produced by a pulsating couple $M \sin \omega t$.

Due to the fact that the problems on vibration of bars are represented by *linear* differential equations, the *principle of superposition* holds and if there are several pulsating forces acting on the beam, the resulting vibration will be obtained by superimposing the vibrations produced by the individual forces. The case of continuously distributed pulsating forces also can be solved in the same manner; the summation only has to be replaced by an integration along the length of the beam. Assume, for instance, that the beam is loaded by a uniformly distributed load of the intensity:

$$w = w_0 \sin \omega t.$$

Such a load condition exists, for instance, in a locomotive side rod under the action of lateral inertia forces. In order to determine the vibrations, $w_0\, dc$ should be substituted for P_0 in eq. (i) and afterwards this equation should be integrated with respect to c within the limits $c = 0$ and $c = l$. In this manner we obtain

$$y = \frac{4gw_0 l^4}{A\gamma\pi} \sum_{i=1}^{i=\infty} \frac{\sin \dfrac{i\pi x}{l}}{i(i^4 \pi^4 a^2 - \omega^2 l^4)} \sin \omega t; \quad i = 1,3,5,\cdots. \qquad (q)$$

If the frequency of the load is very small in comparison with the frequency of the fundamental mode of vibration of the bar, the term $\omega^2 l^4$ in the denominators of the series (q) can be neglected and we obtain,

$$y = \frac{4w l^4}{EI\pi^5} \left(\frac{\sin \dfrac{\pi x}{l}}{1^5} + \frac{\sin \dfrac{3\pi x}{l}}{3^5} + \frac{\sin \dfrac{5\pi x}{l}}{5^5} + \cdots \right). \qquad (r)$$

This very rapidly converging series represents the statical deflection of the beam produced by a uniformly distributed load w. By taking $x = l/2$ we obtain for the deflection at the middle

$$(y)_{x=l/2} = \frac{4w l^4}{EI\pi^5} \left(1 - \frac{1}{3^5} + \frac{1}{5^5} - \cdots \right). \qquad (s)$$

If only the first term of this series be taken, the error in the deflection at the middle will be about $\frac{1}{4}\%$. If the frequency of the pulsating load is not small enought to warrant application of the statical equation, the same method can be used as was shown in the case of a single force and we will arrive at the same conclusion as represented by eq. (o).

In a more general case the intensity of the distributed disturbing force may vary along the span of the beam and may also be some function of time different from sin ωt. Then we take

$$w = f(t) \cdot f_1(x),$$

and represent $f_1(x)$ by the series

$$f_1(x) = a_1 \sin \frac{\pi x}{l} + a_2 \sin \frac{2\pi x}{l} + a_3 \sin \frac{3\pi x}{l} + \cdots,$$

where

$$a_i = \frac{2}{l} \int_0^l f_1(x) \sin \frac{i\pi x}{l} \, dx.$$

In this way the general expression for the distributed disturbing force becomes

$$w = f(t) \Sigma a_i \sin \frac{i\pi x}{l}.$$

To establish, for this general case, the equation for determining the functions ϕ_j in the series (b), we observe that the virtual work of the disturbing force is

$$\int_0^l w \, \delta\phi_i \sin \frac{i\pi x}{l} \, dx = f(t) \, \delta\phi_i \int_0^l \left(\Sigma a_i \sin \frac{i\pi x}{l} \right) \sin \frac{i\pi x}{l} \, dx = f(t) \cdot \frac{a_i l}{2} \delta\phi_i.$$

This expression, instead of expression (e), should be used in the derivation of the equation for ϕ_i; and instead of eq. (143) we obtain

$$\ddot{\phi}_i + \frac{i^4 \pi^4 a^2}{l^4} \phi_i = \frac{a_i g}{A\gamma} f(t).$$

Considering only vibration produced by the disturbing force, we then obtain

$$\phi_i = \frac{l^2}{i^2 \pi^2 a^2} \cdot \frac{a_i g}{A\gamma} \int_0^t f(t) \sin \frac{i^2 \pi^2 a(t - t_1)}{l^2} \, dt_1.$$

In each particular case, for a given $f(t)$, the expression for ϕ_i can be evaluated and, substituting it into the series (b), the required vibration will be obtained. An approximate calculation of ϕ_i can also be made if the function $f(t)$ is given graphically.

Moving Constant Force.—If a constant vertical force P is moving along the length of a beam it produces vibrations which can be calculated as before. Let v denote the constant * velocity of the moving force and let the force be at the left support at the initial moment ($t = 0$); then, at any

* The case when the velocity is not constant has been discussed by A. N. Lowan, *Phil. Mag.*, ser. 7, Vol. 19, p. 708, 1935.

other moment $t = t_1$ the distance of this force from the left support will be vt_1. The virtual work of this force on the displacement $\delta\phi_i \sin i\pi x/l$ is $P \cdot \delta\phi_i \sin i\pi vt_1/l$. Comparing this with expression (e), we see that sin $i\pi vt_1/l$ takes the place of sin $i\pi c/l$. Substituting sin $i\pi vt_1/l$ instead of sin $i\pi c/l$, into the third term of eq. (g), the following expression will be found for the vibrations produced by the moving load: *

$$y = \frac{2gPl^3}{A\gamma\pi^2} \sum_{i=1}^{i=\infty} \frac{\sin \dfrac{i\pi x}{l}}{i^2(i^2\pi^2 a^2 - v^2 l^2)} \sin \frac{i\pi vt}{l}$$

$$- \frac{2gPl^4 v}{A\gamma\pi^3 a} \sum_{i=1}^{i=\infty} \frac{\sin \dfrac{i\pi x}{l}}{i^3(i^2\pi^2 a^2 - v^2 l^2)} \sin \frac{i^2\pi^2 at}{l^2}. \quad (145)$$

The first series in this solution represents forced vibrations and the second series, free vibrations of the beam.

If the velocity v of the moving force be very small, we can put $v = 0$ and $vt = c$ in the solution above; then

$$y = \frac{2gPl^3}{A\gamma\pi^4 a^2} \sum_{i=1}^{i=\infty} \frac{1}{i^4} \sin \frac{i\pi c}{l} \sin \frac{i\pi x}{l}.$$

This is the statical deflection of the beam produced by the load P applied at the distance c from the left support (see eq. j). By using the notation

$$\alpha^2 = \frac{v^2 l^2}{a^2\pi^2}, \quad (t)$$

the forced vibrations in the general solution (145) can be presented in the following form:

$$y = \frac{2Pl^3}{EI\pi^4} \sum_{i=1}^{i=\infty} \frac{\sin \dfrac{i\pi x}{l} \sin \dfrac{i\pi vt}{l}}{i^2(i^2 - \alpha^2)}. \quad (u)$$

* This problem is of practical interest in connection with the study of bridge vibrations. The first solution of this problem was given by A. N. Krylov, *Math. Ann.*, Vol. 61, 1905. See also writer's paper in *Bull. Polytech. Inst. Kiev*, 1908. (German translation in *Z. Math. u. Phys.*, Vol. 59, p. 163, 1911.) Prof. C. E. Inglis in, *Proc. Inst. Civil Engrs.* (*London*), Vol. 218, 1924, came to the same results. If instead of moving force a moving weight is acting on the beam, the problem becomes more complicated. See H. H. Jeffcott, *Phil. Mag.*, Ser. 7, Vol. 8, p. 66, 1929; H. Steuding, *Ing.-Arch.*, Vol. 5, p. 275, 1934; A. Schallenkamp, *ibid.*, Vol. 8, p. 182, 1937; and T. A. Odman, *Bull. Swedish Cement and Concrete Research Inst.*, No. 14, 1948.

It is interesting to note that this deflection completely coincides with the statical deflection of a beam * on which in addition to the lateral load P applied at a distance $c = vt$ from the left support a longitudinal compressive force S is acting, such that

$$\frac{S}{S_{cr}} = \frac{Sl^2}{EI\pi^2} = \alpha^2. \tag{v}$$

Here S_{cr} denotes the known *critical* or *column load* for the beam.

From the eqs. (v) and (t) we obtain

$$\frac{Sl^2}{EI\pi^2} = \frac{v^2l^2}{a^2\pi^2}$$

or

$$S = \frac{v^2A\gamma}{g}. \tag{w}$$

The effect of this force on the statical deflection of the beam loaded by P is equivalent to the effect of the velocity of a moving force P on the deflection (u) representing forced vibrations.

By increasing the velocity v, a condition can be reached where one of the denominators in the series (145) becomes equal to zero and resonance takes place. Assume, for instance, that

$$a^2\pi^2 = v^2l^2. \tag{x}$$

In this case the period of the fundamental vibration of the beam, equal to $2l^2/a\pi$, becomes equal to $2l/v$ and is twice as great as the time required for the force P to pass over the beam. The denominators in the first terms of both series in eq. (145) become, under the condition (x), equal to zero and the sum of these two terms will be

$$\frac{2gPl^3}{A\gamma\pi^2}\sin\frac{\pi x}{l}\frac{\sin\dfrac{\pi vt}{l} - \dfrac{lv}{\pi a}\sin\dfrac{\pi^2 at}{l^2}}{\pi^2a^2 - v^2l^2}.$$

This has the form 0/0 and can be presented in the usual way as follows (see p. 47):

$$-\frac{Pg}{\gamma A\pi v}t\cos\frac{\pi vt}{l}\sin\frac{\pi x}{l} + \frac{Pgl}{\gamma A\pi^2 v^2}\sin\frac{\pi vt}{l}\sin\frac{\pi x}{l}. \tag{y}$$

* See Timoshenko and Lessells, *Applied Elasticity*, p. 163, *loc. cit.* By using the known expression for the statical deflection curve the finite form of the function, from which the series (u) has its origin, can be obtained.

This expression has its maximum value when

$$t = \frac{l}{v}$$

and is then equal to

$$\frac{Pgl}{\gamma A \pi^2 v^2}\left(\sin\frac{\pi vt}{l} - \frac{\pi vt}{l}\cos\frac{\pi vt}{l}\right)_{t=l/v}\sin\frac{\pi x}{l} = \frac{Pl^3}{EI\pi^3}\sin\frac{\pi x}{l}. \qquad (z)$$

Taking into consideration that the expression (y) represents a satisfactory approximation for the dynamical deflection given by eq. (145), it can be concluded that the maximum dynamical deflection at the resonance condition (x) is about 50% greater than the maximum statical deflection which is equal to

$$\frac{Pl^3}{48EI}.$$

It is interesting to note that the maximum dynamical deflection occurs when the force P is leaving the beam. At this moment the deflection under the force P is equal to zero, hence the work done by this force during the passing of the beam is also equal to zero. In order to explain the source of the energy accumulated in the vibrating beam during the passing over of the force P, we should assume that there is no friction and the beam produces a reaction R in the direction of the normal (Fig. 208). In this case, from the condition of equilibrium it follows that there should exist a horizontal force equal to $P(dy/dx)$. The work done by this force during its passage along the beam will be

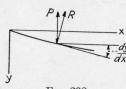

Fig. 208

$$E = -\int_0^{l/v} P\left(\frac{dy}{dx}\right)_{x=vt} v\, dt.$$

Substituting expression (y) for y we obtain

$$E = -\frac{P^2 g}{\gamma A \pi v^2}\int_0^{l/v}\left(\sin\frac{\pi vt}{l} - \frac{\pi vt}{l}\cos\frac{\pi vt}{l}\right)\cos\frac{\pi vt}{l}v\, dt = \frac{P^2 gl}{\gamma A \pi^2 v^2}\cdot\frac{\pi^2}{4},$$

or, by taking into consideration eqs. (x) and (114), we obtain

$$E = \frac{\pi^2}{4}\frac{P^2 l^3}{EI\pi^4}.$$

This amount of work is very close * to the amount of the potential energy of bending in the beam at the moment $t = l/v$.†

In the case of bridges, the time it takes to cross the bridge is usually large in comparison with the period of the fundamental type of vibration and the quantity α^2, given by eq. (t), is small. Then by taking only the first term in each series of eq. (145) and assuming that in the most unfavorable case the amplitudes of the forced and free vibrations are added to one another, we obtain for the maximum deflection,

$$y_{max} = \frac{2gPl^3}{\gamma A \pi^2}\left(\frac{1}{\pi^2 a^2 - v^2 l^2} + \frac{vl}{a\pi}\frac{1}{\pi^2 a^2 - v^2 l^2}\right)$$

$$= \frac{2Pl^3}{EI\pi^4}\frac{1 + \alpha}{1 - \alpha^2} = \frac{2Pl^3}{EI\pi^4}\frac{1}{1 - \alpha}. \tag{146}$$

This is a somewhat exaggerated value of the maximum dynamical deflection, because damping was completely neglected in the above discussion.

By using the principle of superposition, the solution of the problem in the case of a system of concentrated moving forces and in the case of moving distributed forces can also be made without difficulty. ‡

Moving Pulsating Force.§—Consider now the case when a pulsating force is moving along the beam with a constant velocity v. Such a condition may occur, for instance, when an imperfectly balanced locomotive passes over a bridge (Fig. 209). The vertical component of the centrifugal force P,¶ due to the unbalance, is $P \cos \omega t_1$, where ω is the angular velocity of the driving

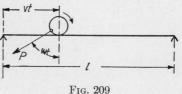

Fig. 209

---

* The potential energy of the beam bent by the force P at the middle is

$$V = \frac{P^2 l^3}{96EI} \quad \text{and} \quad \frac{E}{V} = 2.43.$$

This ratio is very close to the square of the ratio of the maximum deflections for the dynamical and statical conditions which is equal to $(48/\pi^3)^2 = 2.38$. The discrepancy should be attributed to the higher harmonics in the deflection curve.

† For a further discussion of the question see the paper by E. H. Lee, Quarterly of Appl. Math. Vol. X, p. 290, 1952.

‡ See writer's paper, *loc. cit.*, p. 352.

§ See writer's paper, *Phil. Mag.*, Vol. 43, p. 1018, 1922.

¶ It is assumed that at the initial moment $t_1 = 0$ the centrifugal force is acting in downward direction.

wheel. Using the same manner of reasoning as before, we find that the virtual work of the moving pulsating force on the displacement $\delta\phi_i$ $\sin i\pi x/l$ is $P \cos \omega t_1 \cdot \delta\phi_1 \sin i\pi v t_1/l$. Substituting $P \cos \omega t_1 \sin i\pi v t_1/l$ instead of $P \sin i\pi c/l$ in eq. (g), we find ϕ_1 and the series (b) gives

$$y = \frac{Pl^3}{EI\pi^4} \sum_{i=1}^{i=\infty} \sin \frac{i\pi x}{l} \left[\frac{\sin \left(\frac{i\pi v}{l} + \omega \right) t}{i^4 - (\beta + i\alpha)^2} + \frac{\sin \left(\frac{i\pi v}{l} - \omega \right) t}{i^4 - (\beta - i\alpha)^2} \right.$$
$$\left. - \frac{\alpha}{i} \left(\frac{\sin \frac{i^2 \pi^2 at}{l^2}}{-i^2\alpha^2 + (i^2 - \beta)^2} + \frac{\sin \frac{i^2 \pi^2 at}{l^2}}{-i^2\alpha^2 + (i^2 + \beta)^2} \right), \right] \quad (147)$$

where $\alpha = vl/\pi a$ is the ratio of the period $\tau = 2l^2/\pi a$ of the fundamental type of vibration of the beam to twice the time, $\tau_1 = l/v$, it takes the force P to pass over the beam,

$\beta = \tau/\tau_2$ is the ratio of the period of the fundamental type of vibration of the beam to the period $\tau_2 = 2\pi/\omega$ of the pulsating force.

When the period τ_2 of the pulsating force is equal to the period τ of the fundamental type of vibration of the beam, $\beta = 1$ and we obtain the condition of resonance. The amplitude of the vibration during motion of the pulsating force will be gradually built up and attains its maximum at the moment $t = l/v$ when the first term (for $i = 1$) in the series on the right of eq. (147), which is the most important part of y, may be reduced to the form

$$\frac{1}{\alpha} \frac{2Pl^3}{EI\pi^4} \sin \frac{\pi x}{l} \sin \omega t,$$

and the maximum deflection is given by the formula

$$\delta_{\max} = \frac{1}{\alpha} \frac{2Pl^3}{EI\pi^4} = \frac{2\tau_1}{\tau} \cdot \frac{2Pl^3}{EI\pi^4}. \quad (148)$$

Due to the fact that in actual cases the time interval $\tau_1 = l/v$ is large in comparison with the period τ of the natural vibration, the maximum dynamical deflection produced by the pulsating force P will be many times greater than the deflection $2Pl^3/EI\pi^4$, which would be produced by the same force if applied statically at the middle of the beam. Some applications of eq. (148) for calculating the impact effect on bridges will be given in the next article.

PROBLEMS

1. A simply supported beam under the action of a force P, applied at the middle, deflects one inch at the middle. What will be the amplitude of forced vibration produced by a pulsating force $P \sin \omega t$ applied at the middle, if the frequency ω is equal to half of the fundamental frequency of the beam?

Solution. Substituting into eq. (n) $\alpha = 0.5$, $x = 0.5l$, $\omega t = \pi/2$, we obtain the maximum dynamic deflection

$$(y_d)_{x=l/2} = \frac{2Pl^3}{\pi^4 EI} \left(\frac{1}{1 - \frac{1}{4}} + \frac{1}{3^4 - \frac{1}{4}} + \frac{1}{5^4 - \frac{1}{4}} + \cdots \right).$$

Taking only three terms of the series and observing that

$$\frac{Pl^3}{48EI} = 1 \text{ in.,}$$

we find

$$(y_d)_{x=l/2} = \frac{96}{\pi^4} (1.347) = 1.328 \text{ in.}$$

The dynamic deflection is larger than the static deflection by about 33%.

2. The beam of the preceding problem is under the action of two pulsating forces applied at the third points, Fig. 210. Find the amplitude of forced vibration at the middle if P has the same magnitude and frequency as in the preceding problem.

Solution. From symmetry we conclude that the amplitude will be twice as large as that produced by one force. Using then eq. (i), p. 348, we find, for the amplitude of forced vibration,

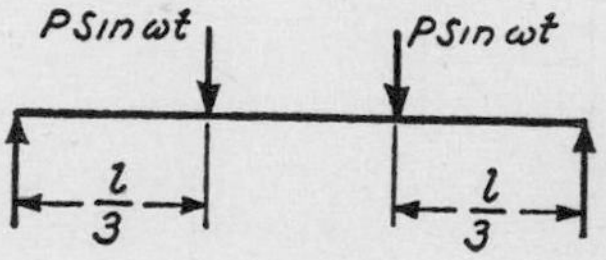

FIG. 210

$$(y_d)_{x=l/2} = \frac{4Pl^3}{\pi^4 EI} \left(\frac{\sin \frac{\pi}{3}}{1 - \frac{1}{4}} + \frac{\sin \frac{5\pi}{3}}{5^4 - \frac{1}{4}} - \frac{\sin \frac{7\pi}{3}}{7^4 - \frac{1}{4}} + \cdots \right) = 2.255 \text{ in.}$$

3. Find the amplitude of forced vibration produced at the middle of a simply supported beam by a distributed pulsating load of intensity $w_0 \sin \omega t$ covering the left-hand half of the span.

Answer. $(y_d)_{x=l/2} = \frac{2w_0 l^4}{\pi^5 EI} \sum \frac{(-1)^{\frac{i-1}{2}}}{i(i^4 - \alpha^2)}.$

4. Find the vibrations produced in a simply supported beam by a force P suddenly applied at the middle of the span.

Answer. $y = \frac{2Pl^3}{\pi^4 EI} \sum_{i=1,3,5,\cdots} \frac{(-1)^{\frac{i-1}{2}}}{i^4} (1 - \cos p_i t) \sin \frac{i\pi x}{l}.$

5. Find the forced vibrations produced in a simply supported beam by a distributed pulsating load $w = w_0 \sin \dfrac{\pi x}{l} \sin \omega t$.

Answer. $y = \dfrac{w_0 l^4}{\pi^4 EI} \cdot \dfrac{\sin \omega t}{1 - \dfrac{\omega^2 l^4}{\pi^4 a^2}} \cdot \sin \dfrac{\pi x}{l}$.

56. Vibration of Bridges.—It is well known that a rolling load produces in a bridge or in a girder a greater deflection and greater stresses than the same load acting statically. Such an *impact effect* of live loads on bridges is of great practical importance and many engineers have worked on the solution of this problem.* There are various causes producing impact effects on bridges of which the following will be discussed: (1) Live-load effect of a smooth-running load, (2) impact effect of the balance weights of the locomotive driving wheels and (3) impact effect due to irregularities of the track and flat spots on the wheels.

Live-load Effect of a Smooth-running Mass.—In discussing this problem two extreme cases will be considered: (1) when the mass of the moving load

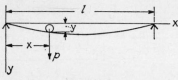

FIG. 211

is large in comparison with the mass of the beam, i.e., girder or rail bearer, and (2) when the mass of the moving load is small in comparison with the mass of the bridge. In the first case the mass of the beam can be neglected. Then the deflection of the beam under the load at any position of this load will be proportional to the pressure R, which the rolling load P produces on the beam (Fig. 211) and can be calculated from the known equation of statical deflection:

$$y = -\frac{R x^2 (l - x)^2}{3 l E I}. \tag{a}$$

In order to obtain the pressure R, the inertia force $-(P/g)(d^2y/dt^2)$ should be added to the rolling load P. Assuming that the load is moving along the beam with a constant velocity v, we obtain

$$\frac{dy}{dt} = v \frac{dy}{dx}; \quad \frac{d^2y}{dt^2} = v^2 \frac{d^2y}{dx^2},$$

---

* The history of the subject is extensively discussed in the famous book by A. Clebsch, *Theorie der Elastizität fester Körper*, French translation by Barré de Saint-Venant (Paris, 1883), see *note finale du paragraphe* 61, p. 597.

and the pressure on the beam will be

$$R = P\left(1 - \frac{v^2}{g}\frac{d^2y}{dx^2}\right). \qquad (b)$$

Substituting in eq. (a) we obtain

$$y = P\left(1 - \frac{v^2}{g}\frac{d^2y}{dx^2}\right)\frac{x^2(l-x)^2}{3lEI}. \qquad (149)$$

This equation determines the path of the point of contact of the rolling load with the beam.* An approximation of the solution of eq. (149) will be obtained by assuming that the path is the same as at zero speed ($v = 0$) and by substituting

$$\frac{Px^2(l-x)^2}{3lEI},$$

for y in the right side of this equation. Then by simple calculations it can be shown that y becomes maximum when the load is at the middle of the span and the maximum pressure will be

$$R_{max} = P\left(1 + \frac{v^2}{g}\frac{Pl}{3EI}\right). \qquad (c)$$

The maximum deflection in the center of the beam increases in the same rate as the pressure on it, so that

$$\delta_d = \delta_{st}\left(1 + \frac{v^2}{g}\frac{Pl}{3EI}\right). \qquad (150)$$

This approximate solution as compared with the result of an exact solution of eq. (149) † is accurate enough for most practical applications. The additional term in the parentheses is usually very small and it can be con-

---

* This equation was established by R. Willis, *Appendix to the Report of the Commissioners . . . to Inquire into the Application of Iron to Railway Structures*, London, 1849. This report was reprinted in P. Barlow, *Treatise on the Strength of Timber, Cast Iron and Malleable Iron*, London, 1851.

† The exact solution of eq. (149) was obtained by G. G. Stokes, *Mathematical and Physical Papers*, Cambridge, Vol. 2, p. 179. The same problem has been discussed also by H. Zimmermann, *Die Schwingungen eines Traegers mit bewegter Last*, Berlin, 1896. It should be noted that the integration of eq. (149) can be made also numerically by using the method explained before, see p. 143. In this manner solutions for a beam on elastic supports and for continuous beams were obtained by Prof. N. P. Petroff, see *Mem. Russian Imperial Tech. Soc.*, 1903.

cluded that the *live-load effect* in the case of small girders has no practical importance.

In the second case when the mass of the load is small in comparison with the mass of the bridge the moving load can be replaced, with sufficient accuracy, by a moving force and then the results given in Art. 55 can be used. Assuming, for instance, that for three single-track railway bridges with spans of 60 ft, 120 ft and 360 ft, the natural frequencies are as shown in the following table,*

$$l = 60 \text{ ft} \qquad 120 \text{ ft} \qquad 360 \text{ ft}$$

	$l = 60$ ft	120 ft	360 ft
$f =$	9	5	2 per sec
$(\alpha)_{v = 120 \text{ ft per sec}} =$	1/9	1/10	1/12

and taking the velocity $v = 120$ ft per sec, the quantity α, representing the ratio of the period of the fundamental type of vibration to twice the time l/v for the load to pass over the bridge, will be as shown in the third line of the table. Now on the basis of solution (146) it can be concluded †
that for a span of 60 ft and with a very high velocity, the increase in deflection due to the live-load effect is about 12% and this is still diminished with a decrease of velocity and with an increase of span. If several moving loads are acting on the bridge, the oscillations associated with these should be superimposed. Only in the exceptional case of synchronism of these vibrations will the resultant live-load effect on the system be equal to the sum of the effects of the separate loads, and the increase in deflection due to this effect be in the same proportion as for a single load. From these examples it can be concluded that the live-load effect of a smooth-running load is not an important factor and in the most unfavorable cases it will hardly exceed 10%. Much more serious effects may be produced, as we will

* Some experimental data on vibrations of bridges can be found in the following papers: A. Bühler, "Stosswirkungen bei eisernen Eisenbahnbrücken," *Druckschrift Intern. Kongr. Brückenbau*, Zürich, 1926; W. Hort, "Stossbeanspruchungen und Schwingungen . . .," *Bautechnik*, 1928. See also N. Streletzky, *Ergebnisse der experimentellen Brückenuntersuchungen*, Berlin, 1928; and C. E. Inglis, *A Mathematical Treatise on Vibrations in Railway Bridges*, Cambridge, 1934. Vibrations produced by a moving force in a two-span beam were studied both theoretically and experimentally by R. S. Ayre, G. Ford and L. S. Jacobsen, *J. Appl. Mech.*, Vol. 17, pp. 1 and 391, 1950.

† The bridge is considered here as a simple beam of a constant cross section. Vibration of trusses has been discussed by H. Reissner, *Z. Baut.*, Vol. 53, p. 135, 1903; E. Pohlhausen, *Z. angew. Math. u. Mech.*, Vol. 1, p. 28, 1921; and K. Federhofer, *Der Stahlbau*, No. 1, 1934. For experimental verification of vibration of trusses, see J. B. Hunley, *Bull. Am. Railway Eng. Assoc.*, Vol. 37, p. 1, 1935.

see, by pulsating forces due to rotating balance weights of steam locomotives.

Impact Effect of Unbalanced Weights.—The most unfavorable condition occurs in the case of resonance when the number of revolutions per second of the driving wheels is equal to the frequency of natural vibration of the bridge. For a short-span bridge the frequency of natural vibration is usually so high that synchronism of the pulsating load and the natural vibration is impossible at any practical velocity. By taking, for instance, 6 revolutions per second of the driving wheels as the highest limit and taking the frequencies of natural vibration from the table above, it can be concluded that the resonance condition, is hardly possible for spans less than 100 ft. For larger spans resonance conditions should be taken into consideration and the impact effect should be calculated from eq. (148).

Let P_1 be the maximum resultant pressure on the rail due to the counterweights when the driving wheels are revolving once per second; n, the total number of revolutions of the driving wheels during passage along the bridge.

Then, from eq. (148), we obtain the following additional deflection due to the impact effect:

$$\delta_{max} = \frac{2n}{\tau^2} \frac{2P_1 l^3}{EI\pi^4}. \tag{151}$$

We see that in calculating the impact effect due to unbalanced weights we have to take consideration of: (1) the statical deflection produced by the force P_1, (2) the period τ of the natural vibration of the bridge and (3) the number of revolutions n. All these quantities are usually disregarded in impact formulas as applied in bridge design.

In order to obtain some idea about the amount of this impact effect let us apply eq. (151) to a numerical example * of a locomotive crossing a bridge of 120-ft span. Assuming that the locomotive load is equivalent to a uniform load of 14,700 lb per linear ft distributed over a length of 15 ft, and that the train load following and preceding the locomotive is equivalent to a uniformly distributed load of 5500 lb per linear ft, the maximum central deflection of each girder is $(2l^3/EI\pi^4)$ (275,000) approximately. The same deflection when the locomotive approaches the support and the train completely covers the bridge is $(2l^3/EI\pi^4)$ (206,000) approximately. Taking the number of revolutions $n = 8$ (the diameter

* The figures below are taken from paper by C. E. Inglis, *op. cit.*, p. 352.

of the wheels equal to 4 ft and 9 in.) and the maximum pulsating pressure on each girder at the resonance condition equal to $P_1/\tau^2 = 18,750$ lb, the additional deflection, calculated from eq. (151), will be $(2l^3/EI\pi^4)$ (300,000). Adding this to the statical deflection, calculated above for the case of the locomotive approaching the end of the bridge, we obtain for the complete deflection at the center $(2l^3/EI\pi^4)$ (506,000). Comparing this with the maximum statical central deflection $(2l^3/EI\pi^4) \times (275,000)$, given above, it can be concluded that the increase in deflection due to impact is in this case about 84%. Assuming the number of revolutions n equal to 6 (the diameter of driving wheels equal to $6\frac{1}{2}$ ft) and assuming again a condition of resonance, we will obtain for the same numerical example an increase in deflection equal to 56%.

In the case of bridges of shorter spans, when the frequency of natural vibration is considerably larger than the number of revolutions per second of the driving wheels, a satisfactory approximation can be obtained by taking only the first term in the series (147) and assuming the most unfavorable condition, namely, that sin $([\pi v/l] + \omega)t$ and sin $([\pi v/l] - \omega)t$ become equal to 1 and sin $\pi^2 at/l^2$ equal to -1 at the moment $t = l/2v$ when the pulsating force arrives at the middle of the span. Then, the additional deflection, from (147), will be

$$y = \frac{Pl^3}{EI\pi^4}\left(\frac{1}{1-(\beta+\alpha)^2} + \frac{1}{1-(\beta-\alpha)^2} + \frac{\alpha}{(1-\beta)^2-\alpha^2} + \frac{\alpha}{(1+\beta)^2-\alpha^2}\right)$$

$$= \frac{2Pl^3}{EI\pi^4}\frac{1-\alpha}{(1-\beta[1+\alpha/\beta])(1+\beta[1-\alpha/\beta])}. \tag{152}$$

Consider, for instance, a 60-ft span bridge and assume the same kind of loading as in the previous example, then the maximum statical deflection is $(2l^3/EI\pi^4)$ (173,000) approximately. If the driving wheels have a circumference of 20 ft and make 6 revolutions per second, the maximum downwards force on the girder will be $18,750(6/5)^2 = 27,000$ lb. Assuming the natural frequency of the bridge equal to 9, we obtain from eq. (143)

$$\delta = \frac{2l^3}{EI\pi^4}(27,000 \times 2.57) = \frac{2l^3}{EI\pi^4}(69,400).$$

Hence,

$$\frac{\text{dynamical deflection}}{\text{statical deflection}} = \frac{173+69.4}{173} = 1.40.$$

The impact effect of the balancing weights in this case amounts to 40%.

In general it will be seen from the theory developed above that the most severe impact effects will be obtained in the shortest spans for which a resonance condition may occur (about 100-ft spans for the assumption made above) because in this case the resonance occurs when the pulsating disturbing force has its greatest magnitude. With increase in the span the critical speed decreases and also the magnitude of the pulsating load, consequently the impact effect decreases. For very large spans, when the frequency of the fundamental type of vibration is low, synchronism of the pulsating force with the second mode of vibration having a node at the middle of the span becomes theoretically possible and, due to this cause, an increase in the impact effect may occur at a velocity of about four times as great as the first critical speed.

It should be noted that all our calculations were based on the assumption of a pulsating force moving along the bridge. In actual conditions we have rolling *masses*, which will cause a variation in the natural frequency of the bridge in accordance with the varying position of the loads. This variability of the natural frequency which is especially pronounced in short spans is very beneficial because the pulsating load will no longer be in resonance all the time during passing over the bridge and its cumulative effect will not be as pronounced as is given by the above theory. From experiments made by the Indian Railway Bridge Committee,* it is apparent that on the average the maximum deflection occurs when the engine has traversed about two-thirds of the span and that the maximum impact effect amounts to only about one-third of that given by eq. (151). It should be noted also that the impact effect is proportional to the force P_1 and depends therefore on the type of engine and on the manner of balancing. While in a badly balanced two-cylinder engine the force P_1 may amount to more than 1000 lb,† in electric locomotives perfect balancing can be obtained without introducing a fluctuating rail pressure. This absence of impact effect may compensate for the increase in axle load in modern heavy electric locomotives.

In the case of short girders and rail bearers whose natural frequencies are very high, the effect of counterweights on the deflection and stresses can be calculated with sufficient accuracy by neglecting vibrations and using the statical formula in which the centrifugal forces of the counter-

---

* See Bridge Subcommittee Reports, 1925; Government of India Central Publication Branch, Calcutta, Tech. Paper No. 247, 1926. Similar conclusions were obtained also by C. E. Inglis, see his book, "Vibrations in Bridges," 1934.

† Some data on the values of P_1 for various types of engines are given in the Bridge Subcommittee Reports mentioned above.

weights should be added to the statical rail pressures. The effect of these centrifugal forces may be especially pronounced in the case of short spans when only a small number of wheels can be on the girder simultaneously.

Impact Effects Due to Irregularities of Track and Flats on Wheels.— Irregularities like low spots on the rails, rail joints, flats on the wheels, etc., may be responsible for considerable impact effect which may become especially pronounced in the case of short spans. If the shape of the low spots in the track or of the flats on the wheels is given by a smooth curve, the methods used before in considering the effect of road unevenness on the vibrations of vehicles and the effect of low spots on deflection of rails (see p. 111) can also be applied here for calculating the additional pressure of the wheel on the rail. This additional pressure will be proportional to the unsprung mass of the wheel and to the square of the velocity of the train. It may attain a considerable magnitude and has practical importance in the case of short bridges and rail bearers. This additional dynamical effect produced by irregularities in the track and flats on the wheels justifies the high impact factor usually applied in the design of short bridges. By removing rail joints from the bridges and by using ballasted spans or those provided with heavy timber floors, the effect of these irregularities can be diminished and the strength condition considerably improved.

57. Forced Vibration of Beams with Various End Conditions.—In the two previous articles various cases of forced vibrations of a bar with simply

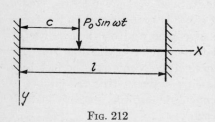

FIG. 212

supported ends were discussed. Let us consider now other cases, when the normal functions are not simple sine curves but have more complicated forms. As an example, we will consider the case of a beam with built-in ends and assume that forced vibrations are produced by a pulsating force P_0 sin ωt applied at the distance c from the end $(x = 0)$, Fig. 212. A general expression for the deflection curve we take, as before, in the form of the series

$$y = \sum_{j=1,2,3,\cdots} \phi_j X_j, \qquad (a)$$

in which X_j are normal functions for a bar with built-in ends (see p. 340) and ϕ_j are functions of time, the equations for which we will now derive by using d'Alembert's principle together with the principle of virtual work.

Assuming a virtual displacement

$$\delta y = \delta\phi_i \, X_i, \qquad (b)$$

and observing that

$$\int_0^l X_i X_j \, dx = 0, \quad \text{and} \quad \int_0^l X_i^2 \, dx = l,$$

we find, for the virtual work of inertia forces:

$$-\frac{\gamma A}{g} \int_0^l \left(\sum_{j=1,2,3,\cdots} \ddot{\phi}_j X_j \right) \delta\phi_i X_i \, dx = -\frac{\gamma Al}{g} \ddot{\phi}_i \delta\phi_i. \qquad (c)$$

For calculating the virtual work of elasticity forces, we use the expression for the strain energy of the bar, which is (see p. 339)

$$V = \frac{EI}{2} \int_0^l \left(\frac{\partial^2 y}{\partial x^2} \right)^2 dx = \frac{EI}{2} \sum_{i=1,2,3,\cdots} k_j^4 \phi_j^2 \int_0^l X_j^2 \, dx,$$

or taking

$$\int_0^l X_j^2 \, dx = l,$$

we obtain

$$V = \frac{EI}{2l^3} \sum_{j=1,2,3,\cdots} (k_j l)^4 \phi_j^2. \qquad (d)$$

Thus the virtual work of elasticity forces is

$$-\frac{\partial V}{\partial \phi_i} \delta\phi_i = -\frac{EI}{l^3} (k_i l)^4 \phi_i \, \delta\phi_i. \qquad (e)$$

The virtual work of the pulsating force is

$$P_0 \sin \omega t \, \delta\phi_i \, (X_i)_{x=c}. \qquad (f)$$

Summing up the expressions (c), (e) and (f), and equating the sum to zero, we obtain, for calculating ϕ_i, the equation

$$\ddot{\phi}_i + \frac{EIg}{A\gamma l^4} (k_i l)^4 \phi_i = \frac{P_0 g}{A\gamma l} \sin \omega t (X_i)_{x=c}, \qquad (g)$$

or using notation (114),

$$\ddot{\phi}_i + \frac{a^2 (k_i l)^4}{l^4} \phi_i = \frac{P_0 g}{A\gamma l} \sin \omega t (X_i)_{x=c}.$$

Disregarding free vibration due to initial conditions and considering only vibration produced by the pulsating force, we obtain the solution

$$\phi_i = \frac{l^2}{(k_il)^2 a} \cdot \frac{g}{A\gamma l} \cdot P_0(X_i)_{x=c} \int_0^t \sin \omega t_1 \sin \frac{(k_il)^2 a(t - t_1)}{l^3} \, dt_1$$

$$= \frac{g}{A\gamma} P_0(X_i)_{x=c} \left[\frac{l^3}{(k_il)^4 a^2 - \omega^2 l^4} \sin \omega t - \frac{\omega l^5 \sin \frac{(k_il)^2 at}{l^2}}{(k_il)^2 a[(k_il)^4 a^2 - \omega^2 l^4]} \right] \quad (h)$$

Substituting into series (a) we obtain the deflection curve of the vibrating bar represented by two series. The first series has a factor $\sin \omega t$ and represents forced vibrations of the beam. The second series represents free vibrations produced by application of the disturbing force. These latter vibrations, due to various kinds of resistance, will gradually be damped out and only the forced vibrations have to be considered.* They are

$$y = \frac{P_0 g l^3 \sin \omega t}{A\gamma} \sum_{i=1,2,3,\cdots} \frac{X_i(X_i)_{x=c}}{(k_il)^4 a^2 - \omega^2 l^4}. \quad (i)$$

If the angular frequency ω of the pulsating force is small in comparison with the frequency of the fundamental mode of vibration of the bar, the second terms in the denominators of the series can be neglected and we will obtain a statical deflection of the bar, which was already investigated (see p. 340).

If the frequency of the pulsating force is smaller than the frequency of the lowest mode of vibration of the bar, and the force is acting at the middle, an approximate expression for the dynamic deflection is obtained by taking only the first term of the series (i). We can conclude, in this way, that the ratio of the dynamic deflection to the static deflection is approximately equal to

$$\frac{y_d}{y_s} = \frac{1}{1 - \alpha^2}, \quad (j)$$

where $\alpha = \omega/k_1^2 a$ is the ratio of the frequency of the pulsating force to the frequency of the fundamental mode of vibration of the bar.

If the frequency of the pulsating force approaches the frequency of one of the natural modes of vibration of the bar, the corresponding term of the series (i) grows indefinitely. We then have the condition of resonance, and to find the vibration we have to take both terms in the parenthesis of expression (h) and make an analysis similar to that on p. 353.

---

* The case of resonance will be discussed later.

By using the method of superposition the case of several pulsating forces acting on the bar can be investigated also.

In the general case of a disturbing force distributed along the span of the beam, we take

$$w = f(t) \cdot f_1(x) \qquad (k)$$

and represent $f_1(x)$ by the series

$$f_1(x) = a_1X_1 + a_2X_2 + a_3X_3 + \cdots,$$

in which *

$$a_i = \frac{1}{l} \int_0^l f_1(x) \cdot X_i \, dx.$$

The virtual work of this force is

$$\int_0^l \delta\phi_i \, X_i w \, dx = \delta\phi_i \, f(t) \int_0^l X_i \Sigma a_j X_j \, dx = \delta\phi_i \, f(t) a_i l.$$

Comparing this result with expression (f), we conclude that in the case of a distributed disturbing force (k), we have to replace $P_0 \sin \omega t (X_i)_{x=c}$ by $a_i l f(t)$. Making this change in the differential eq. (g), we obtain

$$\phi_i = \frac{l^2}{(k_i l)^2 a} \cdot \frac{g}{A\gamma l} \cdot a_i l \int_0^t f(t_1) \sin \frac{(k_i l)^2 a(t - t_1)}{l^2} \, dt_1.$$

Making in each particular case the indicated integration we find ϕ_i and substituting in the series (a) obtain the required vibration.

In our discussion we assumed that the ends of the bar were built in, but eqs. (h) and (i) can also be used for other kinds of end conditions. It is only necessary in each case to use the corresponding normal functions X_i and the corresponding frequencies $k_i l$. For example, to use the series (i) in the case of a bar with simply supported ends we observe that in this case the normal modes of vibration are represented by sine curves and take

$$X_i = \sqrt{2} \sin \frac{i\pi x}{l}, \quad k_i l = i\pi. \qquad (l)$$

The factor $\sqrt{2}$ is introduced to satisfy the requirement

$$\int_0^l (X_i)^2 \, dx = l.$$

Substituting expressions (l) into the series (i), we obtain the result which was previously derived (see p. 348).

* We assume that the normal functions X_i are taken so that $\int_0^l X_i^2 dx = l.$

PROBLEMS

1. Find the forced vibrations of a cantilever beam with a pulsating force $P_0 \sin \omega t$ acting at the free end, Fig. 213.

Answer. $y = \dfrac{P_0 g l^3 \sin \omega t}{A\gamma} \displaystyle\sum_{i=1,2,3 \cdots} \dfrac{X_i (X_i)_{x=l}}{(k_i l)^4 a^2 - \omega^2 l^4},$

where X_i are normal functions for a bar with one end clamped and the other end free, and $k_i l$ are the angular frequencies for normal modes of vibration in that case.

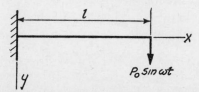

Fig. 213

2. Find the deflection of the free end of the beam in Fig. 213 produced by a load P_0 applied statically at that end. Use the series of the preceding problem.

Solution. $(y)_{x=l} = \dfrac{P_0 g l^3}{A\gamma} \displaystyle\sum_{i=1 \, 2,3 \cdots} \dfrac{(X_i)^2_{x=l}}{(k_i l)^4 a^2}.$

From the tables we find

$$(X_i)_{x=l} = 2(-1)^{i+1}.$$

Then, taking the values of $k_i l$ from the table on p. 338 and using notation (114) (see p. 325), we obtain

$$(y)_{x=l} = \frac{4 P_0 l^3}{EI} \left(\frac{1}{(1.875)^4} + \frac{1}{(4.694)^4} + \frac{1}{(7.855)^4} + \cdots \right)$$

$$= \frac{4 P_0 l^3}{EI} (0.08071 + 0.00206 + 0.00026 + \cdots) = 0.3321 \frac{P_0 l^3}{EI}.$$

With three terms of the series the error is less than 0.5%.

3. Find the forced vibrations of a beam with one end clamped and the other simply supported due to a pulsating force $P_0 \sin \omega t$ applied at the middle of the span.

4. Calculate the deflection at the middle for the beam of the preceding problem by using the numerical values:

$$(X_1)_{x=l/2} = 1.4449, \quad (X_2)_{x=l/2} = 0.5704,$$

$$(X_3)_{x=l/2} = -1.3005, \quad (X_4)_{x=l/2} = -0.5399, \quad (X_5)_{x=l/2} = 1.3068.$$

The frequencies of natural vibrations of this beam are given on p. 339.

58. Vibrations Produced by a Prescribed Motion of Some Cross Sections of a Bar.—In our preceding discussion it was always assumed that forced vibrations were produced by given forces varying with time. There occur in practice also cases in which vibrations are produced by some prescribed motion of some points of the axis or by a prescribed rotation of some cross sections of a beam. The method of handling such problems will now be illustrated by simple examples.* As a first example let us con-

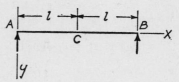

Fig. 214

sider a simply supported beam of length $2l$, Fig. 214, the middle point C of which is performing a motion:

$$(y)_{x=l} = \delta(1 - \cos \omega t). \tag{a}$$

Considering in this symmetrical case the left-hand half of the beam and using the general equation for lateral vibration, which is

$$\frac{\partial^2 y}{\partial t^2} + a^2 \frac{\partial^4 y}{\partial x^4} = 0, \quad \text{where} \quad a^2 = \frac{EIg}{A\gamma}, \tag{b}$$

we see that the end conditions in this case are

$$(y)_{x=0} = \left(\frac{\partial^2 y}{\partial x^2}\right)_{x=0} = 0, \quad \left(\frac{dy}{dx}\right)_{x=l} = 0. \tag{c}$$

In addition, we have the condition (a).

A general solution of eq. (b) we take in the form:

$$y = \delta\left(\frac{3x}{2l} - \frac{1}{2}\frac{x^3}{l^3}\right) + X \cos \omega t, \tag{d}$$

in which the first term represents the statical deflection curve of the beam, for $(y)_{x=l} = \delta$, and X in the second term is the function of x, which is to be selected in such a manner as to make expression (d) satisfy eq. (b) and also the end conditions (a) and (c). Substituting expression (d) into eq. (b), we obtain

$$\frac{d^4X}{dx^4} = \frac{\omega^2}{a^2} X. \tag{e}$$

* Several examples of this kind were discussed by Saint-Venant, *op. cit.*, p. 297. The method used by Saint-Venant was developed by E. Phillips, *J. mathématiques*, Vol. 9, p. 25, 1864. A generalization of the method is discussed by R. D. Mindlin and L. E. Goodman, *J. Appl. Mech.*, Vol. 17, p. 377, 1950; see also G. A. Nothmann, *ibid.*, Vol. 15, p. 327, 1948.

Putting

$$\frac{\omega^2}{a^2} = \alpha^4, \tag{f}$$

we use the previously obtained general solution of eq. (e) (see p. 331):

$$X = C_1(\cos \alpha x + \cosh \alpha x) + C_2(\cos \alpha x - \cosh \alpha x)$$

$$+ C_3(\sin \alpha x + \sinh \alpha x) + C_4(\sin \alpha x - \sinh \alpha x). \tag{g}$$

To satisfy the conditions at the end $x = 0$, we have to put $C_1 = C_2 = 0$. The condition $(dy/dx)_{x=l} = 0$ requires

$$C_4 = -C_3 \frac{\cos \alpha l + \cosh \alpha l}{\cos \alpha l - \cosh \alpha l},$$

and we obtain

$$X = C(\cosh \alpha l \sin \alpha x - \cos \alpha l \sinh \alpha x).$$

To satisfy the condition (a), we put

$$C(\cosh \alpha l \sin \alpha l - \cos \alpha l \sinh \alpha l) = -\delta.$$

Then the solution (d) becomes

$$y = \delta \left(\frac{3x}{2l} - \frac{1}{2} \frac{x^3}{l^3} \right) - \delta \frac{\cosh \alpha l \sin \alpha x - \cos \alpha l \sinh \alpha x}{\cosh \alpha l \sin \alpha l - \cos \alpha l \sinh \alpha l} \cdot \cos \omega t. \tag{h}$$

This expression represents forced vibrations produced by the prescribed motion (a) of the middle cross section C of the beam. To get the complete solution of the problem, we have to superpose on the forced vibrations (h), free vibrations of the beam which must be selected in such a manner as to satisfy the initial conditions of the beam. Let us assume that initially (at $t = 0$) the beam had no deflections and was completely at rest. The second condition is satisfied by expression (h) since its derivative with respect to time vanishes at $t = 0$. To satisfy the first condition, the free vibration must be added to the vibrations (h). Let y_1 denote deflections corresponding to the free vibrations and $f(x)$ denotes expression (h) for $t = 0$. Then y_1 must satisfy eq. (b) and the end conditions (c). In addition, it must vanish at $x = l$, so that condition (a), satisfied by expression (h), will not be violated. From this we conclude that the modes of free vibrations are the same as those for a beam with one end simply supported and the other clamped. Denoting the normal functions for that case by X_i (see p. 342), we can represent the free vibrations by the series

$$y_1 = \sum_{i=1,2,3,\cdots} X_i(A_i \cos p_i t + B_i \sin p_i t). \qquad (i)$$

The initial conditions for y_1 are

$$(y_1)_{t=0} + f(x) = 0; \quad (\dot{y}_1)_{t=0} = 0.$$

From these conditions we conclude that

$$\sum_{i=1,2,3} X_i A_i = -f(x); \quad B_i = 0.$$

The coefficients A_i can now be determined in the usual way and we obtain

$$A_i = -\frac{\displaystyle\int_0^l f(x) X_i \, dx}{\displaystyle\int_0^l X_i^2 \, dx}. \qquad (j)$$

With these values of A_i the free vibrations (i) are completely determined, and superposing them on the forced vibrations (h), the complete solution of the problem is obtained.

As a second example let us consider the case of a cantilever beam, Fig. 215, the left end of which performs a given vertical motion

$$(y)_{x=0} = f(t). \qquad (k)$$

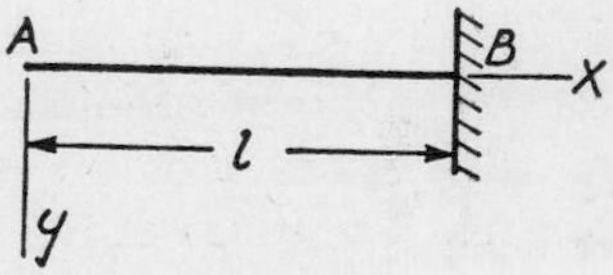

We again use the static deflection curve of a cantilever and take as a portion of the required solution the expression

$$y_1 = f(t) \cdot \left(1 - \frac{3}{2}\frac{x}{l} + \frac{1}{2}\frac{x^3}{l^3}\right). \qquad (l)$$

FIG. 215

This expression satisfies the end conditions

$$(y_1)_{x=0} = f(t), \quad \left(\frac{d^2 y_1}{dx^2}\right)_{x=0} = 0, \quad (y_1)_{x=l} = 0, \quad \left(\frac{dy_1}{dx}\right)_{x=l} = 0, \qquad (m)$$

but it does not satisfy the differential eq. (b) since, by taking the statical deflection curve (l), we disregarded the inertia force distributed along the axis of the beam, the intensity of which is

$$-\frac{A\gamma}{g}\ddot{f}(t)\left(1 - \frac{3}{2}\frac{x}{l} + \frac{1}{2}\frac{x^3}{l^3}\right). \qquad (n)$$

To get the complete solution of the problem, we have to superpose on the motion represented by eq. (l), vibrations produced by the forces (n). To keep the end conditions (m) satisfied, the vibrations which we have to consider must be the same as those for a beam simply supported at the end $x = 0$ and clamped at the end $x = l$. These vibrations will be represented by the series

$$y_2 = \sum_{i=1,2,3,\cdots} \phi_i X_i, \qquad (o)$$

in which ϕ_i are functions of time and X_i, normal functions of x for the beam with the above-mentioned end conditions. The latter can be readily obtained from the general solution (117) which in our case will be

$$X_i \sinh k_i l \sin k_i x - \sin k_i l \sinh k_i x. \qquad (p)$$

The values of k_i are calculated from the frequency equation

$$\tanh k_i l = \tan k_i l \qquad (q)$$

and are given on p. 339.

In deriving the equation for functions ϕ_i we proceed, as before, and consider a virtual displacement

$$\delta y_1 = \delta \phi_i X_i.$$

Then the virtual work of inertia forces is

$$- \frac{A\gamma}{g} \ddot{\phi}_i \, \delta \phi_i \int_0^l X_i^2 \, dx$$

and the virtual work of elasticity forces is

$$- \frac{\partial V}{\partial \phi_i} \delta \phi_i = -EI \phi_i \, \delta \phi_i \int_0^l \left(\frac{d^2 X_i}{dx^2} \right)^2 dx = -EI \phi_i \, \delta \phi_i \, k_i^4 \int_0^l X_1^2 \, dx.$$

In calculating the virtual work of the distributed disturbing force (n), we proceed as explained before (see p. 367) and represent these forces by the series

$$- \frac{A\gamma}{g} \dot{f}(t) \left(1 - \frac{3}{2} \frac{x}{l} + \frac{1}{2} \frac{x^3}{l^3} \right) = - \frac{A\gamma}{g} \ddot{f}(t) \sum_{i=1,2,3,\cdots} b_i X_i, \qquad (r)$$

where the coefficients b_i are obtained from the formula

$$b_i = \frac{\displaystyle\int_0^l X_i \left(1 - \frac{3}{2} \frac{x}{l} + \frac{1}{2} \frac{x^3}{l^3} \right) dx}{\displaystyle\int_0^l X_i^2 \, dx}.$$

Substituting expression (p) for X_i and performing the integration we obtain

$$\int_0^l X_i \left(1 - \frac{3}{2} \frac{x}{l} + \frac{1}{2} \frac{x^3}{l^3} \right) dx = \frac{1}{k_i} (\sin k_i l + \sinh k_i l),$$

$$\int_0^l X_i^2 \, dx = \frac{l}{2} (\sinh^2 k_i l - \sin^2 k_i l).$$

Hence

$$b_i = \frac{2}{k_i l (\sinh k_i l - \sin k_i l)}.$$ (s)

Using the series (r), the virtual work of the disturbing force becomes

$$-\frac{A\gamma}{g}\ddot{f}(t)b_i \,\delta\phi_i \int_0^l X_i^2 \, dx.$$

Equating to zero the entire virtual work, we obtain the equation

$$\ddot{\phi}_i + \frac{EIgk_i^4}{A\gamma}\phi_i = -b_i\ddot{f}(t),$$

the general solution of which is

$$\phi_i = A_i \cos p_i t + B_i \sin p_i t - \frac{b_i}{p_i}\int_0^t \ddot{f}(t_1)\sin p_i(t - t_1)\,dt_1,$$ (t)

where, as before, we use the notations

$$\frac{EIg}{A\gamma} = a^2; \quad ak_i^2 = p_i.$$

Substituting ϕ_i into the series (o), we obtain the vibrations y_2 which must be superposed on the deflections (l) in order to get the complete solution

$$y = y_1 + y_2 = f(t)\left(1 - \frac{3x}{2l} + \frac{1}{2}\frac{x^3}{l^3}\right) + \Sigma\phi_i X_i.$$ (u)

The constants A_i and B_i in each particular case have to be determined from the initial conditions. Assuming that the initial deflections and the initial velocities are given by the equations

$$(y)_{t=0} = u(x), \quad (\ddot{y})_{t=0} = w(x),$$

and observing that from the solution (t)

$$(\phi_i)_{t=0} = A_i, \quad (\dot{\phi}_i)_{t=0} = B_i p_i,$$

we write the initial conditions in the following form:

$$\left. \begin{aligned} u(x) &= (y_1)_{t=0} + (y_2)_{t=0} = f(0)\left(1 - \frac{3}{2}\frac{x}{l} + \frac{1}{2}\frac{x^3}{l^3}\right) + \sum_{i=1,2,3,\cdots} A_i X_i, \\ w(x) &= (\dot{y}_1)_{t=0} + (\dot{y}_2)_{t=0} = \dot{f}(0)\left(1 - \frac{3}{2}\frac{x}{l} + \frac{1}{2}\frac{x^3}{l^3}\right) + \sum_{i=1,2,3,\cdots} B_i p_i X_i. \end{aligned} \right\}$$ (v)

Assuming, for example, that initial displacements and initial velocities vanish and observing, from eq. (r), that

$$1 - \frac{3x}{2l} + \frac{1}{2}\frac{x^3}{l^3} = \sum_{i=1,2,3,\cdots} b_i X_i,$$

we conclude that

$$A_i = -f(0)b_i; \quad B_i = -\frac{1}{p_i}\dot{f}(0)b_i.$$

Thus the general solution (u) becomes

$$y = f(t) \left(1 - \frac{3x}{2l} + \frac{1}{2} \frac{x^3}{l^3} \right) - f(0) \Sigma b_i X_i \cos p_i t$$
$$- \dot{f}(0) \Sigma \frac{b_i}{p_i} X_i \sin p_i t - \Sigma \frac{b_i}{p_i} X_i \int_0^t \ddot{f}(t_1) \sin p_i(t - t_1) \, dt_1. \quad (w)$$

This solution can be somewhat simplified by using the formula for integration by parts, which gives

$$\int_0^t \ddot{f}(t_1) \sin p_i(t - t_1) \, dt_1 = -\dot{f}(0) \sin p_i t + p_i f(t)$$
$$- p_i f(0) \cos p_i t - p_i{}^2 \int_0^t f(t_1) \sin p_i(t - t_1) \, dt_1.$$

Substituting into solution (w), we finally obtain

$$y = f(t) \left(1 - \frac{3x}{2l} + \frac{1}{2} \frac{x^3}{l^3} \right) - \sum_{i=1,2,3,\cdots} b_i X_i f(t) + \sum_{i=1,2,3,\cdots} b_i X_i p_i \int_0^t f(t_1) \sin p_i(t - t_1) \, dt_1.$$

59. Effect of Axial Force on Lateral Vibrations.

—If a vibrating bar is subjected to the action of an axial compressive force S, Fig. 216, the differ-

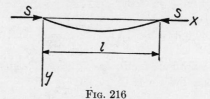

FIG. 216

ential equation of the deflection curve under static lateral load is

$$EI = \frac{d^2 y}{dx^2} = -M - Sy,$$

where M denotes the bending moment produced by lateral load. By double differentiation, we obtain

$$\frac{d^2}{dx^2} \left(EI \frac{d^2 y}{dx^2} \right) = w - S \frac{d^2 y}{dx^2}. \quad (153)$$

To obtain the differential equation for later vibrations, we substitute the inertia forces for w, which gives

$$\frac{\partial^2}{\partial x^2} \left(EI \frac{\partial^2 y}{\partial x^2} \right) + S \frac{\partial^2 y}{\partial x^2} = -\frac{A\gamma}{g} \frac{\partial^2 y}{\partial t^2}.$$

In the case of a prismatical bar, we obtain

$$EI \frac{\partial^4 y}{\partial x^4} + S \frac{\partial^2 y}{\partial x^2} = - \frac{A\gamma}{g} \frac{\partial^2 y}{\partial t^2}. \tag{154}$$

Assuming that the bar performs one of the natural modes of vibration, we take the solution of eq. (154) in the form

$$y = X(A \cos pt + B \sin pt), \tag{a}$$

where X is a function of x.

Substituting back, we find

$$EI \frac{d^4 X}{dx^4} + S \frac{d^2 X}{dx^2} = \frac{A\gamma}{g} p^2 X. \tag{b}$$

The solutions of this equation, satisfying the prescribed end conditions, furnish us the normal functions for these conditions. We have the simplest case if the ends of the bar are simply supported. These conditions are satisfied by taking

$$X_i = \sin \frac{i\pi x}{l}, \tag{c}$$

where i is an integer.

Substituting this expression into eq. (b), we obtain the corresponding angular frequency of vibration

$$p_i = \frac{a i^2 \pi^2}{l^2} \sqrt{1 - \frac{S l^2}{i^2 E I \pi^2}}, \tag{d}$$

where, as before, $a^2 = EIg/A\gamma$.

This frequency is smaller than that obtained before (see eqs. 133), when the axial force S was absent. Its value depends on the magnitude of the ratio $Sl^2/EI\pi^2$, which is the ratio of the axial force to the Euler's critical load. If this ratio approaches unity, the frequency of the lowest mode of vibration approaches zero and we obtain lateral buckling.

Substituting expressions (c) and (d) into solution (a), we obtain a natural mode of vibration with i sinusoidal half waves. Summing up such vibrations, we obtain the general solution for free vibrations of a compressed prismatical bar with simply supported ends:

$$y = \sum_{i=1,2,3,\cdots} \sin \frac{i\pi x}{l} (A_i \cos p_i t + B_i \sin p_i t).$$

If the initial deflections and the initial velocites are given, the constants A_i and B_i can be calculated in the same manner as before (see p. 333).

If, instead of a compressive force, a tensile force S is acting on the bar, the frequencies of natural vibrations increase and we obtain their values by changing S to $-S$ in eq. (d) which gives

$$p_i = \frac{ai^2\pi^2}{l^2}\sqrt{1 + \frac{Sl^2}{i^2 EI\pi^2}}. \tag{e}$$

If we have a very flexible bar, say a wire, under a large tension the second term under the radical in expression (e) becomes very large in comparison with unity and, if i^2 is not large, we can put

$$p_i \approx \frac{ai^2\pi^2}{l^2}\sqrt{\frac{Sl^2}{i^2 EI\pi^2}} = \frac{i\pi}{l}\sqrt{\frac{Sg}{A\gamma}},$$

which are natural frequencies of a stretched string.

In studying forced vibration of a simply supported prismatical bar on which an axial tensile force S is acting, we proceed as before (see p. 345) in the case in which S vanishes and assume that vibrations are represented by a series

$$y = \sum_{i=1,2,3,\cdots} \phi_i \sin\frac{i\pi x}{l}. \tag{f}$$

Taking now a virtual displacement

$$\delta y = \delta\phi_i \sin\frac{i\pi x}{l},$$

and applying the principle of virtual work, we obtain for determining the functions ϕ_i, the equation

$$\ddot{\phi}_i + p_i^2\phi_i = \frac{2g}{A\gamma l}Q_i, \tag{g}$$

in which p_i is given by eq. (e) and $Q_i \,\delta\phi_i$ represents in each particular case the virtual work of the disturbing force. For example, if forced vibrations are produced by a pulsating force $P_0 \sin \omega t$ applied at the distance c from the left end ($x = c$), we have to substitute into eq. (f)

$$Q_i = P_0 \sin \omega t \sin\frac{i\pi c}{l}.$$

The general solution of eq. (g) we take in the form:

$$\phi_i = A_i \sin p_i t + B_i \cos p_i t + \frac{2g}{A\gamma l p_i} \int_0^t (Q_i)_{t\,=\,t_1} \sin [p_i(t - t_1)] \, dt_1.$$

From this ϕ_i can be calculated for any given expression for Q_i. Substituting ϕ_i into the series (f), the general solution of the problem is obtained. In this way, for example, the solution can be obtained for the case of a stretched wire along which a constant lateral force is traveling with constant speed. Such a condition is approximately fulfilled in the case of vibration of an overhead conductor under the action of the collector gear of an electric locomotive. Investigations show * that an undesirable disturbance near the end $x = l$ may occur if the velocity of travel approaches the value $v_{cr} = \sqrt{gS/A\gamma}$. To eliminate this disturbance, it is necessary to use a large tensile stress in the wire so that the above critical speed will be far beyond the speed limit used in service.

60. Vibration of Beams on Elastic Foundation.—Assume that a beam with hinged ends is supported along its length by a continuous elastic foundation, the rigidity of which is given by the magnitude k of the *modulus of foundation*; k is the load per unit length of the beam necessary to produce a compression in the foundation equal to unity. If the mass of the foundation can be neglected the vibrations of such a beam can easily be studied by using the same methods as before.

The differential equation for statical deflection in this case will be

$$EI \frac{d^4y}{dx^4} = w - ky,$$

where w is the intensity of external distributed load. Replacing it by inertia forces, we obtain the differential equation for lateral vibration

$$EI \frac{\partial^4 y}{\partial x^4} + ky = -\frac{A\gamma}{g} \frac{\partial^2 y}{\partial t^2}. \tag{a}$$

Natural modes of vibration we take in the form

$$y = X(A \cos pt + B \sin pt).$$

Substituting into eq. (a), we find the equation for the function X,

$$EI \frac{d^4X}{dx^4} + kX = \frac{A\gamma p^2}{g} X. \tag{b}$$

* See writer's paper in Theodore von Kármán Anniversary Volume, 1941.

Considering the simplest case of a beam with simply supported ends, we take

$$X_i = \sin \frac{i\pi x}{l},$$

which satisfies all the end conditions for this case. Substituting it into eq. (b), we find

$$p_i{}^2 = \frac{a^2 \pi^4}{l^4} (i^4 + \beta), \tag{c}$$

where

$$a^2 = \frac{EIg}{A\gamma}, \quad \beta = \frac{kl^4}{EI\pi^4}. \tag{d}$$

The general expression for free vibrations of the bar then is

$$y = \sum_{i=1,2,3,\cdots} X_i(A_i \cos p_i t + B_i \sin p_i t).$$

The constants A_i and B_i can be calculated in each particular case, if initial deflections and initial velocities are given, by applying the same method as before (see p. 333).

In studying forced vibrations of the bar, we take deflections in the form of the series

$$y = \sum_{i=1,2,3,\cdots} \phi_i \sin \frac{i\pi x}{l}. \tag{e}$$

The differential equation for ϕ_i is obtained as before (see p. 346), by applying the principle of virtual work. In calculating the strain energy, the strain energy of the foundation,

$$\tfrac{1}{2} \int_0^l ky^2 \, dx,$$

must be added to the strain energy of bending of the beam. With only this change in derivation, we obtain the equation

$$\ddot{\phi}_i + p_i{}^2 \phi_i = \frac{2g}{A\gamma l} Q_i, \tag{f}$$

in which the expression for Q_i is to be determined in each particular case from the condition that $Q_i \, \delta\phi_i$ represents the virtual work of the disturbing force.

A general solution of eq. (f) will be

$$\phi_i = A_i \cos p_i t + B_i \sin p_i t + \frac{2g}{\gamma A l} \cdot \frac{1}{p_i} \int_0^t Q_i \sin p_i(t - t_1)\, dt_1. \quad (g)$$

The first two terms of this solution represent free vibrations of the beam, depending on the initial conditions. The third term represents vibrations produced by the disturbing force.

The frequencies of the natural vibrations depend, as seen from (c), not only on the rigidity of the beam but also on the rigidityof the foundation.

As an example consider the case when a pulsating force $P = P_0 \sin \omega t_1$ is acting on the beam at a distance c from the left support (Fig. 207). The quantity Q_i will be in this case

$$Q_i = P_0 \sin \frac{i\pi c}{l} \sin \omega t_1. \quad (h)$$

Substituting in eq. (g) and considering only vibrations produced by the disturbing force, we obtain

$$\phi \cdot = \frac{2g}{\gamma A} P_0 \sin \frac{i\pi c}{l} \left\{ \frac{l^3}{\pi^4 a^2(i^4 + \beta) - \omega^2 l^4} \sin \omega t - \frac{\omega}{l p_i(p_i^2 - \omega^2)} \sin p_i t \right\}.$$

Substituting this into the series (e), gives

$$y = \frac{2g P_0 l^3}{\gamma A} \sum_{i=1}^{i=\infty} \left[\frac{\sin \dfrac{i\pi c}{l} \sin \dfrac{i\pi x}{l} \sin \omega t}{\pi^4 a^2(i^4 + \beta) - \omega^2 l^4} - \frac{\omega \sin \dfrac{i\pi c}{l} \sin \dfrac{i\pi x}{l} \sin p_i t}{l^4 p_i(p_i^2 - \omega^2)} \right]. \quad (i)$$

The first term in this expression represents the forced vibration and the second, the free vibration of the beam. By taking $\omega = 0$ and $P = P_0 \sin \omega t$ the deflection of the beam by a constant force P will be obtained:

$$y = \frac{2P l^3}{E I \pi^4} \sum_{i=1}^{i=\infty} \frac{\sin \dfrac{i\pi c}{l} \sin \dfrac{i\pi x}{l}}{i^4 + \beta}. \quad (155)$$

By taking $c = l/2$, the deflection by the force P at the middle will be obtained as follows:

$$y = \frac{2P l^3}{E I \pi^4} \left(\frac{\sin \dfrac{\pi x}{l}}{1 + \beta} - \frac{\sin \dfrac{3\pi x}{l}}{3^4 + \beta} + \frac{\sin \dfrac{5\pi x}{l}}{5^4 + \beta} - \cdots \right). \quad (156)$$

Comparing this with eq. (l), p. 348, it can be concluded that the additional term β in the denominators represents the effect on the deflection of the beam of the elastic foundation.

By comparing the forced vibrations

$$y = \frac{2gP_0 l^3 \sin \omega t}{\gamma A} \sum_{i=1}^{i=\infty} \frac{\sin \dfrac{i\pi c}{l} \sin \dfrac{i\pi x}{l}}{\pi^4 a^2 (i^4 + \beta) - \omega^2 l^4} = \frac{2P l^3}{EI\pi^4} \sum_{i=1}^{i=\infty} \frac{\sin \dfrac{i\pi c}{l} \sin \dfrac{i\pi x}{l}}{i^4 + \beta - \dfrac{\omega^2 l^4}{\pi^4 a^2}}$$

with the statical deflection (155), it can be concluded that the dynamical deflections can be obtained from the statical formula. It is only necessary to replace β by $\beta - (\omega^2 l^4/\pi^4 a^2)$.

By using notations (d), we obtain

$$\beta - \frac{\omega^2 l^4}{\pi^4 a^2} = \frac{k l^4}{EI\pi^4} - \frac{\omega^2 l^4 \gamma A}{\pi^4 EIg} = \frac{l^4}{EI\pi^4}\left(k - \frac{\gamma \omega^2 A}{g}\right).$$

This means that the dynamical deflection can be obtained from the statical formula by replacing in it the actual modulus of foundation by a diminished value $k - (\gamma \omega^2 A/g)$ of the same modulus. This conclusion remains true also in the case of an infinitely long bar on an elastic foundation. By using it the deflection of a rail produced by a pulsating load can be calculated.[*]

61. Ritz Method. [†]—It has already been shown in several cases (see Art. 4) that in calculating the frequency of the fundamental type of vibration of a complicated system the approximate method of Rayleigh can be applied. In using this method it is necessary to make some assumption as to the shape of the deflection curve of a vibrating beam or vibrating shaft. The corresponding frequency will then be found from the consideration of the energy of the system. The choice of a definite shape for the deflection curve in this method is equivalent to introducing some additional constraints which reduce the system to one having a single degree of freedom. Such additional constraints can only increase the rigidity of the system and make the frequency of vibrations, as obtained by Rayleigh's method, usually somewhat higher than its exact value. Better approximations in calculating the fundamental frequency and also the frequencies of higher modes of vibration can be obtained by Ritz's method which is a further

---

[*] See writer's paper, "Statical and Dynamical Stresses in Rails," *Proc. Intern. Congr. Appl. Mech.*, Zürich, p. 407, 1926.

[†] See Walther Ritz, *Gesammelte Werke*, Paris, p. 265, 1911.

development of Rayleigh's method.* In using this method the equation of the deflection curve representing the mode of vibration is to be taken with several parameters, the magnitudes of which should be chosen in such a manner as to reduce to a minimum the frequency of vibration. The manner of choosing the shape of the deflection curve and the procedure of calculating consecutive frequencies will now be shown for the simple case of the vibration of a uniform string (Fig. 217). Assume that

S is the tensile force in the string,
w is the weight of the string per unit length
$2l$ is the length of the string.

If the string performs one of the normal modes of vibration, the deflection can be represented by the equation

$$y = X \cos pt, \qquad (a)$$

where X is a function of x determining the shape of the vibrating string, and p is the angular frequency of vibration. Assuming that the deflections are very small, the change in the tensile force S during vibration can be neglected and the increase in potential energy of deformation due to the deflection will be obtained by multiplying

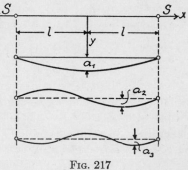

Fig. 217

plying S with the increase in length of the string. In this manner the following expression for the potential energy is found, the energy in the position of equilibrium being taken as zero,†

$$V = S \int_0^l \left(\frac{dy}{dx}\right)^2 dx.$$

The maximum potential energy occurs when the vibrating string occupies its extreme position. In this position $\cos pt = 1$ in eq. (a) and

$$V = S \int_0^l \left(\frac{dX}{dx}\right)^2 dx. \qquad (b)$$

---

* Lord Rayleigh used the method only for an approximate calculation of frequency of the gravest mode of vibration of complicated systems, and was doubtful (see his papers, *Phil. Mag.*, Vol. 47, p. 566, 1899; and Vol. 22, p. 225, 1911) regarding its application to the investigation of higher modes of vibration.

† For both symmetrical and antisymmetrical modes of vibration, it is sufficient to consider only half of the span.

The kinetic energy of the vibrating string is

$$T = \frac{w}{g} \int_0^l (\dot{y})^2 \, dx.$$

Its maximum occurs when the vibrating string is in its middle position, i.e., when $\cos pt = 0$, then

$$T = \frac{p^2 w}{g} \int_0^l X^2 \, dx. \tag{c}$$

Assuming that there are no losses in energy, we may equate (b) and (c), thus obtaining

$$p^2 = \frac{gS}{w} \frac{\displaystyle\int_0^l \left(\frac{dX}{dx}\right)^2 dx}{\displaystyle\int_0^l X^2 \, dx}. \tag{d}$$

Knowing the shapes of various modes of vibration and substituting in (d) the corresponding expressions for X, the frequencies of these modes of vibration can easily be calculated. In the case of a uniform string, the deflection curves during vibration are sinusoidal curves and for the first three modes of vibration, shown in Fig. 217, we have

$$X_1 = a_1 \cos \frac{\pi x}{2l}, \quad X_2 = a_2 \sin \frac{\pi x}{l}, \quad X_3 = a_3 \cos \frac{3\pi x}{2l}.$$

Substituting in (d), we obtain

$$p_1{}^2 = \frac{\pi^2}{4l^2} \frac{gS}{w}, \quad p_2{}^2 = \frac{\pi^2}{l^2} \frac{gS}{w}, \quad p_3{}^2 = \frac{9}{4} \frac{\pi^2}{l^2} \frac{gS}{w}, \tag{e}$$

and the corresponding frequencies will be

$$f_1 = \frac{p_1}{2\pi} = \frac{1}{4l} \sqrt{\frac{gS}{w}}, \quad f_2 = \frac{2}{4l} \sqrt{\frac{gS}{w}}, \quad f_3 = \frac{3}{4l} \sqrt{\frac{gS}{w}}. \tag{f}$$

Let us now apply Ritz's method in calculating, from eq. (d), the frequency f_1 of the fundamental type of vibration. The first step in the application of this method is to choose a suitable expression for the deflection curve. Let $\varphi_1(x)$, $\varphi_2(x)$, $\cdots$ be a series of functions satisfying the end conditions and suitable for representation of X. Then, by taking

$$X = a_1\varphi_1(x) + a_2\varphi_2(x) + a_3\varphi_3(x) + \cdots, \qquad (g)$$

we obtain a suitable deflection curve of the vibrating string.

We know that by taking a finite number of terms in the expression (g) we superimpose certain limitations on the possible shapes of the deflection curve of the string and due to this fact the frequency, as calculated from (d), will usually be higher than the exact value of this frequency. In order to obtain the approximation as close as possible, Ritz proposed to choose the coefficients a_1, a_2, a_3, $\cdots$ in the expression (g) so as to make the expression (d) a minimum. In this manner a system of equations, such as

$$\frac{\partial}{\partial a_n} \frac{\int_0^l \left(\frac{dX}{dx}\right)^2 dx}{\int_0^l X^2 \, dx} = 0, \qquad (h)$$

will be obtained.

Performing the differentiation indicated, we have

$$\int_0^l X^2 \, dx \cdot \frac{\partial}{\partial a_n} \int_0^l \left(\frac{dX}{dx}\right)^2 dx - \int_0^l \left(\frac{dX}{dx}\right)^2 dx \cdot \frac{\partial}{\partial a_n} \int_0^l X^2 \, dx = 0, \qquad (i)$$

or noting that from (d),

$$\int_0^l \left(\frac{dX}{dx}\right)^2 dx = \frac{p^2 w}{gS} \int_0^l X^2 \, dx,$$

we obtain,

$$\frac{\partial}{\partial a_n} \int_0^l \left\{ \left(\frac{dX}{dx}\right)^2 - \frac{p^2 w}{gS} X^2 \right\} dx = 0. \qquad (j)$$

Substituting expression (g) for X and performing the indicated operations, a system of equations homogeneous and linear in a_1, a_2, a_3, $\cdots$ will be obtained, the number of which will be equal to the number of coefficients a_1, a_2, a_3, $\cdots$ in the expression (g). Such a system of equations can yield for a_1, a_2, a_3, $\cdots$ solutions different from zero only if the determinant of these equations is equal to zero. This condition brings us to the *frequency equation* from which the frequencies of the various modes of vibrations can be calculated.

Let us consider the modes of vibration of a taut string symmetrical with respect to the middle plane. It is easy to see that a function such as $l^2 - x^2$, representing a symmetrical parabolic curve and satisfying the end conditions $\{(y)_{x=\pm l} = 0\}$ is a suitable function in this case. By multiplying this function with $x^2, x^4, \cdots$ a series of symmetrical curves satisfying the end conditions will be obtained. In this manner we arrive at the following expression for the deflection curve of the vibrating string:

$$X = a_1(l^2 - x^2) + a_2x^2(l^2 - x^2) + a_3x^4(l^2 - x^2) + \cdots. \qquad (k)$$

In order to show how quickly the accuracy of our calculations increases with an increase in the number of terms of the expression (k) we begin with one term only and put

$$X_1 = a_1(l^2 - x^2).$$

Then,

$$\int_0^l (X_1)^2\, dx = \frac{8}{15}\, a_1{}^2 l^5, \quad \int_0^l \left(\frac{dX_1}{dx}\right)^2 dx = \frac{4}{3}\, a_1{}^2 l^3.$$

Substituting in eq. (d) we obtain

$$p_1{}^2 = \frac{5}{2l^2}\, \frac{gS}{w}.$$

Comparing this with the exact solution (e), it is seen that $5/2$ instead of $\pi^2/4$ is obtained, and the error in frequency is only 0.66%.

It should be noted that by taking only one term in the expression (k) the shape of the curve is completely determined and the system is reduced to one with a single degree of freedom, as in Rayleigh's approximate method.

In order to get a further approximation, let us take two terms in the expression (k). Then we will have two parameters a_1 and a_2 and by changing the ratio of these two quantities we can also change, to a certain extent, the shape of the curve. The best approximation will be obtained when this ratio is such that the expression (d) becomes a minimum, which requires that conditions (j) be satisfied.

By taking as a second approximation

$$X_2 = a_1(l^2 - x^2) + a_2x^2(l^2 - x^2),$$

we obtain

$$\int_0^l X_2{}^2\, dx = \frac{8}{15}\, a_1{}^2 l^5 + \frac{16}{105}\, a_1a_2 l^7 + \frac{8}{315}\, a_2{}^2 l^9,$$

$$\int_0^l \left(\frac{dX_2}{dx}\right)^2 dx = \frac{4}{3}\, a_1{}^2 l^3 + \frac{8}{15}\, a_1a_2 l^5 + \frac{44}{105}\, a_2{}^2 l^7.$$

Substituting in eq. (j) and taking the derivatives with respect to a_1 and a_2, we obtain

$$a_1 \left(1 - \frac{2}{5} k^2 l^2 \right) + a_2 l^2 \left(\frac{1}{5} - \frac{2}{35} k^2 l^2 \right) = 0,$$

$$a_1 \left(1 - \frac{2}{7} k^2 l^2 \right) + a_2 l^2 \left(\frac{11}{7} - \frac{2}{21} k^2 l^2 \right) = 0, \qquad (l)$$

in which

$$k^2 = \frac{p^2 w}{gS}. \qquad (m)$$

The determinant of the eqs. (l) will vanish when

$$k^4 l^4 - 28 k^2 l^2 + 63 = 0.$$

The two roots of this equation are

$$k_1{}^2 l^2 = 2.46744, \quad k_2{}^2 l^2 = 25.6.$$

Remembering that we are considering only modes of vibration symmetrical about the middle and using eq. (m), we obtain for the first and third modes of vibration,

$$p_1{}^2 = \frac{2.46744}{l^2} \frac{gS}{w}, \quad p_3{}^2 = \frac{25.6}{l^2} \frac{gS}{w}.$$

Comparing these with the exact solutions (e):

$$p_1{}^2 = \frac{\pi^2}{4 l^2} \frac{gS}{w} = \frac{2.467401}{l^2} \frac{gS}{w}, \quad p_3{}^2 = \frac{9}{4} \frac{\pi^2}{l^2} \frac{gS}{w} = \frac{22.207}{l^2} \frac{gS}{w},$$

it can be concluded that the accuracy with which the fundamental frequency is obtained is very high (the error is less than 0.001%). The error in the frequency of the third mode of vibration is about 6.5%. By taking three terms in the expression (k) the frequency of the third mode of vibration will be obtained with an error less than $\frac{1}{2}$%.*

It is seen that by using the Ritz method not only the fundamental frequency but also frequencies of higher modes of vibration can be obtained with good accuracy by taking a sufficient number of terms in the expression for the deflection curve. In the next article an application of this method to the study of the vibrations of bars of variable cross section will be shown.

* See W. Ritz, *loc. cit.*, p. 380.

62. Vibration of Bars of Variable Cross Section.—*General.*—In our previous discussion various problems involving the vibration of prismatical bars were considered. There exist, however, several important engineering problems such as the vibration of turbine blades, hulls of ships, beams of variable depth, etc., in which recourse has to be taken to the theory of vibration of a bar of variable cross section. The differential equation of vibration of such a bar has been previously discussed (see p. 324) and has the following form,

$$\frac{\partial^2}{\partial x^2}\left(EI\,\frac{\partial^2 y}{\partial x^2}\right) + \frac{A\gamma}{g}\,\frac{\partial^2 y}{\partial t^2} = 0, \tag{157}$$

in which I and A are certain functions of x. Only in some special cases which will be considered later, can the exact forms of the normal functions be determined in terms of known functions. Thus in the solution of such problems approximate methods like the Rayleigh-Ritz method or numerical integration are used for calculating the natural frequencies of vibration. Using the Ritz method, we take the deflection of the rod, while vibrating, in the form

$$y = X \cos pt, \tag{a}$$

in which X defines the *mode of vibration*. In this way we obtain the following expressions for the maximum potential and the maximum kinetic energy,

$$V = \frac{1}{2}\int_0^l EI\left(\frac{d^2 X}{dx^2}\right)^2 dx, \tag{b}$$

$$T = \frac{p^2}{2g}\int_0^l A\gamma X^2\, dx, \tag{c}$$

from which

$$p^2 = \frac{Eg}{\gamma}\frac{\displaystyle\int_0^l I\left(\frac{d^2 X}{dx^2}\right)^2 dx}{\displaystyle\int_0^l A X^2\, dx}. \tag{d}$$

The exact solution for the frequency of the fundamental mode of vibration will be the one which makes the left side of (d) a minimum. In order to obtain an approximate solution we proceed as in the previous article and take the shape of the deflection curve in the form of a series,

$$X = a_1\varphi_1(x) + a_2\varphi_2(x) + a_3\varphi_3(x) + \cdots, \tag{e}$$

in which every one of the functions φ satisfies the conditions at the ends of the rod. Substituting the series (e) in eq. (d), the conditions of minimum will require that

$$\frac{\partial}{\partial a_n} \frac{\displaystyle\int_0^l I\left(\frac{d^2X}{dx^2}\right)^2 dx}{\displaystyle\int_0^l AX^2 \, dx} = 0, \tag{f}$$

or

$$\int_0^l AX^2 \, dx \cdot \frac{\partial}{\partial a_n} \int_0^l I\left(\frac{d^2X}{dx^2}\right)^2 dx - \int_0^l I\left(\frac{d^2X}{dx^2}\right)^2 dx \cdot \frac{\partial}{\partial a_n} \int_0^l AX^2 \, dx = 0. \tag{g}$$

From (g) and (d) we obtain

$$\frac{\partial}{\partial a_n} \int_0^l \left[I\left(\frac{d^2X}{dx^2}\right)^2 - \frac{p^2 A\gamma}{Eg} X^2 \right] dx = 0. \tag{158}$$

Thus the problem is reduced to finding such values for the constants $a_1, a_2, a_3, \cdots$ in eq. (e) as to make the integral

$$S = \int_0^l \left[I\left(\frac{d^2X}{dx^2}\right)^2 - \frac{p^2 A\gamma}{Eg} X^2 \right] dx \tag{h}$$

a minimum.

Eqs. (158) are homogeneous and linear in $a_1, a_2, a_3, \cdots$ and their number is equal to the number of terms in the expression (e). Equating to zero the determinant of these equations, the *frequency equation* will be obtained from which the frequencies of the various modes can be calculated. Let us consider now several particular cases.

Vibration of a Wedge.—In the case of a wedge of unit thickness with one end free and the other one built in (Fig. 218), we have

$$A = \frac{2bx}{l},$$

$$I = \frac{1}{12}\left(\frac{2bx}{l}\right)^3,$$

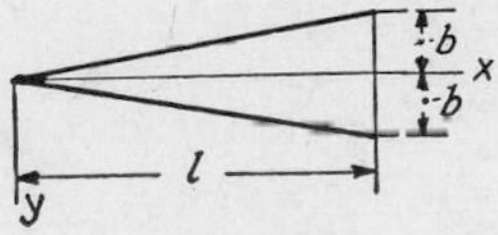

Fig. 218

where l is the length of the cantilever and $2b$ is the depth of the cantilever at the built-in end. The end conditions are:

$$(1) \ \left(EI\frac{d^2X}{dx^2}\right)_{x=0} = 0, \qquad (2) \ \frac{d}{dx}\left(EI\frac{d^2X}{dx^2}\right)_{x=0} = 0,$$

$$(3) \quad (X)_{x=l} = 0, \qquad (4) \quad \left(\frac{dX}{dx}\right)_{x=l} = 0.$$

In order to satisfy the conditions at the ends we take the deflection curve in the form of the series

$$X = a_1 \left(1 - \frac{x}{l}\right)^2 + a_2 \frac{x}{l}\left(1 - \frac{x}{l}\right)^2 + a_3 \frac{x^2}{l^2}\left(1 - \frac{x}{l}\right)^2 + \cdots. \qquad (i)$$

It is easy to see that each term, as well as its derivative with respect to x, becomes equal to zero when $x = l$. Consequently the end conditions (3) and (4) above will be satisfied. Conditions (1) and (2) are also satisfied since I and dI/dx are zero for $x = 0$.

Taking as a first approximation

$$X_1 = a_1 \left(1 - \frac{x}{l}\right)^2,$$

and substituting in eq. (d), we obtain

$$p^2 = 10\,\frac{Eg}{\gamma}\frac{b^2}{l^4}, \qquad f = \frac{p}{2\pi} = \frac{5.48}{2\pi}\frac{b}{l^2}\sqrt{\frac{Eg}{3\gamma}}. \qquad (j)$$

To get a closer approximation we take two terms in the series (i); then

$$X_2 = a_1\left(1 - \frac{x}{l}\right)^2 + a_2\frac{x}{l}\left(1 - \frac{x}{l}\right)^2.$$

Substituting in (h), we obtain

$$S_2 = \frac{2}{3}\frac{b^3}{l^3}\left[(a_1 - 2a_2)^2 + \frac{24}{5}a_2(a_1 - 2a_2) + 6a_2{}^2\right]$$

$$- \frac{2b\gamma l p^2}{Eg}\left[\frac{a_1{}^2}{30} + \frac{2a_1 a_2}{105} + \frac{a_2{}^2}{280}\right].$$

Now from the conditions

$$\frac{\partial S_2}{\partial a_1} = 0, \qquad \frac{\partial S_2}{\partial a_2} = 0,$$

we obtain the following two linear equations:

$$\left(\frac{Eg}{\gamma}\frac{b^2}{3l^4} - \frac{p^2}{30}\right)a_1 + \left(\frac{2}{5}\frac{Eg}{\gamma}\frac{b^2}{3l^4} - \frac{p^2}{105}\right)a_2 = 0,$$

$$\left(\frac{2}{5}\frac{Eg}{\gamma}\frac{b^2}{3l^4} - \frac{p^2}{105}\right)a_1 + \left(\frac{2}{5}\frac{Eg}{\gamma}\frac{b^2}{3l^4} - \frac{p^2}{280}\right)a_2 = 0.$$

Equating to zero the determinant of these equations, we get

$$\left(\frac{Eg}{\gamma}\frac{b^2}{3l^4} - \frac{p^2}{30}\right)\left(\frac{2}{5}\frac{Eg}{\gamma}\frac{b^2}{3l^4} - \frac{p^2}{280}\right) - \left(\frac{2}{5}\frac{Eg}{\gamma}\frac{b^2}{3l^4} - \frac{p^2}{105}\right)^2 = 0. \qquad (k)$$

From this equation p^2 can be calculated. The smallest of the two roots gives

$$f = \frac{p}{2\pi} = \frac{5.319}{2\pi}\frac{b}{l^2}\sqrt{\frac{Eg}{3\gamma}}. \qquad (l)$$

It is interesting to note that for the case under consideration an exact solution exists in which the forms of the normal functions are determined in terms of Bessel's functions.* This exact solution gives

$$f = \frac{p}{2\pi} = \frac{5.315}{2\pi}\frac{b}{l^2}\sqrt{\frac{Eg}{3\gamma}}. \qquad (159)$$

Comparing with (j) and (l), it can be concluded that the accuracy of the first approximation is about 3%, while the error of the second approximation is less than 0.1% and a further increase in the number of terms in expression (e) is necessary only if the frequencies of the higher modes of vibration are also to be calculated.

For comparison we note that in the case of a prismatical cantilever bar having the same section as the wedge at the thick end, the following result was obtained (see p. 338):

$$f = \frac{p}{2\pi} = \frac{a1.875^2}{2\pi l^2} = \frac{3.515b}{2\pi l^2}\sqrt{\frac{Eg}{3\gamma}}.$$

The method developed above can be applied also in cases when A and I are not represented by continuous functions of x. These functions may have several points of discontinuity or may be represented by different mathematical expressions in different intervals along the length l. In such cases the integrals (h) should be subdivided into intervals such that I and A may be represented by continuous functions in each of these intervals.† If the functions A and I are obtained either graphically or

---

* See G. R. Kirchhoff, *Monatsberichte*, Berlin, p. 815, 1879; or *Gesammelte Abhandlungen*, Leipzig, p. 339, 1882. See also I. Todhunter and K. Pearson, *A History of the Theory of Elasticity*, Cambridge, Vol. 2, Part 2, p. 92.

† Examples of such kind were discussed by K. A. Traenkel, *Ing.-Arch.*, Vol. 1, p. 499, 1930.

from numerical tables this method can also be used, it being only necessary to apply one of the approximate methods in calculating the integrals (h).

The calculations can be simplified by using the second form of the Ritz method * in which, instead of calculating strain energy and kinetic energy of a vibrating system, we use directly the differential equation of vibration. Taking, for example, the known case of vibration of a cantilever of constant cross section for which the differential equation defining the normal functions is (see eq. 115)

$$EI \frac{d^4X}{dx^4} - \frac{A\gamma}{g} p^2 X = 0, \qquad (m)$$

with the end conditions

$$(X)_{x=0} = \left(\frac{dX}{dx}\right)_{x=0} = 0, \quad \left(\frac{d^2X}{dx^2}\right)_{x=l} = \left(\frac{d^3X}{dx^3}\right)_{x=l} = 0, \qquad (n)$$

and using the Ritz method, we again take X in the form of the series (e). Since it is not the rigorous solution, it will not satisfy eq. (m) and we will get, after substitution into the left-hand side of the equation, a quantity, different from zero, which represents some load q distributed along the length of the cantilever. The values of the coefficients a_1, a_2, $\cdots$ in the series (e) will now be obtained from the condition that the work of the load q on the virtual displacements

$$\delta a_i \varphi_i(x)$$

vanishes. In this manner we obtain equations of the form

$$\int_0^l \left(EI \frac{d^4X}{dx^4} - \frac{A\gamma}{g} p^2 X\right) \varphi_i(x) \, dx = 0. \qquad (o)$$

After substituting the series (e) and integrating, we obtain a system of linear equations for a_1, a_2, a_3, $\cdots$ and the frequency equation is obtained, as before, by equating to zero the determinant of these equations. Taking only two terms in the series (e), we can assume in our case

$$X = a_1(6l^2x^2 - 4lx^3 + x^4) + a_2(20l^3x^2 - 10l^2x^3 + x^5). \qquad (p)$$

Each of the expressions in the parenthesis satisfies the end conditions (n), the first representing, up to a constant factor, deflections of a uniformly

---

* Such as was used in Art. 27. The method is sometimes attributed to Galerkin, but was first introduced by W. Ritz, see p. 228, *loc. cit.*

loaded cantilever and the second, deflection of a cantilever under triangular load. Substituting expression (p) into eq. (o) and performing the integrations, we obtain

$$\left(\frac{104}{45}\frac{p^2l^4}{a^2} - \frac{144}{5}\right)a_1 + \left(\frac{2644}{315}\frac{p^2l^4}{a^2} - 104\right)a_2 = 0,$$

$$\left(\frac{2644}{315}\frac{p^2l^4}{a^2} - 104\right)a_1 + \left(\frac{21128}{693}\frac{p^2l^4}{a^2} - \frac{2640}{7}\right)a_2 = 0.$$

Equating to zero the determinant of these two equations, we obtain

$$p_1{}^2 = 12.37\frac{a}{l^2} = \frac{12.37}{l^2}\sqrt{\frac{EIg}{A\gamma}}, \quad p_2{}^2 = \frac{518.8}{l^2}\sqrt{\frac{EIg}{A\gamma}}.$$

The value of p_1 is obtained with a high accuracy. The error in p_2 as can be seen from p. 338 is about 3%.

From this simple example, it may be appreciated that the second form of the Ritz method represents a considerable simplification, since it does not require the calculation of the strain energy which was used in our preceding examples.

Vibration of a Conical Bar.—The problem of vibrations of a conical bar which has its tip free and the base built in was first treated by Kirchhoff.* For the fundamental mode he obtained in this case

$$f = \frac{p}{2\pi} = \frac{4.359}{2\pi}\frac{r}{l^2}\sqrt{\frac{Eg}{\gamma}}, \tag{160}$$

where r is radius of the base and l is the length of the bar.

For comparison it should be remembered here that a cylindrical bar of the same length and area of base has the frequency

$$f = \frac{p}{2\pi} = \frac{a}{2\pi}\frac{1.875^2}{l^2} = \frac{1.758}{2\pi}\frac{r}{l^2}\sqrt{\frac{Eg}{\gamma}}.$$

Thus the frequencies of the fundamental modes of a conical and a cylindrical bars are in the ratio $4.359:1.758$. The frequencies of the higher

* *Loc. cit.*, p. 389.

modes of vibration of a conical bar can be calculated from the equation

$$f = \frac{p}{2\pi} = \frac{\alpha}{2\pi} \frac{r}{l^2} \sqrt{\frac{Eg}{\gamma}},$$ (161)

in which α has the values: *

α_1	α_2	α_3	α_4	α_5	α_6
4.359	10.573	19.225	30.339	43.921	59.956

Other Cases of Vibration of a Cantilever of Variable Cross Section.—In the general case the frequency of lateral vibrations of a cantilever can be represented by the equation

$$f = \frac{p}{2\pi} = \frac{\alpha}{2\pi} \frac{i}{l^2} \sqrt{\frac{Eg}{\gamma}},$$ (162)

in which i is radius of gyration of the built-in section,

   l is length of the cantilever,

   α is constant depending on the shape of the bar and on the mode of vibration.

In the following, the values of this constant α for certain particular cases of practical importance are given.

1. If the variations of the cross-sectional area and of the moment of inertia, along the axis x, can be expressed in the form

$$A = ax^m, \quad I = bx^m,$$ (163)

x being measured from the free end, i remains constant along the length of the cantilever and the constant α, in eq. (162) can be represented for the fundamental mode with sufficient accuracy by the equation †

$$\alpha = 3.47(1 + 1.05m).$$

2. If the variation of the cross-sectional area and of the moment of inertia along the x-axis can be expressed in the form

$$A = a\left(1 - c\frac{x}{l}\right), \quad I = b\left(1 - c\frac{x}{l}\right),$$ (164)

x being measured from the built-in end, then i remains constant along the

---

* See Dorothy Wrinch, *Proc. Roy. Soc. (London)*, Vol. 101, p. 493, 1922.

† See Akimasa Ono, *J. Soc. Mech. Engrs. (Tokyo)*, Vol. 27, p. 467, 1924.

length of the rod and the quantity α, in eq. (162), will be as given in table: *

$c =$	0	0.4	0.6	0.8	1.0
$\alpha =$	3.515	4.098	4.585	5.398	7.16

Bar of Variable Cross Section with Free Ends.—Let us consider now the case of a laterally vibrating free-free bar consisting of two equal halves joined together at their thick ends (Fig. 219), the left half being generated by revolving the curve

$$y = ax^n \qquad (q)$$

about the x-axis. The exact solution in terms of Bessel's functions has been obtained in this case for certain values of n † and the frequency of the fundamental mode can be represented in the form

$$= \frac{p}{2\pi} = \frac{\alpha r}{4\pi l^2} \sqrt{\frac{Eg}{\gamma}}, \qquad (165)$$

in which r is radius of the thickest cross section,
    $2l$ is length of the bar,
    α is constant, depending on the shape of the curve (q), the values of which are given in the table:

$n =$	0	$\frac{1}{4}$	$\frac{1}{2}$	$\frac{3}{4}$	1
$\alpha =$	5.593	6.957	8.203	9.300	10.173

The application of integral equations in investigating lateral vibrations of bars of variable cross section has been discussed by E. Schwerin.‡

63. Vibration of Hulls of Ships.—As another example of the application of the theory of vibration of bars of variable cross section, the problem of the vibration of the hull of a ship will now be considered.§ The disturbing force in this case is usually due to unbalance in the engine or to the action of propellers ¶ and, if the frequency of the disturbing force coincides with

---

* Ono, *ibid.*, Vol. 28, p. 429, 1925.

† See J. W. Nicholson, *Proc. Roy. Soc.* (*London*), Vol. 93, p. 506, 1917.

‡ "Über Transversalschwingungen von Stäben veränderlichen Querschnitts," *Z. tech. Phys.*, Vol. 8, p. 264, 1927.

§ A review of the literature dealing with vibration of hulls of ships is given by P. F. Papcovitch, *Appl. Math. and Mech.* (Russian), Vol. 1, p. 97, 1933.

¶ Propeller vibration is discussed in a paper by F. M. Lewis presented before the Society of Naval Architects and Marine Engineers, New York, Nov. 1935.

the frequency of one of the natural modes of vibration of the hull, large forced vibrations may be produced. If the hull of the ship be taken as a bar of variable section with free ends and Ritz's method (see Art. 61) be applied, the frequencies of the various modes of vibration can always be calculated with sufficient accuracy from eq. (158).

To simplify the problem let us assume that the bar is symmetrical with respect to the middle cross section and that, by putting the origin of coordinates in this section, the cross-sectional area and moment of inertia for any cross section can be represented, respectively, by the equations

$$A = A_0(1 - cx^2), \quad I = I_0(1 - bx^2), \tag{a}$$

in which A_0 and I_0 denote the cross-sectional area and the moment of inertia of the middle cross section, respectively. It is understood that x may vary from $x = -l$ to $x = +l$, $2l$ being the length of the ship.

We will further assume that the deflection during vibration may be represented by

$$y = X \cos pt,$$

in which X is taken in the form of the series,

$$X = a_1\varphi_1(x) + a_2\varphi_2(x) + a_3\varphi_3(x) + \cdots. \tag{b}$$

We must choose for φ_1, φ_2, $\cdots$ suitable functions, satisfying the end conditions. The ratios between the coefficients a_1, a_2, a_3, $\cdots$ and the frequencies will be then obtained from eq. (158).

A satisfactory approximation for the frequency of the fundamental mode of vibration can be obtained [*] by taking for the functions $\varphi(x)$ the normal functions for a prismatical bar with free ends:

$$X_i = C_i(\cos k_i x \cosh k_i l + \cosh k_i x \cos k_i l).$$

The arbitrary constant, for simplification, will be taken in the form

$$C_i = \frac{1}{\sqrt{\cos^2 k_i l + \cosh^2 k_i l}}.$$

The normal function, corresponding to the first root, $k_1 l = 0$, will be a constant and the corresponding motion will be a displacement of the bar as a rigid body in the y direction. This constant will be taken equal to $1/\sqrt{2}$.

---

[*] See author's book, *Theory of Elasticity*, St. Petersburg, Vol. 2, p. 229, 1916; also N. W. Akimoff, *Trans. Soc. Nav. Architects and Marine Engrs.*, Vol. 26, 1918. Further discussion of the problem is in papers by J. Lockwood Taylor, *Trans. North-East Coast Inst. Engrs. Shipbuild.*, 1928; and *Trans. Inst. Nav. Architects and Marine Engrs.*, 1930.

Taking the normal functions obtained in this manner as suitable functions $\varphi(x)$ in the series (b), we obtain

$$X = a_1 \frac{1}{\sqrt{2}} + a_2 \frac{\cos k_2 x \cosh k_2 l + \cosh k_2 x \cos k_2 l}{\sqrt{\cos^2 k_2 l + \cosh^2 k_2 l}} + \cdots \qquad (c)$$

Substituting the above in eq. (158), we obtain

$$\frac{\partial}{\partial a_n} \left\{ I_0 \int_{-l}^{+l} (1 - bx^2) \sum_{i=1,2,3} \sum_{j=1,2,3} a_i a_j \varphi_i'' \varphi_j'' \, dx \right.$$

$$\left. - \frac{p^2 A_0 \gamma}{Eg} \int_{-l}^{+l} (1 - cx^2) \sum_{i=1,2,3,\cdots} \sum_{j=1,2,3,\cdots} a_i a_j \varphi_i \varphi_j \, dx \right\} = 0, \quad (d)$$

and denoting

$$\int_{-l}^{+l} (1 - bx^2) \varphi_i'' \varphi_j'' \, dx = \alpha_{ij}, \quad \int_{-l}^{+\iota} (1 - cx^2) \varphi_i \varphi_j \, dx = \beta_{ij}, \qquad (e)$$

we obtain from (d),

$$\sum_{i=1,2,3,\cdots} a_i(\alpha_{in} - \lambda \beta_{in}) = 0, \qquad (f)$$

in which

$$\lambda = \frac{p^2 A_0 \gamma}{E I_0 g}. \qquad (g)$$

For determining the fundamental mode of vibration two terms of the series (c) are practically sufficient. The eqs. (f) in this case become

$$a_1(\alpha_{11} - \lambda \beta_{11}) + a_2(\alpha_{21} - \lambda \beta_{21}) = 0,$$
$$a_1(\alpha_{12} - \lambda \beta_{12}) + a_2(\alpha_{22} - \lambda \beta_{22}) = 0. \qquad (h)$$

In our case,

$$\varphi_1'' = 0, \quad \varphi_2'' = k_2^2 \frac{- \cos k_2 x \cosh k_2 l + \cosh k_2 x \cos k_2 l}{\sqrt{\cos^2 k_2 l + \cosh^2 k_2 l}}.$$

Substituting this in (e) and performing the integration, we obtain

$$\alpha_{11} = 0, \quad \alpha_{12} = 0, \quad \alpha_{21} = 0,$$

$$\alpha_{22} = \int_{-\cdot}^{+l} (1 - bx^2)(\varphi_2'')^2 \, dx = \frac{31.28}{l^3} (1 - 0.087bl^2), \qquad (i)$$

$$\beta_{11} = l(1 - 0.333cl^2), \quad \beta_{12} = \beta_{21} = 0.297cl^3, \quad \beta_{22} = l(1 - 0.481cl^2). \quad (j)$$

Substituting in eqs. (h) and equating the determinant of these equations to zero, the frequency equation becomes:

$$\lambda^2 \left(1 - \frac{\beta_{12}^2}{\beta_{11}\beta_{22}} \right) - \lambda \frac{\alpha_{22}}{\beta_{22}} = 0. \qquad (k)$$

The first root of this equation ($\lambda = 0$) corresponds to a displacement of the bar as a rigid body. The second root,

$$\lambda = \frac{\alpha_{22}}{\beta_{22}} \frac{1}{1 - \dfrac{\beta_{12}^2}{\beta_{11}\beta_{22}}}, \qquad (l)$$

determines the frequency of the fundamental type of vibration. This frequency is

$$f_1 = \frac{p}{2\pi} = \frac{\sqrt{\lambda}}{2\pi} \sqrt{\frac{EI_0 g}{A_0 \gamma}}. \qquad (m)$$

Numerical Example.—Let $2l = 100$ meters; $J_0 = 20$ (meter)^4; $A_0\gamma = 7 \times 9.81$ tons per meter; * $b = c = 0.0003$ per meter square. Then the weight of the ship

$$Q = 2A_0\gamma \int_0^l (1 - cx^2)\, dx = 5150 \text{ tons.}$$

From eqs. (i) and (j) we obtain

$$\alpha_{22} = 23.40 \times 10^{-5}, \quad \beta_{11} = 37.50, \quad \beta_{12} = 11.14, \quad \beta_{22} = 31.95,$$

then, from eq. (l) we get

$$\lambda = 0.817 \times 10^{-5}.$$

Assuming $E = 2.10^7$ tons per meter square, we obtain

$$p = \sqrt{2\tfrac{9}{7} \times 2 \times 10^7 \times 0.817 \times 10^{-5}} = 21.6.$$

The number of oscillations per minute is

$$N = \frac{60p}{2\pi} = 206.$$

The functions $\varphi(x)$, taken above, can be also used when the laws of variation of I and A are different from those given by eqs. (a) and also when I and A are given graphically.

---

* To take into account the pulsating current flow in the water due to vibration, certain mass of water must be added to the mass of the hull. This question is discussed in papers by F. E. Lewis, *Proc. Soc. Nav. Architects Marine Engrs.*, Nov. 1929; E. B. Moulin and A. D. Brown, *Proc. Cambridge Phil. Soc.*, Vol. 24, pp. 400 and 531, 1928; A. D. Brown, E. B. Moulin and A. J. Perkins, *ibid.*, Vol. 26, p. 258, 1930; and J. J. Koch, *Ing.-Arch.*, Vol. 4, p. 103, 1933.

In each case it is only necessary to calculate the integrals (e), which calculation can always be carried out by means of some approximate method.

64. Numerical Methods of Calculating Lateral Vibration Frequencies.—

General.—We have seen that the calculation of frequencies of natural modes of lateral vibration of bars of variable cross section requires the solution of the differential equation

$$\frac{\partial^2}{\partial x^2}\left(EI\,\frac{\partial^2 y}{\partial x^2}\right) + \frac{A\gamma}{g}\,\frac{\partial^2 y}{\partial t^2} = 0. \qquad (a)$$

Taking the solution in the form

$$y = X \cos pt$$

and substituting it into eq. (a), we obtain, for calculating the function X, the equation

$$\frac{d^2}{dx^2}\left(EI\,\frac{d^2 X}{dx^2}\right) = \frac{A\gamma p^2}{g}\,X. \qquad (b)$$

This equation is the same as the equation,

$$\frac{d^2}{dx^2}\left(EI\,\frac{d^2 y}{dx^2}\right) = \frac{A\gamma p^2}{g}\,y, \qquad (c)$$

for the statical deflection of a beam of variable cross section produced by distributed load of intensity $A\gamma p^2 y/g$. Since a rigourous solution of eq. (c) in the general case presents difficulties, various approximate methods of solving the problem have been developed. Most of that work was done in connection with analysis of lateral vibration of hulls of ships, and the approximate solutions were obtained by using step-by-step methods of numerical integration. We can take the solution of the equation in the form

$$y = Cf(x) + C_1 f_1(x), \qquad (d)$$

in which the functions $f(x)$ and $f_1(x)$ are selected in such a way that the conditions at one end, say $x = 0$, are satisfied. Then, starting from this end, and using numerical integration, the expression for y and its derivatives at the end $x = l$ is obtained and the ratio of the constants $C:C_1$ and the magnitude of the angular frequency p are calculated from the conditions at that end.*

---

* L. Gümbel used graphical integration, see *Jahrb. Schiffbautech. Ges.*, p. 211, 1901; A. N. Krylov applied the Störmer-Adams method of numerical integration, see *Bull. Russian Acad. Sci.*, p. 915, 1918; C. E. Inglis approximated a beam of continuously

Bar with Free Ends.—As a first example let us consider the case of a symmetrical beam with free ends, which, for numerical calculations, is replaced by the *stepped* beam in Fig. 220. To get a satisfactory result at least twice as many steps should be used as the number of natural frequencies to be calculated. The continuously distributed masses should be replaced by masses m_1, m_2 $\cdots$ concentrated at discrete points, as shown; then the corresponding inertia forces will be $m_1 p^2 y_1$, $m_2 p^2 y_2$, $\cdots$. Starting with the symmetrical mode of vibration, Fig. 220b, we denote by x_1,

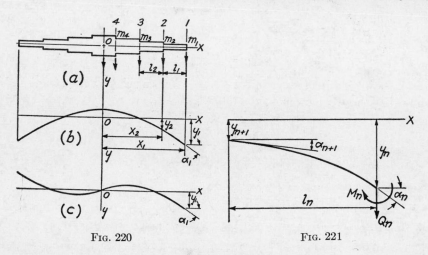

FIG. 220   FIG. 221

x_2, $\cdots$ the distances of the masses m_1, m_2, $\cdots$ from the symmetry axis y and obtain for any cross section n the following values of the shearing force Q_n at the left of mn and the bending moment M_n:

$$Q_n = \sum_{i=1}^{n} m_i p^2 y_i, \quad M_n = \sum_{i=1}^{n-1} m_i p^2 y_i (x_i - x_n). \quad (e)$$

The positive directions of Q_n and M_n are shown in Fig. 221, representing the deflection of one portion of the beam between the cross sections n and

varying moment of inertia by a "stepped" beam and derived an algebraic expression for the deflection curve, see *Trans. Inst. Nav. Architects (London)*, Vol. 71, p. 145, 1929. A very useful scheme of numerical integration for a stepped beam was developed by N. O. Myklestad, *J. Aeronaut. Sci.*, Vol. 11, p. 153, 1944. This scheme is presented in the following discussion. See also papers by M. A. Prohl, *J. Appl. Mech.*, Vol. 12, p. 142, 1945; and by A. I. Bellin, *ibid.*, Vol. 14, p. 1, 1947.

$n + 1$. Using the known formulas for deflection of a cantilever, we obtain

$$\alpha_n = \alpha_{n+1} + \frac{Q_n l_n^2}{2EI_n} + \frac{M_n l_n}{EI_n},$$

$$y_n = y_{n+1} + \alpha_{n+1}l_n + \frac{Q_n l_n^3}{3EI_n} + \frac{M_n l_n^2}{2EI_n}.$$

With notations

$$\left. \begin{array}{ll} \dfrac{l_n^2}{2EI_n} = k_n, & \dfrac{l_n}{EI_n} = k_n', \\[2mm] \dfrac{l_n^3}{3EI_n} = g_n, & \dfrac{l_n^2}{2EI_n} = g_n', \end{array} \right\} \tag{f}$$

we rewrite these equations in the following form:

$$\alpha_{n+1} = \alpha_n - k_n Q_n - k_n' M_n,$$

$$y_{n+1} = y_n - \alpha_{n+1}l_n - g_n Q_n - g_n' M_n.$$

Then using expressions (e), we obtain

$$\left. \begin{array}{l} \alpha_{n+1} = \alpha_n - k_n \displaystyle\sum_{i=1}^{n} m_i p^2 y_i - k_n' \displaystyle\sum_{i=1}^{n-1} m_i p^2 y_i (x_i - x_n), \\[4mm] y_{n+1} = y_n - \alpha_{n+1}l_n - g_n \displaystyle\sum_{i=1}^{n} m_i p^2 y_i - g_n' \displaystyle\sum_{i=1}^{n-1} m_i p^2 y_i (x_i - x_n). \end{array} \right\} \tag{g}$$

Assuming some values α_1 and y_1 for the slope and the deflection at the free end and using eqs. (g) the slopes and the deflections at all consecutive cross sections 2, 3, 4, $\cdots$ can now be calculated. Form eqs. (g) it can be concluded that these quantities depend linearly on the assumed values α_1, y_1 and can be represented in the form:

$$\left. \begin{array}{l} \alpha_n = \alpha_1 \phi_n - y_1 \phi_n', \\ y_n = -\alpha_1 \psi_n + y_1 \psi_n', \end{array} \right\} \tag{h}$$

where $\phi_n, \cdots, \psi_n'$ are some functions of $x_1, x_2, \cdots$, which have to satisfy the following end conditions at the free end:

$$\phi_1 = 1, \quad \phi_1' = 0, \quad \psi_1 = 0, \quad \psi_1' = 1. \tag{i}$$

To establish the forms of these functions, we substitute expressions (h) into the first of eqs. (g), which gives

$$\alpha_1\phi_{n+1} - y_1\phi_{n+1}' = \alpha_1\phi_n - y_1\phi_n' - k_n \sum_{i=1}^{n} m_ip^2(-\alpha_1\psi_i + y_1\psi_i')$$

$$- k_n' \sum_{i=1}^{n-1} m_ip^2(-\alpha_1\psi_i + y_1\psi_i')(x_i - x_n).$$

Since this equation must hold for any assumed values of α_1 and y_1, we can assume first $y_1 = 0$; then the terms containing α_1 as a factor give us the equation

$$\phi_{n+1} = \phi_n + k_n \sum_{i=1}^{n} m_ip^2\psi_i + k_n' \sum_{i=1}^{n-1} m_ip^2\psi_i(x_i - x_n). \tag{j}$$

Taking $\alpha_1 = 0$ and considering terms containing y_1, we obtain

$$\phi_{n+1}' = \phi_n' + k_n \sum_{i=1}^{n} m_ip^2\psi_i' + k_n' \sum_{i=1}^{n-1} m_ip^2\psi_i'(x_i - x_n). \tag{k}$$

Similarly, considering the second of eqs. (g), we obtain

$$\psi_{n+1} = \psi_n + l_n\phi_{n+1} - g_n \sum_{i=1}^{n} m_ip^2\psi_i - g_n' \sum_{i=1}^{n-1} m_ip^2\psi_i(x_i - x_n), \tag{l}$$

$$\psi_{n+1}' = \psi_n' + l_n\phi_{n+1}' - g_n \sum_{i=1}^{n} m_ip^2\psi_i' - g_n' \sum_{i=1}^{n-1} m_ip^2\psi_i'(x_i - x_n) \tag{m}$$

Eqs. (j), $\cdots$, (m) can be simplified by introducing the notations:

$$\sum_{i=1}^{n} m_ip^2\psi_i = B_n, \quad \sum_{i=1}^{n} m_ip^2\psi_i' = G_n. \tag{n}$$

With the notation $m_ip^2\psi_i' = A_i$, we obtain

$$m_ip^2\psi_i'(x_i - x_n) = A_i \sum_{j=i}^{n-1} l_j,$$

and the summation in the last terms of eqs. (k) and (m) become

$$\sum_{i=1}^{n-1} m_i p^2 \psi_i'(x_i - x_n) = \sum_{i=1}^{n-1} \left(A_i \sum_{j=1}^{n-1} l_j\right)$$

$$= A_1(l_1 + l_2 + \cdots + l_{n-1}) + A_2(l_2 + l_3 + \cdots + l_{n-1})$$

$$+ \cdots + A_{n-1}l_{n-1}$$

$$= l_1 A_1 + l_2(A_1 + A_2) + \cdots$$

$$+ l_{n-1}(A_1 + A_2 + \cdots + A_{n-1})$$

$$= \sum_{i=1}^{n-1} \left(l_i \sum_{j=1}^{i} A_j\right) = \sum_{i=1}^{n-1} l_i G_i = G_n'. \qquad (o)$$

Proceeding similarly with the summations in the last terms of eqs. (j) and (l), we obtain

$$\sum_{i=1}^{n-1} m_i p^2 \psi_i(x_i - x_n) = \sum_{i=1}^{n-1} l_i B_i = B_n'. \qquad (p)$$

With these notations, eqs. (j), $\cdots$, (m) become

$$\left.\begin{aligned}
\phi_{n+1} &= \phi_n + k_n B_n + k_n' B_n', \\
\phi_{n+1}' &= \phi_n' + k_n G_n + k_n' G_n', \\
\psi_{n+1} &= \psi_n + l_n \phi_{n+1} - g_n B_n - g_n' B_n', \\
\psi_{n+1} &= \psi_n' + l_n \phi_{n+1}' - g_n G_n - g_n' G_n'.
\end{aligned}\right\} \qquad (q)$$

Starting with the end values (i) and using eqs. (q), the consecutive values of the functions ϕ, ϕ', ψ, ψ' for the cross sections 2, 3, $\cdots$ can be calculated for any assumed value of p^2. Let ϕ_0, ϕ_0', ψ_0 and ψ_0' be the values of the functions at the middle cross section O of the beam Fig. 220. Then, observing that for symmetrical modes of vibration α vanishes at the middle of the beam, we obtain from the first of eqs. (h)

$$0 = \alpha_1 \phi_0 - y_1 \phi_0',$$

which gives

$$\frac{\alpha_1}{y_1} = \frac{\phi_0'}{\phi_0}.$$

With this value of the ratio α_1/y_1 we now calculate deflections of the beam from the second of eqs. (h), which gives

$$y_n = y_1 \left(\psi_n' - \frac{\phi_0'}{\phi_0} \psi_n\right).$$

Substituting this into the first of expressions (e), we obtain the shearing force

$$Q_n = y_1 \sum_{i=1}^{n} m_i p^2 \left(\psi_i' - \frac{\phi_0'}{\phi_0} \psi_i \right) = y_1 \left(G_n - \frac{\phi_0'}{\phi_0} B_n \right).$$

For the middle of the beam this equation gives

$$Q_0 = y_1 \left(G_0 - \frac{\phi_0'}{\phi_0} B_0 \right).$$

The value of the expression in the parenthesis depends, as can be seen from notations (n), on the assumed value of the frequency p. Repeating the calculations for various values of p, a curve such as shown in Fig. 222 can be constructed, which gives Q_0 as a funtion of p.* When the beam performs one of the symmetrical natural modes of vibration the shearing force at the middle vanishes. From this we conclude that the intersection points of the curve in Fig. 222 with the horizontal axis define the angular frequencies of the symmetrical modes of vibration of the beam.

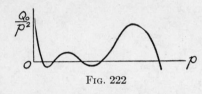

Fig. 222

In calculating frequencies of antisymmetrical modes of vibrations as shown in Fig. 220c, we proceed as in the preceding case and, after calculating the values $\phi_0 \cdots \psi_0'$ for the middle of the beam, use the condition that y vanishes at the middle. From the second of eqs. (h), we then obtain

$$\frac{\alpha_1}{y_1} = \frac{\psi_0'}{\psi_0}.$$

With this value of the ratio α_1/y_1 we now calculate deflections from the second of eqs. (h), which gives

$$y_n = y_1 \left(\psi_n' - \frac{\psi_0'}{\psi_0} \psi_n \right).$$

Substituting this in the second of eqs. (e), we obtain the bending moments

$$M_n = y_1 \sum_{i=1}^{n-1} m_i p^2 \left(\psi_i' - \frac{\psi_0'}{\psi_0} \psi_i \right) (x_i - x_n)$$

* The values $y_1 = 1$ and Q_0/p^2 are used in this construction.

or, with notations (o) and (p),

$$M_n = y_1 \left(G_n' - \frac{\psi_0'}{\psi_0} B_n' \right).$$

Applying this formula to the mid-point O of the beam, we find the frequencies of the antisymmetrical modes of vibration from the condition that the bending moment vanishes at the middle, which gives the equation

$$0 = G_0' - \frac{\psi_0'}{\psi_0} B_0'.$$

To get the required frequencies we calculate the values of the right-hand side of this equation for various values of p and represent it by a curve, as was done in the preceding case. The intersection points of this curve with the horizontal axis define the required frequencies.

Cantilever Beam.—The same method of calculation can be used also in the case of a cantilever, Fig. 223. By using eqs. (r) we calculate $\phi_0, \cdots,$

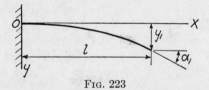

FIG. 223

ψ_0' for the clamped end and, from the condition that the deflection vanishes at that end, we obtain

$$0 = -\alpha_1 \psi_0 + y_1 \psi_0'; \quad \frac{\alpha_1}{y_1} = \frac{\psi_0'}{\psi_0}.$$

Substituting in the first of eqs. (h) and observing that the slope vanishes at the clamped end, we obtain the frequency equation

$$0 = \frac{\psi_0'}{\psi_0} \phi_0 - \phi_0',$$

which again can be solved graphically as already explained.

Bar with Simply Supported Ends.—In the case of a *beam with simply supported ends*, Fig. 224a, we again divide the actual beam in steps and replace its mass by concentrated masses as shown. Considering a portion of the beam between the masses m_n and m_{n+1} and taking the direction of moments and shearing forces as shown in Fig. 225, we obtain

$$\left.\begin{aligned} \alpha_{n+1} &= \alpha_n + k_n Q_n - k_n' M_n, \\ y_{n+1} &= y_n + \alpha_{n+1} l_n - g_n Q_n + g_n' M_n, \end{aligned}\right\} \tag{r}$$

where the coefficients $k_n, \cdots, g_n'$ have the same meaning (f) as before, and the shearing force Q_n and bending moment M_n are given by the equations:

$$\left.\begin{aligned} Q_n &= \sum_{i=1}^{n} m_i y_i p^2 - R_1, \\ M_n &= R_1 \sum_{i=1}^{n-1} l_i - \sum_{i=1}^{n-1} m_i y_i p^2 (x_i - x_n), \end{aligned}\right\} \tag{s}$$

in which R_1 denotes the reactive force at the end $(x = l)$ of the beam. Substituting the expressions for Q_n and M_n into eqs. (r), we obtain ex-

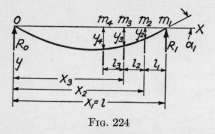

FIG. 224

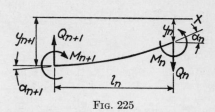

FIG. 225

pressions for calculating the slope α and the deflection y at any cross section of the beam, if for the slope α_1 and the reaction R_1 some values are assumed. Observing that these expressions are linear in α_1 and R_1, we take them in the form

$$\left.\begin{aligned} \alpha_n &= \alpha_1 \phi_n - R_1 \phi_n'', \\ y_n &= \alpha_1 \psi_n - R_1 \psi_n'', \end{aligned}\right\} \tag{t}$$

where $\phi_n, \cdots, \psi_n''$ are functions of x satisfying the following end conditions:

$$\phi_1 = 1, \quad \phi_1'' = 0, \quad \psi_1 = 0, \quad \psi_1'' = 0. \tag{u}$$

Proceeding as before we obtain, for calculating these functions, the equations

$$\left.\begin{aligned} \phi_{n+1} &= \phi_n + k_n B_n + k_n' B_n', \\ \phi_{n+1}'' &= \phi_n'' + k_n D_n + k_n' D_n', \\ \psi_{n+1} &= \psi_n + l_n \phi_{n+1} - g_n B_n - g_n' B_n', \\ \psi_{n+1}'' &= \psi_n'' + l_n \phi_{n+1}'' - g_n D_n - g_n' D_n', \end{aligned}\right\} \tag{v}$$

in which B_n and $B_n{}'$ have the same meaning as before (see eqs. n and p),

$$
\left.
\begin{aligned}
D_n &= 1 + \sum_{i=1}^{n} m_i p^2 \psi_i{}'', \\
D_n{}' &= \sum_{i=1}^{n-1} l_i D_i.
\end{aligned}
\right\} \tag{w}
$$

Starting now with the initial values (u), using eqs. (v) and making step-by-step summations, we finally obtain the values of ϕ_0, $\phi_0{}''$, ψ_0, $\psi_0{}''$ for the left-hand end O of the beam, and observing that the deflection at O vanishes, we find from the second of eqs. (t) that

$$
0 = \alpha_1 \psi_0 - R_1 \psi_0{}'',
$$

which gives

$$
\frac{\alpha_1}{R_1} = \frac{\psi_0{}''}{\psi_0}
$$

and

$$
y_n = R_1 \left(\frac{\psi_0{}''}{\psi_0} \psi_n - \psi_n{}'' \right). \tag{x}
$$

With this value of y_n the bending moment, eq. (s), becomes

$$
\begin{aligned}
M_0 &= R_1 \sum_{i=1}^{0} l_i - R_1 \frac{\psi_0{}''}{\psi_0} \sum_{i=1}^{0} m_i p^2 \psi_i x_i + R_1 \sum_{i=1}^{0-1} m_i p^2 \psi_i{}'' x_i \\
&= R_1 \left(-\frac{\psi_0{}''}{\psi_0} B_0{}' + D_0{}' \right). \tag{y}
\end{aligned}
$$

For calculating the frequencies of natural vibration we proceed as before, calculate the numerical values of the expression in the parentheses for several assumed values of p^2 and represent it by a curve. The intersection points of this curve with the horizontal axis give the required frequencies.

As a simple example in application of the numerical method of calculating frequencies, let us consider the case of a prismatical bar simply supported and carrying three equal masses m, Fig. 226a. Assume that $l_1 = l_2 = l_3$

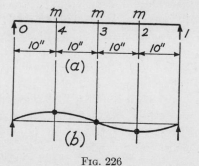

Fig. 226

$= l_4 = 10$ in., $EI = 40 \cdot 10^6$ lb in.^{2}, $m = 1.5$ lb sec^2 in.$^{-1}$ and that it is required to find the frequency of the second mode of vibration, Fig. 226b. This frequency can be readily calculated as for a simply supported bar of length 20 in. and carrying the load mg at the middle. The statical deflection under the load is $\delta = mg.10^3/6EI$ and the angular frequency is

$$p = \sqrt{\frac{g}{\delta}} = \sqrt{\frac{6EI}{m \cdot 10^3}} = 400 \text{ sec}^{-1}.$$

Let us now check this value by the above-described numerical method. For that purpose we have to make step-by-step calculation of the functions ϕ, ϕ'', ψ, ψ'' given by eqs. (v). This calculation is represented in the table below. Taking for p the above calculated value, we fill up the second

n	$\dfrac{mp^2}{10^6}$	ψ_n	B_n	B_n'	ϕ_{n+1}	ψ_n''	D_n	D_n'	ϕ_{n+1}''
1	0	0	0	0	1	0	1	0	$1\frac{1}{4}$
2	0.24	10	2.4	0	4	$4\frac{1}{6}$	2	10	$6\frac{1}{4}$
3	0.24	30	9.6	24	22	37.5	11	30	$27\frac{1}{2}$
4	0.24	140	43.2	120	106	$183\frac{1}{3}$	55	140	$131\frac{1}{4}$
0	0	630	43.2	552		$862\frac{1}{2}$	55	690	

column and, using eqs. (f), we calculate $k = 1\frac{1}{4} \, 10^{-6}$ lb^{-1}; $k' = \frac{1}{4} \cdot 10^{-6}$ lb^{-1}in.$^{-1}$; $g = \frac{25}{3} \, 10^{-6}$ lb^{-1}in.; $g' = 1\frac{1}{4} \, 10^{-6}$ lb^{-1}.

Having these values, we start with the first horizontal line of the table and using the end conditions (u) and eqs. (n), (p), (w), we obtain $\psi_1 = B_1 = B_1' = \psi_1'' = D_1' = 0$, $D_1 = 1$, and from the first two of eqs. (v) we calculate $\phi_2 = 1$ and $\phi_2'' = 1\frac{1}{4}$, which values we also insert in the first line. Thus the first line is completed and the further lines of the table can be readily calculated by using eqs. (v) and notations (n), (p) and (w). Having the values of the functions ψ and ψ'', we obtain the shape of the deflection curve from eq. (x). The corresponding bending moments can be found from eq. (y). For the left-hand end O of the bar, the latter equation gives zero value for the moment, which indicates that the assumed value for p is the true value of the required frequency.

In practical problems the application of the numerical method requires a more complicated calculation since the flexural rigidity EI and the masses m are usually changing from step to step and it is necessary to calculate first the table of the coefficients k, k', g, g'. To get the required frequencies with a satisfactory accuracy it is necessary to make all intermediate calculations with four or more significant figures, which requires the use of a calculating machine. Some examples of such calculation can be found in a paper mentioned on p. 398 and in the book, *Vibration Analysis*, by N. O. Myklestad.

65. Coupled Bending and Torsional Vibrations of Beams.—In the preceding discussion of lateral vibrations of bars it was always assumed that the bar vibrates in its plane of symmetry. If this is not the case, the lateral vibrations will usually be coupled with torsional vibrations. As an example of such coupled vibration, let us consider the case of vibration of a channel, Fig. 227, in the xy-plane perpendicular to the plane of symmetry. In discussing lateral bending of the channel under the action of a statically applied load, we observe that bending will proceed in the vertical plane and will not be accompanied by torsion only if the vertical load is distributed along the shear-center axis $O\text{-}O$ which is parallel to the centroidal axis and lies in the

Fig. 227

plane of symmetry of the bar. This axis is taken as the x-axis. Its distance e from the middle plane of the web is given by the formula *

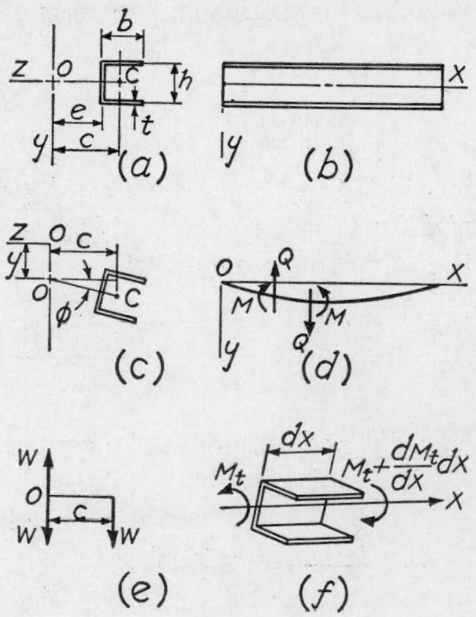

$$e = \frac{b^2 h^2 t}{4 I_z},$$

(a)

in which b is the width of the flanges, h is the distance between the centers of the flanges and t is the thickness of the flanges and of the web. For such a

* See author's *Strength of Materials*, 2d ed., Vol. 2, p. 53, 1941.

load the differential equation of the deflection curve is

$$EI_z \frac{d^4y}{dx^4} = w, \tag{b}$$

in which w is the intensity of the distributed load and EI_z is the flexural rigidity of the bar in the vertical plane.

If the load is distributed along the centroidal axis, we always can proceed as indicated in Fig. 227e and replace the given load by the same load distributed along the shear-center axis x, and a torque of intensity $w \cdot c$ distributed along the same axis. In such a case we will have a combination of (1) bending, defined by eq. (b), and (2) torsion with respect to the shear-center axis x. Since this torsion is nonuniform, the relation between the variable torque M_t and the angle of twist ϕ is given by the equation *

$$M_t = C \frac{d\phi}{dx} - C_1 \frac{d^3\phi}{dx^3}, \tag{c}$$

in which C is the *torsional rigidity* for uniform torsion and C_1 is the *warping rigidity*. Differentiating this equation with respect to x and observing that the positive torque has the direction shown in Fig. 227f, we obtain

$$C \frac{d^2\phi}{dx^2} - C_1 \frac{d^4\phi}{dx^4} = -wc. \tag{d}$$

Eqs. (b) and (d) define the coupled bending and torsion of the bar when a static load is distributed along the centroidal axis.

In the case of vibration of the bar we have to consider inertia forces due to *translation*, of intensity

$$-\frac{A\gamma}{g} \frac{\partial^2}{\partial t^2} (y + c\phi),$$

where $\dfrac{A\gamma}{g}$ is the mass per unit length of the bar, and inertia forces of rotation, which given an inertia torque of intensity

$$-\frac{I_p\gamma}{g} \frac{\partial^2\phi}{\partial t^2},$$

where I_p is the centroidal polar moment of inertia of the cross section.

---

* See *ibid.*, Vol. 2, Art. 53.

Using inertia forces instead of the statically applied load in eqs. (b) and (d), we obtain the following differential equations for the coupled bending and torsional vibrations:

$$EI_z \frac{\partial^4 y}{\partial x^4} = -\frac{A\gamma}{g}\frac{\partial^2 y}{\partial t^2} - \frac{A\gamma c}{g}\frac{\partial^2 \phi}{\partial t^2}, \left.\vphantom{\begin{array}{c} a \\ b \end{array}}\right\}$$
$$C\frac{\partial^2 \phi}{\partial x^2} - C_1 \frac{\partial^4 \phi}{\partial x^4} = \frac{A\gamma c}{g}\frac{\partial^2}{\partial t^2}(y + c\phi) + \frac{I_p \gamma}{g}\frac{\partial^2 \phi}{\partial t^2}. \right\} \qquad (e)$$

Assuming that the bar performs one of the natural modes of vibration, we put

$$y = X \sin pt, \quad \phi = X_1 \sin pt, \qquad (f)$$

where p is the angular frequency of vibration and X and X_1 are the normal functions. Substituting (f) into eqs. (e), we obtain for finding X and X_1 the following equations:

$$EI_z X^{\mathrm{iv}} = \frac{A\gamma p^2}{g}(X + cX_1), \left.\vphantom{\begin{array}{c} a \\ b \end{array}}\right\}$$
$$C_1 X_1{}^{\mathrm{iv}} - CX_1'' = \frac{A\gamma p^2 c}{g}(X + cX_1) + \frac{I_p \gamma p^2}{g}X_1. \right\} \qquad (g)$$

In each particular case we have to find for X and X_1 solutions which satisfy the prescribed conditions at the ends of the bar as well as eqs. (g).

The simplest example is the case of a bar with simply supported ends for which the end conditions are

$$y = \frac{\partial^2 y}{\partial x^2} = \phi = \frac{\partial^2 \phi}{\partial x^2} = 0, \quad \text{for} \quad x = 0 \text{ and } x = l.$$

These requirements are satisfied by taking

$$X = y_0 \sin \frac{i\pi x}{l}, \quad X_1 = \phi_0 \sin \frac{i\pi x}{l},$$

where y_0 and ϕ_0 are constants.

Substituting into eqs. (g) and using the notations

$$\frac{EI_z i^4 \pi^4 g}{l^4 A\gamma} = \omega_b{}^2, \quad \frac{(Ci^2\pi^2 l^2 + C_1 i^4 \pi^4)g}{l^4 \gamma(I_p + Ac^2)} = \omega_t{}^2, \quad \frac{Ac}{I_p + Ac^2} = \lambda, \qquad (h)$$

we obtain

$$(\omega_b{}^2 - p^2)y_0 - p^2 c\phi_0 = 0, \left.\vphantom{\begin{array}{c} a \\ b \end{array}}\right\}$$
$$-\lambda p^2 y_0 + (\omega_t{}^2 - p^2)\phi_0 = 0. \right\} \qquad (i)$$

These equations can give solutions for y_0 and ϕ_0 different from zero only if their determinant vanishes, which gives the frequency equation

$$(\omega_b{}^2 - p^2)(\omega_t{}^2 - p^2) - \lambda p^4 c = 0, \qquad (j)$$

from which we obtain

$$p^2 = \frac{(\omega_t{}^2 + \omega_b{}^2) \pm \sqrt{(\omega_t{}^2 - \omega_b{}^2)^2 + 4\lambda c \omega_b{}^2 \omega_t{}^2}}{2(1 - \lambda c)}. \qquad (k)$$

A similar result will be obtained in all other cases of bars with one plane of symmetry which vibrate perpendicularly to that plane.

If c is zero and the shear center coincides with the centroid, we obtain

$$p^2 = \frac{\omega_t{}^2 + \omega_b{}^2}{2} \pm \frac{\omega_t{}^2 - \omega_b{}^2}{2}$$

which gives us two frequencies:

$$p_1{}^2 = \omega_1{}^2, \quad p_2{}^2 = \omega_b{}^2. \qquad (l)$$

As can be seen from notations (h), these frequencies correspond to the uncoupled torsional and bending vibrations and are independent of each other in this case. If c does not vanish we obtain from the solution (k) two values for p^2, one of which is larger and the other smaller than the values (l). For larger value of p^2 we find, from eqs. (i), that y_0 and ϕ_0 have opposite signs and that for smaller value of p^2 they are of the same sign. The corresponding two configurations are shown in Fig. 228. Similar results will also be obtained in the case of bars with other end conditions. The solutions of eqs. (g) then become more complicated, but we can calculate the approximate values of frequencies of the two kinds of coupled vibrations by using the Rayleigh-Ritz method.*

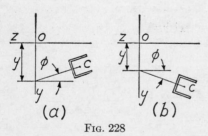

FIG. 228

In the case of bars having no planes of symmetry the problem becomes more involved.† Torsional vibrations are coupled with bending vibrations

---

* In this manner C. F. Garland investigated coupled bending and torsional vibrations of a cantilever, see *J. Appl. Mech.*, Vol. 7, p. 97, 1940.

† The differential equations for the general case are discussed by K. Federhofer *Sitzber. Akad. Wiss. Wien, Abt. IIa*, Vol. 156, p. 343, 1947.

in the two principal planes and, instead of two, we obtain three differential equations of the same kind as eqs. (e).

In practical applications we also encounter the more complicated problem of coupled torsional and bending vibrations of nonsymmetrical bars of variable cross section. Such problems occur, for example, in analyzing vibrations of turbine blades, airplane wings and propellers. For the solution of these problems approximate methods are usually applied. In the case of turbine blades, for example, only bending vibrations are usually considered,[*] although torsion may actually have considerable influence on the frequency of vibration.

66. Lateral Impact of Bars.—*Approximate Solution.*—The problem of stresses and deflections produced in a beam by a falling body is of great practical importance. The exact solution of this problem involves the study of the lateral vibration of the beam. In cases where the mass of the beam is negligible in comparison with the mass of the falling body, an approximate solution can easily be obtained by assuming that the deflection curve of the beam during impact has the same shape as the corresponding statical deflection curve. Then the maximum deflection and the maximum stress will be found from a consideration of the energy of the system. Let us take, for example, a beam supported at the ends and struck midway between the supports by a falling weight W. If δ denotes the deflection at the middle of the beam, the following relation between the deflection and the force P acting on the beam holds:

$$\delta = \frac{Pl^3}{48EI},$$

and the potential energy of deformation will be

$$V = \frac{P\delta}{2} = \frac{24EI\delta^2}{l^3}. \tag{a}$$

If the weight W falls through a height h, the work done by this load during falling will be

$$W(h + \delta_d) \tag{b}$$

and the dynamical deflection δ_d will be found from the equation

$$W(h + \delta_d) = \frac{24EI\delta_d^2}{l^3}, \tag{c}$$

[*] An elaborate investigation of transverse vibrations of turbine blades is found in *Technische Dynamik* (*Berlin*) by C. B. Biezeno and R. Grammel, pp. 726–771, 1939.

from which

$$\delta_d = \delta_{st} + \sqrt{\delta_{st}^2 + 2h\delta_{st}}, \qquad (d)$$

where

$$\delta_{st} = \frac{Wl^3}{48EI}$$

represents the statical deflection of the beam under the action of the load W.

In the above discussion the mass of the beam was neglected and it was assumed that the kinetic energy of the falling weight W was completely transformed into potential energy of deformation of the beam. In actual conditions a part of the kinetic energy will be lost during the impact. Consequently calculations made as above will give an upper limit for the dynamical deflection and the dynamical stresses. In order to obtain a more accurate solution, the mass of a beam subjected to impact must be taken into consideration.

If a moving body, having a mass W/g and a velocity v_0 strikes centrally a stationary body of mass W_1/g and if the deformation at the point of contact is perfectly inelastic, the final velocity v, after the impact (equal for both bodies), may be determined from the equation

$$\frac{W}{g} v_0 = \frac{W + W_1}{g} v,$$

from which

$$v = v_0 \frac{W}{W + W_1}. \qquad (e)$$

It should be noted that for a beam at the instance of impact, it is only at the point of contact that the velocity v of the body W and of the beam will be the same. Other points of the beam may have velocities different from v, and at the supports of the beam these velocities will be equal to zero. Therefore, not the actual mass of the beam, but some *reduced mass* must be used in eq. (e) for calculating the velocity v. The magnitude of this reduced mass will depend on the shape of the deflection curve and can be approximately determined in the same manner as was done in Rayleigh's method, i.e., by assuming that the deflection curve is the same as the one obtained statically. Then,

$$v = v_0 \frac{W}{W + \dfrac{17}{35} W_1},$$

in which $17/35W_1$ is the *reduced weight* of the beam. The kinetic energy of the system will be

$$\frac{\left(W + \frac{17}{35}W_1\right)v^2}{2g} = \frac{Wv_0^2}{2g} \frac{1}{1 + \frac{17}{35}\frac{W_1}{W}}.$$

This quantity should be substituted for $(Wv_0^2/2g) = Wh$ in the previous eq. (c) in order to take into account the effect of the mass of the beam. The dynamical deflection then becomes

$$\delta_d = \delta_{st} + \sqrt{\delta_{st}^2 + 2h\delta_{st}\frac{1}{1 + \frac{17}{35}\frac{W_1}{W}}}. \tag{166}$$

The same method can be used in all other cases of impact in which the displacement of the structure at the point of impact is proportional to the force.*

Impact and Vibrations.—The method described above gives sufficiently accurate results for the cases of thin rods and beams if the mass of the falling weight is large in comparison to the mass of the beam. Otherwise the consideration of vibrations of the beam and of local deformations at the point of impact becomes necessary.

Lateral vibrations of a beam struck by a body moving with a given velocity were considered by St.-Venant.† Assuming that after impact the striking body becomes attached to the beam, the vibrations can be investigated by expressing the deflection as the sum of a series of normal functions. The constant coefficients of this series should be determined in such a manner as to satisfy the given initial conditions. In this manner, St.-Venant was able to show that the approximate solution given above has an accuracy sufficient for practical applications.

The assumption that after impact the striking body becomes attached to the beam is an aribitrary one and in order to get a more accurate picture of the phenomena of impact, the local deformations of the beam and of the striking body at the point of contact should be investigated. Some

* This method was developed by H. Cox, *Trans. Cambridge Phil. Soc.*, Vol. 9, p. 73, 1850. See also Todhunter and Pearson, Vol. 1, p. 895, *loc. cit.*

† *Loc. cit.*, p. 297, *note finale du paragraphe* 61, p. 490. See also W. H. Hoppmann, *J. Appl. Mech.*, Vol. 15, p. 125, 1948; and Vol. 17, p. 409, 1950.

results of such an investigation in which a ball strikes the flat surface of a rectangular beam will now be given.* The local deformation will be given in this case by the known solution of Hertz.† Let α denote the displacement of the striking ball with respect to the axis of the beam due to this deformation and P, the corresponding pressure of the ball on the beam; then

$$\alpha = kP^{\frac{2}{3}}, \tag{f}$$

where k is a constant depending on the elastic properties of the bodies and on the magnitude of the radius of the ball. The pressure P, during impact, will vary with the time and will produce a deflection of the beam which can be expressed by the general solution (g) of Art. 55. If the beam is struck at the middle, the expression for the deflection at the middle produced by the pressure P becomes ‡

$$y = \sum_{i=1,3,5,\cdots}^{i=\infty} \frac{1}{i^2} \frac{l^2}{\pi^2 a} \frac{2g}{\gamma Al} \int_0^t P \sin \frac{i^2 \pi^2 a(t - t_1)\, dt_1}{l^2}. \tag{g}$$

The complete displacement of the ball from the beginning of the impact $(t = 0)$ will be equal to

$$d = \alpha + y. \tag{h}$$

The same displacement can be found now from a consideration of the motion of the ball. If v_0 is the velocity of the ball at the beginning of the impact $(t = 0)$, the velocity v at any moment $t = t_1$ will be equal to

$$v = v_0 - \frac{1}{m} \int_0^{t_1} P\, dt_1, \tag{i}$$

in which m is the mass of the ball and P is the reaction of the beam on the ball varying with the time. The displacement of the ball in the direction of impact will be

$$d = v_0 t - \int_0^t \frac{dt_1}{m} \int_0^{t_1} P\, dt_1. \tag{j}$$

* See author's paper, Z. Math. u. Phys., Vol. 62, p. 198, 1913.

† H. R. Hertz: J. Math. (Crelle), Vol. 92, 1881; A. E. H. Love, p. 198, loc. cit. The case of plastic deformation during impact was studied by D. Tabor, Engineering, Vol. 167, p. 145, 1949.

‡ The effect of shear deflection of a beam under impact was neglected in this investigation. It was discussed later by D. G. Christopherson, see his paper presented to the Institution of Mechanical Engineers, London, Sept. 1951. See also the paper by M. A. Dengler and M. Goland, Proc. First U. S. National Congress of Applied Mechanics, 1951.

Equating (h) and (j), the following equation is obtained:

$$v_0 t - \int_0^t \frac{dt_1}{m} \int_0^{t_1} P\, dt_1$$

$$= kP^{\frac{2}{3}} + \sum_{i=1,3,5,\ldots}^{i=\infty} \frac{1}{i^2} \frac{l^2}{\pi^2 a} \frac{2g}{\gamma Al} \int_0 P \sin \frac{i^2 \pi^2 a(t-t_1)\, dt_1}{l^2}. \qquad (k)$$

This equation can be solved numerically by subdividing the interval of time form 0 to t into small elements and calculating, step by step, the displacements of the ball. In the following, the results of such calculations for two numerical examples are given.

EXAMPLES

In the first example a steel bar of a square cross section 1×1 cm and of length, 15.35 cm is taken. A steel ball of the radius $r = 1$ cm strikes the bar with a velocity $v = 1$ cm per sec. Assuming $E = 2.2 \times 10^6$ kilograms per sq cm and $\gamma = 7.96$ grams

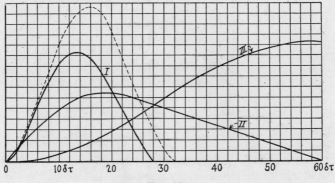

FIG. 229

per cu cm, the period of the fundamental mode of vibration will be $\tau = 0.001$ sec. In the numerical solution of eq. (k) this period was subdivided into 180 equal parts so that $\delta\tau = (\frac{1}{180})\tau$. The pressure P calculated for each step is given in Fig. 229 by the curve I. For comparison, in the same figure the variation of pressure with time for the case when the ball strikes an infinitely large body having a plane boundary surface, is shown by the dotted lines. It is seen that the ball remains in contact with the bar only during an interval of time equal to $28(\delta\tau)$, i.e., about $\frac{1}{6}$ of τ. The displacements of the ball are represented by curve II and the deflection of the bar at the middle by curve III.

A more complicated case is represented in Fig. 230. In this case the length of the bar and the radius of the ball are taken twice as great as in the previous example. The period τ of the fundamental mode of vibration of the bar is four times as large as in the previous case, while the variation of the pressure P is represented by a more complicated curve I. It is seen that the ball remains in contact with the bar from $t = 0$ to $t = 19.5(\delta\tau)$. Then it strikes the bar again at the moment $t = 60(\delta\tau)$ and remains in contact until $t = 80(\delta\tau)$. The deflection of the bar is given by curve II.

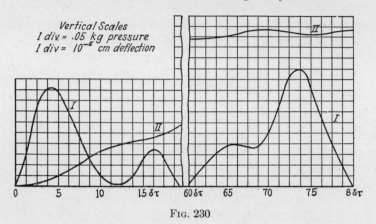

Vertical Scales
1 div = .05 kg pressure
1 div = 10^{-5} cm deflection

FIG. 230

It will be noted from these examples that the phenomenon of elastic impact is much more complicated than that of inelastic impact considered by St.-Venant.*

67. Longitudinal Impact of Prismatical Bars.—*General.*—For the approximate calculation of the stresses and deflections produced in a prismatical bar, struck longitudinally by a moving body, the approximate method developed in the previous article can be used, but for a more accurate solution of the problem a consideration of the longitudinal vibrations of the bar is necessary.

Thomas Young was the first † to point out the necessity of a more detailed consideration of the effect of the mass of the bar on the longitudinal impact. He showed also that any small perfectly rigid body will produce a permanent set in the bar during impact, provided the ratio of the velocity v_1 of motion of the striking body to the velocity v of the propagation of sound waves in the bar is larger than the strain corresponding to the elastic limit in compression of the material. In order to prove this statement,

* For experimental verification of the above theory, see paper by H. L. Mason, *J. Appl. Mech.*, Vol. 3, p. 55, 1936. See also R. N. Arnold, *Proc. Inst. Mech. Engrs. (London)*, Vol. 137, p. 217, 1937; and E. H. Lee, *J. Appl. Mech.*, Vol. 7, p. 129, 1940.

† See his *Lectures on Natural Philosophy*, Vol. 1, p. 144. The history of the longitudinal impact problem is discussed in detail in the book of Clebsch, translated by Saint-Venant, *loc. cit.*, p. 297, *see note finale du paragraphe* 60, p. 480a and appendix.

he assumed that at the moment of impact (Fig. 231) a local compression
will be produced * at the surface of contact of the moving body and the bar,
which compression is propagated along the bar with the velocity of sound.
Let us take a very small interval of time equal to t, such that during this
interval the velocity of the striking body can be considered as unchanged.
Then the displacement of the body will be v_1t and the length of the compressed portion of the bar will be vt.   Consequently the unit
compression becomes equal to v_1/v.   (Hence the statement
mentioned above.)

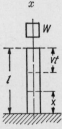

The longitudinal vibrations of a prismatical bar during
impact were considered by C. Navier.† He based his analysis on the assumption that after impact the moving body
becomes attached to the bar at least during a half-period of
the fundamental type of vibration.   In this manner the
problem of impact becomes equivalent to that of the vibrations of a load attached to a prismatical bar and having at
the initial moment a given velocity (see Art. 49).   The solu-

Fig. 231

tion of this problem, in the form of an infinite series given before, is not
suitable for the calculation of the maximum stresses during impact and
in the following a more comprehensive solution, developed by St.-Venant ‡
and J. Boussinesq, § will be discussed.

Bar Fixed at One End and Struck at the Other.¶—Considering first the
bar fixed at one end and struck longitudinally at the other, Fig. 231,
recourse will be taken to the already known equation for longitudinal
vibrations (see p. 299).   This equation is

$$\frac{\partial^2 u}{\partial t^2} = a^2 \frac{\partial^2 u}{\partial x^2}, \qquad (a)$$

in which u denotes the longitudinal displacements from the position of
equilibrium during vibration and

$$a^2 = \frac{Eg}{\gamma}. \qquad (b)$$

The condition at the fixed end is

$$(u)_{x=0} = 0. \qquad (c)$$

---

* It is assumed that the surfaces of contact are two parallel smooth planes.

† *Rapport . . . et mémoire sur les ponts suspendus,* 1823.

‡ *Loc. cit.,* p. 297.

§ *Applications des potentiels,* Paris, p. 508, 1885.

¶ See A. E. H. Love, p. 431, *loc. cit.*

The condition at the free end, at which the force in the bar must be equal to the inertia force of the striking body, will be

$$AE\left(\frac{\partial u}{\partial x}\right)_{x=l} = -\frac{W}{g}\left(\frac{\partial^2 u}{\partial t^2}\right)_{x=l}. \tag{d}$$

Denoting by m the ratio of the weight W of the striking body to the weight $A\gamma l$ of the bar, we obtain from (d)

$$ml\left(\frac{\partial^2 u}{\partial t^2}\right)_{x=l} = -a^2\left(\frac{\partial u}{\partial x}\right)_{x=l}. \tag{e}$$

The conditions at the initial moment $t = 0$, when the body strikes the bar, are

$$u = \frac{\partial u}{\partial t} = 0 \tag{f}$$

for all values of x between $x = 0$ and $x = l$, while at the end $x = l$, since at the instant of impact the velocity of the struck end of the bar becomes equal to that of the striking body, we have:

$$\left(\frac{\partial u}{\partial t}\right)_{t=+0} = -v. \tag{g}$$

The problem consists now in finding such a solution of eq. (a) which satisfies the terminal conditions (c) and (e) and the intial conditions (f) and (g).

The general solution of this equation can be taken in the form

$$u = f(at - x) + f_1(at + x), \tag{h}$$

in which f and f_1 are arbitrary functions.

In order to satisfy the terminal condition (c) we must have,

$$f(at) + f_1(at) = 0$$

or

$$f_1(at) = -f(at) \tag{i}$$

for any value of the argument at. Hence the solution (h) may be written in the form

$$u = f(at - x) - f(at + x). \tag{j}$$

If accents indicate differentiation with respect to the arguments $(at - x)$ or $(at + x)$ and (i) holds, we may put

$$\frac{\partial f}{\partial x} = -\frac{\partial f_1}{\partial x} = f'(at - x), \qquad \frac{\partial^2 f}{\partial x^2} = \frac{\partial^2 f_1}{\partial x^2} = f''(at - x),$$

$$\frac{\partial f}{\partial t} = \frac{\partial f_1}{\partial t} = af'(at - x), \qquad \frac{\partial^2 f}{\partial t^2} = \frac{\partial^2 f_1}{\partial t^2} = a^2 f''(at - x),$$

from which it is seen that the expression (j) satisfies eq. (a).

The solution (j) has a very simple physical meaning which can be easily explained in the following manner. Let us take the first term $f(at - x)$ on the right side of eq. (j) and consider a certain instant t. The function f can be represented for this instant by some curve nsr (Fig. 232), the shape of which will depend on the kind of the function f.

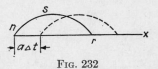

FIG. 232

It is easy to see that after the lapse of an element of time Δt, the argument $at - x$ of the function f will remain unchanged provided only that the abscissas are increased during the same interval of time by an element Δx equal to $a\Delta t$. Geometrically this means that during the interval of time Δt the curve nsr moves without distortion to a new position, shown in the figure by the dotted line. It can be appreciated from this consideration that the first term on the right side of eq. (j) represents a wave traveling along the x-axis with a constant velocity equal to

$$a = \sqrt{\frac{Eg}{\gamma}}, \tag{167}$$

which is also the velocity of propagation of sound waves along the bar. In the same manner it can be shown that the second term on the right side of eq. (j) represents a wave traveling with the velocity a in the negative direction of the x-axis. The general solution (j) is obtained by the superposition of two such waves of the same shape traveling with the same velocity in two opposite directions. The striking body produces during impact a continuous series of such waves, which travel towards the fixed end and are reflected there. The shape of these consecutive waves can now be established by using the initial conditions and the terminal condition at the end $x = l$.

For the initial moment $(t = 0)$ we have, from eq. (j),

$$(u)_{t=0} = f(-x) - f(+x),$$

$$\left(\frac{\partial u}{\partial x}\right)_{t=0} = -f'(-x) - f'(+x),$$

$$\left(\frac{\partial u}{\partial t}\right)_{t=0} = af'(-x) - af'(+x).$$

Now by using the initial conditions (f), we obtain

$$-f'(-x) - f'(+x) = 0, \quad \text{for} \quad 0 < x < l,$$
$$f'(-x) - f'(+x) = 0, \quad \text{for} \quad 0 < x < l. \tag{k}$$

Considering f as a function of an argument z, which can be put equal to $+x$ or $-x$, it can be concluded, from (k), that when $-l < z < l, f'(z)$ is equal to zero, since only under this condition can both eqs. (k) be satisfied simultaneously and hence $f(z)$ is a constant which can be taken equal to zero and we get,

$$f(z) = 0, \quad \text{when} \quad -l < z < l. \tag{l}$$

Now the values of the function $f(z)$ can be determined for the values of z outside the interval $-l < z < l$ by using the end condition (e).

Substituting (j) in eq. (e) we obtain

$$ml\{f''(at - l) - f''(at + l)\} = +f'(at - l) + f'(at + l),$$

or by putting $at + l = z$,

$$f''(z) + \frac{1}{ml}f'(z) = f''(z - 2l) - \frac{1}{ml}f'(z - 2l). \tag{m}$$

By using this equation the function $f(z)$ can be constructed step by step as follows:

From (l) we know that in the interval $l < z < 3l$ the right-hand member of eq. (m) is zero. By integrating this equation the function $f(z)$ in the interval $l < z < 3l$ will be obtained. The right-hand member of eq. (m) will then become known for the interval $3l < z < 5l$. Consequently the integration of this equation will give the function $f(z)$ for the interval $3l < z < 5l$. By proceeding in this way the function $f(z)$ can be determined for all values of z greater than $-l$.

Considering eq. (m) as an equation to determine $f'(z)$, the general solution of this linear equation of the first order will be

$$f'(z) = Ce^{-z/ml} + e^{-z/ml} \int e^{z/ml} \left[f''(z - 2l) - \frac{1}{ml} f'(z - 2l) \right] dz, \quad (n)$$

in which C is a constant of integration.

For the interval $l < z < 3l$, the right-hand member of eq. (m) vanishes and we obtain

$$f'(z) = Ce^{-z/ml}.$$

Now, by using the condition (g), we have

$$a\{f'(-l + 0) - f'(l + 0)\} = -v$$

or

$$f'(l + 0) = Ce^{-1/m} = \frac{v}{a}, \quad C = e^{1/m} \frac{v}{a},$$

and we obtain for the interval $l < z < 3l$

$$f'(z) = \frac{v}{a} e^{-(z-l)/ml}. \tag{o}$$

When $3l < z < 5l$, we have, from eq. (o),

$$f'(z - 2l) = \frac{v}{a} e^{-(z-3l)/ml}$$

and

$$f''(z - 2l) - \frac{1}{ml} f'(z - 2l) = -\frac{2}{ml} \frac{v}{a} e^{-(z-3l)/ml}.$$

Now the solution (n) can be represented in the following form:

$$f'(z) = Ce^{-z/ml} - \frac{2}{ml} \frac{v}{a} (z - 3l) e^{-(z-3l)/ml}. \tag{p}$$

The constant of integration C will be determined from the condition of continuity of the velocity at the end $x = l$ at the moment $t = (2l/a)$. This condition is

$$\left(\frac{\partial u}{\partial t} \right)_{\substack{t=2l/a-0 \\ x=l}} = \left(\frac{\partial u}{\partial t} \right)_{\substack{t=2l/a+0 \\ x=l}},$$

or by using eq. (j),

$$f'(l - 0) - f'(3l - 0) = f'(l + 0) - f'(3l + 0).$$

Using now eqs. (l), (o) and (p) we obtain

$$-\frac{v}{a}e^{-2/m} = \frac{v}{a} - Ce^{-3/m},$$

from which

$$C = \frac{v}{a}(e^{1/m} + e^{3/m}),$$

and we have for the interval $3l < z < 5l$

$$f'(z) = \frac{v}{a}e^{-(z-l)/ml} + \frac{v}{a}\left[1 - \frac{2}{ml}(z - 3l)\right]e^{-(z-3l)/ml}. \qquad (q)$$

Knowing $f'(z)$ when $3l < z < 5l$ and using eq. (m), the expression for $f'(z)$ when $5l < z < 7l$ can be obtained and so on.

The function $f(z)$ can be determined by integration if the function $f'(z)$ be known, the constant of integration being determined from the condition that there is no abrupt change in the displacement u at $x = l$. In this manner the following results are obtained when $l < z < 3l$:

$$f(z) = \frac{mlv}{a}\{1 - e^{-(z-l)/ml}\}, \qquad (r)$$

when $3l < z < 5l$,

$$f(z) = -\frac{mlv}{a}e^{-(z-l)/ml} + \frac{mlv}{a}\left[1 + \frac{2}{ml}(z - 3l)\right]e^{-(z-3l)/ml}. \qquad (s)$$

Knowing $f(z)$, the displacements and the stresses at any cross section of the bar can be calculated by substituting in eq. (j) the corresponding values for the functions $f(at - x)$ and $f(at + x)$. When $0 < t < (l/a)$ the term $f(at - x)$ in eq. (j) is equal to zero, by virtue of (l) and hence we have only the wave $f(at + x)$ advancing in the negative direction of the x-axis. The shape of this wave will be obtained from (r) by substituting $at + x$ for z. At $t = (l/a)$ this wave will be reflected from the fixed end and in the interval $(l/a) < t < (2l/a)$ we will have two waves, the wave $f(at - x)$ traveling in the positive direction along the x-axis and the wave $f(at + x)$ traveling in the negative direction. Both waves can be obtained from (r) by substituting, for z, the arguments $(at - x)$ and $(at + x)$, respectively. Continuing in this way the complete picture of the phenomenon of longitudinal impact can be secured.*

* The phenomenon of longitudinal impact is discussed with great detail in L. H. Donnell's doctoral thesis, University of Michigan. See also his paper in *Trans. A.S.M.E.*, Vol. 52, p. 153, 1930.

The above solution represents the actual conditions only as long as there exists a positive pressure between the striking body and the bar, i.e., as long as the unit elongation

$$\left(\frac{\partial u}{\partial x}\right)_{x=l} = -f'(at - l) - f'(at + l) \tag{t}$$

remains negative. When $0 < at < 2l$, the right-hand member of eq. (t) is represented by the function (o) with the negative sign and remains negative. When $2l < at < 4l$ the right side of the eq. (t) becomes

$$-\frac{v}{a}e^{-at/ml}\left\{1 + 2e^{2/m}\left(1 - \frac{at - 2l}{ml}\right)\right\}.$$

This vanishes when

$$1 + 2e^{2/m}\left(1 - \frac{at - 2l}{ml}\right) = 0$$

or

$$2at/ml = 4/m + 2 + e^{-2/m}. \tag{u}$$

This equation can have a root in the interval, $2l < at < 4l$ only if

$$2 + e^{-2/m} < 4/m,$$

which happens for $m = 1.73$.

Hence, if the ratio of the weight of the striking body to the weight of the bar is less than 1.73 the impact ceases at an instant in the interval $2l < at < 4l$ and this instant can be calculated from eq. (u). For larger values of the ratio m, an investigation of whether or not the impact ceases at some instant in the interval $4l < at < 6l$ should be made, and so on.

The maximum compressive stresses during impact occur at the fixed end and for large values of m $(m > 24)$ can be calculated with sufficient accuracy from the following approximate formula:

$$\sigma_{\max} = E\frac{v}{a}(\sqrt{m} + 1). \tag{168}$$

For comparison it is interesting to note that by using the approximate method of the previous article and neglecting δ_{st} in comparison with h in eq. (d) (see p. 412), we arrive at the equation

$$\sigma_{\max} = E\frac{v}{a}\sqrt{m}. \tag{169}$$

When $5 < m < 24$ the equation

$$\sigma_{max} = E\frac{v}{a}(\sqrt{m} + 1.1) \tag{170}$$

should be used instead of eq. (168). When $m < 5$, St.-Venant derived the following formula,

$$\sigma_{max} = 2E\frac{v}{a}(1 + e^{-2/m}). \tag{171}$$

By using the above method the case of a rod free at one end and struck longitudinally at the other and the case of longitudinal impact of two prismatical bars can be considered.* It should be noted that the investigation of the longitudinal impact given above is based on the assumption that the surfaces of contact between the striking body and the bar are two ideal smooth parallel planes. In actual conditions, there will always be some surface irregularities and a certain interval of time is required to flatten down the high spots. If this interval is of the same order as the time taken for a sound wave to pass along the bar, a satisfactory agreement between the theory and experiment cannot be expected.† Much better results will be obtained if the arrangement is such that the time l/a is comparatively long. For example, by replacing the solid bar by a helical spring, C. Ramsauer obtained ‡ a very good agreement between theory and experiment. For this reason we may also expect satisfactory results in applying the theory to the investigation of the propagation of impact waves in long, uniformly loaded railway trains. Such a problem may be of practical importance in studying the forces acting in couplings between cars.§

Another method of obtaining better agreement between theory and experiment is to make the contact conditions more definite. By taking, for instance, a bar with a rounded end and combining the Hertz theory for the local deformation at the point of contact with St.-Venant's theory of the waves traveling along the bar, J. E. Sears ¶ secured a very good agreement between theoretical and experimental results.

* See A. E. H. Love, p. 435, *loc. cit.*

† Such experiments with solid steel bars were made by W. Voigt, *Ann. Physik*, Vol. 19, p. 43, 1883.

‡ *Ann. Physik*, Vol. 30, p. 416, 1909.

§ This question has been studied by O. R. Wikander, *loc. cit.*

¶ *Trans. Cambridge Phil. Soc.*, Vol. 21, p. 49, 1908. Further experiments are described by J. E. P. Wagstaff, *Proc. Roy. Soc. (London)*, A, Vol. 105, p. 544, 1924. See also W. A. Prowse, *Phil. Mag.*, ser. 7, Vol. 22, p. 209, 1936.

68. Vibration of a Circular Ring.*—The problem of vibration of a circular ring is encountered in the investigation of the frequencies of vibration of various kinds of circular frames for rotating electrical machinery as is necessary in a study of the causes of noise produced by such machinery. In the following, several simple problems on the vibration of a circular ring of constant cross section are considered, under the assumptions that the cross-sectional dimensions of the ring are small in comparison with the radius of its center line and that each cross section has an axis of symmetry situated in the plane of the ring.

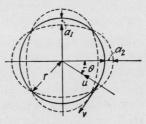

Fig. 233

Pure Radial Vibration.—In this case the center line of the ring forms a circle of periodically varying radius and all the cross sections move radially without rotation.

Referring to Fig. 233, assume that r is the radius of the center line of the ring; u, the radial displacement, positive toward the center and the same for all cross sections; A, the cross-sectional area of the ring. The unit elongation of the ring in the circumferential direction is then $-u/r$. The potential energy of deformation, consisting in this case of the energy of simple tension, will be given by the equation:

$$V = \frac{A E u^2}{2 r^2} 2\pi r, \qquad (a)$$

while the kinetic energy of vibration will be

$$T = \frac{A \gamma}{2g} \dot{u}^2 2\pi r. \qquad (b)$$

From (a) and (b) we obtain

$$\ddot{u} + \frac{Eg}{\gamma} \frac{1}{r^2} u = 0,$$

from which

$$u = C_1 \cos pt + C_2 \sin pt,$$

where

$$p = \sqrt{\frac{Eg}{\gamma r^2}}.$$

* See Zacek, "Radial and Torsional Vibrations of Rings," *Phil. Mag.*, Vol. 25, p. 164, 1938.

The frequency of pure radial vibration is therefore *

$$f = \frac{p}{2\pi} = \frac{1}{2\pi} \sqrt{\frac{Eg}{\gamma r^2}}. \tag{172}$$

A circular ring possesses also modes of vibration analogous to the longitudinal vibrations of prismatical bars. If i denotes the number of wave lengths to the circumference, the frequencies of the higher modes of extensional vibration of the ring will be determined from the equation †

$$f_i = \frac{1}{2\pi} \sqrt{\frac{Eg}{\gamma r^2}} \sqrt{1 + i^2}. \tag{173}$$

Torsional Vibration.—Consideration will now be given to the simplest mode of torsional vibration, i.e., that in which the center line of the ring remains undeformed and all the cross sections of the ring rotate during vibration through the same angle (Fig. 234). Due to this rotation a point M, distant y from the middle plane of the ring, will have a radial displacement equal to $y\varphi$ and the corresponding circumferential elongation can be taken approximately equal to $y\varphi/r$. The potential energy of deformation of the ring can now be calculated as follows:

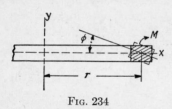

FIG. 234

$$V = 2\pi r \int_A \frac{E}{2} \left(\frac{y\varphi}{r}\right)^2 dA = \frac{\pi E I_x \varphi^2}{r}, \tag{c}$$

where I_x is the moment of inertia of the cross section about the x-axis.
The kinetic energy of vibration will be

$$T = 2\pi r \cdot \frac{I_p \gamma}{2g} \dot{\varphi}^2, \tag{d}$$

where I_p is the polar moment of inertia of the cross section.

* If there is any additional load, which can be considered as uniformly distributed along the center line of the ring, it is only necessary in the above calculation (eq. *b*) to replace $A\gamma$ by $A\gamma + w$, where w denotes the additional weight per unit length of the center line of the ring.

† See A. E. H. Love, p. 454, *loc. cit.*

From (c) and (d) we obtain

$$\ddot{\varphi} + \frac{Eg}{\gamma r^2} \frac{I_x}{I_p} \varphi = 0,$$

from which

$$\varphi = C_1 \cos pt + C_2 \sin pt,$$

where

$$p = \sqrt{\frac{Eg}{\gamma r^2} \frac{I_x}{I_p}}.$$

The frequency of torsional vibration will then be given by

$$f = \frac{1}{2\pi} \sqrt{\frac{Eg}{\gamma r^2} \frac{I_x}{I_p}}. \tag{174}$$

Comparing this result with formula (172), it can be concluded that the frequencies of the torsional and pure radial vibrations are in the ratio $\sqrt{I_x/I_p}$. The frequencies of the higher modes of torsional vibration are given,[*] in the case of a circular cross section of the ring, by the equation

$$f_i = \frac{1}{2\pi} \sqrt{\frac{Eg}{2\gamma r^2}} \sqrt{1 + i^2}. \tag{175}$$

Remembering that

$$\sqrt{\frac{Eg}{\gamma r^2}} = \frac{a}{r},$$

where a is the velocity of propagation of sound along the bar, it can be concluded that the extensional and torsional vibrations considered above usually have high frequencies. Much lower frequencies will be obtained if flexural vibrations of the ring are considered.

Flexural Vibrations of a Circular Ring.—Flexural vibrations of a circular ring fall into two classes, i.e., flexural vibrations in the plane of the ring and flexural vibrations involving both displacements at right angles to the plane of the ring and twist.[†] In considering the flexural vibrations in the plane of the ring (Fig. 233), assume that

θ is the angle determining the position of a point on the center line;
u, the radial displacement, positive towards the center;

* See A. E. H. Love, p. 453, *loc. cit.*
† A. E. H. Love, p. 451, *loc. cit.*

v, the tangential displacement, positive in the direction of increasing θ;
I, the moment of inertia of the cross section with respect to a principal axis at right angles to the plane of the ring.

The unit elongation of the center line at any point, due to the displacements u and v, is

$$e = -\frac{u}{r} + \frac{\partial v}{r\,\partial\theta},\tag{e}$$

and the change in curvature can be represented by the equation *

$$\frac{1}{r + \Delta r} - \frac{1}{r} = \frac{\partial^2 u}{r^2\,\partial\theta^2} + \frac{u}{r^2}.\tag{f}$$

In the most general case of flexural vibration the radial displacement u can be represented in the form of a trigonometric series †

$$u = a_1 \cos\theta + a_2 \cos 2\theta + \cdots + b_1 \sin\theta + b_2 \sin 2\theta + \cdots,\tag{g}$$

in which the coefficients a_1, a_2, $\cdots$ b_1, b_2, $\cdots$ are functions of time.

Considering flexural vibrations without extension,‡ we have, from (e),

$$u = \frac{\partial v}{\partial\theta},\tag{h}$$

from which §

$$v = a_1 \sin\theta + \tfrac{1}{2}a_2 \sin 2\theta + \cdots - b_1 \cos\theta - \tfrac{1}{2}b_2 \cos 2\theta - \cdots.\tag{i}$$

The bending moment at any cross section of the ring will be

$$M = \frac{EI}{r^2}\left(\frac{\partial^2 u}{\partial\theta^2} + u\right),$$

and hence we obtain for the potential energy of bending

$$V = \frac{EI}{2r^4}\int_0^{2\pi}\left(\frac{\partial^2 u}{\partial\theta^2} + u\right)^2 r\,d\theta,$$

* This equation was established by J. Boussinesq, *Comptes rend.*, Vol. 97, p. 843, 1883.

† The constant term of the series, corresponding to pure radial vibration, is omitted.

‡ See discussion of flexural vibrations by taking into account also extension in papers by F. W. Waltking, *Ing.-Arch.*, Vol. 5, p. 429, 1934; and K. Federhofer, *Sitzber. Acad. Wiss. Wien, Abt. IIa*, Vol. 145, p. 29, 1936.

§ The constant of integration representing a rotation of the ring in its plane as a rigid body, is omitted in expression (i).

or, by substituting the series (g) for u and by using the formulas

$$\int_0^{2\pi} \cos m\theta \cos n\theta \, d\theta = 0, \quad \int_0^{2\pi} \sin m\theta \sin n\theta \, d\theta = 0, \quad \text{when} \quad m \neq n,$$

$$\int_0^{2\pi} \cos m\theta \sin m\theta \, d\theta = 0, \quad \int_0^{2\pi} \cos^2 m\theta \, d\theta = \int_0^{2\pi} \sin^2 m\theta \, d\theta = \pi,$$

we get

$$V = \frac{EI\pi}{2r^3} \sum_{i=1}^{i=\infty} (1 - i^2)^2 (a_i^2 + b_i^2). \tag{j}$$

The kinetic energy of the vibrating ring is

$$T = \frac{A\gamma}{2g} \int_0^{2\pi} (\dot{u}^2 + \dot{v}^2) r \, d\theta.$$

By substituting (g) and (i) for u and v, this becomes

$$T = \frac{\pi r A \gamma}{2g} \sum_{i=1}^{i=\infty} \left(1 + \frac{1}{i^2}\right) (\dot{a}_i^2 + \dot{b}_i^2). \tag{k}$$

Proceeding as in the case of straight beams and considering a virtual displacement $\delta u = \delta a_i \cos i\theta$, $\delta v = \dfrac{\delta a_i}{i} \sin i\theta$, the differential equation of motion for any mode of vibration will be obtained as follows:

$$\frac{\pi r A \gamma}{g} \left(1 + \frac{1}{i^2}\right) \ddot{a}_i + \frac{EI\pi}{r^3} (1 - i^2)^2 a_i = 0$$

or

$$\ddot{a}_i + \frac{Eg}{\gamma} \frac{I}{Ar^4} \frac{i^2(1 - i^2)^2}{1 + i^2} a_i = 0.$$

Hence the frequency of any mode of vibration is determined by the equation

$$f_i = \frac{1}{2\pi} \sqrt{\frac{Eg}{\gamma} \frac{I}{Ar^4} \frac{i^2(1 - i^2)^2}{1 + i^2}}. \tag{176}$$

When $i = 1$, we obtain $f_1 = 0$. In this case $u = a_1 \cos \theta$; $v = a_1 \sin \theta$ and the ring moves as a rigid body, a_1 being the displacement in the negative direction of the x-axis, Fig. 233. When $i = 2$ the ring performs the fundamental mode of flexural vibration. The extreme positions of the ring during this vibration are shown in Fig. 233 by dotted lines.

In the case of flexural vibrations of a ring of circular cross section involving both displacements at right angles to the plane of the ring and twist, the frequencies of the principal modes of vibration can be calculated from the equation *

$$f_i = \frac{1}{2\pi} \sqrt{\frac{Eg}{\gamma} \frac{I}{Ar^4} \frac{i^2(i^2 - 1)^2}{i^2 + 1 + \nu}}, \qquad (177)$$

in which ν denotes Poisson's ratio.

Comparing eqs. (176) and (177), it can be concluded that even in the lowest mode ($i = 2$) the frequencies of the two classes of flexural vibrations differ but very slightly. †

Incomplete Ring.—When the ring has the form of an incomplete circular arc, the problem of the calculation of the natural frequencies of vibration becomes very complicated.‡ The results so far obtained can be interpreted only for the case where the length of the arc is small in comparison to the radius of curvature. In such cases, these results show that natural frequencies are slightly lower than those of a straight bar of the same material, length and cross section. Since, in the general case, the exact solution of the problem is extremely complicated, at this date only some approximate values for the lowest natural frequency are available, the Rayleigh-Ritz method § being used in their calculation.

69. Vibration of Membranes.—*General.*—In the following discussion it is assumed that the membrane is a perfectly flexible and infinitely thin lamina of uniform material and thickness. It is further assumed that it is uniformly stretched in all directions by a tension so large that the fluctuation in this tension due to the small deflections during vibration can be

---

* A. E. H. Love, p. 453, *loc. cit.*

† For an experimental investigation of ring vibrations in connection with study of gear noise, see R. E. Peterson, *Trans. A.S.M.E.*, Vol. 52, p. APM-1, 1930.

‡ This problem has been discussed by H. Lamb, *Proc. London Math. Soc.*, Vol. 19, p. 365, 1888. See also paper by F. W. Waltking, p. 409, *loc. cit.*

§ See J. P. Den Hartog, "The Lowest Natural Frequency of Circular Arcs," *Phil. Mag.*, Vol. 5, p. 400, 1928; also "Vibration of Frames of Electrical Machines," *Trans. A.S.M.E.*, Vol. 50, APM-6, 1928. Further discussion of the problem is in papers by K. Federhofer, *Ing.-Arch.*, Vol. 4, pp. 110 and 276, 1933; and *Sitzber. Acad. Wiss. Wien, Abt. IIa*, Vol. 151, p. 89, 1942. See also E. Maier, *Ing.-Arch.*, Vol. 11, p. 73, 1940; and W. Wuest, *ibid.*, Vol. 17, p. 265, 1949. The investigation of the same problem in connection with the question of buckling of an arch was made by K. Federhofer, *Sitzber. Acad. Wiss. Wien, Abt. IIa*, Vol. 143, p. 131, 1934.

neglected.   Taking the plane of the membrane coinciding with the xy-plane, we assume that

v is the displacement of any point of the membrane at right angles to the xy-plane during vibration;
S is the uniform tension per unit length of the boundary;
w is the weight of the membrane per unit area.

The increase in the potential energy of the membrane during deflection will be found in the usual way by multiplying the uniform tension S by the increase in surface area of the membrane.   The area of the surface of the membrane in a deflected position will be

$$A = \iint \sqrt{1 + \left(\frac{\partial v}{\partial x}\right)^2 + \left(\frac{\partial v}{\partial y}\right)^2}\, dx\, dy,$$

or, observing that the deflections during vibration are very small,

$$A = \iint \left\{1 + \frac{1}{2}\left(\frac{\partial v}{\partial x}\right)^2 + \frac{1}{2}\left(\frac{\partial v}{\partial y}\right)^2\right\}\, dx\, dy.$$

Then the increase in potential energy will be

$$V = \frac{S}{2} \iint \left\{\left(\frac{\partial v}{\partial x}\right)^2 + \left(\frac{\partial v}{\partial y}\right)^2\right\}\, dx\, dy. \qquad (a)$$

The kinetic energy of the membrane during vibration is

$$T = \frac{w}{2g} \iint \dot{v}^2\, dx\, dy. \qquad (b)$$

By using (a) and (b) the frequencies of the normal modes of vibration can be calculated, as will now be shown for some particular cases.

Vibration of a Rectangular Membrane.—Let a and b denote the lengths of the sides of the membrane and let the axes be taken as shown in Fig. 235.   Whatever function of the co-ordinates v may be, it always can be represented within the limits of the rectangle by the double series

$$v = \sum_{m=1}^{m=\infty} \sum_{n=1}^{n=\infty} \phi_{mn} \sin\frac{m\pi x}{a} \sin\frac{n\pi y}{b}, \qquad (c)$$

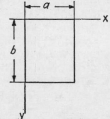

Fig. 235

the coefficients ϕ_{mn} of which are functions of time. It is easy to see that each term of the series (c) satisfies the boundary conditions, namely, $v = 0$, for $x = 0$; $x = a$ and $v = 0$ for $y = 0$; $y = b$.

Substituting (c) in the expression (a) for the potential energy, we obtain

$$V = \frac{S\pi^2}{2} \int_0^a \int_0^b \left\{ \left(\sum \sum \phi_{mn} \frac{m}{a} \cos \frac{m\pi x}{a} \sin \frac{n\pi y}{b} \right)^2 \right.$$
$$\left. + \left(\sum \sum \phi_{mn} \frac{n}{b} \sin \frac{m\pi x}{a} \cos \frac{n\pi y}{b} \right)^2 \right\} dx \, dy.$$

Integrating this expression over the area of the membrane using the formulas of Art. (17) (see p. 97), we find

$$V = \frac{S}{2} \frac{ab\pi^2}{4} \sum_{m=1}^{m=\infty} \sum_{n=1}^{n=\infty} \left(\frac{m^2}{a^2} + \frac{n^2}{b^2} \right) \phi_{mn}^2. \tag{d}$$

Using now d'Alembert's principle and considering a virtual displacement

$$\delta v = \delta \phi_{mn} \sin \frac{m\pi x}{a} \sin \frac{n\pi y}{b},$$

we obtain the differential equation of normal vibration

$$\frac{w}{g} \frac{ab}{4} \ddot{\phi}_{mn} + S \frac{ab\pi^2}{4} \left(\frac{m^2}{a^2} + \frac{n^2}{b^2} \right) \phi_{mn} = 0 \tag{e}$$

from which

$$f_{mn} = \frac{1}{2} \sqrt{\frac{gS}{w} \left(\frac{m^2}{a^2} + \frac{n^2}{b^2} \right)}. \tag{178}$$

The lowest mode of vibration will be obtained by putting $m = n = 1$. Then,

$$f_{11} = \frac{1}{2} \sqrt{\frac{gS}{w} \left(\frac{1}{a^2} + \frac{1}{b^2} \right)}. \tag{f}$$

The deflection surface of the membrane in this case is

$$v = C \sin \frac{\pi x}{a} \sin \frac{\pi y}{b}. \tag{g}$$

In the same manner the higher modes of vibration can be obtained. Take, for instance, the case of a square membrane, when $a = b$. The frequency of the lowest mode is

$$f_{11} = \frac{1}{a\sqrt{2}} \sqrt{\frac{gS}{w}}. \tag{179}$$

The frequency is directly proportional to the square root of the tension S and inversely proportional to the length of sides of the membrane and to the square root of the load per unit area.

The next two higher modes of vibration will be obtained by taking one of the numbers m, n equal to 2 and the other to 1. These two modes have the same frequency, but show different shapes of deflection surface. In Figs. 236a and 236b the node lines of these two modes of vibration are shown. Because of the fact that the frequencies are the same, it is possible to superimpose these two surfaces on each other in any ratio of their maximum deflections. Such a combination is expressed by

$$v = C \sin \frac{2\pi x}{a} \sin \frac{\pi y}{a} + D \sin \frac{\pi x}{a} \sin \frac{2\pi y}{a},$$

where C and D are arbitrary quantities. Four particular cases of such a combined vibration are shown in Fig. 236. Taking $D = 0$, we obtain the vibration mentioned above and shown in Fig. 236a. The membrane,

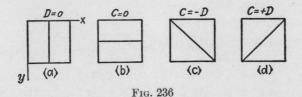

Fig. 236

while vibrating, is subdivided into two equal parts by a vertical nodal line. When $C = 0$, the membrane is subdivided by a horizontal nodal line as in Fig. 236b. When $C = D$, we obtain

$$v = C \left(\sin \frac{2\pi x}{a} \sin \frac{\pi y}{a} + \sin \frac{\pi x}{a} \sin \frac{2\pi y}{a} \right)$$

$$= 2C \sin \frac{\pi x}{a} \sin \frac{\pi u}{a} \left(\cos \frac{\pi x}{a} + \cos \frac{\pi y}{a} \right).$$

This expression vanishes when

$$\sin \frac{\pi x}{a} = 0, \quad \text{or} \quad \sin \frac{\pi y}{a} = 0,$$

or again when

$$\cos \frac{\pi x}{a} + \cos \frac{\pi u}{a} = 0.$$

The first two equations give us the sides of the boundary; from the third equation we obtain

$$\frac{\pi x}{a} = \pi - \frac{\pi y}{a},$$

or

$$x + y = a.$$

This represents one diagonal of the square shown in Fig. 236d. Fig. 236c represents the case when $C = -D$. Each half of the membrane in the last two cases can be considered as an isosceles right-angled triangular membrane. The fundamental frequency of this membrane, from eq. (178), will be

$$f = \frac{1}{2} \sqrt{\frac{gS}{w} \left(\frac{4}{a^2} + \frac{1}{a^2} \right)} = \frac{\sqrt{5}}{2a} \sqrt{\frac{gS}{w}}. \tag{180}$$

In this manner also higher modes of vibration of a square or rectangular membrane can be considered.*

In the case of forced vibration of the membrane the differential equation of motion (e) becomes

$$\frac{w}{g} \frac{ab}{4} \ddot{\phi}_{mn} + S \frac{ab\pi^2}{4} \left(\frac{m^2}{a^2} + \frac{n^2}{b^2} \right) \phi_{mn} = Q_{mn}, \tag{h}$$

in which Q_{mn} is selected in such a manner that $Q_{mn} \phi_{mn}$ represents the virtual work of the disturbing forces.

Let us consider, as an example, the case of a harmonic force $P = P_0 \cos \omega t$, acting at the center of the membrane. By giving an increase $\delta \phi_{mn}$ to a coordinate ϕ_{mn}, in the expression (c), we find for the work done by the force P,

$$P_0 \cos \omega t \delta \phi_{mn} \sin \frac{m\pi}{2} \sin \frac{n\pi}{2},$$

---

* A more detailed discussion of this problem can be found in Rayleigh's book, p. 306, *loc. cit.* See also G. Lamé, *Leçons sur . . .ml'élasticité des corps solides*, Paris, 1852.

from which we see that when m and n are both odd, $Q_{mn} = \pm P_0 \cos \omega t$, otherwise $Q_{mn} = 0$. Substituting in eq. (h), and using eq. (46) (p. 106), we obtain

$$\phi_{mn} = \pm \frac{4g}{abw} \frac{P_0}{p_{mn}} \int_0^t \sin p_{mn}(t - t_1) \cos \omega t_1 \, dt_1$$

$$= \pm \frac{4g}{abw} \frac{P_0}{p_{mn}^2 - \omega^2} (\cos \omega t - \cos p_{mn}t), \qquad (i)$$

where

$$p_{mn}^2 = \frac{gS\pi^2}{w} \left(\frac{m^2}{a_2} + \frac{n^2}{b_2} \right).$$

By substituting (i) in the expression (c), the vibrations produced by the disturbing force $P_0 \cos \omega t$ will be obtained.

When a distributed disturbing force of an intensity Z is acting on the membrane, we have

$$Q_{mn} = \int_0^b \int_0^a Z \sin \frac{m\pi x}{a} \sin \frac{n\pi y}{b} \, dx \, dy. \qquad (j)$$

Assume, for instance, that a uniformly distributed pressure Z is suddenly applied to the membrane at the initial moment $(t = 0)$, then from (j),

$$Q_{mn} = Z \frac{ab}{mn\pi^2} (1 - \cos m\pi)(1 - \cos n\pi)$$

When m and n both are odd, we have

$$Q_{mn} = \frac{4ab}{mn\pi^2} Z; \qquad (k)$$

otherwise Q_{mn} vanishes.

Substituting (k) in eq. (h) and assuming the initial condition that $\phi_{mn} = 0$ at $t = 0$, we obtain

$$\phi_{mn} = \frac{16g}{wmn\pi^2} \frac{Z(1 - \cos p_{mn}t)}{p_{mn}^2}. \qquad (l)$$

Hence the vibrations produced by the suddenly applied pressure Z are

$$v = \frac{16gZ}{\pi^2 w} \sum \sum \frac{1 - \cos p_{mn}t}{mn p_{mn}^2} \sin \frac{m\pi x}{a} \sin \frac{n\pi y}{b}, \qquad (m)$$

where m and n are both odd.

Rayleigh-Ritz Method.—In calculating the frequencies of the natural modes of vibration of a membrane the Rayleigh-Ritz method is very useful. In applying this method we assume that the deflections of the membrane, while vibrating, are given by

$$v = v_0 \cos pt, \tag{n}$$

where v_0 is a suitable function of the coordinates x and y which determines the shape of the deflected membrane, i.e., the mode of vibration. Substituting (n) in the expression (a) for the potential energy, we find

$$V_{\max} = \frac{S}{2} \iint \left\{ \left(\frac{\partial v_0}{\partial x}\right)^2 + \left(\frac{\partial v_0}{\partial y}\right)^2 \right\} dx\, dy. \tag{o}$$

For the maximum kinetic energy we obtain from (b)

$$T_{\max} = \frac{w}{2g} p^2 \iint v_0{}^2\, dx\, dy. \tag{p}$$

Putting (o) equal to (p), we get

$$p^2 = \frac{Sg}{w} \frac{\displaystyle\iint \left\{ \left(\frac{\partial v_0}{\partial x}\right)^2 + \left(\frac{\partial v_0}{\partial y}\right)^2 \right\} dx\, dy}{\displaystyle\iint v_0{}^2\, dx\, dy}. \tag{q}$$

In applying the Rayleigh-Ritz method we take the expression v_0 for the deflection surface of the membrane in the form of a series:

$$v_0 = a_1 \varphi_1(x, y) + a_2 \varphi_2(x, y) + a_3 \varphi_3(x, y) + \cdots, \tag{r}$$

each term of which satisfies the conditions at the boundary. (The deflections at the boundary of the membrane must be equal to zero.) The coefficients a_1, a_2, $\cdots$ in this series should be chosen in such a manner as to make (q) a minimum, i.e., so as to satisfy all equations of the following form:

$$\frac{\partial}{\partial a_n} \frac{\displaystyle\iint \left\{ \left(\frac{\partial v_0}{\partial x}\right)^2 + \left(\frac{\partial v_0}{\partial y}\right)^2 \right\} dx\, dy}{\displaystyle\iint v_0{}^2\, dx\, dy} = 0,$$

or

$$\iint v_0^2 \, dx \, dy \cdot \frac{\partial}{\partial a_n} \iint \left\{ \left(\frac{\partial v_0}{\partial x}\right)^2 + \left(\frac{\partial v_0}{\partial y}\right)^2 \right\} dx \, dy$$

$$- \iint \left\{ \left(\frac{\partial v_0}{\partial x}\right)^2 + \left(\frac{\partial v_0}{\partial y}\right)^2 \right\} dx \, dy \cdot \frac{\partial}{\partial a_n} \iint v_0^2 \, dx \, dy = 0.$$

By using (q), this latter equation becomes

$$\frac{\partial}{\partial a_n} \iint \left\{ \left(\frac{\partial v_0}{\partial x}\right)^2 + \left(\frac{\partial v_0}{\partial y}\right)^2 - \frac{p^2 w}{gS} v_0^2 \right\} dx \, dy = 0. \qquad (s)$$

In this manner we obtain as many equations of the type (s) as there are coefficients in the series (r). All these equations will be linear in a_1, a_2, a_3, $\cdots$, and by equating the determinant of these equations to zero the frequency equation for the membrane will be obtained.

Considering, for example, the modes of vibration of a square membrane symmetrical with respect to the x- and y-axes, Fig. 237, the series (r) can be taken in the following form:

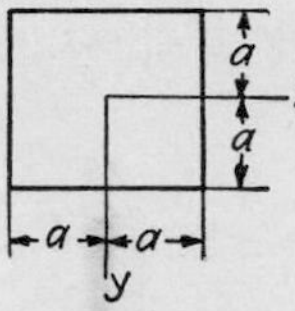

Fig. 237

$$v_0 = (a^2 - x^2)(a^2 - y^2)(a_1 + a_2 x^2 + a_3 y^2 + a_4 x^2 y^2 + \cdots).$$

It is easy to see that each term of this series becomes equal to zero, when $x = y = \pm a$. Hence the conditions at the boundary are satisfied.

In the case of a convex polygon the boundary conditions will be satisfied by taking

$$v_0 = (a_1 x + b_1 y + c_1)(a_2 x + b_2 y + c_2) \cdots (a_n x + b_n y + c_n) \sum\sum a_{mn} x^m y^n,$$

where $a_1 x + b_1 y + c_1 = 0$, $\cdots$ are the equations of the sides of the polygon. By taking only the first term $(m = 0, n = 0)$ of this series, a satisfactory approximation for the fundamental type of vibration usually will be obtained. It is necessary to take more terms if the frequencies of higher modes of vibration are required.

Circular Membrane.—We will consider the simplest case of vibration, where the deflected surface of the membrane is symmetrical with respect to the center of the circle. In this case the deflections depend only on the radial distance r and the boundary condition will be satisfied by taking

$$v_0 = a_1 \cos \frac{\pi r}{2a} + a_2 \cos \frac{3\pi r}{2a} + \cdots, \qquad (t)$$

where a denotes the radius of the boundary.

Because we are using polar coordinates, eq. (o) has to be replaced in this case by the following equation:

$$V_{\max} = \frac{S}{2} \int_0^a \left(\frac{\partial v_0}{\partial r}\right)^2 2\pi r \, dr. \tag{o'}$$

Instead of (p), we obtain

$$T_{\max} = \frac{w}{2g} p^2 \int_0^a v_0^2 2\pi r \, dr, \tag{p'}$$

and eq. (s) assumes the form

$$\frac{\partial}{\partial a_n} \int_0^a \left\{ \left(\frac{\partial v_0}{\partial r}\right)^2 - \frac{p^2 w}{gS} v_0^2 \right\} 2\pi r \, dr = 0. \tag{s'}$$

By taking only the first term in the series (t) and substituting $v_0 = a_1 \cos \pi r/2a$ in eq. (s'), we obtain

$$\frac{\pi^2}{4a^2} \int_0^a \sin^2 \frac{\pi r}{2a} r \, dr = \frac{p^2 w}{gS} \int_0^a \cos^2 \frac{\pi r}{2a} r \, dr,$$

from which

$$\frac{\pi^2}{4a^2} \left(\frac{1}{2} + \frac{2}{\pi^2}\right) = \frac{p^2 w}{gS} \left(\frac{1}{2} - \frac{2}{\pi^2}\right).$$

or

$$p = \frac{2.415}{a} \sqrt{\frac{gS}{w}}.$$

The exact solution * gives for this case,

$$p = \frac{2.404}{a} \sqrt{\frac{gS}{w}}. \tag{181}$$

The error of the first approximation is less than ½%.

In order to get a better approximation for the fundamental mode and also for the frequencies of the higher modes of vibration, a larger number of terms in the series (t) should be taken. These higher modes of vibration will have one, two, three, $\cdots$ nodal circles at which the displacements v are zero during vibration.

In addition to the modes of vibration symmetrical with respect to the center, a circular membrane may also have modes in which one, two, three,

* The problem of the vibration of a circular membrane is discussed in detail by Lord Rayleigh, p. 318, *loc. cit.*

$\cdots$ diameters of the circle are *nodal lines* along which the deflections during vibration are zero. Several modes of vibration of a circular membrane are shown in Fig. 238 where the nodal circles and nodal diameters are indicated by dotted lines.

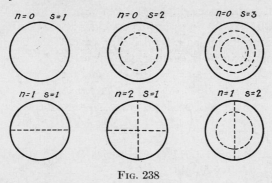

FIG. 238

In all cases the quantity p, determining the frequencies, can be expressed by the equation

$$p_{ns} = \frac{\alpha_{ns}}{a} \sqrt{\frac{gS}{w}}, \tag{182}$$

the constants α_{ns} of which are given in the table below.* In this table

s	$n = 0$	$n = 1$	$n = 2$	$n = 3$	$n = 4$	$n = 5$
1	2.404	3.832	5.135	6.379	7.586	8.780
2	5.520	7.016	8.417	9.760	11.064	12.339
3	8.654	10.173	11.620	13.017	14.373	15.700
4	11.792	13.323	14.796	16.224	17.616	18.982
5	14.931	16.470	17.960	19.410	20.827	22.220
6	18.071	19.616	21.117	22.583	24.018	25.431
7	21.212	22.760	24.270	25.749	27.200	28.628
8	24.353	25.903	27.421	28.909	30.371	31.813

n denotes the number of nodal diameters and s the number of nodal circles. (The boundary circle is included in this number.)

It was assumed in the previous discussion that the membrane has a complete circular area and that it is fixed only on the circular boundary,

* The table was calculated by Bourget, *Ann. l'école normale*, Vol. 3, 1866.

but it is easy to see that the results obtained include also the solution of other problems, such as membranes bounded by two concentric circles and two radii or membranes in the form of a sector. Take, for instance, a membrane semicircular in form. All possible modes of vibration of this membrane will be included in the modes which the circular membrane may perform. It is only necessary to consider one of the nodal diameters of the circular membrane as a fixed boundary. When the boundary of a membrane is approximately circular, the lowest tone of such a membrane is nearly the same as that of a circular membrane having the same area and the same value of Sg/w. Taking the equation determining the frequency of the fundamental mode of vibration of a membrane in the form,

$$p = \alpha \sqrt{\frac{gS}{wA}}, \qquad (183)$$

where A is the area of the membrane, the constant α of this equation will be given by the table below which shows the effect of a greater or less departure from the circular form.*

Circle.......................... $\alpha = 2.404\sqrt{\pi}$ $= 4.261$

Square........................ $\alpha = \pi\sqrt{2}$ $= 4.443$

Quadrant of a circle........... $\alpha = \dfrac{5.135}{2}\sqrt{\pi}$ $= 4.551$

Sector of a circle 60°.......... $\alpha = 6.379\sqrt{\dfrac{\pi}{6}}$ $= 4.616$

Rectangle 3 × 2............... $\alpha = \sqrt{1\frac{3}{6}}\cdot\pi$ $= 4.624$

Equilateral triangle........... $\alpha = 2\pi\sqrt{\tan 30°}$ $= 4.774$

Semi-circle................... $\alpha = 3.832\sqrt{\dfrac{\pi}{2}}$ $= 4.803$

Rectangle 2 × 1............... $\alpha = \pi\sqrt{5\frac{1}{2}}$ $= 4.967$

Rectangle 3 × 1............... $\alpha = \pi\sqrt{10\frac{1}{3}}$ $= 5.736$

* The table is taken from Rayleigh's book, p. 345, *loc. cit.*

In cases where the boundary is different from those discussed above, the investigation of the vibrations presents mathematical difficulties and only the case of an elliptical boundary has been completely solved by E. Mathieu.* A complete discussion of the theory of vibration of membranes from a mathematical point of view is given in a book by F. Pockels.†

70. Vibration of Plates.—*General.*—In the following discussion it is assumed that the plate consists of a perfectly elastic, homogeneous, isotropic material and that it has a uniform thickness h considered small in comparison with its other dimensions. We take for the xy-plane the middle plane of the plate and assume that with small deflections ‡ the lateral sides of an element, cut out from the plate by planes parallel to the zx- and zy-planes (see Fig. 239), remain plane and rotate so as to be normal to the deflected middle surface of the plate. Then the strain in a thin layer of this element, indicated by the shaded area and distant z from the middle plane, can be obtained from a simple geometrical consideration and will be represented by the following equations: §

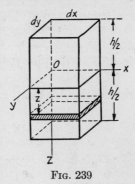

FIG. 239

$$\epsilon_{xx} = \frac{z}{R_1} = -z\frac{\partial^2 v}{\partial x^2},$$

$$\epsilon_{yy} = \frac{z}{R_2} = -z\frac{\partial^2 v}{\partial y^2}, \qquad (a)$$

$$\epsilon_{xy} = -2z\frac{\partial^2 v}{\partial x\,\partial y},$$

in which

ϵ_{xx}, ϵ_{yy} are unit elongations in the x and y directions;

ϵ_{xy} is shear deformation in the xy-plane;

v is deflection of the plate;

$\dfrac{1}{R_1}$, $\dfrac{1}{R_2}$ are curvatures in the xz- and yz-planes;

h is thickenss of the plate.

* *J. Math.* (*Liouville*), Vol. 13, 1868.

† "Über die partielle Differentialgleichung," $\Delta u + k^2 u = 0$, Leipzig, 1891.

‡ The deflections are assumed to be small in comparison with the thickness of the plate.

§ It is assumed that there is no stretching of the middle plane.

The corresponding stresses will then be obtained from the known equa-tions:

$$
\begin{aligned}
\sigma_x &= \frac{E}{1 - \nu^2}(\epsilon_{xx} + \nu\epsilon_{yy}) = -\frac{Ez}{1 - \nu^2}\left(\frac{\partial^2 v}{\partial x^2} + \nu\frac{\partial^2 v}{\partial y^2}\right), \\
\sigma_y &= \frac{E}{1 - \nu^2}(\epsilon_{yy} + \nu\epsilon_{xx}) = -\frac{Ez}{1 - \nu^2}\left(\frac{\partial^2 v}{\partial y^2} + \nu\frac{\partial^2 v}{\partial x^2}\right), \\
\tau &= G\epsilon_{xy} = -\frac{Ez}{(1 + \nu)}\cdot\frac{\partial^2 v}{\partial x\,\partial y},
\end{aligned} \tag{b}
$$

in which ν denotes Poisson's ratio.

The potential energy accumulated in the shaded layer of the element during the deformation will be

$$
dV = \left(\frac{\epsilon_{xx}\sigma_x}{2} + \frac{\epsilon_{yy}\sigma_y}{2} + \frac{\epsilon_{xy}\tau}{2}\right) dx\,dy\,dz,
$$

or by using eqs. (a) and (b),

$$
dV = \frac{Ez^2}{2(1 - \nu^2)}\left\{\left(\frac{\partial^2 v}{\partial x^2}\right)^2 + \left(\frac{\partial^2 v}{\partial y^2}\right)^2 \right.
$$
$$
\left. + 2\nu\frac{\partial^2 v}{\partial x^2}\frac{\partial^2 v}{\partial y^2} + 2(1 - \nu)\left(\frac{\partial^2 v}{\partial x\,\partial y}\right)^2\right\} dx\,dy\,dz, \quad (c)
$$

from which, by integration, we obtain the potential energy of bending of the plate:

$$
V = \iiint dV = \frac{D}{2}\iint\left\{\left(\frac{\partial^2 v}{\partial x^2}\right)^2 + \left(\frac{\partial^2 v}{\partial y^2}\right)^2 \right.
$$
$$
\left. + 2\nu\frac{\partial^2 v}{\partial x^2}\frac{\partial^2 v}{\partial y^2} + 2(1 - \nu)\left(\frac{\partial^2 v}{\partial x\,\partial y}\right)^2\right\} dx\,dy, \quad (184)
$$

where $D = \dfrac{Eh^3}{12(1 - \nu^2)}$ is the *flexural rigidity* of the plate.

The kinetic energy of a vibrating plate will be

$$
T = \frac{\gamma h}{2g}\iint \dot{v}^2\, dx\,dy, \tag{185}
$$

where $\gamma h/g$ is the mass per unit area of the plate.

From these expressions for V and T, the differential equation of vibration of the plate can be obtained.

Vibration of a Rectangular Plate.—In the case of a rectangular plate (Fig. 235) with simply supported edges, we can proceed as in the case of a rectangular membrane and take the deflection of the plate during vibration in the form of a double series:

$$\text{deflection} = v = \sum_{m=1}^{m=\infty} \sum_{n=1}^{n=\infty} \phi_{mn} \sin \frac{m\pi x}{a} \sin \frac{n\pi y}{b}. \tag{d}$$

It is easy to see that that each term of this series satisfies the conditions at the edges, which require that w, $\partial^2 w/\partial x^2$ and $\partial^2 w/\partial y^2$ must be equal to zero at the boundary.

Substituting (d) in eq. (184), the following expression for the potential energy will be obtained:

$$V = \frac{\pi^4 ab}{8} D \sum_{m=1}^{m=\infty} \sum_{n=1}^{n=\infty} \phi_{mn}{}^2 \left(\frac{m^2}{a^2} + \frac{n^2}{b^2}\right)^2. \tag{186}$$

The kinetic energy will be

$$T = \frac{\gamma h}{2g} \frac{ab}{4} \sum \sum \dot{\phi}_{mn}{}^2. \tag{187}$$

p.432

Proceeding as before and considering a virtual displacement

$$\delta v = \qquad \delta\phi_{mn} \sin \frac{m\pi x}{a} \sin \frac{n\pi y}{b}, \qquad Eq(d) \uparrow$$

we obtain the differential equation of normal vibration

$$\frac{\gamma h}{g} \ddot{\phi}_{mn} + \pi^4 D \phi_{mn} \left(\frac{m^2}{a^2} + \frac{n^2}{b^2}\right)^2 = 0,$$

from which

$$\phi_{mn} = C_1 \cos pt + C_2 \sin pt,$$

where

$$p = \pi^2 \sqrt{\frac{gD}{\gamma h}} \left(\frac{m^2}{a^2} + \frac{n^2}{b^2}\right). \tag{188}$$

From this the frequencies of the lowest mode and of the higher modes of vibration can be easily calculated. Taking, for instance, a square plate we obtain for the lowest mode of vibration,

$$f_1 = \frac{p_1}{2\pi} = \frac{\pi}{a^2} \sqrt{\frac{gD}{\gamma h}}. \tag{189}$$

In considering higher modes of vibration and their nodal lines, the discussion previously given for the vibration of a rectangular membrane can be used. Also the case of forced vibrations of a rectangular plate with simply supported edges can be solved without any difficulty. It should be noted that the cases of vibration of a rectangular plate, of which two opposite edges are supported while the other two edges are free or clamped, can also be solved without great mathematical difficulty.*

The problems of the vibration of a rectangular plate, of which all the edges are free or clamped, are, however, much more complicated. For the solution of these problems, Ritz's method has been found to be very useful.† In using this method we assume

$$v = v_0 \cos pt, \tag{e}$$

where v_0 is a function of x and y which determines the mode of vibration. Substituting (e) in eqs. (184) and (185), the following expressions for the maximum potential and kinetic energy of vibration will be obtained:

$$V_{\max} = \frac{D}{2} \iint \left\{ \left(\frac{\partial^2 v_0}{\partial x^2}\right)^2 + \left(\frac{\partial^2 v_0}{\partial y^2}\right)^2 \right.$$
$$\left. + 2\nu \frac{\partial^2 v_0}{\partial x^2} \frac{\partial^2 v_0}{\partial y^2} + 2(1-\nu) \left(\frac{\partial^2 v_0}{\partial x \, \partial y}\right)^2 \right\} dx \, dy,$$

$$T_{\max} = \frac{\gamma h}{2g} p^2 \iint v_0{}^2 \, dx \, dy,$$

from which

$$p^2 = \frac{2g}{\gamma h} \frac{V_{\max}}{\displaystyle\iint v_0{}^2 \, dx \, dy}. \tag{190}$$

---

* See W. Voigt, *Nachr. Ges. Wiss. Göttinger*, p. 225, 1893.

† See W. Ritz, *Ann. Physik*, Vol. 28, p. 737, 1909. The accuracy of the Ritz method has been discussed by S. Tomatika, *Phil. Mag.*, ser. 7, Vol. 21, p. 745, 1936. See also A. Weinstein and Wei-Zang Chien, *Quart. Appl. Math.*, Vol. 1, p. 61, 1943.

Now we take the function v_0 in the form of a series

$$v_0 = a_1\varphi_1(x, y) + a_2\varphi_2(x, y) + \cdots, \qquad (f)$$

where φ_1, φ_2, $\cdots$ are suitable functions of x and y, satisfying the conditions at the boundary of the plate. It is then only necessary to determine the coefficients a_1, a_2, $\cdots$ in such a manner as to make the right member of (190) a minimum. In this way we arrive at a system of equations of the type:

$$\frac{\partial}{\partial a_n} \iint \left\{ \left(\frac{\partial^2 v_0}{\partial x^2}\right)^2 + \left(\frac{\partial^2 v_0}{\partial y^2}\right)^2 + 2\nu \frac{\partial^2 v_0}{\partial x^2} \frac{\partial^2 v_0}{\partial y^2} \right.$$

$$\left. + 2(1 - \nu) \left(\frac{\partial^2 v_0}{\partial x\, \partial y}\right)^2 - \frac{p^2 \gamma h}{gD} v_0{}^2 \right\} dx\, dy = 0, \quad (191)$$

which will be linear with respect to the constants a_1, a_2, $\cdots$, and by equating to zero the determinant of these equations, the frequencies of the various modes of vibration can be approximately calculated.

W. Ritz applied this method to the study of the vibration of a square plate with free edges.* The series (f) was taken in this case in the form

$$v_0 = \sum \sum a_{mn} u_m(x) v_n(y), \qquad (f')$$

where $u_m(x)$ and $v_n(y)$ are the normal functions of the vibration of a prismatical bar with free ends (see p. 336). The frequencies of the lowest and of the higher modes of vibration will be determined by the equation

$$p = \frac{\alpha}{a^2} \sqrt{\frac{gD}{\gamma h}}, \qquad (192)$$

in which α is a constant depending on the mode of vibration. For the three lowest modes, the values of this constant are †

$$\alpha_1 = 14.10 \quad \alpha_2 = 20.56, \quad \alpha_3 = 23.91.$$

---

* *Loc. cit.*, p. 444. Applications of the Ritz method for several other edge conditions were made by Dana Young, *J. Appl. Mech.*, Vol. 17, p. 448, 1950. See also a paper by G. B. Warburton, Institution Mechanical Engrs., London, 1954.

† Poisson's ratio is taken equal to 0.225.

The corresponding modes of vibration are represented by their nodal lines in Fig. 240.

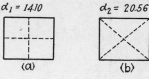

$\alpha_1 = 14.10$ $\alpha_2 = 20.56$ $\alpha_3 = 23.91$

(a)   (b)   (c)

FIG. 240

An extensive study of the nodal lines for this case and a comparison with experimental data are given in the paper by W. Ritz mentioned above.*

From eq. (192) some general conclusions can be drawn which hold also in other cases of vibration of plates:

1. The period of the vibration of any natural mode varies with the square of the linear dimensions, provided the thickness remains the same.

2. If all the dimensions of a plate, including the thickness, be increased in the same proportion, the period increases with the linear dimensions.

3. The period varies inversely with the square root of the modulus of elasticity and directly as the square root of the density of material.

Vibration of a Circular Plate.—The problem of vibration of a circular plate has been solved by G. R. Kirchhoff † who calculated also the frequencies of several modes of vibration for a plate with free boundary. The exact solution of this problem involves the use of Bessel functions. In the following, an approximate solution is developed by means of the Rayleigh-Ritz method, which usually gives for the lowest mode an accuracy sufficient for practical applications. In applying this method it will be useful to transform the expressions (184) and (185) for the potential and kinetic energy to polar coordinates. By taking the coordinates as shown in Fig. 241, we see from the elemental triangle *mns* that

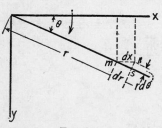

FIG. 241

* The technique of producing Chladni figures was recently greatly improved by using solid carbon dioxide for excitation; see Mary D. Waller, *Proc. Phys. Soc.* (*London*), Vol. 49, p. 522, 1937.

† See *J. Math.* (*Crelle*), Vol. 40, 1850; *Gesammelte Abhandlungen*, Leipzig, p. 237, 1882; or *Vorlesungen über mathematische Physik Mechanik*, Leipzig, *Vorlesung* 30, 1876.

by giving to the coordinate x a small increase dx we obtain

$$dr = dx \cos \theta, \quad d\theta = - \frac{dx \sin \theta}{r}.$$

Then, considering the deflection v as a function of r and θ, we obtain

$$\frac{\partial v}{\partial x} = \frac{\partial v}{\partial r}\frac{\partial r}{\partial x} + \frac{\partial v}{\partial \theta}\frac{\partial \theta}{\partial x} = \frac{\partial v}{\partial r}\cos \theta - \frac{\partial v}{\partial \theta}\frac{\sin \theta}{r}.$$

In the same manner we will find

$$\frac{\partial v}{\partial y} = \frac{\partial v}{\partial r}\sin \theta + \frac{\partial v}{\partial \theta}\frac{\cos \theta}{r}.$$

Repeating the differentiation, we obtain

$$\frac{\partial^2 v}{\partial x^2} = \left(\frac{\partial}{\partial r}\cos \theta - \frac{\partial}{\partial \theta}\frac{\sin \theta}{r}\right)\left(\frac{\partial v}{\partial r}\cos \theta - \frac{\partial v}{\partial \theta}\frac{\sin \theta}{r}\right)$$

$$= \frac{\partial^2 v}{\partial r^2}\cos^2 \theta - 2\frac{\partial^2 v}{\partial \theta \partial r}\frac{\sin \theta \cos \theta}{r} + \frac{\partial v}{\partial r}\frac{\sin^2 \theta}{r}$$

$$+ 2\frac{\partial v}{\partial \theta}\frac{\sin \theta \cos \theta}{r^2} + \frac{\partial^2 v}{\partial \theta^2}\frac{\sin^2 \theta}{r^2}, \tag{g}$$

$$\frac{\partial^2 v}{\partial y^2} = \frac{\partial^2 v}{\partial r^2}\sin^2 \theta + 2\frac{\partial^2 v}{\partial \theta \partial r}\frac{\sin \theta \cos \theta}{r} + \frac{\partial v}{\partial r}\frac{\cos^2 \theta}{r}$$

$$- 2\frac{\partial v}{\partial \theta}\frac{\sin \theta \cos \theta}{r^2} + \frac{\partial^2 v}{\partial \theta^2}\frac{\cos^2 \theta}{r^2}, \tag{h}$$

$$\frac{\partial^2 v}{\partial x \partial y} = \frac{\partial^2 v}{\partial r^2}\sin \theta \cos \theta + \frac{\partial^2 v}{\partial r \partial \theta}\frac{\cos 2\theta}{r} - \frac{\partial v}{\partial \theta}\frac{\cos 2\theta}{r^2}$$

$$- \frac{\partial v}{\partial r}\frac{\sin \theta \cos \theta}{r} - \frac{\partial^2 v}{\partial \theta^2}\frac{\sin \theta \cos \theta}{r^2}, \tag{i}$$

from which we find

$$\frac{\partial^2 v}{\partial x^2} + \frac{\partial^2 v}{\partial y^2} = \frac{1}{R_1} + \frac{1}{R_2} = \frac{\partial^2 v}{\partial r^2} + \frac{1}{r}\frac{\partial v}{\partial r} + \frac{1}{r^2}\frac{\partial^2 v}{\partial \theta^2},$$

$$\frac{\partial^2 v}{\partial x^2}\frac{\partial^2 v}{\partial y^2} - \left(\frac{\partial^2 v}{\partial x \partial y}\right)^2 = \frac{\partial^2 v}{\partial r^2}\left(\frac{1}{r}\frac{\partial v}{\partial r} + \frac{1}{r^2}\frac{\partial^2 v}{\partial \theta^2}\right) - \left\{\frac{\partial}{\partial r}\left(\frac{1}{r}\frac{\partial v}{\partial \theta}\right)\right\}^2.$$

Substituting in eq. (184) and taking the origin at the center of the plate, we obtain

$$V = \frac{D}{2} \int_0^{2\pi} \int_0^a \left[\left(\frac{\partial^2 v}{\partial r^2} + \frac{1}{r} \frac{\partial v}{\partial r} + \frac{1}{r^2} \frac{\partial^2 v}{\partial \theta^2} \right)^2 - 2(1 - \nu) \frac{\partial^2 v}{\partial r^2} \left(\frac{1}{r} \frac{\partial v}{\partial r} + \frac{1}{r^2} \frac{\partial^2 v}{\partial \theta^2} \right) \right.$$
$$\left. + 2(1 - \nu) \left\{ \frac{\partial}{\partial r} \left(\frac{1}{r} \frac{\partial v}{\partial \theta} \right) \right\}^2 \right] r \, d\theta \, dr, \quad (193)$$

where a denotes the radius of the plate.

When the deflection of the plate is symmetrical about the center, v will be a function of r only and eq. (193) becomes

$$V = \pi D \int_0^a \left\{ \left(\frac{d^2 v}{dr^2} + \frac{1}{r} \frac{dv}{dr} \right)^2 - 2(1 - \nu) \frac{d^2 v}{dr^2} \cdot \frac{1}{r} \frac{dv}{dr} \right\} r \, dr. \quad (194)$$

In the case of a plate clamped at the edge, the integral

$$\iint \left[\frac{\partial^2 v}{\partial r^2} \left(\frac{1}{r} \frac{\partial v}{\partial r} + \frac{1}{r^2} \frac{\partial^2 v}{\partial \theta^2} \right) - \left\{ \frac{\partial}{\partial r} \left(\frac{1}{r} \frac{\partial v}{\partial \theta} \right) \right\}^2 \right] r \, dr \, d\theta$$

vanishes and we obtain from (193)

$$V = \frac{D}{2} \int_0^{2\pi} \int_0^a \left(\frac{\partial^2 v}{\partial r^2} + \frac{1}{r} \frac{\partial v}{\partial r} + \frac{1}{r^2} \frac{\partial^2 v}{\partial \theta^2} \right)^2 r \, d\theta \, dr. \quad (195)$$

If the deflection of such a plate is symmetrical about the center, we have

$$V = \pi D \int_0^a \left(\frac{\partial^2 v}{\partial r^2} + \frac{1}{r} \frac{\partial v}{\partial r} \right)^2 r \, dr. \quad (196)$$

The expression for the kinetic energy in polar coordinates will be

$$T = \frac{\gamma h}{2g} \int_0^{2\pi} \int_0^a \dot{v}^2 r \, d\theta \, dr, \quad (197)$$

and in symmetrical cases,

$$T = \frac{\pi \gamma h}{g} \int_0^a \dot{v}^2 r \, dr. \quad (198)$$

By using these expressions for the potential and kinetic energy, the frequencies of the natural modes of vibration of a circular plate for various particular cases can be calculated.*

* Forced vibrations of circular plates were studied by W. Flügge, *Z. tech. Phys.*, Vol. 13, p. 139, 1932.

Circular Plate Clamped at the Boundary.—The problem of a circular plate clamped at the edges is of practical interest in connection with the application to telephone receivers and other devices. In using the Rayleigh-Ritz method we assume

$$v = v_0 \cos pt, \qquad (j)$$

where v_0 is a function of r and θ.

In the case of the lowest mode of vibration, the shape of the vibrating plate is symmetrical about the center of the plate and v_0 will be a function of r only. By taking v_0 in the form of a series like

$$v_0 = a_1 \left(1 - \frac{r^2}{a^2} \right)^2 + a_2 \left(1 - \frac{r^2}{a^2} \right)^3 + \cdots, \qquad (k)$$

the condition of symmetry will be satisfied. The conditions at the boundary also will be satisfied because each term of the series (k), together with its first derivative, vanishes when $r = a$.

The differential equation (191) in the case under consideration becomes

$$\frac{\partial}{\partial a_n} \int_0^a \left\{ \left(\frac{d^2 v_0}{dr^2} + \frac{1}{r} \frac{dv_0}{dr} \right)^2 - \frac{p^2 \gamma h}{gD} v_0{}^2 \right\} r \, dr = 0. \qquad (199)$$

By taking only one term of the series (k) and substituting it in (199), we obtain

$$\frac{96}{9a^2} - \frac{p^2 \gamma h}{gD} \frac{a^2}{10} = 0,$$

from which

$$p = \frac{10.33}{a^2} \sqrt{\frac{gD}{\gamma h}}. \qquad (200)$$

In order to get a closer approximation, we take the first two terms of the series (k), then

$$\int_0^a \left(\frac{d^2 v_0}{dr^2} + \frac{1}{r} \frac{dv_0}{dr} \right)^2 r \, dr = \frac{96}{9a^2} \left(a_1{}^2 + \frac{3}{2} a_1 a_2 + \frac{9}{10} a_2{}^2 \right),$$

$$\int_0^a v_0{}^2 r \, dr = \frac{a^2}{10} \left(a_1{}^2 + \frac{5}{3} a_1 a_2 + \frac{5}{7} a_2{}^2 \right).$$

Eqs. (199) become

$$a_1 \left(\frac{192}{9} - \frac{x}{5}\right) + a_2 \left(\frac{144}{9} - \frac{x}{6}\right) = 0,$$
$$a_1 \left(\frac{144}{9} - \frac{x}{6}\right) + a_2 \left(\frac{96}{5} - \frac{x}{7}\right) = 0,$$

(l)

where

$$x = a^4 p^2 \frac{\gamma h}{gD}.$$

(m)

Equating to zero the determinant of eqs. (l), we obtain

$$x^2 - \frac{204 \times 48}{5} x + 768 \times 36 \times 7 = 0,$$

from which

$$x_1 = 104.3, \quad x_2 = 1854.$$

Substituting in (m), we obtain

$$p_1 = \frac{10.21}{a^2} \sqrt{\frac{gD}{\gamma h}}, \quad p_2 = \frac{43.04}{a^2} \sqrt{\frac{gD}{\gamma h}},$$

(201)

where p_1 gives the second approximation to the frequency of the lowest mode of vibration of the plate and p_2 gives a rough approximation to the frequency of the second mode of vibration in which the vibrating plate has one nodal circle. By using the same method the modes of vibration having nodal diameters can also be investigated.

In all cases the frequency of vibration will be determined by the equation

$$p = \frac{\alpha}{a^2} \sqrt{\frac{gD}{\gamma h}},$$

(202)

the constant α of which, for a given number s of nodal circles and of a given number n of nodal diameters, is given in the following table:

s	$n = 0$	$n = 1$	$n = 2$
0	10.21	21.22	34.84
1	39.78	.....	.....
2	88.90	.....	.....

In the case of thin plates the mass of the air or of the liquid in which the plate vibrates may affect the frequency considerably. In order to take this into account in the case of the lowest mode of vibration, eq. (202) above should be replaced by the following equation,*

$$p_1 = \frac{10.21}{a^2\sqrt{1+\beta}}\sqrt{\frac{gD}{\gamma h}}, \tag{203}$$

in which

$$\beta = 0.6689\,\frac{\gamma_1}{\gamma}\frac{a}{h}$$

and (γ_1/γ) is the ratio of the density of the fluid to the density of the material of the plate.

Taking, for instance, a steel plate 7 in. in diameter and 1/8 in. thick vibrating in water, we obtain

$$\beta = 0.6689 \times \frac{1}{7.8} \times 28 = 2.40, \quad \frac{1}{\sqrt{1+\beta}} = 0.542.$$

The frequency of the lowest mode of vibration will be lowered to 0.542 of its original vlaue.

Other Kinds of Boundary Conditions.—In all cases the frequencies of a vibrating circular plate can be calculated from eq. (202). The numerical values of the factor α are given in the tables below.

For a free circular plate with n nodal diameters and s nodal circles, α has the following values: †

s	$n = 0$	$n = 1$	$n = 2$	$n = 3$
0	. . . . . .	. . . . .	5.251	12.23
1	9.076	20.52	35.24	52.91
2	38.52	59.86		

* This problem has been discussed by H. Lamb, *Proc. Roy. Soc. (London)*, Vol. 98, p. 205, 1921.

† Poisson's ratio is taken equal to $\frac{1}{3}$.

For a circular plate with its center fixed and having s nodal circles, α has the following values *:

$s =$	0	1	2	3
$\alpha =$	3.75	20.91	60.68	119.7

The frequencies of vibration having nodal diameters will be the same as in the case of a free plate.

The Effect of Stretching of the Middle Surface of the Plate.—In the previous theory it was assumed that the deflection of the plate is small in comparison with its thickness. If a vibrating plate is under considerable static pressure such that the deflection produced by this pressure is not small in comparison with the thickness of the pate, the stretching of the middle surface of the plate should be taken into account in calculating the frequency of vibration. Due to the resistance of the plate to such a stretching, the rigidity of the plate and the frequency of vibration increase with the pressure acting on the plate.† In order to show how the stretching of the middle surface may affect the frequency, let us consider again the case of a circular plate clamped at the boundary and assume that the deflection of the plate under a uniformly distributed pressure is given by the equation ‡

$$v_0 = a_1 \left(1 - \frac{r^2}{a^2} \right)^2. \tag{k'}$$

In addition to the displacements v_0 at right angles to the plate, the points in the middle plane of the plate will perform radial displacements u which vanish at the center and at the clamped boundary of the plate. The unit elongation of the middle surface in a radial direction, due to the displacements v_0 and u, is

$$\epsilon_r = \frac{1}{2} \left(\frac{dv_0}{dr} \right)^2 + \frac{du}{dr}. \tag{n}$$

The elongation in a circumferential direction will be,

$$\epsilon_t = \frac{u}{r}. \tag{o}$$

* See paper by R. V. Southwell, *Proc. Roy. Soc.* (*London*), A, Vol. 101, p. 133, 1922; $\mu = 0.3$ is taken in these calculations.

† Such an increase in frequency was established experimentally, see paper by J. H. Powell and J. H. T. Roberts, *Proc. Phys. Soc.* (*London*), Vol. 35, p. 170, 1923.

‡ This equation represents the deflections when the stretching of the middle surface is neglected. It can be used also for approximate calculation of the effect of the stretching.

For an approximate solution of the problem we assume that the radial displacements are represented by the following series:

$$u = r(a - r)(c_1 + c_2 r + c_3 r^2 + \cdots), \tag{p}$$

each term of which satisfies the boundary conditions.

Taking only the first two terms in the series (p) and substituting (p) and (k) in eqs. (n) and (o), the strain in the middle surface will be obtained and the energy corresponding to the stretching of the middle surface can now be calculated as follows:

$$V_1 = \frac{\pi E h}{1 - \nu^2} \int_0^a (\epsilon_r{}^2 + \epsilon_t{}^2 + 2\nu\epsilon_r\epsilon_t) r \, dr$$

$$= \frac{\pi E h a^2}{1 - \nu^2} \left(0.250 c_1{}^2 a^2 + 0.1167 c_2{}^2 a^4 + 0.300 c_1 c_2 a^3 - 0.00846 c_1 a \frac{8 a_1{}^2}{a^2} \right.$$

$$\left. + 0.00682 c_2 a^2 \frac{8 a_1{}^2}{a^2} + 0.00477 \frac{64 a_1{}^4}{a^4} \right). \tag{q}$$

Determining the constants c_1 and c_2 so as to make V_1 a minimum, we get, from the equations

$$\frac{\partial V_1}{\partial c_1} = 0, \quad \frac{\partial V_1}{\partial c_2} = 0,$$

$$c_1 = 1.185 \frac{a_1{}^2}{a^3}, \quad c_2 = -1.75 \frac{a_1{}^2}{a^4}.$$

Substituting in eq. (q), we find

$$V_1 = 2.59 \pi D \frac{a_1{}^4}{a^2 h^2}.$$

Adding this energy of stretching to the energy of bending (eq. 196), we obtain

$$V = \frac{32}{3} \pi D \frac{a_1{}^2}{a^2} + 2.59 \pi D \frac{a_1{}^4}{a^2 h^2} = \frac{32}{3} \pi D \frac{a_1{}^2}{a^2} \left(1 + 0.244 \frac{a_1{}^2}{h^2} \right). \tag{r}$$

The second term in the parentheses represents the correction due to the extension of the middle surface of the plate. It is easy to see that this correction is small and can be neglected only when the deflection a_1 at the center of the plate is small in comparison with the thickness h. The static deflection of the plate under the action of a uniformly distributed pressure w can now be found from the equation of virtual displacements,

$$\frac{\partial V}{\partial a_1}\, \delta a_1 = 2\pi w\, \delta a_1 \int_0^a \left(1 - \frac{r^2}{a^2}\right)^2 r\, dr = \delta a_1\, \frac{\pi w a^2}{3},$$

from which

$$a_1 = \frac{w a^4}{64D} \cdot \frac{1}{1 + 0.488\, \dfrac{a_1{}^2}{h^2}}. \tag{204}$$

The last factor on the right side represents the effect of the stretching of the middle surface. Due to this effect the deflection a_1 is no longer proportional to w and the rigidity of the plate increases with the deflection. Taking, for instance, $a_1 = \tfrac{1}{2}h$, we obtain from (204)

$$a_1 = 0.89\, \frac{w a^4}{64D}.$$

The deflection is 11% less than that obtained by neglecting the stretching of the middle surface.

From the expression (r) of the potential energy, which contains not only the square but also the fourth power of the deflection a_1, it can be concluded at once that the vibration of the plate about its flat configuration will not be *isochronic* and the frequency will increase with the amplitude of vibration. Consider now small vibrations of the plate about a bent position given by eq. (k'). This bending is supposed to be due to some constant, uniformly distributed static pressure w. If Δ denotes the amplitude of this vibration, the increase in the potential energy of deformation due to additional deflection of the plate will be obtained from eq. (r) and is equal to *

$$\delta\bar{V} = \frac{32}{3}\frac{\pi D}{a^2}\left[2a_1\Delta + \Delta^2 + \frac{0.244}{h^2}\left(4a_1{}^3\Delta + 6a_1{}^2\Delta^2\right)\right].$$

The work done by the constant pressure w during this increase in deflection is

$$\delta W = \frac{\pi a^2 w \Delta}{3} = \frac{\pi a^2 \Delta}{3}\cdot\frac{64 a_1 D\left(1 + 0.488\, \dfrac{a_1{}^2}{h^2}\right)}{a^4}.$$

* Terms with Δ^3 and Δ^4 are neglected in this expression.

The complete change in the potential energy of the system will be

$$\delta V - \delta W = \frac{32}{3} \frac{\pi D \Delta^2}{a^2} \left(1 + \frac{1.464 a_1^2}{h^2} \right).$$

Equating this to the maximum kinetic energy,

$$T_{\max} = \frac{\pi \Delta^2 p^2 \gamma h}{g} \int_0^a \left(1 - \frac{r^2}{a^2} \right)^4 r \, dr = \frac{\pi \Delta^2 a^2 \gamma h}{10g} p^2,$$

we obtain

$$p = \frac{10.33}{a^2} \sqrt{\frac{gD}{\gamma h}} \sqrt{1 + 1.464 \frac{a_1^2}{h^2}}. \tag{205}$$

Comparing this result with eq. (200) it can be concluded that the last factor on the right side of eq. (205) represents the correction due to the stretching of the middle surface of the plate.

It should be noted that in the above theory eq. (k') for the deflection of the plate was used and the effect of tension in the middle surface of the plate on the form of the deflection surface was neglected. This is the reason why eq. (205) will be accurate enough only if the deflections are not large, say $a_1 \leq h$. Otherwise the effect of tension in the middle surface on the form of the deflection surface must be taken into consideration.*

71. Vibration of Turbine Discs.—*General.*—It is now fairly well established that fractures which occur in turbine discs and which cannot be explained by defects in the material or by excessive stresses due to centrifugal forces may be attributed to flexural vibrations of these discs. In this respect it may be noted that direct experiments have shown † that such vibrations, at certain speeds of the turbine, become very pronounced and produce considerable additional bending stresses which may result in fatigue of the metal and in the gradual development of cracks, which usually start at the boundaries of the steam balance holes and other discontinuities in the web of the turbine disc, where stress concentration is present.

There are various causes which may produce these flexural vibrations in turbine discs but the most important is that due to nonuniform steam pressure. A localized pressure acting on the rim of a rotating disc is sufficient at certain speeds to maintain lateral vibrations in the disc and

---

* This question was discussed by K. Federhofer, *Österr. Ing.-Arch.*, Vol. 2, p. 325, 1948.

† See papers by Wilfred Campbell, *Trans. A.S.M.E.*, Vol. 46, p. 31, 1924; and by Dr. J. von Freudenreich, *Engineering*, Vol. 119, p. 2, 1925.

experiments show that the application of a localized force of only a few pounds, such as produced by a small direct current magnet, to the side of a rotating turbine disc makes it respond violently at a whole series of critical speeds.

Assume now that there exists a certain irregularity in the nozzles which results in a nonuniform steam pressure and imagine that a turbine disc is rotating with a constant angular velocity ω in the field of such a pressure. Then for a certain spot on the rim of the disc the pressure will vary with the angle of the rotation of the wheel and this may be represented by a periodic function, the period of which is equal to the time of one revolution of the disc. In the most general case such a function may be represented by a trigonometric series

$$w = a_0 + a_1 \sin \omega t + a_2 \sin 2\omega t + \cdots b_1 \cos \omega t + b_2 \cos 2\omega t + \cdots.$$

By taking only one term of the series such as $a_1 \sin \omega t$ we obtain a periodic disturbing force which may produce large lateral vibration of the disc if the frequency $\omega/2\pi$ of the force coincides with one of the natural frequencies $p/2\pi$ of the disc. From this it can be appreciated that the calculation of the natural frequencies of a disc may have a great practical importance.

A rotating disc, like a circular plate, may have various modes of vibration which can be subdivided into two classes:

1. Vibrations symmetrical with respect to the center, having nodal lines in the form of concentric circles.
2. Unsymmetrical vibrations having diameters for nodal lines.

Experiments show that the symmetrical type of vibration very seldom occurs and no disc failure can be attributed to this kind of vibration.

In discussing the unsymmetrical vibrations it can be assumed that the deflection of the disc has the form

$$v = v_0 \sin n\theta \cos pt, \tag{a}$$

in which, as before, v_0 is a function of the radial distance r only, θ determines the angular position of the point under consideration and n represents the number of nodal diameters.

The deflection can be taken also in the form

$$v = v_0 \cos n\theta \sin pt. \tag{a'}$$

Combining (a) and (a'), we obtain

$$v = v_0(\sin n\theta \cos pt \pm \cos n\theta \sin pt) = v_0 \sin (n\theta \pm pt),$$

which represents traveling waves. The angular speed of these waves traveling around the disc will be found from the condition

$$n\theta \pm pt = \text{const.}$$

or

$$\theta = \pm \frac{p}{n} t + \text{const.}$$

Thus we obtain two speeds $-p/n$ and $+p/n$ which are the speeds of the backward and forward traveling waves, respectively. The experiments of Campbell * proved the existence of these two trains of waves in a rotating disc and showed also that the amplitudes of the backward-moving waves are usually larger than those of the forward-moving waves. Backward-moving waves become especially pronounced under conditions of resonance when the backward speed of these waves in the disc coincides exactly with the forward angular velocity of the rotating disc so that the waves become *stationary in space*. The experiments show that this type of vibration is responsible in a majority of cases for disc failures.

Calculation of the Frequencies of Disc Vibrations.—In calculating the frequencies of the various modes of vibration of turbine discs the Rayleigh-Ritz method is very useful.† In applying this method we assume that the deflection of the disc has a form

$$v = v_0 \sin n\theta \cos pt. \tag{a''}$$

In the particular case of vibration symmetrical with respect to the center, the deflection will be:

$$v = v_0 \cos pt. \tag{b}$$

Starting with this particular case the maximum potential energy of deformation will be, from eq. (194),

$$V_{\max} = \pi \int_b^a D \left\{ \left(\frac{d^2 v_0}{dr^2} + \frac{1}{r}\frac{dv}{dr} \right)^2 - 2(1 - \nu) \frac{d^2 v}{dr^2} \frac{1}{r}\frac{dv}{dr} \right\} r\, dr, \tag{c}$$

---

* *Loc. cit.*, p. 455.

† The vibration of turbine discs by using this method was investigated by A. Stodola, *Schweiz. Bauzeitung*, Vol. 63, p. 112, 1914. For a further study of the problem, see I. Malkin, *J. Franklin Inst.*, Vol. 234, p. 355, 1942.

where a, b are outer and inner radii of the disc and

$D = \dfrac{Eh^3}{12(1 - \nu^2)}$ is flexural rigidity of the disc, which in this case will be
variable due to variation in thickness h of the disc.

In considering vibration of a rotating disc, not only the energy of deformation but also the energy corresponding to the work done during

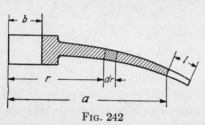

FIG. 242

deflection by the centrifugal forces must be taken into consideration. It is easy to see that the centrifugal forces resist any deflection of the disc and this results in an increase in the frequency of its natural vibration. In calculating the work done by the centrifugal forces let us take an element cut out from the disc by two cylindrical surfaces of the radii r and $r + dr$ (Fig. 242). The radial displacement of this element towards the center due to the deflection will be

$$\frac{1}{2} \int_b^r \left(\frac{dv_0}{dr}\right)^2 dr.$$

The mass of the element is

$$\frac{2\pi r h \gamma}{g} dr$$

and the work done during the deflection by the centrifugal forces acting on this element will be

$$-\frac{2\pi r^2 \omega^2 h \gamma}{g} dr \cdot \frac{1}{2} \int_b^r \left(\frac{dv_0}{dr}\right)^2 dr. \qquad (d)$$

The energy corresponding to the work of the centrifugal forces will be obtained by summation of such elements as (d) in the following form:

$$(V_1)_{\max} = \int_b^a \frac{\pi r^2 \omega^2 h \gamma}{g} dr \int_b^r \left(\frac{dv_0}{dr}\right)^2 dr. \qquad (e)$$

The maximum kinetic energy is given by the equation

$$T = \int_b^a \frac{2\pi r \gamma h}{2g} \dot{v}^2 dr.$$

Substituting expression (b) for v we obtain

$$T_{max} = \frac{\pi \gamma p^2}{g} \int_b^a h v_0^2 \, r dr. \tag{f}$$

Now, from the equation

$$V_{max} + (V_1)_{max} = T_{max}$$

we deduce

$$p^2 = \frac{V_{max} + (V_1)_{max}}{\dfrac{\pi \gamma}{g} \displaystyle\int_b^a h v_0^2 r \, dr}. \tag{g}$$

In order to obtain the frequency the deflection curve v_0 should be chosen so as to make the expression (g) a minimum. This can be done graphically by assuming for v_0 a suitable curve from which v_0, dv_0/dr and d^2v_0/dr^2 can be taken for a series of equidistant points and then the expressions (c), (e) and (f) can be calculated. By gradual changes in the shape of the curve for v_0, a satisfactory approximation for the lowest frequency can be obtained * from eq. (g).

In order to take into account the effect of the blades on the frequency of natural vibration, the integration in the expressions (e) and (f) for the work done by the centrifugal forces and for the kinetic energy must be extended from b to $a + l$, where l denotes the length of the blade. In this calculation the blades can be assumed to be straight during vibration of the disc so that no addition to the expression for the potential energy (c) will be necessary.

In an analytical calculation of the lowest frequency of a vibrating disc we take v_0 in the form of a series such as

$$v_0 = a_1(r - b)^2 + a_2(r - b)^3 + a_3(r - b)^4 + \cdots,$$

which satisfies the conditions at the built-in inner boundary of the disc, where v_0 and dv_0/dr become equal to zero. The coefficients a_1, a_2, a_3 should now be chosen so as to make expression (g) a minimum. Proceeding as explained in the previous article (see p. 449), a system of equations analogous to eqs. (199) and linear in a_1, a_2, a_3, $\cdots$ can be obtained. Equating to zero the determinant of these equations, the frequency equation will be found.

---

* Such a graphical method has been developed by A. Stodola, *loc. cit.*, p. 457. It was applied also by E. Oehler, *Z. Ver. duet. Ing.* Vol. 69, p. 335, 1925 and gave good agreement with experimental data.

In the case of a mode of vibration having diameters as nodal lines the expression (a'') instead of (b) must be used for the deflections. The potential energy will be found from eq. (193): it is only necessary to take into consideration that in the case of turbine discs the thickness and the flexural rigidity D are varying with the radial distance r so that D must be retained under the sign of integration. Expressions for V_1 and T can be established also for this case and finally the frequency can be calculated from eq. (g) exactly in the same manner as explained above for the case of a symmetrical mode of vibration.*

When the disc is stationary, V_1 vanishes and we obtain from eq. (g),

$$p_1{}^2 = \frac{V_{\max}}{\dfrac{\pi\gamma}{g} \displaystyle\int_b^a h v_0{}^2 r \, dr}, \qquad (g')$$

which determines the frequency of vibration due to elastic forces alone.

Another extreme case is obtained when the disc is very flexible and the restoring forces during vibration are due entirely to centrifugal forces. Such conditions are encountered, for instance, when experimenting with flexible discs made of rubber. The frequency will be determined in this case from the equation

$$p_2{}^2 = \frac{(V_1)_{\max}}{\dfrac{\pi\gamma}{g} \displaystyle\int_b^a h v_0{}^2 r \, dr}. \qquad (g'')$$

Now, from eq. (g), we have

$$p^2 = p_1{}^2 + p_2{}^2. \qquad (h)$$

If the frequencies p_1 and p_2 are determined in some way, the resulting frequency of vibration of the disc will be found from eq. (h). In the case of discs of constant thickness and fixed at the center an exact solution for p_1 and p_2 has been obtained by R. V. Southwell.† He gives for $p_1{}^2$ the equation,

$$p_1{}^2 = \frac{\alpha}{a^4} \frac{Dg}{\gamma h}. \qquad (i)$$

---

* The formulas for this calculation are developed in detail by A. Stodola, *loc. cit.*, p. 457.

† *Loc. cit.*, p. 452.

The values of the constant α for a given number n of nodal diameters and a given number s of nodal circles are as follows: *

	$n = 0$	$n = 1$	$n = 2$	$n = 3$
$s = 0$	14.1	0	29.0	156
$s = 1$	438	422	1210	2840

The equation for calculating $p_2{}^2$ is

$$p_2{}^2 = \lambda\omega^2, \qquad\qquad (j)$$

in which ω is the angular velocity and λ is a constant given in the following table:

	$n = 0$	$n = 1$	$n = 2$	$n = 3$
$s = 0$	0	1	2.35	4.05
$s = 1$	3.3	5.95	8.95	12.3

Determining $p_1{}^2$ and $p_2{}^2$ from eqs. (i) and (j), the frequency of vibration of the rotating disc will then be found from eq. (h).†

In the above theory of the vibration of discs the effect of nonuniform heating of the disc was not considered. In a turbine in service the rim of the disc will be warmer than the web. Due to this factor compressive stresses in the rim and tensile stresses in the web will be set up which may affect the frequencies of the natural vibrations considerably. The experiments and calculations ‡ show that for vibrations with 0 and 1 nodal diameters the frequency is increased, whereas with a larger number of nodal diameters the frequency is lowered by such a nonuniform heating.

---

* All other notations are the same as for circular plates (see p. 449). Poisson's ratio is taken equal to 0.3 in these calculations.

† A discussion of the differential equation of vibration for the case of a disc of variable thickness is given in a paper by Dr. F. Dubois, *Schweiz. Bauzeitung*, Vol. 89, p. 149, 1927.

‡ von Freudenreich, *loc. cit.*, p. 455.

AUTHOR INDEX

SUBJECT INDEX